Houghton Mifflin

Math Expressions

Teacher's Guide • Grade 3 • Volume 1

**Developed by
The Children's Math Worlds
Research Project**

PROJECT DIRECTOR AND AUTHOR

Dr. Karen C. Fuson

This material is based upon work supported by the
National Science Foundation
under Grant Numbers
ESI-9816320, REC-9806020, and RED-935373.

Any opinions, findings, and conclusions or recommendations expressed in this
material are those of the author and do not necessarily reflect the views of the
National Science Foundation.

 HOUGHTON MIFFLIN   BOSTON

Blended Usage Planning Guide: *Houghton Mifflin Math* and *Math Expressions*
Matt Larson, Senior Advisor

Special Thanks
Special thanks to the many teachers, students, parents, principals, writers, researchers, and work-study students who participated in the Children's Math Worlds Research Project over the years.

Credits
Cover art: (scale) © HMCo./Richard Hutchings. (elephant) © Art Wolfe/Stone/Getty Images. (chipmunk) © David W. Hamilton/The Image Bank/Getty Images.

Illustrative art: Robin Boyer/Deborah Wolfe, LTD
Technical art: Nesbitt Graphics, Inc.
Photos: Nesbitt Graphics, Inc.

Printed in the U.S.A.

ISBN-13: 978-0-618-51009-2
ISBN-10: 0-618-51009-5

3 4 5 6 7 8 9 WEB 11 10 09 08 07

Introducing

Math Expressions

A Fresh Approach to

Math Expressions is a comprehensive Kindergarten–Grade 5 mathematics curriculum that offers new ways to teach and learn mathematics. Combining the most powerful elements of standards-based instruction with the best of traditional approaches, *Math Expressions* uses objects,

Stairsteps

Standards-Based Instruction

drawings, conceptual language, and real-world situations to help
students build mathematical ideas that make sense to them.

Secret Code Cards

Math Expressions implements
state standards as well as the
recommendations and findings from
recent reports on math learning:

- *Principles and Standards for
  School Mathematics* (NCTM, 2000)

- *Adding It Up* (National Research
  Council, 2001)

- *How Students Learn Mathematics
  in the Classroom* (National
  Research Council, 2005)

- *Knowing and Teaching Elementary
  Mathematics* (Dr. Liping Ma, 1999)

Focused on Inquiry

Math Expressions balances deep understanding with essential skills and problem solving. Students invent, question, and discover, but also learn and practice important math strategies. Through daily

and Fluency

Math Talk, students explain their methods and, in turn, become more fluent with them.

> "As students are asked to communicate about the mathematics they are studying ... they gain insights into their thinking. In order to communicate their thinking to others, students naturally reflect on their learning and organize and consolidate their thinking about mathematics."

– Principles and Standards for School Mathematics, National Council of Teachers of Mathematics (2000)

Organized for

Math Expressions is organized around five
crucial classroom structures that allow

Quick Practice
Routines involve whole-class
responses or individual partner
practice and are frequently led
by student leaders.

Math Talk
Children share strategies and
solutions orally and through
proof drawings.

Building Concepts
Objects, drawings, conceptual language
and real-world situations strengthen
mathematical ideas and understanding.

UNIT 4
LESSON
2

Explore Teen Num

Lesson Objectives
• Relate teen numbers to a ten and extra ones.
• Represent teen numbers in different ways.

The Day at a Glance

Today's Goals

Daily Routines See Introduction (page xxiii).
Quick Practice Count to 100 by tens.

1 **Teaching the Lesson**
  A1: Recognize the embedded ten in
  teen numbers.
  A2: Represent teen numbers.

2 **Extending the Lesson**
  ▶ Differentiated Instruction

3 **Homework and Spiral Review**

Quick Practice

⏱ 5 MINUTES   Goal: Count to 100 by tens.

Count by Tens Have children count to 100 by tens,
for each 10-group. Repeat several times.

10   20

Remember to continue the *Money Routine* throu
Introduce the two new routines for Unit 4, *Calen*
Introducing the Calendar and *Partner Houses*. (S

300 UNIT 4 LESSON 2

---

① Teaching the Lesson

Activity 1

Modeling Ten-Structured Teens

⏱ **20 MINUTES**

Goal: Recognize the embedded ten
in teen numbers.

Materials: Demonstration Secret
Code Cards 1–10 (Copymasters
M31–M40)

✔ **NCTM Standards:**
Number and Operations
Communication
Representation

Teaching Note

What to Expect from Students
A few children may already know
something about place value. If so,
invite them to explain why each teen
number begins with a 1, but be sure
to make this a quick discussion. Do
not attempt a full explanation of
place value at this time. Children will
develop this understanding in the
days to come. Right now, children
only need to see that each teen
number contains 1 ten.

📁 Class Management

Looking Ahead Keep the
Demonstration Secret Code Cards on
the ledge of the board. They will be
needed for the next activity. Children
will also need their MathBoards (or
the 10 × 10 Grid Copymaster).

▶ **Elicit Prior Knowledge** WHOLE CLASS

Write the numbers 10 through 19 on the board. Ha
aloud as you point to each number. Discuss what c
these numbers.

• How are these numbers alike? They all begin w

• What does the 1 mean? 1 ten

▶ **Demonstrate a Ten and Extra On**

Use the board. Introduce tens-and-ones languag
the board, point out the tens place and the one

| 1 | 4 |
| tens | ones |

• The number 14 has 1 ten and 4 extra ones. D
tens place? Do you see the 4 in the ones plac

Use the Demonstration Secret Code Cards. Lin
on the ledge of the board, starting with the 1
Demonstration Secret Code Cards have been u
Routines in Unit 3, this lesson provides an opp
explore the cards in more depth.

| 1 | 0 | 1 | 2 | 3 | 4 | 5 |

Demonstrate how the Secret Code Cards can
numbers by stacking two cards to show 14.

• I can make the number 14 with these Sec
big 10-card. Which card shows how many
we make 10? 4 I can put the 4-card over
10-card is like a secret code telling us tha

| 1 | 0 | 4 |

Emphasize the hidden 10 by drawing a d
14 you had written on the board earlier.

| 1 | 4 |
| tens | ones |

▶ **A Story with Tens and Extra Ones** WHOLE CLASS

Present a teen-grouping story problem to the class and have them so
it any way they can.

• Sara has a bag of 10 tennis balls and 6 extra balls. How many balls
does she have altogether? 16 balls

• 16 means 1 ten and 6 extra ones. Let's write an equation to show this
10 + 6 = 16.

Use the Demonstration Secret Code Cards to show 16. Again, point out
the ten "hiding" inside the number.

| 1 | 0 | | 6 | → | 1 | 6 |

Then point out the small number in the top corner of the 10- and 6-cards.

• What do you think those little numbers tell us about the number 16?
16 is made up of 10 and 6. Even when you can't see the 10, it is there.

Activity 2

Visualizing Teen Numbers

▶ **Represent 15** WHOLE CLASS

Explain that children will be making some teen numbers on the 10 × 10
Grid. You can demonstrate by attaching an enlarged photocopy of the
10 × 10 Grid (Copymaster M46) to the board.

Have children begin by drawing 10 circles in the first column of the grid.

• Every teen number has a ten, so you will always need this group of ten.

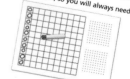

✔ As ch
numb
able t
for ex
grid to
some
equati

Activity continued ▶

Explo

Classroom Success

children to develop deep conceptual understanding, and then practice, apply, and discuss what they know with skill and confidence.

Helping Community
A classroom in which everyone is both a teacher and a learner enhances mathematical understanding, competence, and confidence.

Student Leaders
Teachers facilitate students' growth by helping them learn to lead practice and discussion routines.

...hing the Lesson (continued)

...ing Classroom
...epts After learning the ...ers, children begin ...tegrated concept of ...beginning with teen ...grating tens and ones ...tanding of 2-digit ...sents an enormous ...ance over simply ...s, and this skill

...e
...e children may not ...d 12 are teen ...they don't end with ...scuss this problem ...emonstrate that ...en and extra ones

Now have children ...
children how many ...
show that number ...
ask children to write ...
somewhere on their ...
that they can write ...

▶ **Represent O...**
Have the class name ...
class show the numb...
volunteer use Secret...
children write an eq...
with 10, such as 10 ...

Be sure to include t...
numbers as part of t...

• These numbers do ...
They are made up...

---

② Extending the Lesson

Differentiated Instruction Activities for Individualizing

Intervention
for students having difficulty
SMALL GROUPS

How Many?
Materials: index cards (9 per group), bags of 11–19 beans or other small objects (1 bag per child), paper plates (1 per child)

Have children in the group work together to write the numbers 11 through 19 on the index cards, one number on each card. Then put bags with a different number of beans (11–19) on the table at the center of the group. Give each child a paper plate with the number 10 written on it. Each child picks a bag and determines how many beans it has by counting 10 on the plate and the extra ones on the side. Then they choose the correct card and place it next to the plate. Have children check each other's cards and plates before they put the beans back in the bag. Then children pick a different bag and repeat the activity.

Math Writing Prompt
Intervention
Draw a Picture
Draw 17 triangles as a group of ten and extra ones.

On Level
for students having success
SMALL GROUPS

Number Change
Materials: MathBoard materials or 10 × 10 Grid (Copymaster M46)

Have one child call out a number between 10 and 20. Each child in the group writes the number on his or her MathBoard or paper and draws that number of circles on the grid. Next, another child calls out a different number between 10 and 20. Children record the number and decide if the number is greater or less than the number before. Then they show the new number by erasing some circles or drawing some circles, instead of erasing all the circles and starting over.

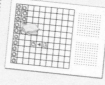

Math Writing Prompt
On Level
Use an Equation
Why is the equation 10 + 9 = 19 a good way to show the number 19? Write or draw your answer.

Challenge
for students seeking a challenge
INDIVIDUALS

Write a Teen Number Poem
Explain to children that a poem is a story that sometimes rhymes. Write the poem shown below on the board, and explain to the children that their task is to write a poem about a teen number. Discuss how the word "green" rhymes with "fifteen." Invite children to choose a teen number. Suggest they write all the words they can think of that rhyme with that number. When children have completed their poem, have them draw a picture to illustrate it. Then have them share their poems with the class or display them on a bulletin board.

Five little monkeys
sitting on the green.
Ten more monkeys came.
Now there are fifteen

Also use
Challenge Master for 4-2

Math Writing Prompt
Challenge
Explain Your Thinking
Suppose you are explaining to a friend that 13 has 1 ten and some extra ones. Write or draw how you would show this to your friend. Explain why you would show it that way.

Explore Teen Numbers **303**

---

③ Homework and Spiral Review

...practice

4-2
Remembering Goal: Spiral Review
This Remembering activity would be appropriate anytime after today's lesson.

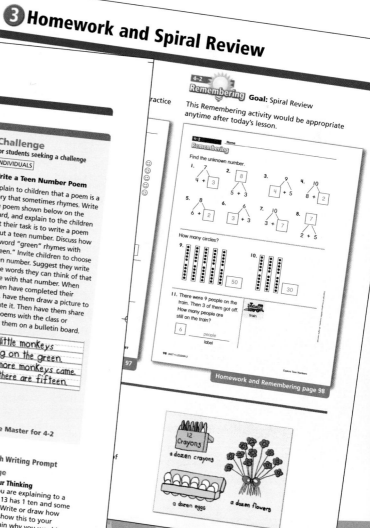

Remembering

Find the unknown number.

How many circles?

11. There were 9 people on the train. Then 3 of them got off. How many people are still on the train?

6 people

98 UNIT 4 LESSON 2

Homework and Remembering page 98

ix

Differentiated for

Every *Math Expressions* lesson includes intervention, on level, and challenge differentiation to support classroom needs. In addition, leveled math writing prompts provide opportunities for in-depth

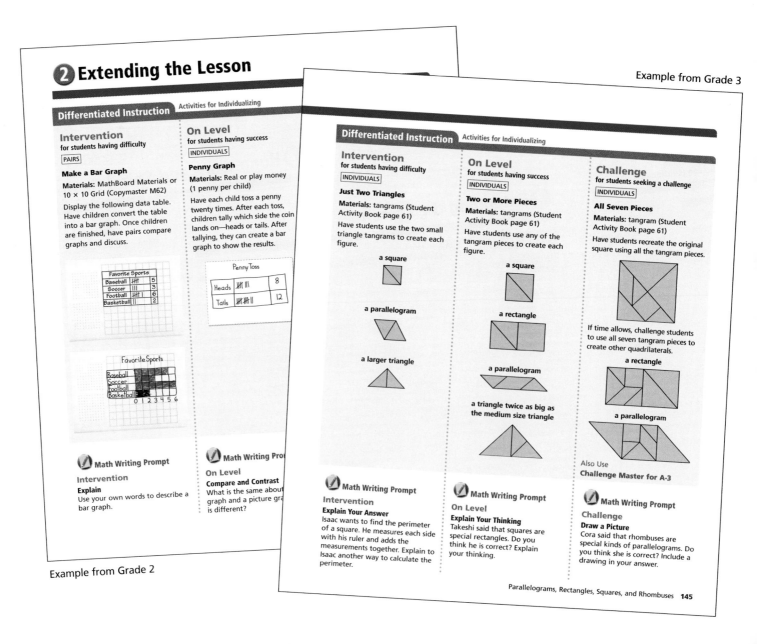

② Extending the Lesson

Example from Grade 3

Differentiated Instruction Activities for Individualizing

Intervention
for students having difficulty

PAIRS

Make a Bar Graph

Materials: MathBoard Materials or 10 × 10 Grid (Copymaster M62)

Display the following data table. Have children convert the table into a bar graph. Once children are finished, have pairs compare graphs and discuss.

Favorite Sports		
Baseball	ЖЖ	5
Soccer	III	3
Football	ЖЖ I	6
Basketball	II	2

Favorite Sports

Baseball
Soccer
Football
Basketball
0 1 2 3 4 5 6

Math Writing Prompt

Intervention

Explain
Use your own words to describe a bar graph.

On Level
for students having success

INDIVIDUALS

Penny Graph

Materials: Real or play money (1 penny per child)

Have each child toss a penny twenty times. After each toss, children tally which side the coin lands on—heads or tails. After tallying, they can create a bar graph to show the results.

Penny Toss

Heads	ЖЖ III	8
Tails	ЖЖ ЖЖ II	12

Math Writing Prompt

On Level

Compare and Contrast
What is the same about [a bar] graph and a picture gra[ph] is different?

Differentiated Instruction Activities for Individualizing

Intervention
for students having difficulty

INDIVIDUALS

Just Two Triangles

Materials: tangrams (Student Activity Book page 61)

Have students use the two small triangle tangrams to create each figure.

a square

a parallelogram

a larger triangle

Math Writing Prompt

Intervention

Explain Your Answer
Isaac wants to find the perimeter of a square. He measures each side with his ruler and adds the measurements together. Explain to Isaac another way to calculate the perimeter.

On Level
for students having success

INDIVIDUALS

Two or More Pieces

Materials: tangrams (Student Activity Book page 61)

Have students use any of the tangram pieces to create each figure.

a square

a rectangle

a parallelogram

a triangle twice as big as the medium size triangle

Math Writing Prompt

On Level

Explain Your Thinking
Takeshi said that squares are special rectangles. Do you think he is correct? Explain your thinking.

Challenge
for students seeking a challenge

INDIVIDUALS

All Seven Pieces

Materials: tangram (Student Activity Book page 61)

Have students recreate the original square using all the tangram pieces.

If time allows, challenge students to use all seven tangram pieces to create other quadrilaterals.

a rectangle

a parallelogram

Also Use
Challenge Master for A-3

Math Writing Prompt

Challenge

Draw a Picture
Cora said that rhombuses are special kinds of parallelograms. Do you think she is correct? Include a drawing in your answer.

Example from Grade 2

Parallelograms, Rectangles, Squares, and Rhombuses **145**

All Learners

thinking and analysis, and help prepare students for high-stakes tests. Support for English Language Learners is integrated throughout.

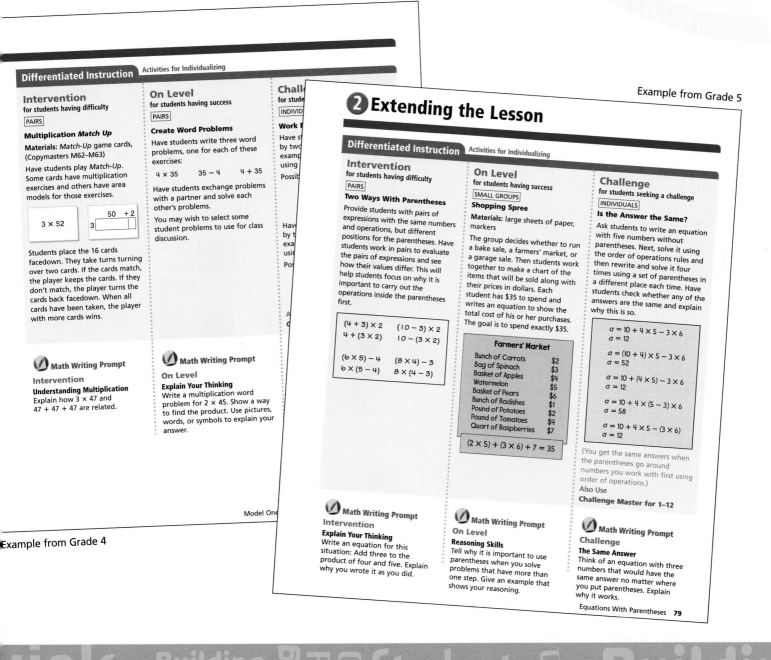

Example from Grade 5

Differentiated Instruction Activities for Individualizing

Intervention
for students having difficulty
PAIRS

Multiplication *Match Up*

Materials: *Match-Up* game cards, (Copymasters M62–M63)

Have students play *Match-Up*. Some cards have multiplication exercises and others have area models for those exercises.

3 × 52

3 | 50 +2

Students place the 16 cards facedown. They take turns turning over two cards. If the cards match, the player keeps the cards. If they don't match, the player turns the cards back facedown. When all cards have been taken, the player with more cards wins.

Math Writing Prompt

Intervention
Understanding Multiplication
Explain how 3 × 47 and 47 + 47 + 47 are related.

On Level
for students having success
PAIRS

Create Word Problems

Have students write three word problems, one for each of these exercises:

4 × 35   35 − 4   4 + 35

Have students exchange problems with a partner and solve each other's problems.

You may wish to select some student problems to use for class discussion.

Math Writing Prompt

On Level
Explain Your Thinking
Write a multiplication word problem for 2 × 45. Show a way to find the product. Use pictures, words, or symbols to explain your answer.

Chall for stude
INDIVID

Work Have st by two examp using

Possib

Have by t exa usi Po

A C

Model One

Example from Grade 4

2 Extending the Lesson

Differentiated Instruction Activities for Individualizing

Intervention
for students having difficulty
PAIRS

Two Ways With Parentheses

Provide students with pairs of expressions with the same numbers and operations, but different positions for the parentheses. Have students work in pairs to evaluate the pairs of expressions and see how their values differ. This will help students focus on why it is important to carry out the operations inside the parentheses first.

(4 + 3) × 2   (10 − 3) × 2
4 + (3 × 2)   10 − (3 × 2)

(6 × 5) − 4   (8 × 4) − 3
6 × (5 − 4)   8 × (4 − 3)

(2 × 5) + (3 × 6) + 7 = 35

Math Writing Prompt

Intervention
Explain Your Thinking
Write an equation for this situation: Add three to the product of four and five. Explain why you wrote it as you did.

On Level
for students having success
SMALL GROUPS

Shopping Spree

Materials: large sheets of paper, markers

The group decides whether to run a bake sale, a farmers' market, or a garage sale. Then students work together to make a chart of the items that will be sold along with their prices in dollars. Each student has $35 to spend and writes an equation to show the total cost of his or her purchases. The goal is to spend exactly $35.

Farmers' Market	
Bunch of Carrots	$2
Bag of Spinach	$3
Basket of Apples	$4
Watermelon	$5
Basket of Pears	$6
Bunch of Radishes	$1
Pound of Potatoes	$2
Pound of Tomatoes	$4
Quart of Raspberries	$7

Math Writing Prompt

On Level
Reasoning Skills
Tell why it is important to use parentheses when you solve problems that have more than one step. Give an example that shows your reasoning.

Challenge
for students seeking a challenge
INDIVIDUALS

Is the Answer the Same?

Ask students to write an equation with five numbers without parentheses. Next, solve it using the order of operations rules and then rewrite and solve it four times using a set of parentheses in a different place each time. Have students check whether any of the answers are the same and explain why this is so.

$a = 10 + 4 × 5 − 3 × 6$
$a = 12$

$a = (10 + 4) × 5 − 3 × 6$
$a = 52$

$a = 10 + (4 × 5) − 3 × 6$
$a = 12$

$a = 10 + 4 × (5 − 3) × 6$
$a = 58$

$a = 10 + 4 × 5 − (3 × 6)$
$a = 12$

(You get the same answers when the parentheses go around numbers you work with first using order of operations.)
Also Use
Challenge Master for 1–12

Math Writing Prompt

Challenge
The Same Answer
Think of an equation with three numbers that would have the same answer no matter where you put parentheses. Explain why it works.

Equations With Parentheses **79**

Validated Through Ten

For twenty-five years, Dr. Karen Fuson, Professor Emeritus of Education and Psychology at Northwestern University, researched effective methods of teaching and learning mathematics. During the last ten years, with the support of the

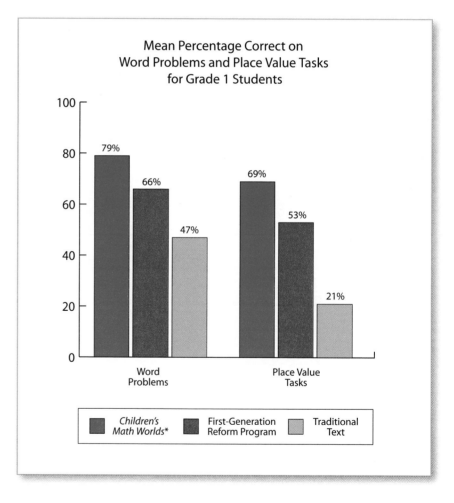

Mean Percentage Correct on
Word Problems and Place Value Tasks
for Grade 1 Students

Math Expressions is the curriculum developed from the *Children's Math Worlds Research Project.*

"I have many children who cheer when it's math time."
– Grade 2 Teacher

Years of Research

National Science Foundation for the *Children's Math Worlds Research Project*, Dr. Fuson began development of what is now the *Math Expressions* curriculum in real classrooms across the country.

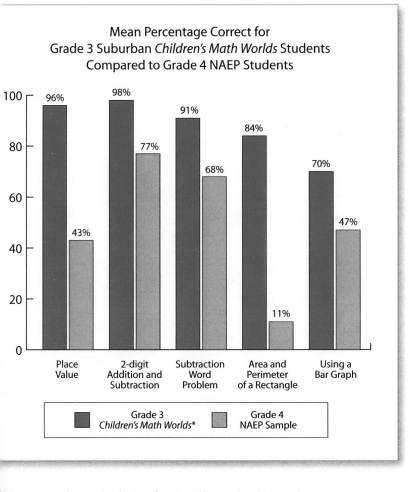

Mean Percentage Correct for
Grade 3 Suburban *Children's Math Worlds* Students
Compared to Grade 4 NAEP Students

- Place Value: 96% (Grade 3 Children's Math Worlds), 43% (Grade 4 NAEP Sample)
- 2-digit Addition and Subtraction: 98%, 77%
- Subtraction Word Problem: 91%, 68%
- Area and Perimeter of a Rectangle: 84%, 11%
- Using a Bar Graph: 70%, 47%

Grade 3 *Children's Math Worlds**   Grade 4 NAEP Sample

th Expressions is the curriculum developed from the *Children's Math Worlds Research Project*.

> "The mathematical growth was tremendous and the children had a great attitude about math. I would say their overall comment about math is, 'It is fun!'"
> – Grade 3 Teacher

Powered by Professional

Math Expressions incorporates a "learn while you teach" philosophy, in which elements of the Teacher's Edition—such as Mathematics Background, Class Management, and the Learning Classroom—work in conjunction with the program's thoughtful, research-based content to educate both teachers and students.

Development

To further help teachers and administrators implement *Math Expressions* with the highest levels of expertise, commitment, and confidence, Houghton Mifflin also offers specialized professional institutes.

Math Expressions Institutes

- **Administrator Institute**
  For administrators with school-based curriculum responsibilities

- **Level I Institute**
  For teachers who are new to *Math Expressions*

- **Level II Institute**
  For teachers who have at least six months' experience teaching *Math Expressions*

- **Math Expressions Blended Usage Institute**
  For teachers using *Math Expressions* with *Houghton Mifflin Math*

"**I**mproving teachers' subject matter knowledge and improving students' mathematics education are ... interwoven and interdependent processes.... What is needed, then, is a teaching context in which it is possible for teachers to improve their knowledge of school mathematics as they work to improve their teaching of mathematics."

– *Knowing and Teaching Elementary Mathematics*, Dr. Liping Ma (1999), p. 147

Math Expressions
Components

	Grades					
	K	1	2	3	4	5
Teacher's Guide, Volumes 1 and 2	•	•	•	•	•	•
Student Activity Book, Volumes 1 and 2	•	•	•	•	•	•
Homework and Remembering, Volumes 1 and 2	•	•	•	•	•	•
Teacher's Resource Book	•	•	•	•	•	•
Assessment Guide	•	•	•	•	•	•
Challenge Masters	•	•	•	•	•	•
Manipulatives and Materials Kit	•	•	•	•	•	•
Student MathBoard		•	•	•	•	•
Teacher MathBoard		•	•	•	•	•
Lesson Planner CD-ROM	•	•	•	•	•	•
***Ways to Assess* Test Generator**	•	•	•	•	•	•

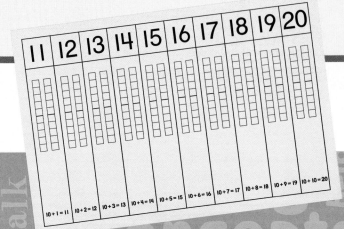

Materials and Manipulatives Kit for Grade 3

The essential materials needed for teaching *Math Expressions* are provided in the Student Activity Book and/or can be made from Copymasters in the Teacher's Resource Book. However, many teachers prefer to use the more sturdy materials from the Materials and Manipulatives Kit. This allows the students to take home the paper materials (from the Student Activity Book) or the cardstock materials (made from the Copymasters) to facilitate the connection between home and school.

Material or Manipulative in Grade 3 Kit	Pages in Student Activity Book	Copymasters in Teacher's Resource Book
Demonstration Secret Code Cards*		M3–M18
Secret Code Cards*	7–10	M19–M22
Strategy Cards*	245–270	M63–M88
120 Poster*		M60
Time Poster*		
Geometry and Measurement Poster*		
Class Multiplication Table Poster*		M50
Pointer		
Math Expressions 25-cm ruler		M26
Play Coins (pennies, nickels, dimes, and quarters)		M40
Play Bills (1-dollar, 5-dollar, 10-dollar)		
2-Color Counters		
Connecting Cubes		
Number Cubes		
Base Ten Blocks		
Pattern Blocks		M27
3-D Shapes		

* These materials were developed specifically for this program during the Children's Math Worlds Research Project.

Using the Materials and Manipulatives Kit for Each Unit

Material or Manipulative in Grade 3 Kit	Unit													
	1	A	2	B	3	C	4	D	5	E	6	F	7	G
Demonstration Secret Code Cards	•				•									
Secret Code Cards	•				•									
Strategy Cards							•		•					
120 Poster							•							
Time Poster										•				
Geometry and Measurement Poster														
Class Multiplication Table Poster							•		•					
Pointer	•	•	•	•	•	•	•	•	•	•	•	•	•	•
Math Expressions 25-cm ruler		•		•				•					•	
Play Coins (pennies, nickels, dimes, and quarters)	•				•		•				•			
Play Bills (1-dollar, 5-dollar, 10-dollar)	•				•						•			
Two-Color Counters	•		•			•	•		•		•			•
Connecting Cubes					•		•		•		•	•		
Number Cubes	•		•		•				•			•		•
Base Ten Blocks	•				•		•				•	•		
Pattern Blocks		•		•		•					•			
3-D Shapes												•		

All materials for each unit (including those not in the kit) are listed in the planning chart for that unit.

Introduction

History and Development

Math Expressions is a complete mathematics program for kindergarten through grade 5. It is a result of the Children's Math Worlds (CMW) Research Project conducted by Dr. Karen C. Fuson, Professor Emeritus at Northwestern University. This project was funded in part by the National Science Foundation.

The project studied the ways children around the world understand mathematical concepts, approach problem solving, and learn to do computation; included ten years of classroom research; and incorporated the ideas of participating students and teachers into the developing curriculum. The research focused on building conceptual supports that include special language, drawings, manipulatives, and classroom communication methods that facilitate language competence.

Within the curriculum a series of learning progressions reflect recent research regarding children's natural stages when mastering concepts such as addition, subtraction, multiplication, and problem solving. These learning stages help determine the order of concepts across grades, the sequence of units within grades, and the positioning of topics within units. The curriculum is designed to help teachers apply the most effective conceptual supports so that each child progresses as rapidly as possible.

The curriculum was developed within a context of both national and international mathematics education reform movements. These movements have focused on creating high standards that emphasize students' construction of mathematical knowledge. The curriculum meets the standards of the National Council of Teachers of Mathematics (NCTM) as well as various state and district goals.

During the ten years of research, students have shown increases in standardized test scores as well as in broader measures of student understanding. These results have been found for a wide range of both urban and suburban students from a variety of socio-economic groups.

Philosophy

Math Expressions is designed to incorporate the best of both traditional and reform mathematics curricula. The program strikes a balance between promoting children's natural solution methods and introducing effective procedures.

Because research has demonstrated that premature instruction in formalized procedures can lead to mechanical, unthinking behavior, established procedures for solving problems are not introduced until students have developed a solid conceptual foundation. Children begin by using their own knowledge to solve problems and then are introduced to research-based accessible methods, which are discussed so that children understand them.

In the process, many teachers discover new meanings behind their own solution methods and come to understand the methods that students use.

In order to promote children's natural solution methods, as well as to encourage students to become reflective and resourceful problem solvers, teachers need to develop a helping and explaining culture in their classrooms. Collaboration and peer helping deepen children's commitment to values such as responsibility and respect for others. *Math Expressions* offers opportunities for students to interact in pairs, small groups, whole-class activities, and special scenarios.

As students collaboratively investigate math situations, they develop communication skills, sharpen their mathematical reasoning, and enhance their social awareness. Integrating students' social and cultural worlds into their emerging math worlds in this way allows them to find their own voices and to connect real-world experiences to math concepts.

Main Concept Streams

Math Expressions focuses on crucially important core concepts at each grade level. This is the approach taken by most international curricula. These core topics are placed at grade levels that enable students to do well on standardized tests. Main related concept streams at all grade levels are number concepts and an algebraic approach to word problems.

Breaking apart numbers, or finding the embedded numbers, is a key concept running through the number concept units. Kindergarteners and first-graders find the numbers embedded within single-digit numbers and find the tens and ones in multi-digit numbers. Second- and third-graders continue breaking apart multi-digit numbers into ones and groups of tens, hundreds, and thousands. This activity facilitates their understanding of multi-digit addition, subtraction, and word problems. Second-, third-, and fourth-graders work on seeing the repeated groups within numbers, and this awareness helps them to master multiplication and division. Fourth- and fifth-graders approach fractions as sums of unit fractions using length models. This permits them to see and comprehend operations on fractions.

Students begin working with story problems early in kindergarten and continue throughout the other grades. They not only solve but also construct word problems. As a result, they become comfortable and flexible with mathematical language and can connect concepts and terminology with meaningful referents from their own lives. As part of this process, students learn to make meaningful math drawings that are both easier to use and more permanent than manipulatives. Such drawings enable teachers to see student thinking and facilitate communication.

Concepts and skills in algebra, geometry, measurement, and graphing are woven in among these two main streams throughout the grades. In grades two through five, geometry and measurement mini-units follow each regular unit.

Program Features

A number of special features and approaches contribute to the effectiveness of *Math Expressions*.

Quick Practice

The opening 5–10 minutes of each math period are dedicated to activities (often student-led) that allow students an opportunity to practice newly-acquired knowledge. These *consolidating activities* help students to become faster and more accurate with the concepts. Occasionally, *leading activities* prepare the ground for new concepts before they are introduced. Quick Practice activities are repeated so that they become familiar routines that students can do quickly and confidently.

Drawn Models

Special manipulatives are used at key points. However, students move toward math drawings as rapidly as possible. These drawn models help students relate to the math situation. The drawings facilitate students' explanations of the steps they took to solve the problem and help listeners comprehend these explanations. The drawings also give teachers insight into students' mathematical thinking, and they leave a durable record of student work that can be examined after class.

Language Development

Math Expressions offers a wealth of learning activities that directly support language development. In addition to verbalizing procedures and explanations, students are encouraged to write their own problems and describe their problem-solving strategies in writing as soon as they are able.

Homework Assignments

To help students achieve a high level of mathematical performance, students complete homework assignments every night. Families are expected to identify a homework helper to be responsible for monitoring the student's homework completion and to help if necessary. Homework not only develops and consolidates students become organized and self-regulatory.

Remembering Activities

Remembering Activities provide practice with the important concepts covered in all the units to date, and are ideal for spare classroom moments when students need a quick refresher of what they have learned so far. These pages are also valuable as extra homework pages that promote cumulative review as an ongoing synthesis of concepts.

Student Leaders

Student leaders lead Quick Practice activities and can help as needed during the solving phase of Solve and Discuss. They can manage materials. Such experiences build independence and confidence.

Math Talk

A significant part of the collaborative classroom culture is the frequent exchange of mathematical ideas and problem-solving strategies, or Math Talk. The benefits of Math Talk are multiple. Describing one's methods to another person can clarify one's own thinking as well as clarify the matter for others. Another person's approach can supply a new perspective, and frequent exposure to different approaches tends to engender flexible thinking.

In the collaborative Math Talk classroom, students can ask for and receive help, and errors can be identified and discussed so that everyone understands why they are wrong and shares better approaches. Student math drawings accompany early explanations in all domains, so that all students can understand and participate in the discussion.

Math Talk permits teachers to assess students' understanding on an ongoing basis. It encourages students to develop their language skills, both in math and in everyday English. Finally, Math Talk enables students to become active helpers and questioners, creating student-to-student talk that stimulates engagement and community.

The key supports for Math Talk are the various participant structures, or ways of organizing class guides the activity and helps students function productively, and students learn to work together as a community and also independently. Description of the most common participant structures follows.

Participant Structures

Solve and Discuss (Solve, Explain, Question, and Justify) at the Board

The teacher selects 4 to 5 students (or as many as space allows) to go to the classroom board and solve a problem, using any method they choose. Their classmates work on the same problem at their desks. Then the teacher picks 2 or 3 students to explain their methods. Students at their desks are encouraged to ask questions and to assist their classmates in understanding.

> **Benefits:** The board work reveals multiple methods of solving a problem, making comparisons possible and communicating to students that different methods are acceptable. The teacher can select methods to highlight in subsequent discussions. Spontaneous helping occurs frequently by students working next to each other at the board. Time is used efficiently because everyone in the class is working. In addition, errors can be identified in a supportive way and corrected and understood by students.

Student Pairs

Two students work together to solve a problem, to explain a solution method to each other, to role play within a mathematical situation (for example, buying and selling), to play a math game, or to help a partner having difficulties. They are called *helping pairs* when more advanced students are matched with students who are struggling. Pairs may be organized formally, or they may occur spontaneously as help is needed. Initially, it is useful to model pair activities, contrasting effective and ineffective helping. Continued discussion about how to help (for example, helping someone do it their way, not doing it for someone) can lead to improved helping by all.

Benefits: Pair work supports students in learning from each other, particularly in applying and practicing concepts introduced in whole-class discussion. Helping pairs often foster learning by both students as the helper strives to adopt the perspective of the novice. Helping almost always enables the helper to understand more deeply.

Whole-Class Practice and Student Leaders

This structure can be either teacher-led or student-led. When students lead it, it is usually at the consolidation stage, when children understand the concept and are beginning to achieve speed and automaticity. It is an excellent way for students to work together and learn from each other.

Benefits: Whole-class practice lets the less advanced students benefit from the knowledge of the more advanced students without having to ask for help directly. It also provides the teacher with a quick and easy means of assessing the progress of the class as a whole.

Scenarios

The main purpose of scenarios is to demonstrate mathematical relationships in a visual and memorable way. In scenario-based activities, a group of students is called to the front of the classroom to act out a particular situation. Scenarios are useful when a new concept is being introduced for the first time. They are especially valuable for demonstrating the physical reality that underlies such math concepts as embedded numbers (break-aparts) and regrouping.

Benefits: Because of its active and dramatic nature, the scenario structure often fosters a sense of intense involvement among children. In addition, scenarios create meaningful contexts in which students can reason about numbers and relate math to their everyday lives.

This is a variation of the Solve and Discuss structure. Again, several children go to the board to solve a problem. This time, however, a different student performs each step of the problem, describing the step before everyone does it. Everyone else at the board and at their desks carries out that step. This approach is particularly useful in learning multi-digit addition, subtraction, multiplication, and division. It assists the least-advanced students the most, providing them with accessible, systematic methods.

Benefits: This structure is especially effective when students are having trouble solving certain kinds of problems. The step-by-step structure allows students to grasp a method more easily than doing the whole method at once. It also helps students learn to verbalize their methods more clearly, as they can focus on describing just their own step.

Small Groups

Unstructured groups can form spontaneously if physical arrangements allow (for example, desks arranged in groups of four or children working at tables). Spontaneous helping between and among students as they work on problems individually can be encouraged.

For more structured projects, assign students to specific groups. It is usually a good idea to include a range of students and to have a strong reader in each group. Explain the problem or project and guide the groups as necessary. When students have finished, call a pair from each group to present and explain the results of their work or have the entire group present the results, with each member explaining one part of the solution or project. Having lower-performing students present first allows them to contribute, while higher-performing students expand on their efforts and give the fuller presentation.

Benefits: Students learn different strategies from each other for approaching a problem or task. They are invested in their classmates' learning because the presentation will be on behalf of the whole group.

VOLUME 1 CONTENTS

Unit 1 Place Value and Multi-Digit Addition and Subtraction

Big Idea Understand Place Value

Big Idea Group to Add

Mini Unit A Lines, Line Segments and Quadrilaterals

Big Idea Properties of Quadrilaterals

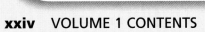

Unit 2 Addition and Subtraction Word Problems

Big Idea Solve Word Problems

Big Idea Solve Multi-Digit Word Problems

Overview 229A

Big Idea Properties of Quadrilaterals and Triangles

Unit 3 Use Addition and Subtraction

Overview 265A

Big Idea Round, Estimate, and Compare

Mini Unit C Patterns

 **Patterns**

Unit 4 Multiplication and Division with 0-5, 9 and 10

Big Idea Meanings of Multiplication and Division

Big Idea Practice Routines

Big Idea Strategies for Products and Factors

Mini Unit D Area and Perimeter

Big Idea Area and Perimeter

Unit 5 Multiplication and Division with 6, 7, and 8 and Problem Solving

Big Idea The Remaining Multiplications

Big Idea Multiplication Comparisons and Square Numbers

Big Idea Word Problems

Mini Unit E Time

Big Idea Time and Date

Unit 6 Exploring Fractions, Probability, and Division with Remainders

Mini Unit F Three-Dimensional Figures

Unit 7 Measurement

Mini Unit G Directions and Locations

Pacing Guide

Unit 1 is designed as a review of topics from Grade 2 but extends multi-digit addition and subtraction to larger numbers. Unit 6 builds strong conceptual development and skill fluency at a level often seen in the curricula of other countries that rank high in math performance. In the first year many classes may not cover all of the content of the later unit(s). But as more students experience *Math Expressions* in the previous grade(s) and teachers become familiar with *Math Expressions*, movement through the earlier units is more rapid and

classes are able to do more of the later material in greater depth. Some lessons in every unit, but especially the geometry and measurement mini-units, can be omitted if they do not focus on important state or district goals.

Be sure to do the Quick Practice activities with student leaders that begin each lesson, as they provide needed practice on core grade-level skills as well as supporting the growth of students as they lead these activities.

Unit	First Year — Pacing Suggestions	Days	Later Years — Pacing Suggestions	Days
1	Elicit student ideas and build community. Develop place value and grouping concepts. Mastery can build throughout Units 2 and 3, so move along quickly.	25	Many ideas are review for students who had Grade 2 *Math Expressions.* Move as quickly as you can while eliciting student ideas and building community.	19
A	Be sure that students understand these ideas.	9	These are central Grade 3 ideas.	7
2	The multi-digit word problems will be challenging. Unit 3 will continue to develop understanding, so continue on without mastery.	16	The multi-digit word problems will be challenging. Unit 3 will continue to develop understanding, so continue on without mastery.	12
B	Be sure that students understand these ideas.	7	These are central Grade 3 ideas.	6
3	Two-step word problems are difficult for some. Continue on and build fluency in multi-digit addition and subtraction.	28	Continue to move more quickly as fluency in multi-digit addition and subtraction builds.	21
C	Do only important district and state goals.	3	Do only important district and state goals.	4
4	Spend time on patterns, word problem situations, and building fluency in multiplication and division. Most ideas will continue into Unit 5.	26	Move more quickly than in Year 1. In Unit 6, target word problems and basic multiplication and division fluency for individual students.	19
D	Area and perimeter are key Grade 3 topics.	6	Area and perimeter are key Grade 3 topics.	4
5	Fluency with 6s, 7s, and 8s can continue to build all year. Two-step word problems will remain difficult for some. All students should be mastering single-step (but not multi-step) word problems with all 4 operations.	26	Fluency with all numbers can build in Units 6 and 7 where basic multiplication and division are used, so go on. All students should be mastering single-step (but not multi-step) problems with all 4 operations.	21
E	Lesson 3 is optional.	4	Lesson 3 is optional, but students enjoy Lesson 3.	4
6	Lessons 1 through 5 are a nice introduction. The ideas in this unit will be built in depth in Grade 4.	5	This unit provides experiences to support earlier ideas and will provide a strong basis for Grade 4 fractions.	21
F	Teach the important goals and content of the lesson.	2	This lesson is good for building students' spatial visualization.	6
7	Concentrate on important district and state goals. Lessons 7 and 8 continue Unit 6 fraction ideas.	2	Concentrate on important district and state goals. Lessons 7 and 8 continue Unit 6 fraction ideas.	12
G	Maps and directions relate to other subject areas.	1	Explore coordinate graphing if these are part of your state goals.	4
All Units	Total Days	160	Total Days	160

NCTM Correlation

Number and Operations Standards and Expectations	Math Expressions Correlation to Expectations for Grade 3
Understand numbers, ways of representing numbers, relationships among numbers, and number systems	
• understand the place-value structure of the base-ten number system and be able to represent and compare whole numbers and decimals;	Unit 1, Lesson 1–Lesson 4; Unit 3, Lesson 3
• recognize equivalent representations for the same number and generate them by decomposing and composing numbers;	Unit 1, Lesson 1–Lesson 4; Unit 3, Lesson 4–Lesson 5
• develop understanding of fractions as parts of unit wholes, as parts of a collection, as locations on number lines, and as divisions of whole numbers;	Unit 5, Lesson 6–Lesson 7; Lesson 12; Unit 6, Lesson 1–Lesson 7; Unit 7, Lesson 7
• use models, benchmarks, and equivalent forms to judge the size of fractions;	Unit 6, Lesson 1–Lesson 3; Lesson 7; Lesson 9–Lesson 13
• recognize and generate equivalent forms of commonly used fractions, decimals, and percents;	Unit 6, Lesson 7; Lesson 9–Lesson 13; Lesson 16
• explore numbers less than 0 by extending the number line and through familiar applications;	Unit 7, Lesson 10
• describe classes of numbers according to characteristics such as the nature of their factors.	Unit 5, Lesson 6
Understand meanings of operations and how they relate to one another	
• understand various meanings of multiplication and division;	Unit 4, Lesson 1–Lesson 16; Unit 5, Lesson 1–Lesson 14
• understand the effects of multiplying and dividing whole numbers;	Unit 4, Lesson 1–Lesson 16; Unit 5, Lesson 1–Lesson 14
• identify and use relationships between operations, such as division as the inverse of multiplication, to solve problems;	Unit 2, Lesson 1–Lesson 3; Unit 4, Lesson 5–Lesson 16; Unit 5, Lesson 1–Lesson 14
• understand and use properties of operations, such as the distributivity of multiplication over addition.	Unit 4, Lesson 3; Unit 5, Lesson 9

NCTM Correlation

Number and Operations (continued) Standards and Expectations	Math Expressions Correlation to Expectations for Grade 3
Compute fluently and make reasonable estimates	
• develop fluency with basic number combinations for multiplication and division and use these combinations to mentally compute related problems, such as 30 × 50;	Unit 4, Lesson 1–Lesson 16; Unit 5, Lesson 1–Lesson 14
• develop fluency in adding, subtracting, multiplying, and dividing whole numbers;	Unit 1, Lesson 5–Lesson 15; Unit 2, Lesson 1–Lesson 8; Unit 4, Lesson 1–Lesson 16; Unit 5, Lesson 1–Lesson 14; Unit 6, Lesson 18–Lesson 20
• develop and use strategies to estimate the results of whole-number computations and to judge the reasonableness of such results;	Unit 3, Lesson 1–Lesson 3
• develop and use strategies to estimate computations involving fractions and decimals in situations relevant to students' experience;	Unit 3, Lesson 7
• use visual models, benchmarks, and equivalent forms to add and subtract commonly used fractions and decimals;	Unit 6, Lesson 14–Lesson 17; Unit 7, Lesson 4
• select appropriate methods and tools for computing with whole numbers from among mental computation, estimation, calculators, and paper and pencil according to the context and nature of the computation and use the selected method or tool.	Unit 1, Lesson 8; Lesson 9; Lesson 14; Lesson 15; Unit 3, Lesson 7

Algebra Standards and Expectations	Math Expressions Correlation to Expectations for Grade 3
Understand patterns, relations, and functions	
• describe, extend, and make generalizations about geometric and numeric patterns;	Unit C, Lesson 1, Lesson 3; Unit 4, Lesson 14; Unit 5, Lesson 3; Lesson 5; Lesson 8
• represent and analyze patterns and functions, using words, tables, and graphs.	Unit 3, Lesson 8; Unit C, Lesson 3; Unit 4, Lesson 5; Lesson 12; Unit 5, Lesson 1; Lesson 8; Lesson 13; Unit 7, Lesson 8–Lesson 9
Represent and analyze mathematical situations and structures using algebraic symbols	
• identify such properties as commutativity, associativity, and distributivity and use them to compute with whole numbers;	Unit 4, Lesson 3, Lesson 14; Unit 5, Lesson 11–Lesson 12
• represent the idea of a variable as an unknown quantity using a letter or a symbol;	Unit 2, Lesson 1–Lesson 3; Lesson 6; Unit D, Lesson 3; Unit 5, Lesson 2
• express mathematical relationships using equations.	Unit 2, Lesson 1–Lesson 3; Lesson 6; Lesson 8; Unit D, Lesson 3; Unit 3, Lesson 13; Unit 5, Lesson 8; Lesson 11–Lesson 12; Lesson 14

NCTM Correlation

Algebra (continued) Standards and Expectations	Math Expressions Correlation to Expectations for Grade 3
Use mathematical models to represent and understand quantitative relationships	
• model problem situations with objects and use representations such as graphs, tables, and equations to draw conclusions.	Unit 2, Lesson 1–Lesson 3; Unit 3, Lesson 8; Lesson 10; Lesson 16; Unit C, Lesson 3; Unit 5, Lesson 1–Lesson 2; Lesson 7; Lesson 11–Lesson 12; Unit 6, Lesson 7; Unit 7, Lesson 8
Analyze change in various contexts	
• investigate how a change in one variable relates to a change in a second variable;	Unit 5, Lesson 1; Lesson 7–Lesson 8; Lesson 13; Unit 7, Lesson 8–Lesson 9
• identify and describe situations with constant or varying rates of change and compare them.	Unit 5, Lesson 7; Unit 7, Lesson 8–Lesson 9

Geometry Standards and Expectations	Math Expressions Correlation to Expectations for Grade 3
Analyze characteristics and properties of two- and three-dimensional geometric shapes and develop mathematical arguments about geometric relationships	
• identify, compare, and analyze attributes of two- and three-dimensional shapes and develop vocabulary to describe the attributes;	Unit A, Lesson 3–Lesson 5; Unit B, Lesson 1; Lesson 3; Lesson 4; Unit F, Lesson 1–Lesson 5
• classify two- and three-dimensional shapes according to their properties and develop definitions of classes of shapes such as triangles and pyramids;	Unit A, Lesson 3–Lesson 5; Unit B, Lesson 1–Lesson 3; Unit F, Lesson 3–Lesson 5
• investigate and predict the results of putting together and taking apart two- and three-dimensional shapes.	Unit A, Lesson 3; Lesson 4; Unit B, Lesson 1–Lesson 3 Unit F, Lesson 1; Lesson 2
• investigate, describe, and reason about the results of subdividing, combining, and transforming shapes;	Unit A, Lesson 3; Lesson 4, Unit B, Lesson 1; Lesson 2; Unit C, Lesson 1
• explore congruence and similarity;	Unit B, Lesson 1; Lesson 2
• make and test conjectures about geometric properties and relationships and develop logical arguments to justify conclusions.	Unit A, Lesson 4; Lesson 5; Unit B, Lesson 1; Lesson 3; Unit D, Lesson 2; Unit F, Lesson 1

NCTM Correlation

Geometry (continued) Standards and Expectations	Math Expressions Correlation to Expectations for Grade 3
Specify locations and describe spatial relationships using coordinate geometry and other representational systems	
• describe location and movement using common language and geometric vocabulary;	Unit G, Lesson 1–Lesson 3
• make and use coordinate systems to specify locations and to describe paths;	Unit G, Lesson 1–Lesson 3
• find the distance between points along horizontal and vertical lines of a coordinate system.	Unit G, Lesson 1–Lesson 3
Apply transformations and use symmetry to analyze mathematical situations	
• predict and describe the results of sliding, flipping, and turning two-dimensional shapes;	Unit B, Lesson 1; Lesson 2, Unit C, Lesson 1–Lesson 3
• describe a motion or a series of motions that will show that two shapes are congruent;	Unit B, Lesson 1; Lesson 2; Unit C, Lesson 1
• identify and describe line and rotational symmetry in two- and three-dimensional shapes and designs.	Unit B, Lesson 1; Lesson 2; Unit C, Lesson 1
Use visualization, spatial reasoning, and geometric modeling to solve problems	
• build and draw geometric objects;	Unit A, Lesson 4; Lesson 5; Unit B, Lesson 1; Lesson 2; Unit C, Lesson 1–Lesson 3; Unit D, Lesson 1–Lesson 3; Unit F, Lesson 1–Lesson 5; Unit G, Lesson 1–Lesson 3
• create and describe mental images of objects, patterns, and paths;	Unit A, Lesson 2; Lesson 3; Unit C, Lesson 1; Lesson 3; Unit D, Lesson 1; Unit F, Lesson 1
• identify and build a three-dimensional object from two-dimensional representations of that object;	Unit F, Lesson 1–Lesson 4
• identify and build a two-dimensional representation of a three-dimensional object;	Unit F, Lesson 2–Lesson 4
• use geometric models to solve problems in other areas of mathematics, such as number and measurement;	Unit C, Lesson 3; Unit 4, Lesson 10; Unit D, Lesson 1–Lesson 3; Unit F, Lesson 2
• recognize geometric ideas and relationships and apply them to other disciplines and to problems that arise in the classroom or in everyday life.	Unit C, Lesson 3; Unit D, Lesson 1; Unit F, Lesson 2, Unit G, Lesson 2

NCTM Correlation

Measurement Standards and Expectations	Math Expressions Correlation to Expectations for Grade 3
Understand measurable attributes of objects and the units, systems, and processes of measurement	
• understand such attributes as length, area, weight, volume, and size of angle and select the appropriate type of unit for measuring each attribute;	Unit A, Lesson 1–Lesson 4; Unit B, Lesson 1; Lesson 2; Lesson 4; Unit 4, Lesson 10; Unit D, Lesson 1–Lesson 3; Unit 5, Lesson 2; Lesson 4; Lesson 8; Unit 7, Lesson 1; Lesson 3–Lesson 6; Lesson 9; Unit E, Lesson 1–Lesson 3; Unit F, Lesson 5; Unit G, Lesson 1; Lesson 3
• understand the need for measuring with standard units and become familiar with standard units in the customary and metric systems;	Unit A, Lesson I; Unit 7, Lesson 1–Lesson 3; Lesson 5–Lesson 6; Lesson 9–Lesson 10; Unit E, Lesson 1–Lesson 3
• carry out simple unit conversions, such as from centimeters to meters, within a system of measurement;	Unit 7, Lesson 2–Lesson 3; Lesson 5–Lesson 9
• understand that measurements are approximations and how differences in units affect precision;	Unit A, Lesson 1; Unit 7, Lesson 1; Lesson 4
• explore what happens to measurements of a two-dimensional shape such as its perimeter and area when the shape is changed in some way.	Unit A, Lesson 4; Unit D, Lesson 1; Lesson 2
Apply appropriate techniques, tools, and formulas to determine measurements	
• develop strategies for estimating the perimeters, areas, and volumes of irregular shapes;	Unit D, Lesson 1; Unit F, Lesson 5
• select and apply appropriate standard units and tools to measure length, area, volume, weight, time, temperature, and the size of angles;	Unit A, Lesson 1–Lesson 4; Unit B, Lesson 2; Lesson 3; Unit D, Lesson 1–Lesson 3; Unit 7, Lesson 1–Lesson 5; Lesson 9–Lesson 10; Unit E, Lesson 1–Lesson 3; Unit F, Lesson 5; Unit G, Lesson 1–Lesson 3
• select and use benchmarks to estimate measurements;	Unit 7, Lesson 2–Lesson 3; Lesson 5; Lesson 9–Lesson 10
• develop, understand, and use formulas to find the area of rectangles and related triangles and parallelograms;	Unit D, Lesson 2; Lesson 3
• develop strategies to determine the surface areas and volumes of rectangular solids.	Unit F, Lesson 2

NCTM Correlation

Data Analysis and Probability Standards and Expectations	Math Expressions Correlation to Expectations for Grade 3
Formulate questions that can be addressed with data and collect, organize, and display relevant data to answer them	
• design investigations to address a question and consider how data-collection methods affect the nature of the data set;	Unit 3, Lesson 15; Lesson 17
• collect data using observations, surveys, and experiments;	Unit 3, Lesson 10; Lesson 15; Lesson 17
• represent data using tables and graphs such as line plots, bar graphs, and line graphs;	Unit 3, Lesson 8–Lesson 10; Lesson 15; Lesson 16; Lesson 17; Unit 4, Lesson 5
• recognize the differences in representing categorical and numerical data.	Unit 3, Lesson 17; Unit 6, Lesson 8
Select and use appropriate statistical methods to analyze data	
• describe the shape and important features of a set of data and compare related data sets, with an emphasis on how the data are distributed;	Unit 3, Lesson 10; Lesson 15; Lesson 17
• use measures of center, focusing on the median, and understand what each does and does not indicate about the data set;	Unit 3, Lesson 17
• compare different representations of the same data and evaluate how well each representation shows important aspects of the data.	Unit 3, Lesson 16–Lesson 17
Develop and evaluate inferences and predictions that are based on data	
• propose and justify conclusions and predictions that are based on data and design studies to further investigate the conclusions or predictions.	Unit 3, Lesson 15–Lesson 17; Unit 4, Lesson 5; Unit 5, Lesson 7; Unit 6, Lesson 3–Lesson 5; Lesson 7; Lesson 8
Understand and apply basic concepts of probability	
• describe events as likely or unlikely and discuss the degree of likelihood using such words as *certain, equally likely,* and *impossible;*	Unit 6, Lesson 8
• predict the probability of outcomes of simple experiments and test the predictions;	Unit 6, Lesson 8
• understand that the measure of the likelihood of an event can be represented by a number from 0 to 1.	Unit 6, Lesson 8

NCTM Correlation

Problem Solving Standards and Expectations	Math Expressions Correlation to Expectations for Grade 3
• build new mathematical knowledge through problem solving;	Unit 1, Lesson 5; Lesson 10; Unit 2, Lesson 3–Lesson 4; Unit 3, Lesson 4–Lesson 6; Lesson 10; Lesson 13–Lesson 14; Lesson 17; Unit 4, Lesson 3–Lesson 4; Lesson 10; Lesson 12; Unit 5, Lesson 2; Lesson 6–Lesson 7; Lesson 10–Lesson 11; Lesson 14; Unit 6, Lesson 3; Lesson 6; Lesson 11; Lesson 14–Lesson 15; Lesson 17–Lesson 20; Unit 7, Lesson 5
• solve problems that arise in mathematics and in other contexts;	Unit 1, Lesson 3–Lesson 7; Lesson 10–Lesson 15; Unit 2, Lesson 1–Lesson 8; Unit 3, Lesson 4–Lesson 7; Lesson 9–Lesson 15; Unit 4, Lesson 1; Lesson 3–Lesson 6; Lesson 8; Lesson 10–Lesson 11; Unit 5, Lesson 2; Lesson 4; Lesson 6–Lesson 7; Lesson 10–Lesson 14; Unit 6, Lesson 3; Lesson 5–Lesson 6; Lesson 11–Lesson 13; Unit 7, Lesson 6–Lesson 7
• apply and adapt a variety of appropriate strategies to solve problems;	Unit 1, Lesson 3–Lesson 7; Lesson 10–Lesson 15; Unit 2, Lesson 1; Unit 3, Lesson 4–Lesson 7; Lesson 9–Lesson 15; Lesson 17; Unit 4, Lesson 1; Lesson 3–Lesson 4; Lesson 6; Lesson 8; Lesson 10–Lesson 12; Lesson 16; Unit 5, Lesson 4; Lesson 6–Lesson 7; Lesson 10–Lesson 14; Unit 6, Lesson 3; Lesson 5–Lesson 6; Lesson 11–Lesson 15; Lesson 17–Lesson 20
• monitor and reflect on the process of mathematical problem solving.	Unit 1, Lesson 3–Lesson 7; Lesson 10–Lesson 15; Unit 2, Lesson 1–Lesson 8; Unit 3, Lesson 4–Lesson 7; Lesson 9–Lesson 15; Unit 4, Lesson 3–Lesson 4; Lesson 6; Lesson 10–Lesson 11; Lesson 16; Unit 5, Lesson 3; Lesson 6; Lesson 7; Lesson 10–Lesson 14; Unit 6, Lesson 3; Lesson 5–Lesson 6; Lesson 11–Lesson 15; Lesson 17–Lesson 20; Unit 7, Lesson 5–Lesson 7

Reasoning and Proof Standards and Expectations	Math Expressions Correlation to Expectations for Grade 3
• recognize reasoning and proof as fundamental aspects of mathematics;	Unit 3, Lesson 1–Lesson 2; Lesson 9; Unit 5, Lesson 10
• make and investigate mathematical conjectures;	Unit B, Lesson 1–Lesson 3; Unit 3, Lesson 1–Lesson 2; Unit C, Lesson 2, Lesson 3; Lesson 5; Lesson 10; Unit 7, Lesson 5; Lesson 7
• develop and evaluate mathematical arguments and proofs;	Unit 3, Lesson 1–Lesson 2; Unit C, Lesson 3; Lesson 5; Lesson 10; Unit 7, Lesson 5; Lesson 7
• select and use various types of reasoning and methods of proof.	Unit 2, Lesson 7; Unit 3, Lesson 1–Lesson 2; Lesson 9, Unit C, Lesson 3; Lesson 4; Lesson 10–Lesson 11; Lesson 13–Lesson 14; Unit 5, Lesson 10; Unit 7, Lesson 5; Lesson 7

NCTM Correlation

Communication Standards and Expectations	*Math Expressions* Correlation to Expectations for Grade 3
• organize and consolidate their mathematical thinking through communication;	Unit 1, Lesson 3–Lesson 4; Unit B, Lesson 4; Lesson 6; Lesson 12–Lesson 15; Unit 2, Lesson 1–Lesson 5; Unit 3, Lesson 3–Lesson 6; Lesson 8–Lesson 12; Lesson 15–Lesson 16; Unit 4, Lesson 11; Unit 5, Lesson 10; Unit 6, Lesson 15–Lesson 16; Unit 7, Lesson 1–Lesson 4; Lesson 9–Lesson 10
• communicate their mathematical thinking coherently and clearly to peers, teachers, and others;	Unit 1, Lesson 3–Lesson 4; Unit B, Lesson 4; Lesson 6; Lesson 12–Lesson 15; Unit 2, Lesson 1–Lesson 5; Unit 3, Lesson 4–Lesson 6; Lesson 8–Lesson 9; Lesson 11–Lesson 12; Lesson 14; Lesson 16; Unit 4, Lesson 11; Lesson 13; Lesson 16; Unit 5, Lesson 6; Lesson 10; Unit 6, Lesson 15–Lesson 16; Unit 7, Lesson 1–Lesson 4; Lesson 9–Lesson 10
• analyze and evaluate the mathematical thinking and strategies of others;	Unit 1, Lesson 3–Lesson 4; Lesson 6; Lesson 12–Lesson 15; Unit 2, Lesson 1–Lesson 5; Unit 3, Lesson 4–Lesson 5; Lesson 8–Lesson 12; Lesson 14; Lesson 16; Unit 4, Lesson 11; Lesson 13; Lesson 16; Unit 5, Lesson 10; Unit 6, Lesson 16; Unit 7, Lesson 1–Lesson 4; Lesson 9–Lesson 10
• use the language of mathematics to express mathematical ideas precisely.	Unit 1, Lesson 3–Lesson 4; Lesson 6; Lesson 12–Lesson 15; Unit A, Lesson 5; Unit 2, Lesson 1–Lesson 5; Unit 3, Lesson 3–Lesson 6; Lesson 8–Lesson 12; Lesson 16; Unit 4, Lesson 11; Lesson 16; Unit 5, Lesson 10; Unit 6, Lesson 15–Lesson 16; Unit 7, Lesson 1–Lesson 4; Lesson 9–Lesson 10

Connections Standards and Expectations	*Math Expressions* Correlation to Expectations for Grade 3
• recognize and use connections among mathematical ideas;	Unit B, Lesson 1; Lesson 3; Lesson 4; Unit 3, Lesson 4; Lesson 10; Lesson 12; Lesson 14; Unit 4, Lesson 12–Lesson 13; Unit D, Lesson 1–Lesson 3; Unit 5, Lesson 10; Lesson 14; Unit E, Lesson 1–Lesson 3; Unit F, Lesson 1–Lesson 5; Unit G, Lesson 2
• understand how mathematical ideas interconnect and build on one another to produce a coherent whole;	Unit 3, Lesson 4; Lesson 10; Lesson 12; Lesson 14; Unit 4, Lesson 12–Lesson 13; Unit 5, Lesson 10; Lesson 14
• recognize and apply mathematics in contexts outside of mathematics.	Unit 1, Lesson 2–Lesson 3; Lesson 6–Lesson 15; Unit 2, Lesson 2–Lesson 8; Unit 3, Lesson 2–Lesson 11; Lesson 13–Lesson 16; Unit 4, Lesson 2; Lesson 4; Lesson 6; Lesson 8–Lesson 13; Lesson 15–Lesson 16; Unit 5, Lesson 2–Lesson 13; Unit 6, Lesson 2–Lesson 7; Lesson 9–Lesson 21; Unit 7, Lesson 1–Lesson 10; Unit E, Lesson 1–Lesson 3; Unit F, Lesson 2; Unit G, Lesson 2

NCTM Correlation

Representation Standards and Expectations	Math Expressions Correlation to Expectations for Grade 3
• create and use representations to organize, record, and communicate mathematical ideas;	Unit 1, Lesson 1–Lesson 4; Unit A, Lesson 2; Lesson 4; Unit 2, Lesson 6–Lesson 8; Unit B, Lesson 2; Unit 3, Lesson 4; Lesson 7; Lesson 10–Lesson 11; Lesson 14; Lesson 16; Unit C, Lesson 1; Unit 4, Lesson 1–Lesson 5; Lesson 7–Lesson 8; Lesson 16; Unit 5, Lesson 1–Lesson 3; Lesson 5–Lesson 8; Lesson 11; Lesson 13; Unit 6, Lesson 1–Lesson 7; Lesson 9–Lesson 17; Unit 7, Lesson 1–Lesson 4; Lesson 10; Unit E, Lesson 2; Unit F, Lesson 2–Lesson 4; Unit G, Lesson 1–Lesson 3
• select, apply, and translate among mathematical representations to solve problems;	Unit 1, Lesson 3–Lesson 5; Unit 2, Lesson 6–Lesson 8; Unit 3, Lesson 4; Lesson 7; Lesson 10–Lesson 11; Lesson 16; Unit 4, Lesson 1–Lesson 5; Lesson 7–Lesson 8; Lesson 16; Unit 5, Lesson 1; Lesson 3; Lesson 5–Lesson 8; Lesson 11; Unit 6, Lesson 1–Lesson 7; Lesson 9–Lesson 17; Unit E, Lesson 2
• use representations to model and interpret physical, social, and mathematical phenomena.	Unit 2, Lesson 6–Lesson 8; Unit 3, Lesson 4; Lesson 7; Lesson 10–Lesson 11; Lesson 14; Unit 4, Lesson 1–Lesson 5; Lesson 7–Lesson 8; Lesson 16; Unit 5, Lesson 1–Lesson 3; Lesson 5–Lesson 8; Lesson 11; Unit 6, Lesson 1–Lesson 7; Lesson 9–Lesson 17; Unit 7, Lesson 1–Lesson 4; Lesson 10

Place Value and Multi-Digit Addition and Subtraction

THE GOAL FOR UNIT 1 is to develop multi-digit addition and subtraction methods that are meaningful and easily used by students. Place-value activities build understanding of the base-ten numeration system and provide the foundation to understand grouping and ungrouping. Students will use drawings to show grouping and ungrouping, and then will describe and discuss the process.

UNIT 1 CONTENTS

Unit 1 Assessment

✓ Unit Objectives Tested	Unit Test Items	Lessons
1.1 Read, write, identify, and represent the place value of whole numbers.	1–9, 20	1–4
1.2 Add and subtract whole numbers.	10–14	5, 6, 8–15
1.3 Add and subtract money amounts.	15–17	7
1.4 Write a related subtraction word problem for an addition problem and vice versa.	18, 19	13

Formal Assessment	Informal Assessment	Review Opportunities
Open or Free Response Tests • Quick Quizzes (Assessment Guide) • Unit Review and Test (Student Activity Book pages 45–46, Teacher's Guide pages 121–124. • Unit 1 Test Form A (Assessment Guide) • Unit 1 Open Response Test (Test Generator) • Test Bank Items for Unit 1 (Test Generator) **Multiple Choice Tests** • Unit 1 Test Form B (Assessment Guide) • Unit 1 Multiple Choice Test (Test Generator) • Test Bank Items for Unit 1 (Test Generator) **Performance Tasks** • Unit 1 Performance Assessment (Assessment Guide)	**Ongoing Assessment** • In every Teacher's Guide lesson **Performance Assessment** • Class discussions • Small-group work • Quick Practice (in every lesson) • Individual work on teacher-selected tasks **Portfolios** • See Unit 1 Review and Test for suggestions for selecting items for portfolios. • Some Homework pages are noted as suitable for portfolio inclusion.	**Homework and Remembering** • Homework pages provide review of recently taught topics. • Remembering pages provide spiral review. **Teacher's Guide** • Unit Review and Test (page 121) **Test Generator CD-ROM** • Test Bank Items can be used to create custom review sheets.

Planning Unit 1

See pages xvii and xviii for a list of unit materials and manipulatives that are available in the *Math Expressions* Kit.

Lesson Title	Lesson Resources	Materials and Manipulatives	
		Math Expressions	**Other**
1 Make Place Value Drawings	Family Letter Student Activity Book pages 1–6 Homework and Remembering pages 1–2	MathBoard materials, Dot Array (Copymaster M1)	Base ten blocks, number cubes (1–6), Math Journals
2 Build Numbers and Represent Money Amounts	Student Activity Book pages 7–12 Homework and Remembering pages 2–4	MathBoard materials, pointer, Demonstration Secret Code Cards (Copymasters M3–M18), Secret Code Cards (Copymasters M19–M22), Dot Array (Copymaster M1), Ten Frame (Copymaster M2), Play Money (Copymaster M40)	Envelopes or small bags, scissors, two-color counters, index cards, Math Journals
3 Place Value in Word Problems	Student Activity Book pages 13–14 Homework and Remembering pages 4–6	MathBoard materials, Demonstration Secret Code Cards (Copymasters M3–M18), Secret Code Cards (Copymasters M19–M22)	Base ten blocks, sentence strips, sticky notes, Math Journals
4 Practice with Place Value	Student Activity Book pages 15–18 Homework and Remembering pages 6–8 Quick Quiz 1	MathBoard materials, Demonstration Secret Code Cards (Copymasters M3–M18), Secret Code Cards (Copymasters M19–M22), Ten Frame (Copymaster M2), Place Value Strips (Copymaster M23)	Scissors, index cards, two-color counters, Math Journals
5 Explore Multi-Digit Addition	Family Letter Student Activity Book pages 19–22 Homework and Remembering pages 9–10	MathBoard materials, Demonstration Secret Code Cards (Copymasters M3–M18), Secret Code Cards (Copymasters M19–M22), Game Cards (Copymaster M25)	Base ten blocks, index cards, Math Journals
6 Discuss Addition Methods	Student Activity Book pages 23–24 Homework and Remembering pages 11–12	MathBoard materials, Demonstration Secret Code Cards (Copymasters M3–M18), Secret Code Cards (Copymasters M19–M22), Game Cards (Copymaster M25), Spinner A (Copymaster M24)	Base ten blocks, paper clips, Math Journals
7 Addition with Dollars and Cents	Student Activity Book pages 25–26 Homework and Remembering pages 13–14	MathBoard materials, Demonstration Secret Code Cards (Copymasters M3–M18), Play Money (Copymaster M40),	Grocery store ads, index cards, Math Journals
8 The Grouping Concept in Addition	Student Activity Book pages 27–28 Homework and Remembering pages 15–16	MathBoard materials, Demonstration Secret Code Cards (Copymasters M3–M18), Game Cards (Copymaster M25)	Restaurant menus, index cards, rulers, Math Journals
9 Practice Addition	Student Activity Book pages 29–30 Homework and Remembering pages 17–18 Quick Quiz 2	MathBoard materials, Demonstration Secret Code Cards (Copymasters M3–M18), Play Money (Copymaster M40)	Restaurant menus, Math Journals

Planning Unit 1

Lesson Title	Lesson Resources	Materials and Manipulatives	
		Math Expressions	**Other**
10 Ungroup to Subtract	Student Activity Book pages 31–32 Homework and Remembering pages 19–20	MathBoard materials, Demonstration Secret Code Cards (Copymasters M3–M18), Game Cards (Copymaster M25)	Base ten blocks, index cards, Math Journals
11 Subtract Across Zeros	Student Activity Book pages 33–36 Homework and Remembering pages 21–22	MathBoard materials, Demonstration Secret Code Cards (Copymasters M3–M18), Play Money (Copymaster M40)	Paper bags, Math Journals
12 Discuss Methods of Subtracting	Student Activity Book pages 37–38 Homework and Remembering pages 23–24	MathBoard materials, Demonstration Secret Code Cards (Copymasters M3–M18)	Base ten blocks, number cubes, Math Journals
13 Relate Addition and Subtraction	Student Activity Book pages 39–40 Homework and Remembering pages 25–26	MathBoard materials, Demonstration Secret Code Cards (Copymasters M3–M18)	Base ten blocks, chart paper, index cards, sticky notes, Math Journals
14 Subtraction Practice	Student Activity Book pages 41–42 Homework and Remembering pages 27–28	Demonstration Secret Code Cards (Copymasters M3–M18), Game Cards (Copymaster M25)	Crayons, colored pencils, or markers, chart paper, index cards, Math Journals
15 Addition and Subtraction Practice	Student Activity Book pages 43–44 Homework and Remembering pages 29–30 Quick Quiz 3	MathBoard materials, Demonstration Secret Code Cards (Copymasters M3–M18), Game Cards (Copymaster M25), Play Money (Copymaster M40)	Index cards, paper bags, calculators, Toy Store ads from Lesson 14, Math Journals
✅ **Unit Review and Test**	Student Activity Book pages 45–46 Assessment Guide		

Unit 1 Teaching Resources

Differentiated Instruction

Reaching All Learners

Extra Help

Lesson 1, page 6
Lesson 1, page 8
Lesson 3, page 23
Lesson 6, page 47
Lesson 7, page 55
Lesson 9, page 67
Lesson 11, page 88
Lesson 12, page 95
Lesson 13, page 103
Lesson 14, page 111

English Learners

Lesson 1, page 3
Lesson 1, page 7
Lesson 2, page 13
Lesson 7, page 56
Lesson 12, page 96
Lesson 13, page 104

Individualizing Instruction

Activities
- Intervention (in every lesson)
- On Level (in every lesson)
- Challenge (in every lesson)

Math Writing Prompts
- Intervention (in every lesson)
- On Level (in every lesson)
- Challenge (in every lesson)

Challenge Masters
- (for every Lesson)

Cross-Curricular Links • Home or School Activities

 Social Studies Connections

Timelines (Lesson 3, page 28)
Design a Coin (Lesson 7, page 58)
Number Code (Lesson 8, page 64)
Inventions (Lesson 11, page 90)
Where Can You Find 100? (Lesson 15, page 120)

 Math-to-Math Connection

Abacus (Lesson 4, page 36)

 Science Connections

Breakfast Calories (Lesson 6, page 52)
Subtracting Sunny Days (Lesson 10, page 80)
Migration (Lesson 13, page 108)

 Multicultural Connections

International Coins (Lesson 2, page 20)
Foods from Around the World (Lesson 9, page 70)

 Sports Connection

Baseball Ticket Prices (Lesson 14, page 114)

 Literature Connection

Some Favorite Books (Lesson 12, page 98)

Teaching Unit 1

Putting Research into Practice for Unit 1

From the CMW Research Project: Multi-Digit Addition and Subtraction Methods

We show three methods for multi-digit addition: the common algorithm (New Groups Above), plus two methods found to be effective during the research project, New Groups Below and Show All Totals. These methods are introduced to help students see and discuss core mathematical ideas about addition and subtraction. When using the New Groups Below method, students record a regrouped digit on the line below the addition exercise, instead of above the addition exercise. This New Groups Below method allows students to see the tens and ones, or hundreds and tens, more closely together than in the New Groups Above method. In the Show All Totals method, students add in each place, record the total for each place, then add these totals to find the sum.

To subtract multi-digit numbers, we teach students to ungroup all the places before they subtract. This approach reduces errors and helps develop conceptual understanding of multi-digit subtraction. Some students make the common error of consistently subtracting the smaller digit in a place-value column from the larger digit, even if the smaller digit is on top. To help students remember to ungroup in subtraction, they are encouraged to draw a "magnifying glass" around the top number to prepare for ungrouping. They "look inside" the magnifying glass to see which places need to be ungrouped.

Fuson, Karen C. *Children's Math World Video Research Report,* 2005

Fuson, Karen C. *Children's Math World Field Test Teacher's Guide Grade 3*

From Current Research: Accessible Methods for Multi-Digit Addition

Method B [New Groups Below] is taught in China and has been invented by students in the United States. . . . [T]his method [where] the new 1 or regrouped 10 (or new hundred) is recorded on the line separating the problem from the answer . . . requires that children understand what to do when they get 10 or more in a given column. . . . Method C [Show All Totals], reflecting more closely many students' invented procedures, reduces the problem [of carrying] by writing the total for each kind of unit on a new line. The carrying-regrouping-trading is done as part of the adding of each kind of unit. Also, Method C can be done in either direction.

National Research Council. "Developing Proficiency with Whole Numbers." *Adding It Up: Helping Children Learn Mathematics.* Washington, D.C.: National Academy Press, 2001. p. 203.

Other Useful References: Addition and Subtraction

Number and Operations Standard for Grades 3–5. *Principles and Standards for School Mathematics.* Reston, VA: National Council of Teachers of Mathematics, 2000. pp. 148–155.

Van de Walle, John A., *Elementary and Middle School Mathematics: Teaching Developmentally.* 3rd ed. New York: Longman, 1998. pp. 213–221.

Math Background

Concept Building

Place Value Drawings

Students represent 3-digit numbers with drawings that show hundreds, tens, and ones. To start, students make drawings on the dot arrays on their MathBoards. They show ones by circling individual dots, tens by drawing lines through groups of ten dots, and hundreds by drawing squares around groups of 100 dots. *Math Expressions* uses the terms *ones, ten-sticks,* and *hundred-boxes* to describe the three representations.

Dot Drawing of 178

1 hundred-box   7 ten-sticks   8 ones

Students soon move on to free-hand drawings, making squares for hundreds, lines for tens, and circles for ones. Students group ten-sticks and circles in subgroups of five to avoid errors and to make their drawings easier to read. These drawings are used to visually illustrate the grouping process in addition and the ungrouping process in subtraction.

Place Value Drawing of 178

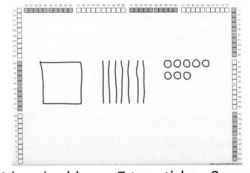

1 hundred-box   7 ten-sticks   8 ones

Students choose to use any method they understand and can explain. Some enjoy using several methods, while others concentrate on one method. The most important part of the learning process is to link each step of a proof drawing to each step of a numerical method. This gives meaning to the numerical method and helps students self-correct later on. Students then begin to do only the numerical method but they can think of a drawing to self-correct. Occasionally, it is helpful for students to make a proof drawing to explain their numerical method to someone else and to keep the meanings attached to the numerical method.

Alternative Accessible Algorithms for Multi-Digit Addition and Subtraction

Addition: New Groups Below Method

Students record a regrouped digit on the line below the addition example, instead of above them.

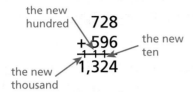

the new hundred
728
+ 596
the new ten
1 1 1
the new thousand
1,324

Addition: Show All Totals Method

Students add in each place, record the total for each place, then add these totals to find the sum.

$$
\begin{array}{r}
728 \\
+ 596 \\
\hline
1,200 \\
110 \\
14 \\
\hline
1,324
\end{array}
$$

the new thousand → 1,200
the new hundred → 110
the new ten → 14

Subtraction: Ungroup First

Students draw a "magnifying glass" around the top number to see which places need to be ungrouped. After ungrouping, they subtract in any direction. Students make proof drawings with boxes, sticks, and circles to show ungrouping.

$$
\begin{array}{r}
\overset{15}{0\ \cancel{16}\ 13} \\
\cancel{163} \\
- 75 \\
\hline
88
\end{array}
$$

Place value drawing of 163
1 hundred + 6 tens + 3 ones
Drawing ungrouped to subtract
Cross out 75. There are 88 left.

Subtraction: Expanded Method

Students write each number in expanded form. They ungroup as needed to subtract. They subtract in each place. Then they add the differences.

$$
\begin{array}{r}
163 = \overset{0}{\cancel{100}} + \overset{150}{\cancel{60}} + \overset{13}{\cancel{3}} \\
- 75 = 70 + 5 \\
\hline
80 + 8 = 88
\end{array}
$$

Representation

Using Secret Code Cards to Form Multi-Digit Numbers

Students explore place value by assembling Secret Code Cards to form multi-digit numbers. To make the number 1,983 students select the cards representing 1 thousand, 9 hundreds, 8 tens, and 3 ones and then assemble them, as shown:

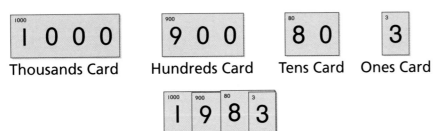

Thousands Card   Hundreds Card   Tens Card   Ones Card

Assembled Cards

Each card has a small version of the number in the upper left corner. So even after the number 1,983 is assembled, students can see that the 1 represents 1,000, the 9 represents 900, and so on.

Place Value Drawings on Secret Code Cards

The back of each Secret Code Card has a place-value drawing representation of the number shown on the front. This drawing helps students to further understand the value of each number by showing a pictorial representation of the base-ten form. Students can also easily compare the value of two numbers, or the value of different digits, visually.

Students can also use the place-value drawing sides of the Secret Code Cards to model numbers. Then students can determine what the related numeral is or find the value of the digits within the numeral, and then turn over the cards to check their answers.

Thousands Card   Hundreds Card   Tens Card   Ones Card

Make Place Value Drawings

Lesson Objectives

- Make and interpret place value drawings.
- Recognize that 1,000 is 10 hundreds.

The Day at a Glance

Today's Goals	Materials	Math Talk
1 Teaching the Lesson **A1:** Create place value drawings for 2- and 3-digit numbers. **A2:** Interpret and make place value drawings for hundreds, tens, and ones. **A3:** Represent 1,000 with a place value drawing. **2 Extending the Lesson** ▶ Going Further: Compare Numbers ▶ Differentiated Instruction **3 Homework and Spiral Review**	MathBoard materials Dot Array (Copymaster M1) in the Teacher's Resource Book Base ten blocks Number cubes Student Activity Book pages 1–6 Homework and Remembering pages 1–2 Math Journals Family Letter	In today's activities, the students are involved in discussion as they ▶ discuss the place value of digits in a multi-digit number ▶ explain how to represent a number with a place value drawing

Quick Practice

This section provides repetitive, short activities that either help students become faster and more accurate at a skill or help to prepare ground for new concepts.

Quick Practice for this unit will start in Lesson 2.

Class Management

If your students are not familiar with place value drawings, you may need to spend more than one day on this lesson.

① Teaching the Lesson

Represent Hundreds, Tens, and Ones

 20 MINUTES

Goal: Create place value drawings for 2- and 3-digit numbers.

Materials: MathBoard materials or Dot Array (Copymaster M1) in the Teacher's Resource Book, base ten blocks

 NCTM Standards:
Number and Operations
Representation

Class Management

If you do not have a Class MathBoard, you may wish to make a transparency of Dot Array (Copymaster M1) and display it on the overhead.

If you do not have student MathBoards, you may wish to put copies of Dot Array (Copymaster M1) in sheet protectors for students to use.

Teaching Note

Faster Ten-Sticks Point out the small circles along two edges of the dot array. Explain that there are 5 dots between each pair of circles. Students can use the circles as a guide to help them draw ten-sticks quickly.

Teaching Note

Language and Vocabulary When describing *ten-sticks*, some of your students may use the term *quick tens* which they used in the previous grade.

▶ Place Value Drawings on the Dot Array WHOLE CLASS

Ones Have students use the dot side of their MathBoards to make drawings of numbers. Make sure students hold their MathBoards as shown below. Each dot on the array represents 1. To show the number 6, circle 6 dots.

Circle 6 dots in a column on the Class MathBoard as students follow along. Point out to students that the small circles along the top and left edges will help them with their circling. There are 5 dots between each pair of circles.

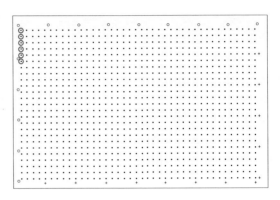

Ten-Stick Circle 4 more dots in the column so there are a total of 10.

● How many dots are circled now? 10

Draw a line through the 10 dots as shown below on the left.

● Use a shortcut to represent 10 by drawing a line through a group of 10 dots instead of circling 10 dots. Call the line a *ten-stick*.

Draw a ten-stick next to the column of 10 circles.

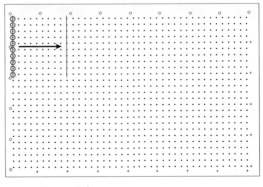

Ten-stick

On the Class MathBoard write: **76**   *seventy-six*

Ask students to use ten-sticks and circles to show the number as a volunteer works at the Class MathBoard. Students should draw 7 ten-sticks and then circle 6 single dots as shown on the next page.

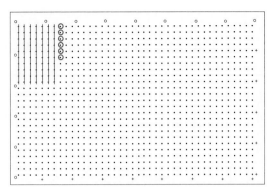

Dot Drawing of 76

● How can you check to make sure you have drawn 76 correctly without counting each individual dot? First count the tens: 10, 20, 30, 40, 50, 60, 70. Then count the ones: 71, 72, 73, 74, 75, 76.

Hundred-Box Write on the Class MathBoard:

123   *one hundred twenty-three*

Ask students to show 123 on their MathBoards as a volunteer shows it on the Class MathBoard. Most students will draw 12 ten-sticks and circle 3 individual dots. (Some students may draw a box or circle around 100 dots, and then draw 2 ten-sticks and circle 3 dots. This should be considered correct.)

● Let's count by tens and ones to make sure we have drawn 123 correctly: 10, 20, 30, 40, 50, 60, 70, 80, 90, 100, 110, 120, 121, 122, 123.

Have students draw a box around 10 of the ten-sticks.

● What amount does this box show? 100

Explain that just as a ten-stick is a quick way of drawing 10, a *hundred-box* is a quick way of drawing 100.

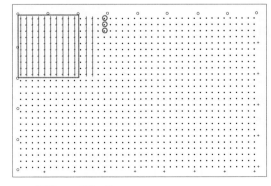

100 + 20+3
Dot Drawing of 123

Activity continued ▶

Alternate Approach

Base Ten Blocks In this lesson and in the lessons that follow, students could also show the numbers using base ten blocks. In the figure below, for instance, 1 thousands block, 3 hundreds blocks, 2 tens rods, and 7 ones cubes are used to represent 1,327.

The major difference between the base ten blocks and the *Math Expression* drawings is in the thousands (see pages 6 and 7). The 2-dimensional long thousands bar used to show 10 hundreds is clearer to some students than the thousands base ten block, because some students see only the 6 faces of the block and think there are 6 hundreds rather than 10 in one thousand.

The Learning Classroom

Building Concepts As a review during the lesson, ask students for the place value of each number. For example, point to each digit in the number 76 and ask for the value. 7 tens, 6 ones

Differentiated Instruction

English Learners Although these activities are not labeled as English Learner activities, they are ideal for English Learners. In this activity, visual and numerical representations of a number are connected to the number's word form.

Make Place Value Drawings   **3**

The Learning Classroom

Helping Community Create a classroom where students are not competing, but desire to collaborate and help one another. Communicate often that your goal as a class is that everyone understands the math you are studying. Tell students that this will require everyone working together to help each other.

Teaching Note

What to Expect from Students
Students may draw 5-groups in different ways. For example, here are four ways to show 10 ones with 5-groups. Similar arrangements may be used for ten-sticks and hundred-boxes.

Emphasize that 100 can be thought of *either* as 10 tens (ten-sticks) *or* as 100 ones (dots). Students need to understand both of these representations to add and subtract multi-digit numbers. They will need to group 10 tens to get 1 hundred or ungroup 1 hundred to get 10 tens.

Draw the number 247 on the Class MathBoard as shown below. Ask students to identify the number by counting hundreds, then tens, then ones: 100, 200, 210, 220, 230, 240, 241, 242, 243, 244, 245, 246, 247.

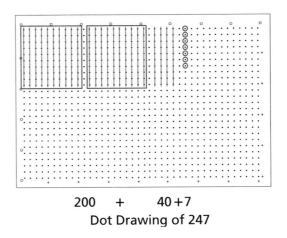

200 + 40 + 7
Dot Drawing of 247

▶ Place Value Drawings Without Dots | WHOLE CLASS |

Have students erase their MathBoards and turn them over.

● How can you show 76 without dots? Draw 7 sticks for 7 tens and 6 circles for 6 ones.

Help students make the drawing below, which shows a stick for each ten and a circle for each one. Explain that drawing "5-groups" makes counting easier because you can see at a glance that there are five without counting each item individually.

Place Value Drawing of 76

● How can you represent a hundred without using the dots. Draw a box.

Tell students to make a place value drawing for 123 on the blank part of their MathBoards. Ask for a volunteer to draw the place value drawing on the Class MathBoard.

Place Value Drawing of 123

Practice Place Value Drawings for Hundreds, Tens, and Ones

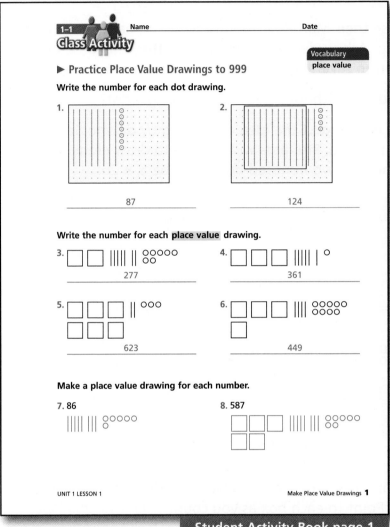

Student Activity Book page 1

 20 MINUTES

Goal: Interpret and make place value drawings for hundreds, tens, and ones.

Materials: Student Activity Book page 1

 NCTM Standards:
Number and Operations
Representation

The Learning Classroom

Math Talk Make your classroom a place where all students listen to understand one another. Explain to students that this involves thinking about what a person is saying so that you can explain it yourself or help them explain it more clearly. By listening carefully, students will be able to ask a question or help the explainer.

▶ Practice Place Value Drawings to 999 INDIVIDUALS

Have students complete Student Activity Book page 1. Exercises 1–8 provide practice with interpreting and making place value drawings. Encourage students to work independently, and then discuss the results as a class. Focus on place value by asking these questions:

● How much is a box worth? one hundred

● How much is a stick worth? ten

● How much is a circle worth? one

● How can you count to find the number shown in the drawing? First count the hundreds, then the tens, and then the ones.

Activity 3

Conceptualize and Represent 1,000

 20 MINUTES

Goal: Represent 1,000 with a place value drawing.

Materials: MathBoard materials, Student Activity Book page 2

 NCTM Standards:
Number and Operations
Representation

Differentiated Instruction

Extra Help If students are not convinced these 5 × 20 boxes represent 100, have them draw horizontal ten-sticks.

▶ **Introduce the Thousand-Bar** WHOLE CLASS

Have students erase their MathBoards and turn them back over so the dot array is face up. Ask students how many dots they think are on the entire board. Listen to several guesses.

● How can we find out without counting every single dot?

If no one brings it up, suggest the idea of starting by drawing as many hundred-boxes as possible. Students will be able to draw eight 10 × 10 hundred-boxes. The last two hundred-boxes will be 5 × 20.

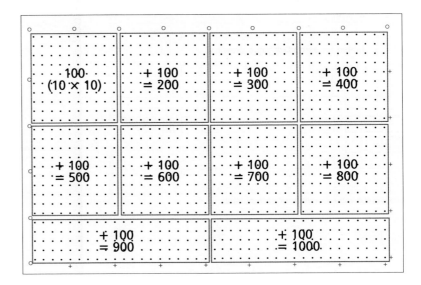

● Now, count by hundreds to find out how many dots there are. Let's count together. Point to each box as you count. 100, 200, 300, 400, 500, 600, 700, 800, 900, 1000.

Some students may get confused about what number comes after 900. They may say "10 hundred." Explain that "a thousand" is another name for "10 hundred." Write 1,000 in numerals and in words on the board.

Thousand-Bar Turn over the Class MathBoard and draw a column of 10 hundred boxes. Ask a volunteer to count by hundreds to find what number you have represented. 1,000

Next to the column of hundred-boxes, draw a column of the same height, without hundreds divisions. Explain that a *thousand-bar* is a fast way of drawing 1,000. Emphasize that a thousand-bar should be long and skinny so it doesn't get confused with a hundred-box. See sample to the left.

Column of Hundred Boxes   Thousand Bar

Student Activity Book page 2

1-1
Class Activity

Name _____ Date _____

▶ Practice with the Thousand Model

Write the number for each place value drawing.

9. _____ 1,238

10. _____ 1,093

Make a drawing for each number.

11. 2,368

12. 5,017

▶ Write Numbers for Word Names

Write the number for the words.

13. eighty-two _____82_____

14. ninety-nine _____99_____

15. four hundred sixty-seven _____467_____

16. nine hundred six _____906_____

17. one thousand, fifteen _____1,015_____

18. eight thousand, one hundred twenty _____8,120_____

2 UNIT 1 LESSON 1   Make Place Value Drawings

Differentiated Instruction

English Learners Pair English Learner "drawer/listeners" with English-speaking "word name readers." Have the "drawer/listeners" write a number up to 3,000 and make a place-value drawing to represent it. Then have the "word name reader" read the number. After doing this for five numbers, have students switch roles.

▶ Practice with the Thousand Model WHOLE CLASS

As a class, work through exercises 9–12 on Student Activity Book page 2.

▶ Write Numbers for Word Names INDIVIDUALS

Have students complete exercises 13–18 independently.

Exercises 13–18 provide practice for reading and writing numbers.

When students have finished, ask volunteers to write their answers on the board and read the answers aloud to check that they wrote them correctly. Be sure to correct any students who say the word "and" when reading a number. For example, 467 should not be read "four hundred and sixty seven." Explain that we will say "and" for the decimal point when we say decimal numbers later in the year so it is better to learn not to say it now.

Then, ask students:

● **What word do you notice the volunteers saying at the comma in the number?** thousand

Ongoing Assessment

Have students use dot drawings or place value drawings to explain how the number 251 is different from the number 521.

Make Place Value Drawings **7**

② Extending the Lesson

Going Further: Compare Numbers

Goal: Compare 4-digit numbers using the greater than and less than symbols.

Materials: MathBoard materials, base ten blocks

 NCTM Standards:
Number and Operations
Representation

📁 Class Management

Going Further activities may be difficult for some students. These activities are intended to challenge students and to include mathematical topics required by state standards. Use these activities based on the individual needs of your students and/or according to specific state standards.

▶ Compare Numbers Using Place Value

WHOLE CLASS

Write the numbers 2,312 and 2,176 on the board. Ask a volunteer to make place value drawings for the numbers.

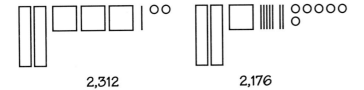

2,312   2,176

Ask students which of the numbers is greater and to explain why. Be sure that students use the drawings to explain that there are 2 more hundreds in 2,312 than in 2,176 and that even 100 is more than 76.

Then make the typical error that students make in such comparisons:

● Look at the numbers. I know 76 is more than 12, so I think 2,176 is greater.

If necessary, help students explain that you look at the bigger place values farther left to decide, not the smaller places to the right.

● Describe whether you should put > or < after 2,312 and why? *the greater than symbol because the bigger part of this symbol points to the greater number*

Write the following on the board so students can see how to say a comparison and how to write a comparison using symbols.

2,312 is greater than 2,176.

2,312 > 2,176

Repeat the same procedure for 1,326 and 1,371, where students will need to look at the tens place to compare. Again, make the error of looking at the ones place and have students correct you by looking at the drawings.

▶ Practice Comparing Numbers PAIRS

Write the following exercises on the board. Tell students to make place value drawings for exercises 1–4. Ask students to put >, <, or = in the circle and to be thinking of a general numerical method they could use for all such problems.

1. 8,056 ⟩ 8,037   2. 5,460 ⟨ 8,560
3. 1,429 ⟨ 1,550   4. 1,932 ⟩ 198

▶ Critical Thinking Questions

WHOLE CLASS

Discuss general patterns students found and exemplify with drawings as needed.

● When you compare two numbers, where do you start comparing the digits? *At the left so you compare digits with the greatest place value.*

● What is always true when you compare a 3-digit number to a 4-digit number? *The 4-digit number is larger.*

● If two 4-digit numbers have the same 4 digits, are the numbers equal? Explain. *The numbers are equal if the same digits are in same places in both numbers.*

Differentiated Instruction

Extra Help Students can model each number in the pair with base ten blocks, then make the comparisons.

Intervention

for students having difficulty

PAIRS

Race to 100

Materials: Base ten blocks (1 hundreds block, 20 tens rods, 20 ones cubes per pair) number cubes labeled 1–6 (2 per pair)

Give each pair of students base ten blocks and two number cubes. Partners take turns rolling the number cubes. Each student takes the number of ones indicated by the sum of the numbers that were rolled. Whenever students can exchange 10 ones for 1 ten, they should do so. The first student who can exchange 10 tens for 1 hundred wins the game.

On Level

for students having success

SMALL GROUPS

Pass the Number

Materials: MathBoard materials

Each student in the group makes a dot drawing of a three-digit number on a MathBoard, then passes the MathBoard to the right. Students write the number on the MathBoard in words, then pass the MathBoard to the right. Next, students write the number on the MathBoard in numerals and then pass the MathBoard to the student who made the original dot drawing. That student must check that the words and numerals on the MathBoard are correct.

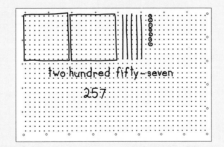

two hundred fifty-seven

257

Challenge

for students seeking a challenge

INDIVIDUALS

Number Riddles

Give students the following riddles to solve. Tell them to find all possible answers.

> I am a 3-digit number.
> The digit in my tens place is 5.
> The sum of all my digits is 7.
> What number could I be?

151 or 250

> I am a 4-digit number.
> The digit in my tens place is 5.
> The sum of all my digits is 8.
> What number could I be?

1,052, 1,151, 1,250, 2,051, 2,150, or 3,050

Also Use
Challenge Master for 1-1

 Math Writing Prompt

Intervention

Investigate Math
Explain to a friend how the two 4s in the number 1,445 are different from each other.

 Math Writing Prompt

On Level

Explain Your Thinking
Explain why you do *not* read the number 308 as "thirty-eight."

Math Writing Prompt

Challenge

Bagging Marbles
A toy factory made 1,800 marbles yesterday. How many bags can they fill with 10 marbles in each bag? Explain your answer.

③ Homework and Spiral Review

Homework **Goal:** Additional Practice

This Homework page gives students practice making and interpreting place value drawings.

1–1
Remembering **Goal:** Spiral Review

This Remembering page would be appropriate anytime after today's lesson.

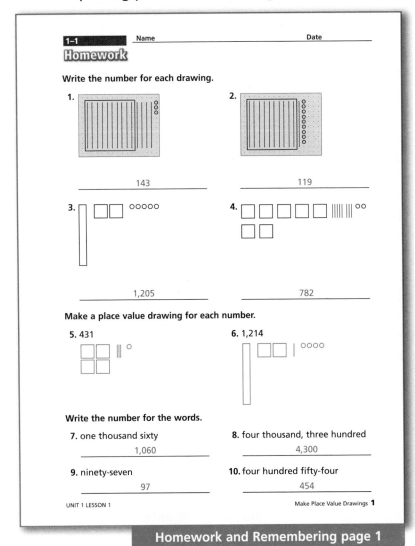

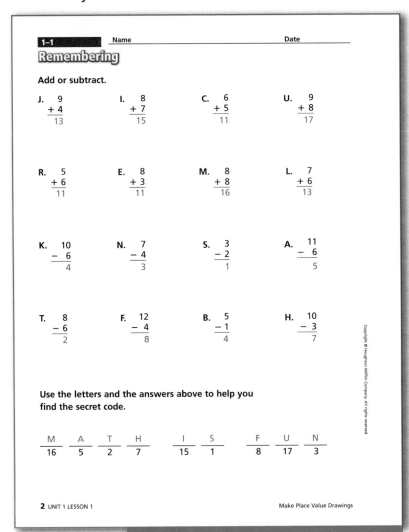

Home and School Connection

Family Letter Have children take home the Family Letter on Student Activity Book pages 3–4. A Spanish translation of this letter is on the following pages in the Student Activity Book. This letter explains how the concept of place value is developed in *Math Expressions.* It gives parents and guardians a better understanding of the learning that goes on in math class and creates a bridge between school and home.

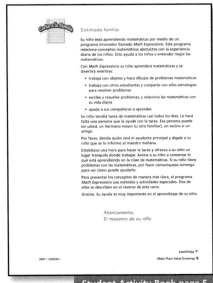

Build Numbers and Represent Money Amounts

Lesson Objectives

- Identify the value of a digit.
- Make drawings to represent money amounts.

Vocabulary	
digit	dollars place
expanded form	Secret Code Cards
standard form	Counting on strategy
pennies place	Make a Ten strategy
dimes place	

The Day at a Glance

Today's Goals	Materials	123 Math Talk
Quick Practice Identify 3-digit numbers by counting hundreds, tens, and ones.	Demonstration Secret Code Cards (Copymasters M3–M18)	In today's activities, the students are involved in discussion as they
1 Teaching the Lesson **A1:** Read 3-digit numbers from models. **A2:** Build 2- and 3-digit numbers with Secret Code Cards. **A3:** Make drawings to represent money amounts. **A4:** Review strategies for adding 1-digit numbers.	Secret Code Cards Pointer Scissors Envelopes or small bags MathBoard materials Ten Frame (Copymaster M2) Two-color counters Index cards	▶ discuss the place value of digits ▶ relate place value to money amounts ▶ explain strategies for adding 1-digit numbers
2 Extending the Lesson ▶ Going Further: Place Value Through Ten Thousands ▶ Differentiated Instruction	Play money (Copymaster M40) Student Activity Book pages 7–12	
3 Homework and Spiral Review	Homework and Remembering pages 2–4 Math Journals	

Quick Practice

Explain to students that tomorrow and on future days they will do Quick Practice activities. Tell them they will all have opportunities to be the Student Leader and lead these activities. The first activity in today's lesson will prepare them for tomorrow's Quick Practice.

Teaching Note

Homework Homework is crucial for learning in this program. Ask those students who did not complete the homework from the previous day to complete it and turn it in the following day. Establish a routine so that students know they are expected to complete their homework every day. Encourage students to see doing homework as a usual part of the daily routine.

Teaching the Lesson

Model Place-Value with Secret Code Cards

 10 MINUTES

Goal: Read 3-digit numbers from models.

Materials: Demonstration Secret Code Cards (Copymasters M3–M18), pointer

✓ **NCTM Standards:**
   Number and Operations
   Representation

The Learning Classroom

Student Leaders Once students see how a Quick Practice activity works, invite two students to serve as leaders. Invite two new student leaders to direct the Quick Practice each day.

The following approach can assist your students in developing their leadership skills while taking turns leading the Quick Practice. For the first several sessions, select students who can take on the leadership role easily. They can serve as models for their classmates. After a few sessions, let other students volunteer for the leadership role. Since many Quick Practice activities call for two student leaders, you can ease students into the leadership role by pairing some students with a strong partner. Soon, all students will be able to conduct Quick Practice effectively and with confidence.

 Class Management

If you have access to the *Math Expressions* Materials Kit, the Demonstration Secret Code Cards and Secret Code Cards are included, so you will not have to prepare these materials.

► **Introduce Demonstration Secret Code Cards**

WHOLE CLASS

In this activity, students review place value by assembling Demonstration Secret Code Cards to form multi-digit numbers. To make the number 372, for example, students select the cards representing 3 hundreds, 7 tens, and 2 ones and then assemble them as shown below. Each card has a small version of the number in the upper left corner. So even after 372 is assembled, students can see that the 3 represents 300, the 7 represents 70, and the 2 represents 2.

Using the Demonstration Secret Code Cards, have a Student Leader select a hundreds card, a tens cards, and a ones card and display the cards as shown.

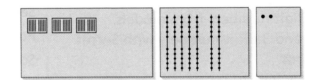

To identify the number, the class counts by hundreds, then tens, then ones, as the Student Leader uses a pointer to point to each quantity.

Leader: Count to find the number.

Class: 100, 200, 300, 310, 320, 330, 340, 350, 360, 370, 371, 372

Then the leader turns over the cards to reveal the hundreds, tens, and ones and assembles the cards to show the number.

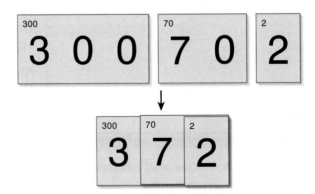

Repeat the activity, using several different numbers.

Use Secret Code Cards

▶ Build and Discuss 148 | WHOLE CLASS |

Have students cut out the Secret Code Cards on Student Activity Book pages 7–10.

Tell students they will use the Secret Code Cards to build numbers. Write the number 148 in numerals and in words on the board.

● What digit is in the hundreds place of 148? 1 Find the card that represents 1 hundred.

● What digit is in the tens place of 148? 4 Find the card that represents 4 tens.

● What digit is in the ones place of 148? 8 Find the card that represents 8 ones.

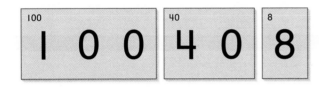

Have students slide the 8 card over the 40 card and the 40 card over the 100 card to form the number 148 as shown below. Ask students what number they have made. 148

Direct students' attention to the small 100 in the upper left corner of the 100 card. Explain that this is a reminder that the 1 in 148 means 100 because it is in the hundreds place.

● What small number do you see above the 4? 40

● What does this tell us? The 4 in 148 is 40 or 4 tens.

Write the following on the board:

148 = 1 hundred + 4 tens + 8 ones

148 = 100 + 40 + 8

Point out that these are two ways to write 148 in expanded form. Discuss the fact that these two equations are different ways of saying the same thing. The Secret Code Cards also show both ways.

Activity continued ▶

---

 20 MINUTES

Goal: Build 2- and 3-digit numbers with Secret Code Cards.

Materials: Secret Code Cards (Student Activity Book pages 7–10), envelopes or small bags (1 per student), scissors (1 per student)

 NCTM Standards:
Number and Operations
Representation

Teaching Note

Watch For! When modeling numbers, such as 148, some students may choose the 1 card when they really should choose the 100 card and the 4 card when they need the 40. Encourage students to use the small numbers in the left hand corner of their cards to help them choose the right cards.

The Learning Classroom

Math Talk Elicit students' ideas when introducing a new topic. Students will become more engaged if they believe their contributions will be heard. You may want to allow for interruptions from students during the explanation of the content. When this occurs, decide what is important to continue exploring, but allow students to "own" new ideas or strategies. Students may volunteer to explain strategies that you are about to teach. Encourage **English Learners** to raise their hands when they require repetition or clarification of any words or concepts they do not understand.

▶ Build and Discuss Other Numbers WHOLE CLASS

In a different area of the board, write the numbers 264, 37, and 493 in numerals and in words. Have students build these numbers with their Secret Code Cards.

Discuss the number 264:

● What digit is in the hundreds place in 264? 2 in the tens place? 6 in the ones place? 4

● Which hundreds card did you use to make 264? 200 Which tens card? 60 Which ones card? 4

● What does the small 200 tell us? that the 2 in 264 means 200 What does the small 60 tell us? that the 6 in 264 means 60

Ask a volunteer to write 264 in expanded form in two ways like you wrote for 148.

Repeat this type of questioning for the other numbers. If you think students need more practice, have them build and discuss other numbers.

Activity 3

Draw Money Amounts

 20 MINUTES

Goal: Make drawings to represent money amounts.

Materials: MathBoard materials or Dot Array (Copymaster M1), Student Activity Book page 11

 NCTM Standards:
Number and Operations
Representation

▶ Introduce Money Drawings on the Dot Array
WHOLE CLASS

Ask students to make a dot drawing of 157 on the dot side of their MathBoards.

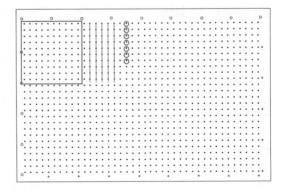

Ask questions to help students relate the drawing to money.

● Imagine that each dot represents a penny. What does each ten-stick represent? 10 cents, or a dime

● What does the hundred-box represent? 100 cents, or a dollar

● What amount of money does the whole drawing represent? $1.57

Have students label the drawing $1.57.

The Learning Classroom

Math Talk Encourage students to stand beside their work and point to parts of it as they explain it. Using a pointer that does not obscure any work enables watchers to see the part of the drawing or math symbols that is being discussed at that moment.

Write $2.74 on the board. Point out the pennies place, the dimes place, and the dollars place. Have students make a dot drawing to represent this amount. Choose one student to work at the Class MathBoard.

● How many hundred-boxes did you draw? 2 What do the 2 hundred-boxes represent? 2 dollars, or 200 cents

● How many ten-sticks did you draw? 7 What do these ten-sticks represent? 7 dimes, or 70 cents

● How many individual dots did you circle? 4 What do these circles represent? 4 pennies, or 4 cents

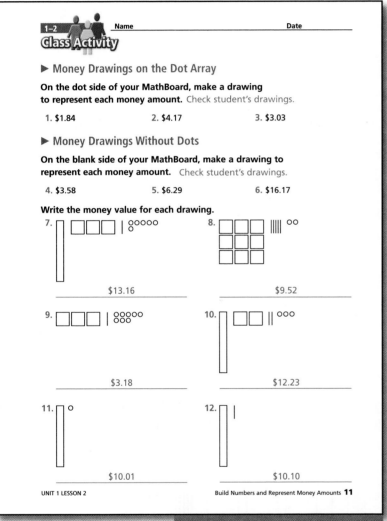

Student Activity Book page 11

▶ Money Drawings on the Dot Array INDIVIDUALS

Direct the students' attention to Student Activity Book page 11. Have them complete exercises 1–3. Discuss exercises that caused difficulty.

Teaching Note

Math Background This program refers to the places in dollar notation as the *dollars place,* the *dimes place,* and the *pennies place.*

At this time, students only need to know that the "dot," or decimal point, separates the dollars from the dimes and pennies. Later, when students study decimals, they will learn that a dime is a tenth of a dollar and a penny is a hundredth of a dollar. This will make clear the meaning of the decimal point in dollar notation.

Review the relationship between cent notation and dollar notation with your students, 73¢ and $0.73, for example. Thinking of money amounts in terms of dollars, dimes, and pennies makes it easier for students to convert from one notation to another.

You may wish to discuss the reading of the decimal point as "and" here in this money context: $3.47 is *Three dollars and forty-seven cents.* This is good preparation for when 3.47 will be read as *three and forty-seven hundredths.*

① Teaching the Lesson (continued)

The Learning Classroom

Building Concepts Over the next several lessons, review strategies for solving basic additions and subtractions with your students (for example, 7 + 8 = ? and 15 + 7 = ?) and extensions of these basic additions and subtractions (for example, 70 + 80 = ? or 150 − 70 = ?). For multi-digit calculation it is important for students to have fast and accurate methods for the single-digit addition and subtraction within each column. It is also important that students understand methods for adding and subtracting tens and hundreds. Watch your less-advanced students during this unit to see if they need help moving to counting on with fingers for addition or subtraction. It is a rapid and accurate method for less-advanced children.

✓ Ongoing Assessment

Ask students these questions.

▶ How are 7 + 4 and 70 + 4 different?

▶ In a money drawing, explain why a thousand-bar represents ten dollars.

▶ Compare adding 7 + 4 to adding 8 + 4. How are they the same? How are they different?

▶ Introduce Money Drawings Without Dots

WHOLE CLASS

Have students make a drawing for $2.74 on the number path side of their MathBoard. Choose a volunteer to discuss his or her drawing.

Now draw a thousand-bar on the board.

● Can anyone tell me how much money a thousand-bar shows? $10

● How do you know? A thousand-bar is 10 hundred-boxes, and each hundred-box is $1.

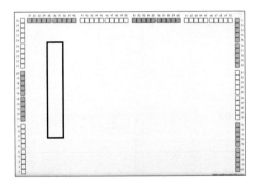

Make this drawing for $13.51 on the board. Ask a volunteer to tell what amount the drawing represents and how he or she found the answer.

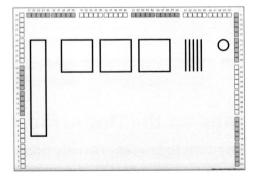

▶ Money Drawings without Dots INDIVIDUALS

Have students complete exercises 4–12 on Student Activity Book page 11. Discuss exercises that caused difficulty for students.

Review Addition Strategies

▶ Discuss Addition Strategies WHOLE CLASS

Review Homework and Remembering page 2 from Lesson 1. Ask students what strategies they used to add 9 + 4. Make sure to discuss the Counting On and Make a Ten strategies. Have volunteers demonstrate these strategies, or demonstrate them yourself.

Counting On by Ones Strategy

Mentally
- Say the first number to yourself: "9". Count on 4 more: "10, 11, 12, 13"

With Fingers
- Say the first number to yourself: "9". Count on, raising one finger for each number you say, until you have raised 4 fingers:

"10"   "11"   "12"   "13"

With a Drawing
- Write the number 9 (pretending you have already counted 9 dots) followed by four dots. Count on from the 9 to find the total.

Make a Ten Strategy

- To add 9 + 4 by making a ten, take 1 from the 4 and add it to the 9 to make 10, then add the 3 that is left to get 13.

Mentally
- Start with 9. Add 1 to get 10. Add 3 more to get 13

Numerically
- $9 + 4 = 9 + 1 + 3 = 10 + 3 = 13$

With a Drawing
- Write 9 and draw 4 dots. Group the 9 with 1 of the dots to get a group of 10, plus 3 more.

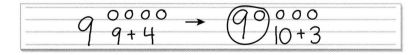

Review the remaining exercises on that page. If your students are not proficient with addition, have them find the answers by using the Counting On and Make a Ten strategies.

 10 MINUTES

Goal: Review strategies for adding 1-digit numbers.

Materials: MathBoard materials, Homework and Remembering page 2, Ten Frame (Copymaster M2), two-color counters

 NCTM Standards:
Number and Operations
Representation

Teaching Note

What to Expect from Students In this activity, we review the Counting On and Make a Ten addition strategies. If your students are not proficient with addition, help them learn one or both of these strategies and give them opportunities for practice. With practice, these strategies will become efficient, reliable addition methods.

Alternate Approach

Counters and Ten Frames When adding 1-digit numbers, students could also make a ten using two-color counters and a Ten Frame (Copymaster M2).

9 + 4 = 13

Invite students to explain how to fill the ten frame with the counters and how to count the counters that remain outside the frame.

$9 + 1 = 10$ $10 + 3 = 13$

② Extending the Lesson

Going Further: Place Value Through Ten Thousands

▶ Place Value to 99,999 [WHOLE CLASS]

Explain that it takes Neptune 60,190 days to orbit the Sun. Draw a place value chart on the board to help students understand the value of the number.

ten thousands	thousands	hundreds	tens	ones
6	0	1	9	0

Starting with the ones place, point to each place and ask:

● What is the value of this place? ones

Then, ask students to suppose there are Secret Code Cards for numbers this large. Ask a volunteer to sketch the Secret Code Cards under the chart that they would use to build the number.

ten thousands	thousands	hundreds	tens	ones
6	0	1	9	0

(60,000)   (100)   (90)

Ask students the following questions:

● What is the value of the digit 6 in the place value chart? 60,000

● What is the value of the digit 1 in the place value chart? 100

● What is the value of the digit 9 in the place value chart? 90

Summarize by writing the labels standard form, expanded form, and word form on the board and ask a volunteer to write the number in these ways next to the labels:

> Standard form: 60,190
> Expanded form: 60,000 + 100 + 90
> Word form: Sixty thousand, one hundred ninety

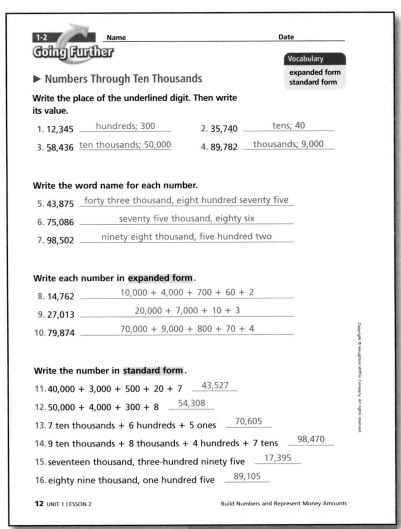

Student Activity Book page 12

▶ Numbers Through Ten Thousands
[WHOLE CLASS]

Ask a volunteer to think of a 5-digit number, say it in words, and write it on the board in standard form.

Example: 54,138

● What place is the digit 4 in? thousands

● What is the value of the digit 4? 4,000

● How would you write the number in expanded form? 50,000 + 4,000 + 100 + 30 + 8

Then, have students complete Student Activity Book page 12.

Intervention
for students having difficulty

 PAIRS

Mixed-up Money

Materials: index cards (3 per student), play money (20 dollars, 20 dimes, and 20 pennies per pair)

Ask students to choose any number from 1–9 and draw that number of hundred-boxes on the first index card. Again have students choose a number and draw ten-sticks on the second card and circles on the third card. Partners should not look at each other's cards.

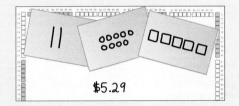

$5.29

Tell the students to mix up their set of cards and exchange sets of cards with their partners. Each partner should then place coins on the cards that match the amount shown. Have students write the amount of money the set of cards represents. Have partners check each other's answers and discuss the results.

 Math Writing Prompt

Intervention

Explain Your Thinking
Explain how you know that 7 + 5 is greater than 10.

On Level
for students having success

 PAIRS

Money Match

Materials: index cards (12 per pair)

Have students write a money amount on an index card with the matching place value drawing on another card. They should make six sets using different amounts on each set of cards. Mix up the cards and turn them face down to play *Money Match*. Have each pair of students take turns turning two cards face up in order to find a matching pair. If a match is made, they take the cards off the table. If a match is not made, they turn the selected cards face down, and the other partner takes a turn. Students repeat the activity until all the pairs are found.

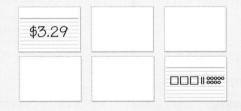

 Math Writing Prompt

On Level

Investigate Math
Explain why you can use a hundred-box to show both the number *one hundred* and the money amount *one dollar*.

Challenge
for students seeking a challenge

 PAIRS

Money Riddles

Materials: MathBoard materials, index cards

One student begins the game by choosing a money amount and writing it on an index card. Encourage students to use amounts over $10.00. On the back, the student must present the amount in the form of a place value drawing riddle. The other partner must try to guess the amount correctly.

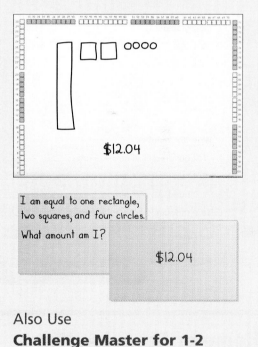

Also Use
Challenge Master for 1-2

 Math Writing Prompt

Challenge

Create Your Own
What amount of money do you think 10 thousand-bars represent? Create your own picture to show that amount and explain why you chose that picture.

③ Homework and Spiral Review

1-2
Homework **Goal:** Additional Practice

This Homework page gives students an opportunity to practice making and interpreting drawings for money amounts.

1-2
Remembering **Goal:** Spiral Review

This Remembering page would be appropriate anytime after today's lesson.

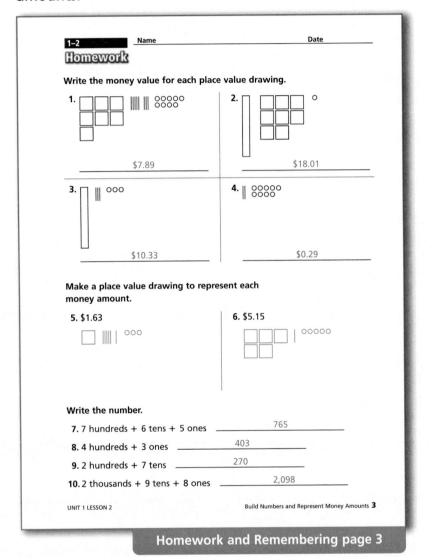

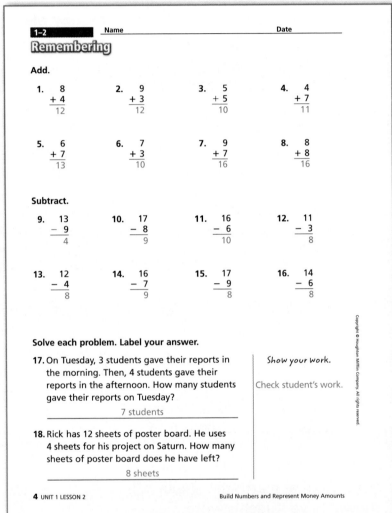

Home or School Activity

 Multicultural Connection

International Coins Have students bring in real coins or pictures of coins from other countries to share with the class. Compare the design of the coins to one another and to U.S. coins.

Place Value in Word Problems

Lesson Objectives

- Group and ungroup multi-digit numbers.
- Solve word problems that require understanding of place value.

Vocabulary

place value drawing
Counting On strategy
Make a Ten strategy

The Day at a Glance

Today's Goals	Materials	Math Talk
Quick Practice Read and form 3-digit numbers with Secret Code Cards.	Quick Practice materials	In today's activities, the students are involved in discussion as they
1 Teaching the Lesson **A1:** Represent multi-digit numbers as sums of thousands, hundreds, tens, and ones. **A2:** Solve place value word problems. **A3:** Review subtraction strategies.	Demonstration Secret Code Cards Secret Code Cards (Copymasters M19–M22) MathBoard materials Base ten blocks	▶ discuss the place value of digits in multi-digit numbers ▶ solve and discuss word problems
2 Extending the Lesson ▶ Differentiated Instruction	Sentence Strips Sticky notes	▶ explain subtraction strategies
3 Homework and Spiral Review	Student Activity Book pages 13–14 Homework and Remembering pages 4–6 Math Journals	

Quick Practice

 5 MINUTES   **Goal:** Read and form 3-digit numbers with Secret Code Cards.
Materials: Demonstration Secret Code Cards (Copymasters M3–M18)

Read Place Value Drawings Have a Student Leader form a 3-digit number with the place value drawings on the back of the Demonstration Secret Code Cards. After the class identifies the number, have the Student Leader demonstrate how to form the 3-digit number using the numerals on the cards. (See Unit 1 Lesson 2 Activity 1.)

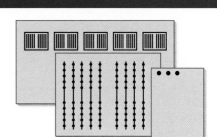

Teaching the Lesson

Analyze Numbers

 20 MINUTES

Goal: Represent multi-digit numbers as sums of thousands, hundreds, tens, and ones.

Materials: Demonstration Secret Code Cards (Copymasters M3–M18), Secret Code Cards (Copymasters M19–M22 or from Lesson 2) (1 set per student)

✓ **NCTM Standards:**
Number and Operations
Representation

▶ Build 4-digit Numbers WHOLE CLASS

Have students use the Secret Code Cards they cut out in Lesson 2 for this activity. Use Copymasters M19–M22 to provide replacement sets if needed.

Write the number 1,237 on the board and ask students to build it with their Secret Code Cards. When they have finished, discuss the place value of each number.

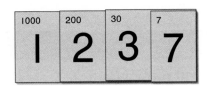

Have a volunteer make a place value drawing for 1,237 on the board.

Next, write the numbers below on the board.

1,659   1,302   1,847   1,263

Have students build the numbers, one at a time, with their Secret Code Cards. For each number, ask questions about place value, in mixed order. For example:

● What digit is in the tens place?

● What is the value of the digit in the tens place?

● What digit is in the thousands place?

● What is the value of the digit in the thousands place?

● What digit is in the ones place?

● What is the value of the digit in the ones place?

● What digit is in the hundreds place?

● What is the value of the digit in the hundreds place?

Write these equations on the board:

$$1{,}263 = 1{,}000 + 200 + 60 + 3$$

$$1{,}263 = 1 \text{ thousand} + 2 \text{ hundreds} + 6 \text{ tens} + 3 \text{ ones}$$

Point out that these are two ways to write the number in expanded form. Then, point to 1,263.

- One way to read this number is "one thousand, two hundred sixty-three." Does anyone know another way to read it?

If no one responds correctly, explain that some people read 1,263 as "twelve hundred sixty-three." Ask students to explain why this way of reading the number is also correct. Remind them that 1 thousand is equal to 10 hundreds. Because 1 thousand is 10 hundreds, 1,263 actually has 12 hundreds altogether.

Write the following beneath the equations that are already on the board:

$$1{,}263 = 12 \text{ hundreds} + 6 \text{ tens} + 3 \text{ ones}$$

Now, focus on the tens.

- What if we want to think of 1,263 as being made up of only tens and ones. How many tens are there in 1,263 altogether? 126

Have students explain how they found the answer. They should understand that 12 hundreds is the same as 120 tens. Combining 120 tens with the 6 tens shown in the tens place equals 126 tens. Write the following beneath the other equations:

$$1{,}263 = 126 \text{ tens} + 3 \text{ ones}$$

Finally, focus on the ones.

- Now, think of 1,263 as being made only of ones. How many ones are there altogether? 1,263

Write this last equation under the others.

$$1{,}263 = 1{,}263 \text{ ones}$$

Give students several numbers less than 2,000 to analyze in this way.

Solve Place Value Word Problems

 25 MINUTES

Goal: Solve place value word problems.

Materials: MathBoard materials, Student Activity Book page 13, base ten blocks

 NCTM Standards:
Number and Operations
Problem Solving
Communication
Representation

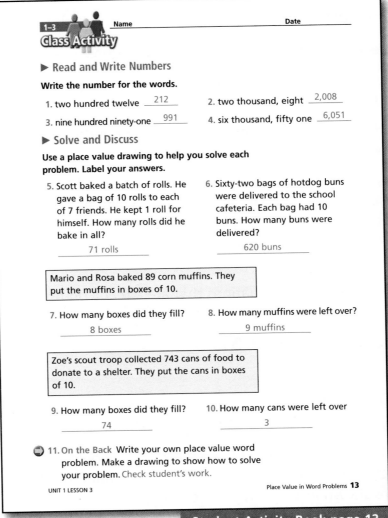

1-3 Class Activity

Name _____ Date _____

▶ **Read and Write Numbers**

Write the number for the words.

1. two hundred twelve __212__
2. two thousand, eight __2,008__
3. nine hundred ninety-one __991__
4. six thousand, fifty one __6,051__

▶ **Solve and Discuss**

Use a place value drawing to help you solve each problem. Label your answers.

5. Scott baked a batch of rolls. He gave a bag of 10 rolls to each of 7 friends. He kept 1 roll for himself. How many rolls did he bake in all?
   __71 rolls__

6. Sixty-two bags of hotdog buns were delivered to the school cafeteria. Each bag had 10 buns. How many buns were delivered?
   __620 buns__

Mario and Rosa baked 89 corn muffins. They put the muffins in boxes of 10.

7. How many boxes did they fill?
   __8 boxes__

8. How many muffins were left over?
   __9 muffins__

Zoe's scout troop collected 743 cans of food to donate to a shelter. They put the cans in boxes of 10.

9. How many boxes did they fill?
   __74__

10. How many cans were left over
    __3__

11. On the Back Write your own place value word problem. Make a drawing to show how to solve your problem. Check student's work.

UNIT 1 LESSON 3   Place Value in Word Problems **13**

Student Activity Book page 13

▶ **Read and Write Numbers** INDIVIDUALS

Have students complete exercises 1–4 on Student Activity Book page 13 to practice reading and writing numbers.

▶ **Solve and Discuss** WHOLE CLASS

Read aloud problem 5 on Student Activity Book page 13.

123 Math Talk Use the **Solve and Discuss** structure for problem 5. Invite a few students to work at the board, while the other students work on their MathBoards. Ask students to solve using a place value drawing. Select two or three students to show their place value drawings and explain their thinking. Encourage other students to listen carefully and ask questions. Make sure students give the label, or unit, for their answer. If they forget, ask questions like the following:

● You said the answer is 71. 71 what? 71 rolls

The Learning Classroom

Math Talk When using **Solve and Discuss**, choose presenters who used different solution strategies and have the class compare and contrast the strategies.

The following is one possible solution for problem 5.

- Make a ten-stick for each bag of 10 rolls and a circle for the extra roll.

7 bags of 10 rolls   1 roll

- Count to find the total: 10, 20, 30, 40, 50, 60, 70, 71
- Scott made 71 rolls.

Continue using **Solve and Discuss** for problems 6–10 on Student Activity Book page 13. Choose different students to work at the board for each problem. Then have students complete problem 11 and share their problems with the class. These problems are difficult for some students. Solving them is not a central unit goal.

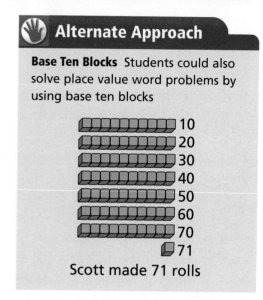

Alternate Approach

Base Ten Blocks Students could also solve place value word problems by using base ten blocks

10
20
30
40
50
60
70
71

Scott made 71 rolls

Review Subtraction Strategies

▶ Discuss Subtraction Strategies WHOLE GROUP

Review the subtraction exercises on Homework and Remembering page 4 from Lesson 2. Ask students what strategies they used to find the answer to 13 − 9. Discuss the Counting On and Make a Ten strategies for subtraction described below.

Counting On by Ones to Subtract To subtract by counting on, think of the related addition and count on to the total. There are three ways to think about counting on to find the answer to 13 − 9.

Mentally
- Think: $9 + ? = 13$.
- Say the known addend: "9" Count on to 13: "10, 11, 12, 13"
- You have counted 4 more, so $9 + 4 = 13$, or equivalently $13 − 9 = 4$.

With Fingers
- Think: $9 + ? = 13$. Say the first number to yourself: "9"
- Count on, raising one finger for each number you say, until you reach 13.

"10"   "11"   "12"   "13"

- You have raised 4 fingers, so $9 + 4 = 13$, or equivalently $13 − 9 = 4$.

Activity continued ▶

🕐 **10 MINUTES**

Goal: Review subtraction strategies.

Materials: Homework and Remembering page 4

✔ **NCTM Standards:**
Number and Operations
Representation

Place Value in Word Problems   **25**

① Teaching the Lesson (continued)

Teaching Note

Subtraction Strategies In this activity, we review how to subtract using the counting on and make a ten strategies. Students experiencing difficulty with subtraction should learn one or both of these methods. With practice, these strategies will become efficient, reliable subtraction methods.

✓ Ongoing Assessment

▶ How many tens are in 300?

▶ Each basket can hold 10 apples. Describe what happens when 58 apples are put into the baskets.

▶ Explain how you can use an addition problem to help you solve 14 − 8.

With a Drawing

● Think: 9 + ? = 13

● Pretend you have already counted 9 dots. Write the number 9. Draw and count dots, one at a time, until you reach 13.

$$9 \quad \underset{10 \;\; 11 \;\; 12 \;\; 13}{\circ \;\; \circ \;\; \circ \;\; \circ}$$
$$9 + 4 = 13$$
$$13 - 9 = 4$$

● You have drawn 4 dots, so 9 + 4 = 13, or equivalently, 13 − 9 = 4.

Make a Ten to Subtract In order to subtract by making a ten, think of the related addition. Add to get to ten and then add to get to the total. There are two ways to think about making a ten to find the answer to 13 − 9.

Mentally

● Think: 9 + ? = 13

● Start with 9. Add 1 to get 10 and then 3 more to get 13. You have added a total of 4, so 9 + 4 = 13, or equivalently, 13 − 9 = 4.

Numerically

(9 + 1) + 3 = 13

9 + (1 + 3) = 13; 9 + 4 = 13, or equivalently, 13 − 9 = 4

With a Drawing

● Think: 9 + ? = 13

● Draw 9 to represent 9 dots. Draw 1 more dot to get 10. Add 3 more to get 13. You have drawn 4 dots, so 9 + 4 = 13, or equivalently, 13 − 9 = 4.

$$9 \rightarrow \boxed{9 \; \circ} \rightarrow \boxed{9 \; \circ} \circ \circ \circ \rightarrow \boxed{9} \; \circ \circ \circ \circ$$
$$ 10 \qquad 10 + 3 = 13 \qquad 9 + 4 = 13$$
$$13 - 9 = 4$$

Review the remaining subtraction exercises on page 4 as a class. If students are not proficient with subtraction, have them use the Counting On and Make a Ten strategies to subtract.

② Extending the Lesson

Differentiated Instruction
Activities for Individualizing

Intervention
for students having difficulty

INDIVIDUALS

Number Names

Materials: MathBoard materials

Have students use their MathBoards to visualize equivalent names for the same number. For example, tell students to make a dot drawing for 245 using hundred-boxes, ten-sticks, and circles. Then ask them to make another drawing for 245 beneath it, using only ten-sticks and circles. Have them label each drawing as shown below.

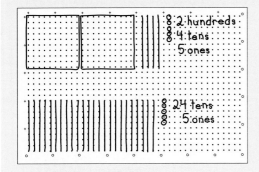

Repeat the activity with other numbers as needed.

 Math Writing Prompt

Intervention

Write a Problem
Write a place value word problem involving groups of 10.

On Level
for students having success

PAIRS

Scrambled Word Problems

Materials: Sentence Strips

Write the sentences of a story problem on separate sentence strips. Mix up the strips so the sentences are out of order. Have pairs of students work together to arrange the strips in the correct order and solve the problem.

> How many vases did Jen fill?
>
> Jen had 83 daisies.
>
> How many daisies were left over?
>
> Jen put 10 daisies in each vase.

Then have each student write a place value word problem and repeat the activity. Partners exchange sentence strips and solve each other's problems.

 Math Writing Prompt

On Level

Explain Your Thinking
Explain how to use the Make a Hundred strategy to add 90 + 40.

Challenge
for students seeking a challenge

PAIRS

Write a Place Value Problem

Materials: Index cards

Give students the three answers below written on index cards. Have students write a place value word problem for each answer. Partners exchange papers and match the word problem with the correct answer.

> 21 boxes and 7 cookies left over
>
> 2 boxes and 17 cookies left over
>
> 217 cookies

Also Use
Challenge Master for 1-3

 Math Writing Prompt

Challenge

Investigate Math
What pattern do you see in the value of the places in a number when you go from right to left?

3 Homework and Spiral Review

1–3 Homework **Goal:** Additional Practice

✓ Include students' completed Homework page as part of their portfolios.

1–3 Homework

Name ____________________ Date __________

Use place value drawings to help you solve each problem. Label your answers.

> At Kyle's birthday party, he gave each of his 8 friends a bag. Each bag had 10 party favors.

1. How many favors did Kyle give out altogether? 80 favors

> A farmer had 612 tomatoes. He put them in baskets of 100.

2. How many baskets did he fill completely? 6 baskets
3. How many tomatoes were left over? 12 tomatoes

> At the library, Eric is placing 112 books on shelves. Each shelf holds 10 books.

4. How many shelves can Eric fill completely? 11 racks
5. How many books will be left over? 2 books

Write the number for the words.

6. one hundred sixty-seven 167
7. eighty-two 82
8. one hundred twenty 120
9. fifteen 15
10. four thousand one hundred six 4,106
11. one thousand ninety-nine 1,099

Homework and Remembering page 5

1–3 Remembering **Goal:** Spiral Review

This Remembering page would be appropriate anytime after today's lesson.

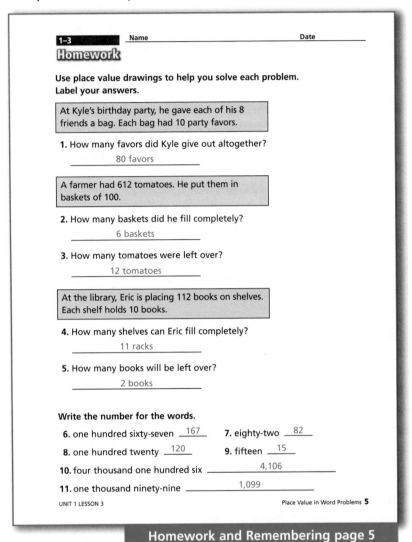

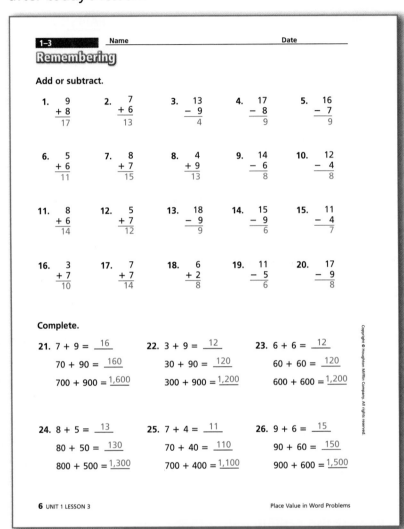

1–3 Remembering

Name ____________________ Date __________

Add or subtract.

1. 9 + 8 = 17	2. 7 + 6 = 13	3. 13 − 9 = 4	4. 17 − 8 = 9	5. 16 − 7 = 9
6. 5 + 6 = 11	7. 8 + 7 = 15	8. 4 + 9 = 13	9. 14 − 6 = 8	10. 12 − 4 = 8
11. 8 + 6 = 14	12. 5 + 7 = 12	13. 18 − 9 = 9	14. 15 − 9 = 6	15. 11 − 4 = 7
16. 3 + 7 = 10	17. 7 + 7 = 14	18. 6 + 2 = 8	19. 11 − 5 = 6	20. 17 − 9 = 8

Complete.

21. 7 + 9 = 16	22. 3 + 9 = 12	23. 6 + 6 = 12
70 + 90 = 160	30 + 90 = 120	60 + 60 = 120
700 + 900 = 1,600	300 + 900 = 1,200	600 + 600 = 1,200
24. 8 + 5 = 13	25. 7 + 4 = 11	26. 9 + 6 = 15
80 + 50 = 130	70 + 40 = 110	90 + 60 = 150
800 + 500 = 1,300	700 + 400 = 1,100	900 + 600 = 1,500

Homework and Remembering page 6

Home or School Activity

Social Studies Connection

Timelines Have students find three events that happened between 1500 and today. They should write the year and event on sticky notes. Then, have students make a timeline by placing their sticky notes in the correct place on the poster board.

DaVinci paints Mona Lisa 1503
Thomas Jefferson elected President 1800
Armstrong walks on Moon 1969

Practice with Place Value

Lesson Objectives
- Identify numbers from scrambled place value names.
- Solve place value word problems.

Vocabulary
Counting On strategy
Make a Ten strategy
place value

The Day at a Glance

Today's Goals	Materials	Math Talk
Quick Practice Read and form 3-digit numbers with Demonstration Secret Code Cards.	Quick Practice materials	In today's activities, the students are involved in discussion as they

1 Teaching the Lesson
A1: Identify numbers expressed in scrambled order.
A2: Solve place value word problems.
A3: Extend the Counting On and Make a Ten strategies.
	Secret Code Cards
	MathBoard materials
	Ten Frame
	  Two-color counters
	Place Value Strips
	  (Copymaster M23)
	Scissors
		▶ talk about the place value of digits in a multi-digit number
		▶ solve and discuss word problems
		▶ explain addition strategies

2 Extending the Lesson
▶ Going Further: Place Value Through Hundred Thousands
▶ Differentiated Instruction
	Index cards
	Student Activity Book
	  pages 15–18
	Homework and
	  Remembering pages 6–8	

3 Homework and Spiral Review	Math Journals Quick Quiz 1 (Assessment Guide)	

Quick Practice

🕐 **5 MINUTES**   **Goal:** Read and form 3-digit numbers with Demonstration Secret Code Cards.
Materials: Demonstration Secret Code Cards (Copymasters M3–M18)

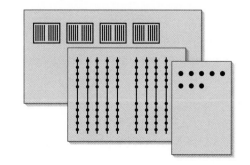

Read Place Value Drawings Have a Student Leader form a 3-digit number with the place value drawings on the back of the Demonstration Secret Code Cards. After the class identifies the number, the Student Leader demonstrates how to form the 3-digit number using the numerals on the cards. (See Unit 1 Lesson 2 Activity 1.)

1 Teaching the Lesson

Scrambled Places

 15 MINUTES

Goal: Identify numbers expressed in scrambled order.

Materials: Secret Code Cards (Copymasters M19–M22 or from Lesson 2), Student Activity Book page 15

 NCTM Standards:
Number and Operations
Representation

▶ **Scrambled Place Value Names** [WHOLE CLASS]

Write the expanded form of 1,653 on the board:

1 thousand + 6 hundreds + 5 tens + 3 ones

Have students build the number using their Secret Code Cards. 1,653

Now, write 1,278 in scrambled form on the board:

7 tens + 1 thousand + 2 hundreds + 8 ones

Have students build the number using their Secret Code Cards.

● What number did you build? 1,278

● How is this exercise different from the first one? The place values are given out of order.

Have students complete exercises 1–10 on Student Activity Book page 15. Review and discuss their answers.

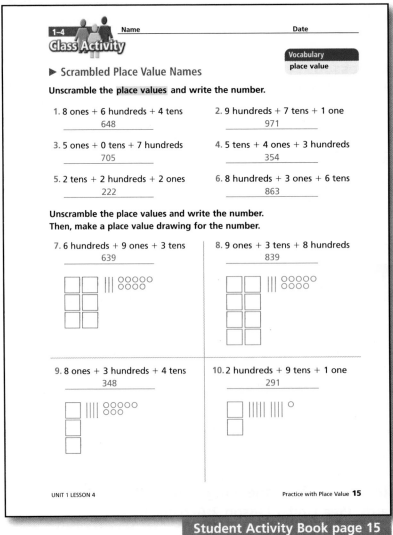

1–4 **Class Activity**   Name _____ Date _____

Vocabulary
place value

▶ Scrambled Place Value Names

Unscramble the **place values** and write the number.

1. 8 ones + 6 hundreds + 4 tens
   648

2. 9 hundreds + 7 tens + 1 one
   971

3. 5 ones + 0 tens + 7 hundreds
   705

4. 5 tens + 4 ones + 3 hundreds
   354

5. 2 tens + 2 hundreds + 2 ones
   222

6. 8 hundreds + 3 ones + 6 tens
   863

Unscramble the place values and write the number. Then, make a place value drawing for the number.

7. 6 hundreds + 9 ones + 3 tens
   639

8. 9 ones + 3 tens + 8 hundreds
   839

9. 8 ones + 3 hundreds + 4 tens
   348

10. 2 hundreds + 9 tens + 1 one
    291

UNIT 1 LESSON 4   Practice with Place Value **15**

Student Activity Book page 15

Activity 2

Place Value Word Problems

Student Activity Book page 16

The Student Activity Book page shows:

1–4 Class Activity

Name   Date

▶ Solve and Discuss

Solve each problem. Label your answer.

11. The bookstore received 35 boxes of books. Each box held 10 books. How many books did the store receive?

   350 books

Maya's family picked 376 apples and put them in baskets. Each basket holds 10 apples.

12. How many baskets did they fill?

   37 baskets

13. How many apples were left over?

   6 apples

Aidee had 672 buttons. She put them in bags with 100 buttons each.

14. How many bags did Aidee fill?

   6 bags

15. How many buttons were left over?

   72 buttons

When Joseph broke open his piggy bank, there were 543 pennies inside. He grouped the pennies into piles of 100.

16. How many piles of 100 did Joseph make?

   5 piles

17. How many extra pennies did he have?

   43 pennies

16 UNIT 1 LESSON 4   Practice with Place Value

▶ Solve and Discuss [WHOLE GROUP]

Direct students' attention to problems 11–17 on Student Activity Book page 16. Read aloud problem 11.

 Math Talk Using the **Solve and Discuss** structure, have students solve problem 11. Allow students to use any method they choose. If students have difficulty, suggest they try making place value drawings. Choose presenters who used different methods. A sample method is shown in the side column.

Using **Solve and Discuss,** have students solve problems 12–15.

 30 MINUTES

Goal: Solve place value word problems.

Materials: Math Board materials, Student Activity Book page 16

✓ **NCTM Standards:**
Numbers and Operations
Problem Solving
Communication
Representation

The Learning Classroom

Helping Community By discussing multiple methods for solving math problems, students become aware of other students' thinking. As students better understand other students' thinking, they become better helpers. Instead of showing how they would solve problems using their methods, they are able to look at another student's work and help that student find errors using that student's method.

Sample Method

Use place value drawings

• Draw a ten-stick for each box of books.

• Make a hundred box for each group of 10 ten-sticks.

• Count to find the total: 100, 200, 300, 310, 320, 330, 340, 350. There are 350 books in all.

Practice with Place Value   **31**

Extend Addition Strategies to Tens and Hundreds

 10 MINUTES

Goal: Extend the Counting On and Make a Ten strategies.

Materials: Homework and Remembering page 6, Ten Frame (Copymaster M2), two-color counters

 NCTM Standards:
Number and Operations
Representation

▶ Discuss Addition Strategies [WHOLE CLASS]

Review exercises 24–26 on Homework and Remembering page 6 from Lesson 3. Ask what strategies students used to find the answer to exercise 24, 80 + 50. Make sure the Counting On by Tens and Make a Hundred strategies are discussed. These strategies are described below and on the following page.

Counting On by Tens Strategy

There are a couple of ways to think about counting on. Students can use their fingers as long as they realize each finger represents 10. Students may also find it helpful to draw and count ten-sticks.

Mentally

● Say the first number to yourself: "80"

● Count on by tens, until you have counted 5 tens: "90, 100, 110, 120, 130"

● The answer is 130.

With a Drawing

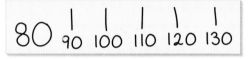

Use Place Value

● Think of the problem as 8 tens + 5 tens.

● Say the first number to yourself: "8 tens"

● Count on, until you have counted 5 tens: "9 tens, 10 tens, 11 tens, 12 tens, 13 tens."

● The answer is 13 tens, or 130.

 Ongoing Assessment

Write this place value problem on the board.

Avi has 634 pennies.

Ask students

▶ how many piles of 100 pennies can he make?

▶ How many extra pennies does he have?

Make A Hundred Strategy

Students can make a hundred to solve 80 + 50. There are at least two ways to make a hundred.

Numerically

- Start with 80. Take 20 from the 50 to get 100. Add the 30 that is left.

$$80 + 50 = 80 + 20 + 30 = 100 + 30 = 130$$

With a Drawing

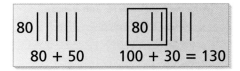

Use Place Value

- Think of the problem as 8 tens + 5 tens.

- Take 2 tens from 5 tens to get 10 tens and then add the 3 tens that are left.

- 8 tens + 5 tens = 8 tens + 2 tens + 3 tens

    = 10 tens + 3 tens

    = 1 hundred + 3 tens

    = 130

Counting on by Hundreds Strategy

Write 800 + 500 = ? on the board. Ask a volunteer to count on by hundreds to find the answer.

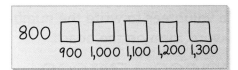

Make a Thousand Strategy

Challenge another volunteer to solve the problem by making a new thousand.

 Alternate Approach

Counters and Ten Frames When adding tens, students could also make a hundred using two-color counters and Ten Frame (Copymaster M2).

Invite students to describe how the frame could be used to add tens. Students should explain that each counter represents 10 and the frame represents 100.

80 + 20 = 100   100 + 30 = 130

 **Quick Quiz**

See Assessment Guide for Unit 1 Quick Quiz 1.

Extending the Lesson

Going Further: Place Value Through Hundred Thousands

Goal: Identify the place value of the digits in numbers to 999,999.

Materials: Student Activity Book pages 17–18

✓ **NCTM Standards:**
Numbers and Operations
Representation

▶ Place Value to 999,999 WHOLE CLASS

Tell students that the Moon is 238,900 miles from the Earth. Draw a place value chart on the board with this number in it to help students understand the value of the number.

hundred thousands	ten thousands	thousands	hundreds	tens	ones
2	3	8	9	0	0

Starting with the ones place, point to each place and ask:

● What is the value of this place? ones

Then ask students to suppose there are Secret Code Cards for numbers this large. Ask a volunteer to sketch the Secret Code Cards under the chart that they would use to build the number.

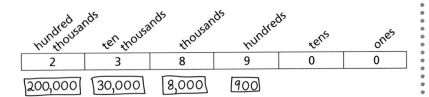

Ask students the following questions:

● What is the value of the digit 2 in the place value chart? 200,000

● What is the value of the digit 3 in the place value chart? 30,000

● What is the value of the digit 8 in the place value chart? 8,000

● What is the value of the digit 9 in the place value chart? 900

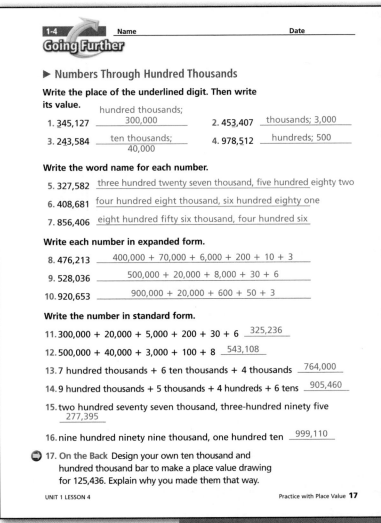

Student Activity Book page 17

Ask a volunteer to write the number in expanded form and word form on the board.

$$200,000 + 30,000 + 8,000 + 900$$

two hundred thirty eight thousand, nine hundred

Summarize by writing the labels *standard form, expanded form,* and *word form* on the board and ask a volunteer to write the number in these ways next to the labels.

▶ Numbers Through Hundred Thousands INDIVIDUALS

Have students complete Student Activity Book page 17.

Intervention
for students having difficulty

PAIRS

Matching Number Names

Materials: Place Value Strips (Copymaster M23), scissors

Have each pair of students cut Place Value Strips (Copymaster M23) to make eighteen number strips. Pairs work together to match each number with its word name and its place value name.

259

two hundred fifty-nine

two hundreds + 9 ones + 5 tens

After students have matched the three place value strips, have them draw a place value drawing of the number.

On Level
for students having success

SMALL GROUPS

Build Five

Materials: Index cards (30 per group)

On index cards have students write all the ones, tens, and hundreds from 0 through 9.

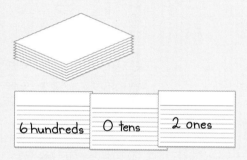

6 hundreds   0 tens   2 ones

Students shuffle and receive 2 cards. The remaining cards are placed facedown in a stack. Partners take turns choosing the top card from the stack. If the three cards form a three-digit number, the player names the number and earns 1 point. One card is discarded on each turn whether or not a number has been formed. The discarded card is placed at the bottom of the stack. The first player to earn 5 points wins the game.

Challenge
for students seeking a challenge

SMALL GROUPS

Make an Organized List

Materials: Math Journals

Have each group create and organize a list to show all possible place value combinations of the number 138. Then, have them discuss any patterns they see in their list.

Hundreds	Tens	Ones
1	3	8
1	2	18
1	1	28
1	0	38
0	13	8
0	12	18
0	11	28
0	10	38
0	9	48
0	8	58
0	7	68
0	6	78
0	5	88
0	4	98
0	3	108
0	2	118
0	1	128
0	0	138

As time permits, challenge students to repeat the activity using the number 238.

Also Use
Challenge Master for 1-4

 Math Writing Prompt

Intervention

Compare and Contrast
Compare 1,234 and 4,321. How are they alike? How are they different? Explain your thinking.

 Math Writing Prompt

On Level

Investigate Math
Describe a way to find the total number of paperclips needed so every student in a class has 10 paperclips.

 Math Writing Prompt

Challenge

Explain Your Thinking
How many ways are there to scramble the place values in four hundred fifty-seven? Explain your answer.

③ Homework and Spiral Review

Homework **Goal:** Additional Practice

✓ Include students' completed Homework page as part of their portfolios.

Remembering **Goal:** Spiral Review

This Remembering page would be appropriate anytime after today's lesson.

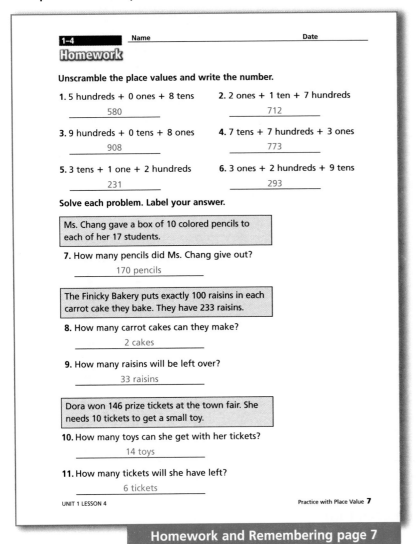

1–4 Name _____ Date _____

Homework

Unscramble the place values and write the number.

1. 5 hundreds + 0 ones + 8 tens
   _____ 580 _____

2. 2 ones + 1 ten + 7 hundreds
   _____ 712 _____

3. 9 hundreds + 0 tens + 8 ones
   _____ 908 _____

4. 7 tens + 7 hundreds + 3 ones
   _____ 773 _____

5. 3 tens + 1 one + 2 hundreds
   _____ 231 _____

6. 3 ones + 2 hundreds + 9 tens
   _____ 293 _____

Solve each problem. Label your answer.

Ms. Chang gave a box of 10 colored pencils to each of her 17 students.

7. How many pencils did Ms. Chang give out?
   _____ 170 pencils _____

The Finicky Bakery puts exactly 100 raisins in each carrot cake they bake. They have 233 raisins.

8. How many carrot cakes can they make?
   _____ 2 cakes _____

9. How many raisins will be left over?
   _____ 33 raisins _____

Dora won 146 prize tickets at the town fair. She needs 10 tickets to get a small toy.

10. How many toys can she get with her tickets?
    _____ 14 toys _____

11. How many tickets will she have left?
    _____ 6 tickets _____

UNIT 1 LESSON 4   Practice with Place Value **7**

Homework and Remembering page 7

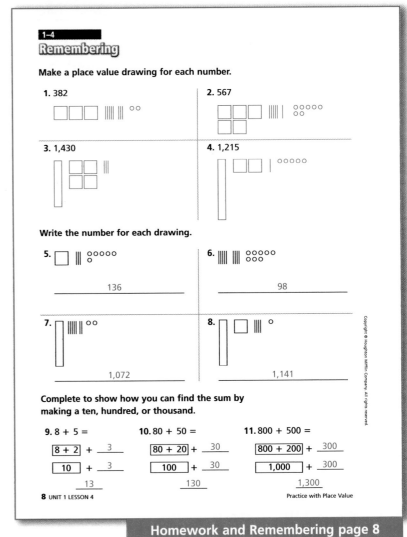

1–4

Remembering

Make a place value drawing for each number.

1. 382

2. 567

3. 1,430

4. 1,215

Write the number for each drawing.

5. _____ 136 _____

6. _____ 98 _____

7. _____ 1,072 _____

8. _____ 1,141 _____

Complete to show how you can find the sum by making a ten, hundred, or thousand.

9. 8 + 5 =
   [8 + 2] + _3_
   [10] + _3_
   _____ 13 _____

10. 80 + 50 =
    [80 + 20] + _30_
    [100] + _30_
    _____ 130 _____

11. 800 + 500 =
    [800 + 200] + _300_
    [1,000] + _300_
    _____ 1,300 _____

8 UNIT 1 LESSON 4   Practice with Place Value

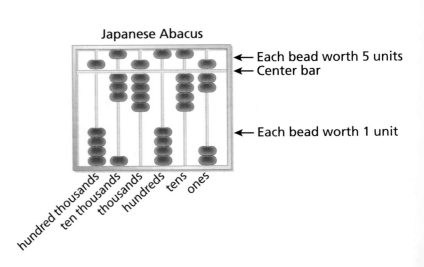

Homework and Remembering page 8

Home or School Activity

Math-to-Math Connection

Abacus Tell students that before place value charts were invented, people used an abacus to show numbers and perform computations. Have students find out how to show a number on an abacus.

To read the number on this abacus, count the beads moved to the center bar in each place value. The number 539,047 is shown on the Japanese abacus to the right.

Japanese Abacus

← Each bead worth 5 units
← Center bar

← Each bead worth 1 unit

hundred thousands   ten thousands   thousands   hundreds   tens   ones

Explore Multi-Digit Addition

Lesson Objectives

- Discuss and apply multi-digit addition methods.
- Make proof drawings to show that addition methods are correct.

The Day at a Glance

Today's Goals	Materials	Math Talk
Quick Practice Use the Make a Hundred strategy to add tens.	Quick Practice materials	In today's activities, the students are involved in discussion as they
① Teaching the Lesson **A1:** Make proof drawings to illustrate adding. **A2:** Compare and discuss different multi-digit addition methods.	MathBoard materials Secret Code Cards Base ten blocks Game Cards Index cards	▶ describe methods for adding 3-digit numbers ▶ solve and discuss word problems
② Extending the Lesson ▶ Differentiated Instruction	Student Activity Book pages 19–22	
③ Homework and Spiral Review	Homework and Remembering pages 9–10	
	Math Journals	
	Family Letter	

Quick Practice

 5 MINUTES   **Goal:** Use the Make a Hundred strategy to add tens.
Materials: Demonstration Secret Code Cards
(Copymasters M3–M18)

Add Tens Using the Demonstration Secret Code Cards, have a Student Leader hold up two tens cards. The leader gives students a few seconds to mentally add the numbers, and then says, "Add." The class says the addition equation aloud. The leader then chooses one student to explain the Make a Hundred strategy. Repeat for several pairs of cards.

Leader: Add.
Class: 50 plus 70 equals 120.
Student: 70 plus 30 equals 100, plus 20 more is 120.

Class Management

The student explainer may add from the larger addend (easier) or add from the first addend.

```
50        70
5 0      7 0
```

Teaching the Lesson

Activity 1

Solve Addition Problems

 25 MINUTES

Goal: Make proof drawings to illustrate adding.

Materials: MathBoard materials, Student Activity Book page 19

✔ **NCTM Standards:**
Number and Operations
Problem Solving
Representation

New Groups Above Method (Common U.S.)

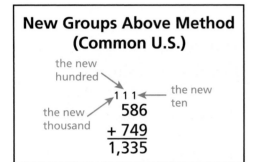

the new hundred

the new ten

the new thousand

$$\begin{array}{r} 1\ 1\ 1 \\ 586 \\ +\ 749 \\ \hline 1,335 \end{array}$$

New Groups Below Method

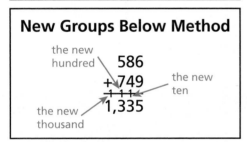

the new hundred

the new ten

the new thousand

$$\begin{array}{r} 586 \\ +\ 749 \\ \hline 1\ 1\ 1 \\ 1,335 \end{array}$$

Show All Totals Method

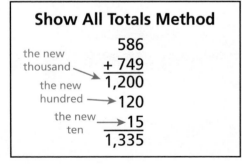

the new thousand

the new hundred

the new ten

$$\begin{array}{r} 586 \\ +\ 749 \\ \hline 1,200 \\ 120 \\ 15 \\ \hline 1,335 \end{array}$$

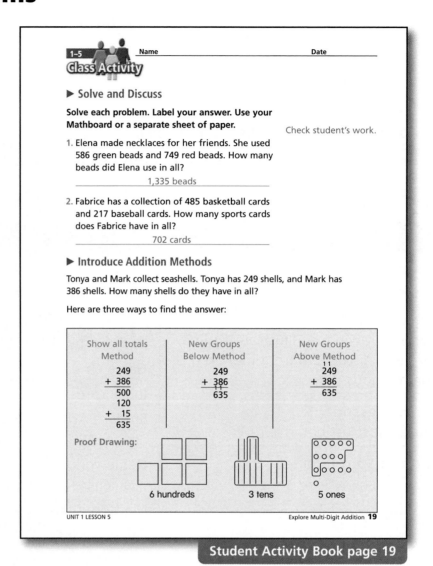

Student Activity Book page 19

▶ Solve and Discuss [WHOLE CLASS]

Using the **Solve and Discuss** structure, have students solve problem 1 on Student Activity Book page 19. Students may use any method they wish as long as they can explain it using place value language. Encourage students to make place value drawings to show their methods. Students who used this program in a previous grade may use the New Groups Below method or Show All Totals method. Other students are likely to use the New Groups Above method, which is the method taught in most U.S. classrooms. These addition methods are shown to the left with groupings labeled.

Invite students who used different addition methods to explain how their drawings relate to the numerical method. If no presenter makes a place value drawing, choose one of the addition methods and work as a class to make a drawing as described below.

Make place value drawings for the numbers being added on the board.

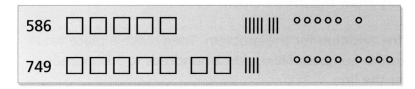

First group 10 ones to make a new ten, 10 tens to make a new hundred, and 10 hundreds to make a new thousand. (Do this step-by-step in order. The order in which the grouping is done depends on the numerical method used.)

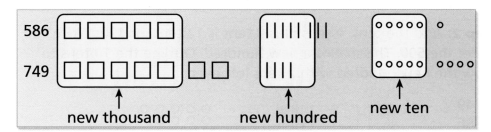

- Now, how many thousands are there? 1
- How many hundreds are there? 3 Tens? 3 Ones? 5
- What is the total? 1,335

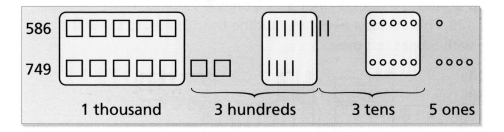

Explain to students that these drawings are called *proof drawings* because they *prove* that the addition method and the answer are correct.

Continue using **Solve and Discuss** for problem 2. Tell students to make proof drawings for their additions. See a sample proof drawing to the right. Students' proof drawings may vary in the way the tens and ones are positioned in the place value drawing for the numbers being added. Be sure to discuss the reason the total has a zero in the tens place: 10 ones are grouped to form a new ten, giving a total of 10 tens. These 10 tens are then grouped to form a new hundred, leaving no tens.

Sample Proof Drawing for problem 2.

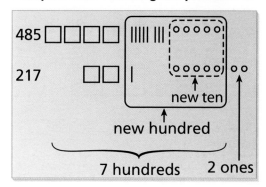

Activity 2

Three Addition Methods

 30 MINUTES

Goal: Compare and discuss different multi-digit addition methods.

Materials: MathBoard materials, Student Activity Book pages 19–20 Secret Code Cards (Copymasters M19–M22)

 NCTM Standards:
Number and Operations
Problem Solving
Representation

 Alternate Approach

Secret Code Cards If students have trouble understanding the Show All Totals method, consider having them build the addends with Secret Code Cards. They can then "open up" each addend to show hundreds, tens, and ones. Then they can add each place value group separately.

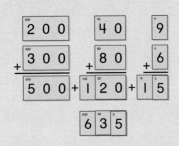

▶ **Introduce Addition Methods** WHOLE CLASS

Read the problem about Tonya and Mark's sea shells on Student Activity Book page 19.

Show All Totals Method Have students focus on the Show All totals method first. Ask for a volunteer to go to the board and explain each step relating the numerical method to a proof drawing. Student's proof drawings may vary from the ones below.

Step 1: Write the addition for the problem. Then make a place value drawing next to the numbers. Next, add 2 hundreds to 3 hundreds. Write 500 under the line.

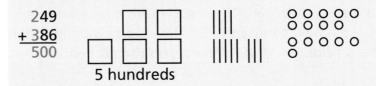

5 hundreds

Step 2: Add the tens. 4 tens plus 8 tens is 12 tens, or 120. Write 120 under the 500. This makes a new hundred. Outline the 10 tens to show the new hundred with 2 tens left over.

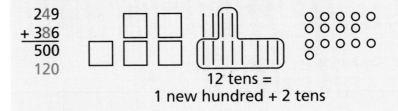

12 tens =
1 new hundred + 2 tens

Step 3: Add the ones. 9 ones plus 6 ones is 15 ones. Write 15 under the 120. This makes a new ten. Outline the 10 ones to show the new ten with 5 ones left over.

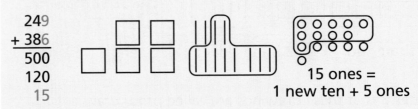

15 ones =
1 new ten + 5 ones

Step 4: Add 500, 120, and 15. Write 635 under the line.

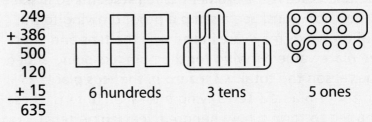

6 hundreds   3 tens   5 ones

New Groups Below Method Ask if anyone can explain the New Groups Below method. If someone can, have that student go to the board and show each step, illustrating with proof drawings. Provide help and clarify explanations as needed. If no one can explain, guide students through the method yourself, eliciting as much information from students as you can.

As you (or a student) explain, relate the numerical method to a proof drawing. As before, start by writing the addition for the problem and making place value drawings for each addend.

Step 1: This time, start by adding the ones. What do we get? 15 Can we make a new ten? yes How many ones are left over? 5. Write a "1" for the 1 new ten under the tens column. The 1 ten will wait there until we add the tens. I'll write a 5 for the 5 leftover ones in the ones column, under the line. Show the new ten in the drawing.

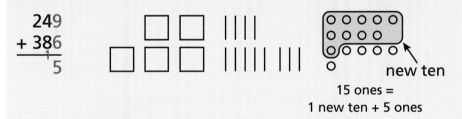

15 ones =
1 new ten + 5 ones

Step 2: Next, add the tens. Add 4 tens and 8 tens and then add the 1 new ten that has been waiting. What is the total? 13 tens Can we make a new hundred? yes How many tens are left over? 3 Write a "1" for the 1 new hundred under the hundreds column. Write a 3 for the 3 leftover tens in the tens column, under the line. Show the new hundred in the drawing.

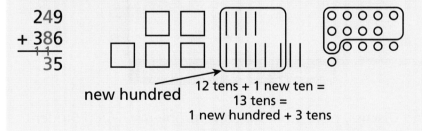

new hundred

12 tens + 1 new ten =
13 tens =
1 new hundred + 3 tens

Step 3: Finally, add the hundreds. Add 2 hundreds and 3 hundreds and then add the 1 hundred that has been waiting. What is the total? 6 hundreds Write 6 in the hundreds column, under the line. What is the final answer? 635

Have students compare the New Groups Below method to the Show All Totals method. Ask them which they find easier and why.

Activity continued ▶

Math Background New Groups Above is the method taught in most U.S. classrooms. However, the New Groups Below method has advantages that make it easier to use for some students. For example, it allows students to see the sum that results from adding the tens or the ones, even after regrouping. In the example below, the 15 that results from adding 9 ones and 6 ones is clearly visible with the New Groups Below method but not with the New Groups Above method.

New Groups Below	New Groups Above
249	$\overset{1}{2}49$
+ 386	+ 386
5	5

Many students also find it easier to add the new 1 last, after adding the other numbers in the column. In the problem above, students using the New Groups Below method would add 4 tens and 8 tens to get 12 tens and then simply add 1 more to get 13 tens. With the New Groups Above method, they need to add 1 ten and 4 tens to get 5 tens, remember that sum, and then add 8 tens.

The Learning Classroom

Helping Community When students present their solutions, encourage those listening to pay attention to how they are talking about place value. When a presenter forgets to mention place value, encourage other students to wave their fingers in the air – that is, to "wave tens or hundreds"—as a reminder.

New Groups Above Method Have students look at the New Groups Above method. Ask them how it is similar to the New Groups Below method and how it is different. Students should observe that the methods are identical, except in the New Groups Above method, the new ten or hundred is written at the top of the column, rather than beneath the column.

▶ **Practice Addition Methods** INDIVIDUALS

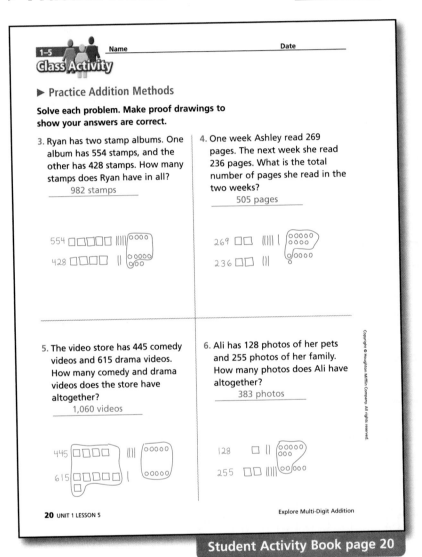

Student Activity Book page 20

Using **Solve and Discuss,** have students solve problems 3–6 on Student Activity Book page 20. Encourage them to try the methods discussed in this activity, but allow them to use any method they understand. Students should make proof drawings to show their answers are correct.

Choose students who used different methods to share their solutions. Encourage presenters to talk about grouping ones to make a new ten, tens to make a new hundred, and hundreds to make a new thousand. Also, make sure they say add 5 tens, 2 tens, and 1 new ten to get 8 tens (or 50 and 20 and 10 to get 80), rather add 5, 2, and 1 to get 8.

Class Management

Looking Ahead You will need grocery store advertisements for Lesson 7. Ask students to bring them in from home.

Ongoing Assessment

Give students this addition exercise and ask them to find the sum.

$$\begin{array}{r} 614 \\ + 893 \\ \hline 1{,}507 \end{array}$$

Check their understanding of the process by asking questions such as:

▶ How do you know the answer has to be more than 1,000?

▶ Why is there a zero in the tens place of your answer?

Differentiated Instruction — Activities for Individualizing

Intervention
for students having difficulty

PAIRS

Adding with Base Ten Blocks

Materials: Base ten blocks (20 hundreds, 20 tens, 20 ones per pair), MathBoard materials

Write several 3-digit numbers on index cards and place them in a pile. Have each student select a card from the pile, and use base ten blocks to model the number.

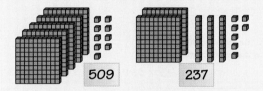

509   237

Next, partners combine their blocks and show the total with as few blocks as possible. They should exchange any group of 10 ones for 1 ten, any group of 10 tens for 1 hundred, and so on. Have them write the number for the total on their MathBoards.

If time permits, have pairs choose different cards and repeat the activity.

On Level
for students having success

PAIRS

On Target

Draw the target pictured below on the board or on chart paper. Tell students that the numbers indicate how many points are scored when a dart lands in that section of the target. Have them find all the ways to score a total greater than 1,000 points when two darts are thrown at the target.

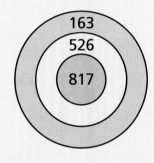

163
526
817

If time permits, have students repeat the activity, substituting for three darts.

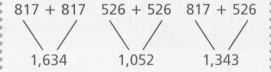

$$817 + 817 \qquad 526 + 526 \qquad 817 + 526$$

$$1,634 \qquad\qquad 1,052 \qquad\qquad 1,343$$

Challenge
for students seeking a challenge

PAIRS

Addition Shuffle

Materials: Index cards (22 per pair) or Game Cards (Copymaster M25)

Have each pair of students write the digits from 1 to 9 on index cards, one digit per card. Ask students to make 2 cards for each digit, then shuffle the cards and place them facedown in a stack.

Each student draws 6 cards from the stack and uses them to create 2 three-digit numbers. The student adds the numbers and writes the sum on a blank index card. The student then shuffles all of the cards (except the answer card) and gives them to his or her partner.

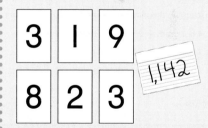

The partner arranges the cards for the addends so they add to the given sum.

Also Use
Challenge Master for 1-5

 **Math Writing Prompt**

Intervention

Find the Error
A student said the answer to 536 + 481 is 917. Explain why this answer is incorrect.

 Math Writing Prompt

On Level

Explain Your Thinking
Write two 3-digit numbers that have a sum less than 1,000. Write two 3-digit numbers that have a sum greater than 1,000. Explain how you chose the numbers.

 Math Writing Prompt

Challenge

Guess and Check
Using six different digits, write 2 three-digit numbers whose sum is exactly 1,000. Explain how you chose the numbers.

③ Homework and Spiral Review

1-5 Homework Goal: Additional Practice

This Homework page gives students practice solving addition problems and scrambled place value problems.

1-5 Remembering Goal: Spiral Review

This Remembering page would be appropriate anytime after today's lesson.

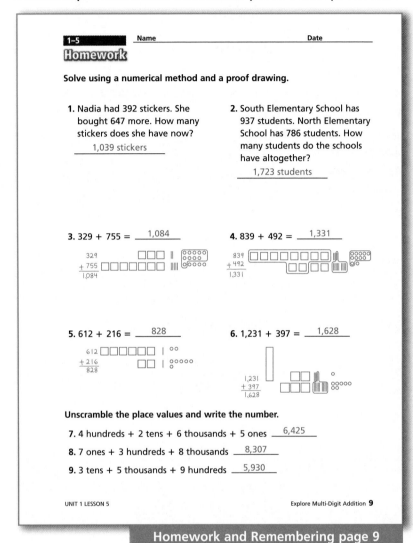

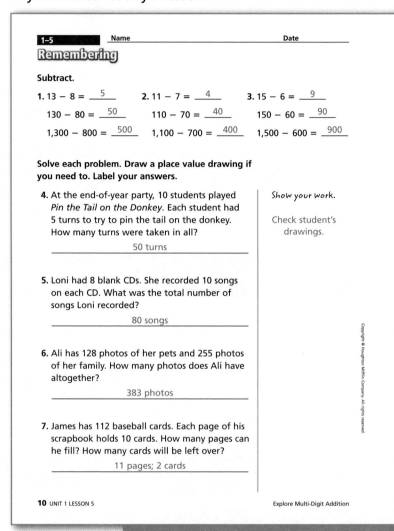

Homework and Remembering page 9

Homework and Remembering page 10

Home and School Connection

Family Letter Have children take home the Family Letter on Student Activity Book page 21. A Spanish translation of this letter is on the following page in the Student Activity Book. This letter explains how the concepts of addition and subtraction are developed in *Math Expressions.* It gives parents and guardians a better understanding of the learning that goes on in math class and creates a bridge between school and home.

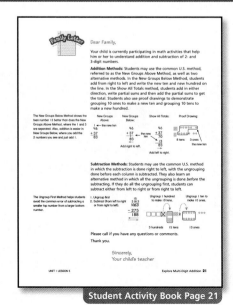

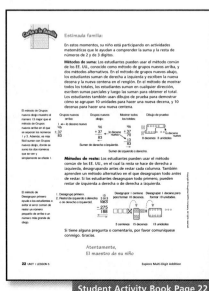

Student Activity Book Page 21

Student Activity Book Page 22

44 UNIT 1 LESSON 5

UNIT 1 LESSON 6

Discuss Addition Methods

Lesson Objectives
- Apply and discuss multi-digit addition methods.
- Discuss why it is necessary to align places before adding.

Vocabulary
Counting On strategy
Make a Ten strategy
expression
proof drawing

The Day at a Glance

Today's Goals	Materials	Math Talk
Quick Practice Add tens. **1 Teaching the Lesson** A1: Solve multi-digit addition problems and discuss solution methods. A2: Discuss the importance of aligning place value columns before adding. A3: Extend Counting On and Make a Ten subtraction strategies. **2 Extending the Lesson** ▶ Going Further: Sums to 10,000 ▶ Differentiated Instruction **3 Homework and Spiral Review**	Quick Practice materials MathBoard materials Secret Code Cards Spinner A (Copymaster M24) Paper clips Base ten blocks Game Cards Student Activity Book pages 23–24 Homework and Remembering pages 11–12 Math Journals	In today's activities, the students are involved in discussion as they ▶ explain different addition methods ▶ discuss the importance of aligning place value columns before adding ▶ extend Counting On and Make a Ten subtraction strategies

Quick Practice

⏱ **5 MINUTES**　**Goal:** Use the Make a Hundred strategy to add tens.
Materials: Demonstration Secret Code Cards (Copymasters M3–M18)

Add Tens Using the Demonstration Secret Code Cards, have a Student Leader hold up two tens cards. The leader gives students a few seconds to mentally add the numbers, and then says, "Add." The class says the addition equation aloud. The leader then chooses one student to explain the Make a Hundred strategy. Repeat for several pairs of cards.

Leader: Add.
Class: 60 plus 80 equals 140.
Student: 60 plus 40 equals 100, plus 40 more is 140.

❶ Teaching the Lesson

Solve Word Problems and Discuss Solutions

 25 MINUTES

Goal: Solve multi-digit addition problems and discuss solution methods.

Materials: Student Activity Book page 23

✔ **NCTM Standards:**
Number and Operations
Problem Solving
Communication

The Learning Classroom

Building Concepts At this point, all students should include Proof Drawings with their numerical solutions. These drawings will provide conceptual support and facilitate students' explanations. After two or three days, you may decide to make drawings optional for students who are consistently accurate with addition and can explain their method, while continuing to require them from students who need more support.

Teaching Note

Language and Vocabulary When adding tens in the first problem, 359 + 245, some students may say they are adding 50 and 40 and 10 to get 100, rather than saying they are adding 5 tens and 4 tens and 1 ten to get 10 tens, or 1 hundred. Similarly, students may say they are adding 300 and 200 and 100 to get 600, rather than 3 hundreds and 2 hundreds and 1 hundred to get 6 hundreds. This language is correct and acceptable. If no students use this language, consider modeling it for them. Students should be comfortable with both kinds of place value language.

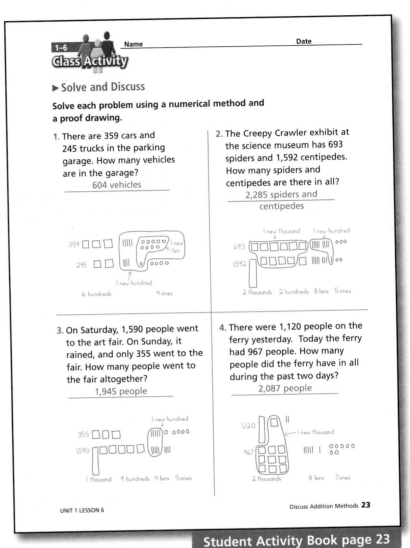

Student Activity Book page 23

▶ Solve and Discuss WHOLE CLASS

Math Talk Use the **Solve and Discuss** structure for problem 1. Invite three to six students to go to the classroom board and solve the problem relating each step of a proof drawing to each step of a numerical method while others work at their seats on MathBoards.

Ask students who used different addition methods to share their solutions. Encourage them to talk about grouping and make sure they are using correct language to talk about place value. Remind students to "wave tens or hundreds" if a presenter talks about tens and hundreds as if they were ones. Compare the solution methods that are presented.

Continue to use **Solve and Discuss** to complete problems 2–4.

Activity 2

Align Places to Add

1–6 **Class Activity**

Name ______________________ Date ______________

Possible response: You added tens to hundreds and ones to tens because you did not line up the numbers correctly.

▶ **The Puzzled Penguin**

Dear Math Students:

Today I found the answer to 163 + 78, but I don't know if I added correctly. Please look at my work. Is my answer right? If not, please correct my work and tell what I did wrong.

168	168
+78	+ 78
948	246

Thank you,

The Puzzled Penguin

▶ **Line Up the Places to Add**

Write each addition vertically. Line up the places correctly. Then add and make a proof drawing.

5. 179 + 38 = 217

6. 1,250 + 345 = 1,595

7. 907 + 877 = 1,784

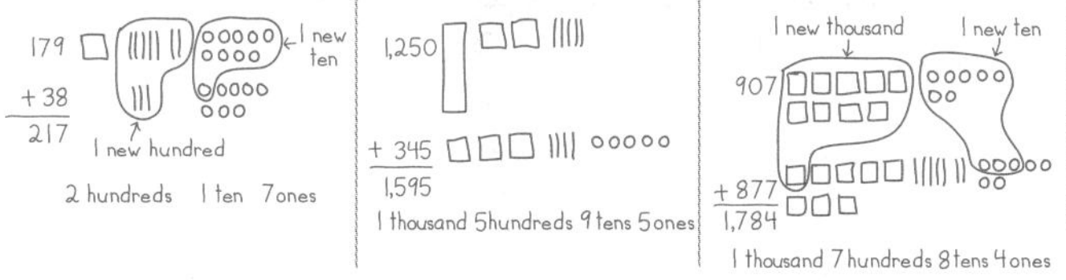

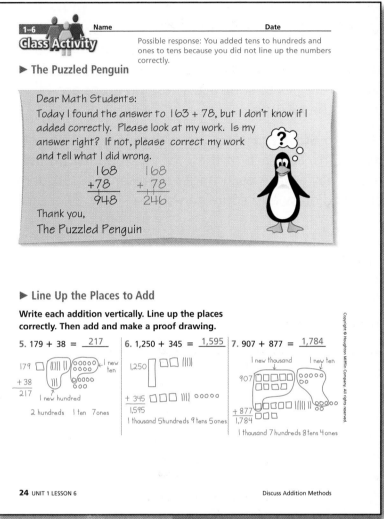

Student Activity Book page 24

▶ The Puzzled Penguin WHOLE CLASS

Have students read the letter from the Puzzled Penguin on Student Activity Book page 24 and correct his work if necessary.

Ask volunteers to explain what the penguin did wrong. Students should notice that, because the penguin did not line up the numbers correctly, he added the tens to hundreds and ones to tens. Ask students why it is important to align the place value columns. Then have a student come to the board to show and explain how to do the addition correctly.

▶ Line Up the Places to Add WHOLE CLASS

Have students complete problems 5–7 on page 24. Assist students who are having trouble.

15 MINUTES

Goal: Discuss the importance of aligning place value columns before adding.

Materials: Student Activity Book page 24

NCTM Standards:
Number and Operations
Communication
Problem Solving

The Learning Classroom

Building Concepts The Puzzled Penguin feature presents common math errors for students to catch and correct. More importantly, it encourages students to articulate basic math concepts.

Teaching Note

Reasonable Answers You might ask students how the penguin could have used common sense to figure out that his answer is not reasonable. Because 168 is less than 200, and 78 is less than 100, 168 + 78 must be less than 300. The penguin's answer, 948, is much too big. Tell students that they can use a similar type of thinking to check whether their own answers are reasonable.

Differentiated Instruction

Extra Help If students have trouble aligning the place value columns, use grid paper to help them line up their numbers correctly.

Activity 3

Extend Subtraction Strategies

 15 MINUTES

Goal: Extend Counting On and Make a Ten subtraction strategies.

Materials: Homework and Remembering page 10

 NCTM Standards:
Number and Operations
Communication

Teaching Note

What to Expect from Students
How did your students explain their math thinking today? Students are often unfamiliar with this process; they are accustomed to providing math answers only. Supporting students to talk more fully about their thinking will take repeated efforts on your part. Expect this to be a building process that lasts for several weeks.

Early on, when a student provides an answer and then wants to sit down, try asking them to stay at the board and explain just one or two more things about the problem or math thinking first. For example, a student may be encouraged to tell more about a drawing they drew to solve a word problem or how they used the drawing to come up with an answer.

Teaching Note

Math Background In 1489, John Widman, an English mathematician, first used the + and − signs. In 1557, Robert Record, also an English mathematician, introduced the = sign. Until then the word *equals* was written out in an equation.

▶ **Discuss Subtraction Strategies** [WHOLE CLASS]

Review problems from Homework and Remembering page 10 from Lesson 5. Ask what strategies students used to find the answer to 130 − 80. Make sure the Counting On by Tens and Make a Hundred strategies are discussed. Then introduce the Counting On by Hundreds, and Make a Thousand strategies to subtract. These methods are described below and on the next page.

Counting On by Tens to Subtract Here are different ways to think about Counting On by Tens. For each of these ways, students can use their fingers as long as they realize each finger represents 10. Students may also find it helpful to draw and count ten-sticks.

Mentally

● Think: 80 + ? = 130

● Say the first number to yourself: 80

● Count on by tens, until you reach 130: 90, 100, 110, 120, 130

● You have counted 5 tens, or 50, so 80 + 50 = 130, or equivalently, 130 − 80 = 50.

With a Drawing

$$80 \mid \ \mid \ \mid \ \mid \ \mid \qquad 80 + 50 = 130 \rightarrow 130 - 80 = 50$$
$$\quad \ \ 90 \ 100 \ 110 \ 120 \ 130$$

Use Place Value

● Think: 8 tens + ? tens = 13 tens.

● Say the first number to yourself: "8 tens"

● Count on until you reach 13 tens: "9 tens, 10 tens, 11 tens, 12 tens, 13 tens." You have counted 5 tens, or 50, so 80 + 50 = 130, or equivalently, 130 − 80 = 50.

Make a Hundred to Subtract Here are different ways to think about Making a Hundred to Subtract. Again, for each of these methods, students can use their fingers to represent 10s. Students may also find it helpful to draw and count ten-sticks.

Mentally

Think: 80 + ? = 130.

Start with 80. Add 20 to get 100 and then 30 more to get 130.

You have added a total of 50, so 80 + 50 = 130, or equivalently, 130 − 80 = 50.

With a Drawing

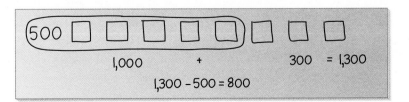

$80 \rightarrow \boxed{80 \; \text{II}} \rightarrow \boxed{80 \; \text{II}} \; \text{III} \rightarrow 80 \; \text{IIIII}$

80 + 20 = 100   100 + 30 = 130   80 + 50 = 130
                                   130 − 80 = 50

Use Place Value

Think: 8 tens + ? tens = 13 tens.

Add 2 tens to 8 tens to get 10 tens and then add 3 more tens to get 13 tens.

You have added a total of 50, so 80 + 50 = 130, or equivalently, 130 − 80 = 50.

Counting On by Hundreds Write 1,300 − 500 = ? on the board. Ask a volunteer to find the answer by counting on by hundreds.

500 ☐ ☐ ☐ ☐ ☐ ☐ ☐ ☐
    600 700 800 900 1,000 1,100 1,200 1,300

500 + 800 = 1,300
1,300 − 500 = 800

Make a Thousand to Subtract Ask another volunteer to find the answer to 1,300 − 500 by making a thousand.

500 ☐ ☐ ☐ ☐ ☐ ☐ ☐ ☐

1,000   +   300   = 1,300
      1,300 − 500 = 800

📁 **Class Management**

Looking Ahead: You will need grocery store ads for Lesson 7. Encourage students to bring them from home.

✓ **Ongoing Assessment**

Write 764 + 87 on the board. Have students write the expression vertically, find the answer, and make a proof drawing.

Write 150 − 70 on the board. Have students find the answer by counting on by tens.

Extending the Lesson

Going Further: Sums to 10,000

 15 MINUTES

Goal: Find sums to 10,000.
Materials: MathBoard materials, Secret Code Cards
(Copymasters M19–22)

✔ **NCTM Standards:**
Number and Operations
Communication

▶ **Discuss Sums to 10,000** | WHOLE CLASS |

Write the following expressions on the board.

1. 3,945 + 2,176	2. 1,049 + 6,853
3. 4,284 + 3,716	4. 3,431 + 1,398
5. 3,765 + 5,437	6. 2,577 + 2,562

 Math Talk Use the **Step-by-Step at the Board**
structure to complete exercise 1. Write the first
expression vertically. Invite four students to come to
the board. Have a different student complete the
addition in each place. As each student performs the
addition, he or she describes the step. The class
performs the same steps at their seats on their
MathBoards.

The **Step-by-Step at the Board** structure is similar to
Solve and Discuss. **Step-by-Step at the Board** allows
students to grasp a method more easily than doing the
whole method at once. It also helps students verbalize
their methods more clearly as they only have to explain
one step at a time.

As students discuss each step, make sure that students
understand the grouping that is involved. Students
should understand that:

• adding 5 ones and 6 ones gives 1 new ten and 1 one

• adding the new ten, 4 tens, and 7 tens gives 1 new
hundred and 2 tens

• adding the new hundred, 9 hundreds, and 1
hundred gives 1 new thousand and 1 hundred

• adding the new thousand, 3 thousands, and 2
thousands gives 6 thousands.

When the addition is completed, have a volunteer
make a proof drawing on the board while the class
works at their desks.

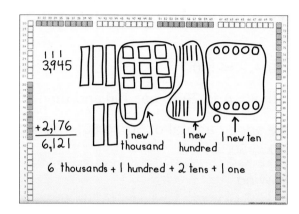

▶ **Sums to 10,000** | INDIVIDUALS |

Have students complete the rest of the exercises
independently. Then have volunteers use **Step-by-Step
at the Board** to explain their work.

📁 **Class Management**

Walk around the room and observe as students complete the
addition exercises. Watch for students who forget to record or
add a new ten, hundred, or thousand. Use questioning to help
students group and record the grouping. For example:

▶ Can you make a thousand in the proof drawing? How many
hundreds are left if you make the thousand?

▶ How do you show the thousand you made numerically?
Where will you write it in the addition example?

Extend If time permits, students can play *What's the
Sum?* First, pairs form two numbers in the thousands
using their Secret Code Cards. Then, they add both
numbers to find the sum. Students should check their
work by drawing Proof Drawings on their MathBoards.

Intervention
for students having difficulty

PAIRS

Model Sums

Materials: Spinner A (Copymaster M24) (1 per pair), paper clips, base ten blocks (1 thousand cube, 20 hundreds, 20 tens rods, 20 ones per pair)

Each student spins three times to create a 3-digit number. Students then use base ten blocks to represent their number. One student combines the blocks and makes tens, hundreds, and thousands where possible. The other student writes a vertical addition example that shows the results of adding the two numbers.

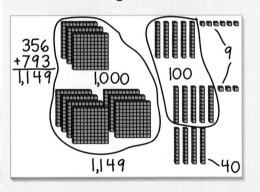

On Level
for students having success

PAIRS

What's My Number?

Students will work together to solve the riddles using the clues. Write the clues on the board or on a sheet of paper.

> **What's my number?**
>
> The number is less than 154 + 285.
>
> The number is greater than 318 + 96.
>
> The tens digit is even.
>
> When the digits in the number are added, the total is 11.

> **What's my number?**
>
> The number is greater than 117 + 113.
>
> The number is less than 76 + 173.
>
> The number is odd.
>
> The ones digit is 4 more than the tens digit.

Challenge
for students seeking a challenge

PAIRS

The Greatest Sum

Materials: two sets of Game Cards (Copymaster M25) (per pair)

Have students shuffle the digit cards and place them in a pile facedown. Each student chooses eight cards from the pile and uses them to create a 4-digit addition exercise that has the greatest possible sum. Have students check each other's work. The student with the greater sum wins 1 point.

Students repeat the activity until one player wins 5 points.

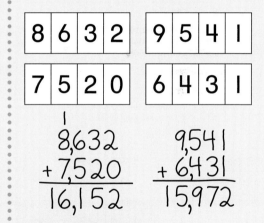

Also Use
Challenge Master for 1-6

 Math Writing Prompt

Intervention

Explain Your Thinking
When adding two numbers in the hundreds, when do you need to make a thousand?

 Math Writing Prompt

On Level

Apply
Explain how to count on to solve this equation:
$1{,}400 - 600 = \square$

 Math Writing Prompt

Challenge

Thousands
Kim's father flew 596 miles from Washington, D.C. to Chicago and then flew another 4,256 miles to Hawaii. Kim said that her father flew over 9,000 miles. Is she correct? Explain why or why not.

③ Homework and Spiral Review

 **Goal:** Additional Practice

This Homework page provides practice with solving addition word problems and with aligning place value columns before adding.

 **Goal:** Spiral Review

This Remembering page would be appropriate anytime after today's lesson.

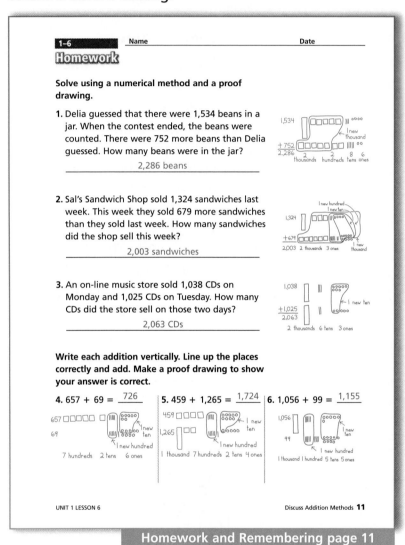

1-6 Homework Name _____ Date _____

Solve using a numerical method and a proof drawing.

1. Delia guessed that there were 1,534 beans in a jar. When the contest ended, the beans were counted. There were 752 more beans than Delia guessed. How many beans were in the jar?
   _____ 2,286 beans _____

2. Sal's Sandwich Shop sold 1,324 sandwiches last week. This week they sold 679 more sandwiches than they sold last week. How many sandwiches did the shop sell this week?
   _____ 2,003 sandwiches _____

3. An on-line music store sold 1,038 CDs on Monday and 1,025 CDs on Tuesday. How many CDs did the store sell on those two days?
   _____ 2,063 CDs _____

Write each addition vertically. Line up the places correctly and add. Make a proof drawing to show your answer is correct.

4. 657 + 69 = _726_

5. 459 + 1,265 = _1,724_

6. 1,056 + 99 = _1,155_

UNIT 1 LESSON 6   Discuss Addition Methods **11**

Homework and Remembering page 11

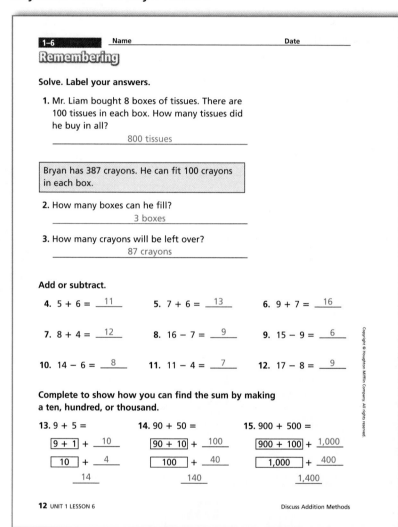

1-6 Remembering Name _____ Date _____

Solve. Label your answers.

1. Mr. Liam bought 8 boxes of tissues. There are 100 tissues in each box. How many tissues did he buy in all?
   _____ 800 tissues _____

Bryan has 387 crayons. He can fit 100 crayons in each box.

2. How many boxes can he fill?
   _____ 3 boxes _____

3. How many crayons will be left over?
   _____ 87 crayons _____

Add or subtract.

4. 5 + 6 = _11_   5. 7 + 6 = _13_   6. 9 + 7 = _16_

7. 8 + 4 = _12_   8. 16 − 7 = _9_   9. 15 − 9 = _6_

10. 14 − 6 = _8_   11. 11 − 4 = _7_   12. 17 − 8 = _9_

Complete to show how you can find the sum by making a ten, hundred, or thousand.

13. 9 + 5 =
    9 + 1 + _10_
    10 + _4_
    14

14. 90 + 50 =
    90 + 10 + _100_
    100 + _40_
    140

15. 900 + 500 =
    900 + 100 + _1,000_
    1,000 + _400_
    1,400

12 UNIT 1 LESSON 6   Discuss Addition Methods

Homework and Remembering page 12

Home or School Activity

 ### Science Connection

Breakfast Calories Provide students with the calorie chart shown at the right. Have students create a breakfast by choosing two to four of the items listed on the chart. Then have students find the total number of calories in the breakfast. Ask students to explain how they added.

Breakfast Food	Calories
Bagel	260
Banana	130
Cereal with lowfat milk	120
Hard boiled egg	76
Orange juice (8 oz.)	115
Whole wheat toast (two slices)	150
Yogurt (8 oz.)	240

Addition with Dollars and Cents

Vocabulary

proof drawing
Show All Totals method
New Groups Below method
New Groups Above method

Lesson Objective

- **Add money amounts.**

The Day at a Glance

Today's Goals	Materials	123 Math Talk
Quick Practice Add tens.	Quick Practice materials	In today's activities, the students are involved in discussion as they
1 **Teaching the Lesson** **A1:** Review addition methods. **A2:** Solve problems that involve adding money amounts and discuss solution methods. **A3:** Find the total cost of items selected from a grocery store advertisement.	MathBoard materials Grocery store ads Play money Index cards Student Activity Book pages 25–26	▶ discuss methods for adding 3-digit numbers ▶ talk about methods for adding money amounts
2 **Extending the Lesson** ▶ Differentiated Instruction	Homework and Remembering pages 13–14	
3 **Homework and Spiral Review**	Math Journals	

Quick Practice

 5 MINUTES **Goal:** Use the Make a Hundred strategy to add tens.
Materials: Demonstration Secret Code Cards
(Copymasters M3–M18)

Add Tens Using the Demonstration Secret Code Cards, have a Student Leader hold up two tens cards. The leader gives students a few seconds to mentally add the numbers, and then says, "Add." The class says the addition equation aloud. The leader then chooses one student to explain the Make a Hundred strategy. Repeat for several pairs of cards.

Leader: Add.
Class: 40 plus 90 equals 130.
Student: 90 plus 10 equals 100, plus 30 more is 130.

40   90
4 0   9 0

1 Teaching the Lesson

Activity 1

Review Addition Methods

 15 MINUTES

Goal: Review addition methods.

Materials: MathBoard materials

 NCTM Standards:
Number and Operations
Communication

▶ **Discuss Addition Methods** [WHOLE CLASS]

Write 273 + 539 on the board. Ask for volunteers to solve using New Groups Below and Show All Totals at the board. Other students may solve using any method. Discuss how each method shows the new groups.

Activity 2

Adding Grocery Store Prices

 20 MINUTES

Goal: Solve problems that involve adding money amounts and discuss solution methods.

Materials: Student Activity Book page 25

 NCTM Standards:
Number and Operations
Problem Solving
Communication

 Class Management

Looking Ahead Students will need Student Activity Book page 25 to complete the Homework page 13.

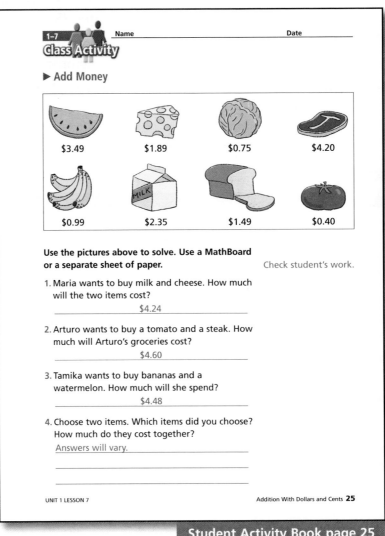

Student Activity Book page 25

▶ Add Money WHOLE CLASS

Read aloud the first problem on Student Activity Book page 25. Ask these questions to encourage discussion.

- How much does the milk cost? $2.35
- How much does the cheese cost $1.89
- How can we find out how much they cost together? Add the two prices.

Write $2.35 + $1.89 vertically on the board, noting the alignment of places. Explain that hundred-boxes can be used to represent dollars, ten-sticks to represent dimes, and circles to represent pennies. Elicit solution strategies from students.

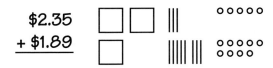

Encourage students to think about grouping 10 pennies to make a dime and 10 dimes to make a dollar. Work through a complete solution with proof drawings, using the New Groups Below method.

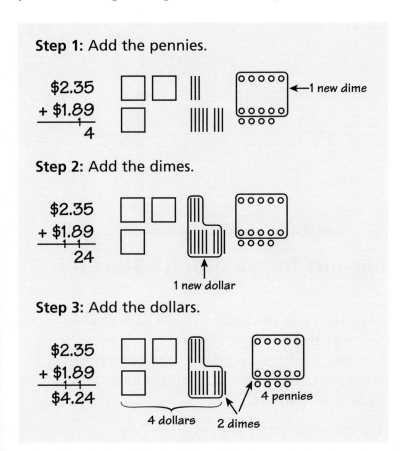

Step 1: Add the pennies.

Step 2: Add the dimes.

Step 3: Add the dollars.

Have students work independently on problems 2–4.

❶ Teaching the Lesson (continued)

Activity 3

Use a Real Grocery Store Ad

 20 MINUTES

Goal: Find the total cost of items selected from a grocery store advertisement.

Materials: Student Activity Book page 26, grocery store ads

✓ **NCTM Standards:**
Number and Operations
Problem Solving

Differentiated Instruction

English Learners Students generally learn more easily when they can relate a new idea to something in their own world. Most students will have selected items to buy in a grocery store. This activity reinforces the names of grocery store items and how to write these names.

✓ Ongoing Assessment

A carton of orange juice costs $2.49 and a box of cereal costs $4.37. How much do they cost together?

1–7
Class Activity

Name _____ Date _____

▶ **Add Money Amounts from a Grocery Store Ad**

Use an ad from a grocery store. List the names and prices of five or six items you would like to buy. Then answer the questions below.

_____   _____
_____   _____
_____   _____

5. How much would the two most expensive items on your list cost altogether?   *Show your work.*
   Answers will vary. Check student's answer.   Check student's work.

6. How much would the two least expensive items cost in all?
   Answers will vary.

7. What would be the total cost of your two favorite items?
   Answers will vary.

8. Which items would you buy if you had $5.00 to spend?
   Answers will vary.

9. Use the grocery ad to write and solve a word problem involving money.
   Answers will vary.

   _____
   _____
   _____

26 UNIT 1 LESSON 7   Addition With Dollars and Cents

Student Activity Book page 26

▶ Add Money Amounts from a Grocery Store Ad

PAIRS

Give a grocery store ad to each pair of students. Have each student make a list of five or six items he or she would like to buy, along with the prices. (If there are not enough ads, make a list of items and prices on the board for the entire class to use.) Have students use their lists to complete Student Activity Book page 26.

If students finish quickly, ask them to try adding prices of three or four items; or tell them that they have only a given amount of money to spend and ask them to find combinations of items they can afford to buy.

② Extending the Lesson

Intervention
for students having difficulty

PAIRS

Model Addition

Materials: Play money (Copymaster M40) (5 one-dollar bills, 10 dimes, and 10 pennies per student)

Have each student use play money to show a money amount between $1.00 and $5.00. While one partner writes and solves a vertical addition exercise, the other partner combines the play money, trading pennies for a dime, and dimes for a dollar when possible. Partners then compare their results. The sum of the vertical addition problem should match the play money representation.

Have students switch roles and repeat the activity.

$2.43
+$3.18
$5.61

On Level
for students having success

PAIRS

Playing Store

Materials: Index cards (6 per pair)

Write the name of an object and its price on each index card as follows:

> Wind-up car, $3.59
>
> Whistle, $1.79
>
> Playing cards, $0.68
>
> Stuffed animal, $2.59
>
> Crayons, $4.62
>
> Stickers, $2.97

One student is the customer and chooses two items to purchase by selecting two index cards. The customer gives the index cards to the other student, who is the cashier. The cashier computes the total on a piece of paper. The customer then checks the total.

Students switch roles and repeat the activity.

$1.79
+$2.59
$4.38

Challenge
for students seeking a challenge

PAIRS

Predict and Verify

Materials: MathBoard materials

Have students copy the price list below on their MathBoards.

Souvenirs at Baseball Stadium

baseball........$3.59
team flag.....$1.25
poster..........$0.95
cap..............$4.29
horn............$0.79
postcard pack....$2.59

Then have them predict, without adding, which pairs of items will cost more or less than $5.00.

• a baseball and a team flag

• a poster and a cap

• a cap and a horn

• a postcard pack and a team flag

Have students add to check their predictions and answer the following questions.

Which was the hardest prediction?

Which was the easiest?

Also Use
Challenge Master for 1-7

 Math Writing Prompt

Intervention

Explain Your Thinking
Explain how to add $1.59 + $2.64.

 Math Writing Prompt

On Level

Compare and Contrast
How is adding dollars, dimes, and pennies like adding hundreds, tens, and ones? How is it different?

 Math Writing Prompt

Challenge

Making Predictions
Explain how you can predict what the cost will be for three items that cost $3.79 each, if you do not need to find the exact total.

# ③ Homework and Spiral Review

Homework **Goal:** Additional Practice

This Homework page gives students practice adding money amounts and aligning place value columns.

Remembering **Goal:** Spiral Review

This Remembering page would be appropriate anytime after today's lesson.

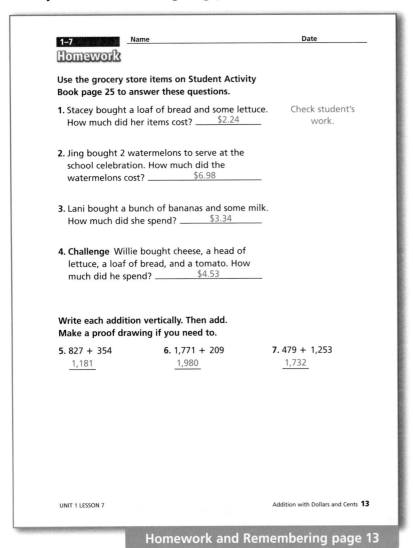

| 1–7 | Name | Date |

Homework

Use the grocery store items on Student Activity Book page 25 to answer these questions.

Check student's work.

1. Stacey bought a loaf of bread and some lettuce. How much did her items cost? ___$2.24___

2. Jing bought 2 watermelons to serve at the school celebration. How much did the watermelons cost? ___$6.98___

3. Lani bought a bunch of bananas and some milk. How much did she spend? ___$3.34___

4. **Challenge** Willie bought cheese, a head of lettuce, a loaf of bread, and a tomato. How much did he spend? ___$4.53___

Write each addition vertically. Then add. Make a proof drawing if you need to.

5. 827 + 354   6. 1,771 + 209   7. 479 + 1,253
    1,181   1,980   1,732

UNIT 1 LESSON 7   Addition with Dollars and Cents **13**

Homework and Remembering page 13

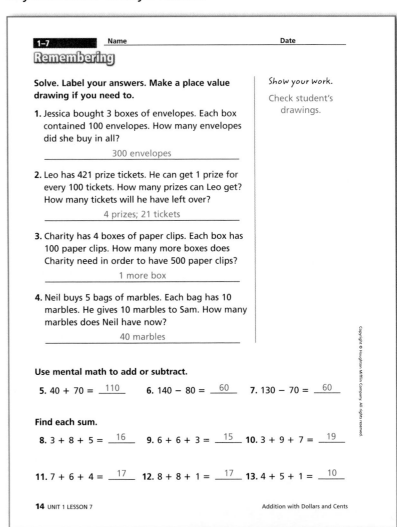

| 1–7 | Name | Date |

Remembering

Solve. Label your answers. Make a place value drawing if you need to.

Show your work.
Check student's drawings.

1. Jessica bought 3 boxes of envelopes. Each box contained 100 envelopes. How many envelopes did she buy in all?
    ___300 envelopes___

2. Leo has 421 prize tickets. He can get 1 prize for every 100 tickets. How many prizes can Leo get? How many tickets will he have left over?
    ___4 prizes; 21 tickets___

3. Charity has 4 boxes of paper clips. Each box has 100 paper clips. How many more boxes does Charity need in order to have 500 paper clips?
    ___1 more box___

4. Neil buys 5 bags of marbles. Each bag has 10 marbles. He gives 10 marbles to Sam. How many marbles does Neil have now?
    ___40 marbles___

Use mental math to add or subtract.

5. 40 + 70 = ___110___   6. 140 − 80 = ___60___   7. 130 − 70 = ___60___

Find each sum.

8. 3 + 8 + 5 = ___16___   9. 6 + 6 + 3 = ___15___   10. 3 + 9 + 7 = ___19___

11. 7 + 6 + 4 = ___17___   12. 8 + 8 + 1 = ___17___   13. 4 + 5 + 1 = ___10___

14 UNIT 1 LESSON 7   Addition with Dollars and Cents

Homework and Remembering page 14

Home or School Activity

🔵 Social Studies Connection

Design a Coin Tell students that the United States used to make many different kinds of coins and paper bills. For example, in the 1800s, coins worth 2¢ and 3¢ were minted. Until 1969, the United States Treasury distributed paper money for $500, $1,000.

Have students design a new coin or bill. Students can give the value of the new piece of money, then tell how many other coins or bills they would need to show an equivalent amount.

58 UNIT 1 LESSON 7

UNIT 1

LESSON

8

The Grouping Concept in Addition

Lesson Objectives

- Decide when and how to group in multi-digit addition.
- Practice adding money amounts.

Vocabulary

grouping
Make a Thousand strategy

The Day at a Glance

Today's Goals	Materials	Math Talk
Quick Practice Mentally add numbers in the hundreds. Students use the Make a Thousand strategy to add numbers greater than a hundred.	Quick Practice materials MathBoard materials Restaurant menus Index cards	In today's activities, the students are involved in discussion as they
1 Teaching the Lesson A1: Discuss when and how to group when adding. A2: Add prices of items on a menu.	Game Cards Rulers Student Activity Book pages 27–28	▶ explain the process of grouping in addition ▶ discuss problem situations
2 Extending the Lesson ▶ Going Further: Guess and Check ▶ Differentiated Instruction	Homework and Remembering pages 15–16 Math Journals	
3 Homework and Spiral Review		

Quick Practice

 5 MINUTES   **Goals:** Add numbers in the hundreds using mental math. Use the Make a Thousand strategy to add numbers greater than a thousand.
Materials: Demonstration Secret Code Cards (Copymasters M3–M18)

Add Hundreds The Student Leader selects two hundreds cards from the Demonstration Secret Code Cards and holds them up to the class. The leader gives students a few seconds to add the numbers mentally, and then says "Add." The class says the addition equation aloud. The leader then chooses one student to demonstrate the Make a Thousand strategy. Repeat for several pairs of cards.

Leader: Add.
Class: 500 plus 700 equals 1,200.
Student: 700 plus 300 is 1,000, plus 200 more is 1,200.

500	700
5 0 0	**7 0 0**

Class Management

As with the Make a Hundred strategy, the student explainer may add from the larger addend (easier) or add from the first addend.

Teaching the Lesson

Deciding When to Group

 20 MINUTES

Goal: Discuss when and how to group when adding.

Materials: MathBoard materials

✔ **NCTM Standard:**
Number and Operations

▶ **Group Ones, Tens, or Both** INDIVIDUALS

Write the four exercises below on the board. Have students copy the exercises and complete them on their MathBoards.

	A.	467 + 268 735		B.	384 + 263 647
	C.	765 + 117 882		D.	524 + 263 787

Students may use any method to solve these exercises. The New Groups Below method is shown here.

Math Talk When most students are finished, have a discussion about grouping.

● For which exercises did you need to group ones to make a new ten? A and C

● For which exercises did you need to group tens to make a new hundred? A and B

● Is there any exercise that didn't require any grouping? yes; exercise D

● How can you tell when you need to group? when the total number of ones or tens is more than 9

● What do you do when the total of the ones is greater than 9? Write 1 for the new ten in the tens column and then write the number of ones left over under the line in the ones column.

● What do you do when the total of the tens is greater than 9? Write 1 for the new hundred in the hundreds column and then write the number of tens left over under the line in the tens column.

Ask students to give word problem situations for exercise A. It is important to keep multi-digit calculation connected to real-world situations.

The Lunchtime Diner

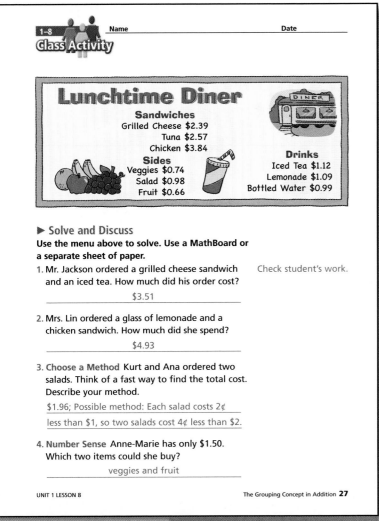

Student Activity Book page 27

The student activity page shows:

1-8 Class Activity Name _____ Date _____

Lunchtime Diner

Sandwiches
Grilled Cheese $2.39
Tuna $2.57
Chicken $3.84

Sides
Veggies $0.74
Salad $0.98
Fruit $0.66

Drinks
Iced Tea $1.12
Lemonade $1.09
Bottled Water $0.99

▶ Solve and Discuss
Use the menu above to solve. Use a MathBoard or a separate sheet of paper.

1. Mr. Jackson ordered a grilled cheese sandwich and an iced tea. How much did his order cost?   Check student's work.
   $3.51

2. Mrs. Lin ordered a glass of lemonade and a chicken sandwich. How much did she spend?
   $4.93

3. **Choose a Method** Kurt and Ana ordered two salads. Think of a fast way to find the total cost. Describe your method.
   $1.96; Possible method: Each salad costs 2¢
   less than $1, so two salads cost 4¢ less than $2.

4. **Number Sense** Anne-Marie has only $1.50. Which two items could she buy?
   veggies and fruit

UNIT 1 LESSON 8   The Grouping Concept in Addition **27**

⏱ **35 MINUTES**

Goal: Add prices of items on a menu.

Materials: Student Activity Book page 27

✔ **NCTM Standards:**
Number and Operations
Problem Solving

The Learning Classroom

Building Concepts Students should not be required to make proof drawings once they have demonstrated that they have a solid understanding of place value and grouping and can explain their addition using place value language. Students who are struggling with these concepts should continue to make drawings until they are comfortable with these ideas.

▶ Solve and Discuss WHOLE CLASS

Have students turn to Student Activity Book page 27 and briefly look at the menu for the Lunchtime Diner. Read aloud the first problem and give students a few minutes to solve it.

Use **Solve and Discuss** for the remaining problems. Suggest that before students add, they should think about whether they will need to trade pennies for a new dime or dimes for a new dollar. Try to choose students who used different methods to present, and encourage other students to ask questions if the explanations are unclear.

Ongoing Assessment

▶ Choose two items from the Lunchtime Diner menu and add to find the total cost.

② Extending the Lesson

Going Further: Guess and Check

Goal: Use the Guess and Check strategy to solve a problem.

Materials: Student Activity Book page 28

 NCTM Standard:
Problem Solving

▶ Use the Guess and Check Strategy

WHOLE CLASS

Introduce the Guess and Check strategy, with this analogy. You want to buy a pair of shoes but you don't know what size you wear. You make a guess and try a pair on and see if it fits. If it doesn't fit, you know whether you need a smaller or larger size. Then you use what you learned to try another pair. When solving math problems, sometimes we begin by guessing the answer and seeing if it works. If it doesn't work, we use what we've learned and try again.

Have students use the Guess and Check strategy to solve the problem on Student Activity Book page 28. Have students explain their answer. See Math Talk in Action for a sample classroom dialogue.

🔢 Math Talk in Action

Cora: How can I figure out which items José bought, if I don't know how much José spent?

Mario: Well you can figure out how much he spent because you know how much change he got back.

Cora: O.K., he got back 50 cents and he started with $7.00, so his clothing cost $6.50.

Mario: So now you can use the Guess and Check strategy to find the items that add up to $6.50. Rounding can also help you make your first two guesses.

Cora: Well, first of all I know that José didn't buy the jacket because that costs more money than he has, so I'll cross that off of my sheet. I'll guess that the socks and the shorts are what he bought because $5.00 and $1.00 is close to $6.00.

Mario: But he spent $6.50.

Cora: Yes, I know, but maybe the change will make the total add up to $6.50. $5.45 plus $.95 is only $6.40.

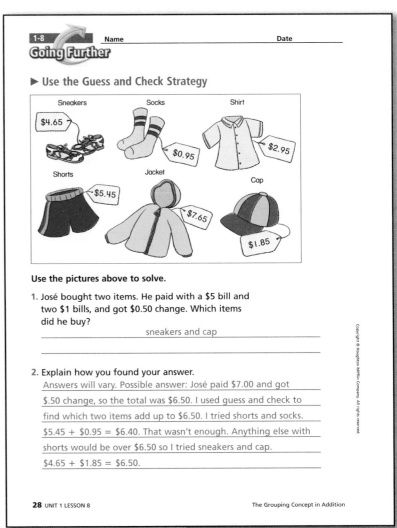

Student Activity Book page 28

Mario: You only were a dime off. Check your other clothing prices and see if there are other prices that are 10 cents higher than the socks or the shorts.

Cora: I didn't find any other prices that had a ten cents difference, so I'll just try two different combinations. Mario, why don't you try two also. That will work faster for us.

Mario: O.K. I'll try sneakers and T-shirt.

Cora: I'll try cap and sneakers.

Mario: I was way over. That would cost $7.60. I should have known not to pick those two pieces of clothing anyway because adding the numbers in the ten cents place wouldn't have totaled 50 cents after grouping.

Cora: I was right on. $4.65 plus $1.85 was $6.50.

Intervention
for students having difficulty
PAIRS

Act it Out!

Materials: Restaurant menus

Bring in a variety of menus and have pairs of students act out a restaurant scene. One student can order from the menu while the other student takes the order and adds to find the total cost. The student ordering then checks the bill to make sure it's right. Students can then switch roles.

On Level
for students having success
INDIVIDUALS

Number Puzzler

Materials: MathBoard materials

Have students copy the three number puzzles below on their Mathboards and try to solve them.

```
  6 [5] 2
+ 2  4 [9]
---------
  9  0  1
```

```
 [3] 4  7
+ 2  3 [6]
---------
  5  8  3
```

```
  7 [2] 8
+[6] 4  5
---------
1, 3 7  3
```

Challenge
for students seeking a challenge
INDIVIDUALS

Mix and Match

Materials: Game Cards (Copymaster M25) (1 set per student), index cards (1 per student), rulers (1 per student)

Have students write a plus sign on an index card. Students should then try to arrange their game cards to make and solve a 3–digit + 3–digit addition exercise. They can use a ruler to show the line under the addends.

Possible solutions:

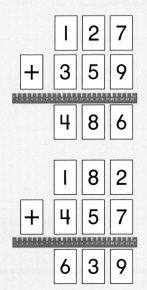

Also Use
Challenge Master for 1-8

Math Writing Prompt
Intervention
Explain Your Thinking
Explain to a friend how you know when to group the tens in an addition problem.

Math Writing Prompt
On Level
Choose a Method
If you only had $5.00 to spend at the Lunchtime Diner, what's a quick way to make sure you don't go over that amount?

Math Writing Prompt
Challenge
Investigate Math
If you add a number in the hundreds and a number in the tens, will the total ever be a number in the thousands? How do you know?

③ Homework and Spiral Review

This Homework page gives students practice deciding when to group when solving addition problems.

This Remembering page would be appropriate anytime after today's lesson.

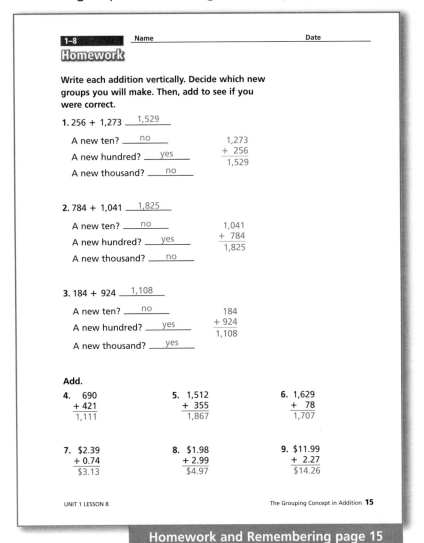

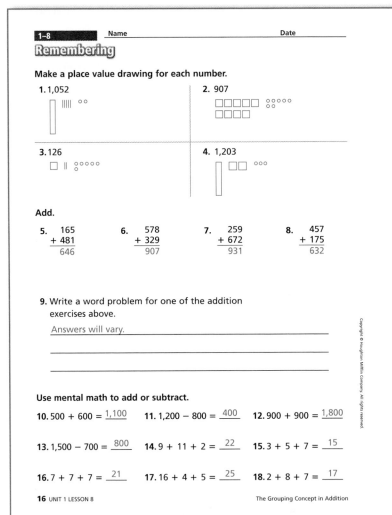

Home or School Activity

 Social Studies Connection

Number Code Explain to students that Egyptian numbers were called hieroglyphic numbers and were used thousands of years ago. The numbers were based on important symbols in the Egyptian culture. For example, the number 100 was a coil of rope, and the number 1,000 was a lotus flower.

Have students create their own set of numbers, a key to their code, and a few addition exercises for someone else to solve.

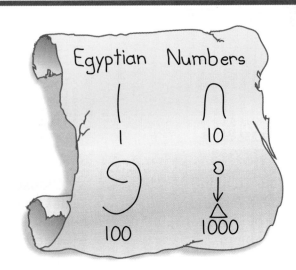

Practice Addition

Lesson Objectives

- Practice adding money amounts.
- Identify and explain errors in addition problems.

Vocabulary
grouping

The Day at a Glance

Today's Goals	Materials	Math Talk
Quick Practice Use mental math to add numbers in hundreds.	Quick Practice materials	In today's activities, the students are involved in discussion as they
① Teaching the Lesson A1: Identify and correct addition errors. A2: Find the total cost of items on a menu.	MathBoard materials Restaurant menus Play money	▶ identify and explain computation errors
② Extending the Lesson ▶ Going Further: Add Money Amounts with Sums Greater than $20 ▶ Differentiated Instruction	Student Activity Book pages 29–30 Homework and Remembering pages 17–18	▶ explain the process of adding money amounts
③ Homework and Spiral Review	Math Journals Quick Quiz 2 (Assessment Guide)	

Quick Practice

 5 MINUTES   **Goal:** Use mental math to add numbers in the hundreds.
Materials: Demonstration Secret Code Cards (Copymasters M3–M18)

Add Hundreds From the Demonstration Secret Code Cards, have a Student Leader select and hold up two hundreds cards. The leader gives students a few seconds to mentally add the numbers, and then says "Add." The class says the addition equation aloud. Repeat for several pairs of cards. (See Unit 1 Lesson 8)

Class Management

Class Management All students should have a turn at being a Student Leader in order to develop their communication skills. Select students who have not been Student Leaders yet to lead this activity.

Teaching the Lesson

Identify Errors

 20 MINUTES

Goal: Identify and correct addition errors.

✔ **NCTM Standard:**
Number and Operations

Teaching Note

Be sure that students understand that this is a *Help the Teacher* activity. Encourage them to be alert just in case you make a mistake, and to point out your mistakes in a helpful way.

▶ **Identify Errors** | WHOLE CLASS |

Tell students you are going to solve some addition exercises on the board. Tell them that you might make errors, so they should watch carefully and help you catch mistakes. Ask students to explain each mistake and to suggest strategies for avoiding the errors you make.

Be sure to make each of the common errors you have seen your students make. Below are some examples that illustrate common errors.

Example: $\begin{array}{r} 744 \\ + 172 \\ \hline 816 \end{array}$	**Example:** $\begin{array}{r} \overset{2}{6}39 \\ + 183 \\ \hline 731 \end{array}$
Error: Forgot to make a new hundred.	**Error:** Wrote the ones above the tens column and the new 1 ten in the ones column.
Correct answer: 916	**Correct answer:** 822
Example: $\begin{array}{r} 477 \\ + 344 \\ \hline 811 \end{array}$	**Example:** $\begin{array}{r} 329 \\ + 483 \\ \hline 702 \end{array}$
Error: Forgot to make a new ten.	**Error:** Forgot to make a new ten and a new hundred.
Correct answer: 821	**Correct answer:** 812

Carmen's Café

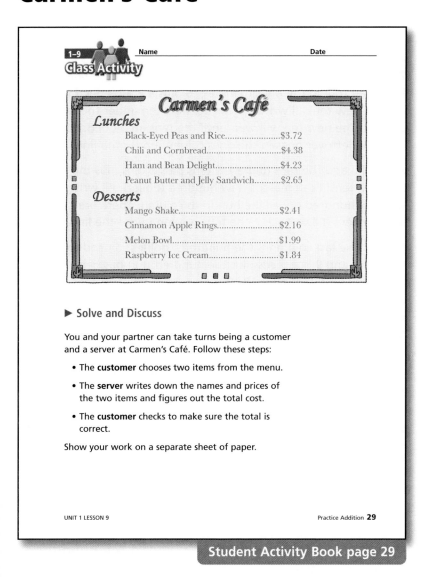

Student Activity Book page 29

(Menu shown in Student Activity Book page 29:)

1–9 Class Activity
Name _____ Date _____

Carmen's Café

Lunches
Black-Eyed Peas and Rice.......................$3.72
Chili and Cornbread..............................$4.38
Ham and Bean Delight..........................$4.23
Peanut Butter and Jelly Sandwich...........$2.65

Desserts
Mango Shake.......................................$2.41
Cinnamon Apple Rings.........................$2.16
Melon Bowl..$1.99
Raspberry Ice Cream.............................$1.84

▶ Solve and Discuss

You and your partner can take turns being a customer and a server at Carmen's Café. Follow these steps:

• The **customer** chooses two items from the menu.

• The **server** writes down the names and prices of the two items and figures out the total cost.

• The **customer** checks to make sure the total is correct.

Show your work on a separate sheet of paper.

UNIT 1 LESSON 9   Practice Addition **29**

▶ Solve and Discuss PAIRS

Have students look at the menu for Carmen's Café on Student Activity Book page 29. Read aloud the directions.

For this activity, one partner will be the customer and the other will be the server. Explain that after the customer chooses items from the menu, the server should use a separate sheet of paper to write down the names and prices of the two items, then add to find the total amount. You may want to hand out quarter sheets of paper for servers to take orders. The customer should check that the total is correct. Encourage students to think about whether they will need to trade pennies for a new dime or dimes for a new dollar.

Choose pairs that used different methods to discuss how they found the total cost.

 30 MINUTES

Goal: Find the total cost of items on a menu.

Materials: Student Activity Book, page 29

 NCTM Standard:
Number and Operations

Differentiated Instruction

Extra Help You might need to help some students understand money amounts written symbolically. Using play money, have students show the cost of two items; then, count the total amount and write that amount using dollar and cent notation.

Ongoing Assessment

Ask students to explain what the error is in this example. Then they should find the correct answer.

$$\begin{array}{r} 478 \\ +\ 123 \\ \hline 591 \end{array}$$

Class Management

Looking Ahead Students will need to use Student Activity Book page 29 for homework.

Quick Quiz

See Assessment Guide for Unit 1 Quick Quiz 2.

Extending the Lesson

Going Further: Add Money Amounts with Sums Greater than $20

Goal: Find sums of money more than $10.00.

Materials: Student Activity Book page 30

✔ **NCTM Standards:**
Number and Operations
Problem Solving

1–9
Going Further

Name _____ Date _____

▶ **Add Larger Money Amounts**

$6.38 $9.29 $7.39 $9.89 $8.79 $12.69 $9.99
$8.95 MESA TOY STORE

Use the pictures above to solve. Use your MathBoard
or a separate sheet of paper.

1. Jeremy bought a dog and a cat. How much did
   he spend in all?   Check student's work.
   _____ $18.24

2. Keisha bought a horse. Juan bought a pig. How
   much did they spend together?
   _____ $21.48

3. Chan bought a cat, a duck, and a horse. What
   was the total cost?
   _____ $24.46

4. **Choose a Method** Rani wants to buy two
   rabbits. Think of a fast way to find the total
   cost. Describe your method.
   Possible method: 1 rabbit costs 1¢ less than
   $10.00, so 2 rabbits cost 2¢ less than $20.00 or $19.98

5. **Number Sense** Betty has $20.00. Is that enough
   money for her to buy a cow and a horse?
   Explain why or why not.
   Possible answer: yes, because a cow costs less
   than $10.00 and a horse costs less than $9.00
   and $10.00 + $9.00 = $19.00

30 UNIT 1 LESSON 9   Practice Addition

Student Activity Book page 30

▶ Add Larger Money Amounts

WHOLE CLASS

Have students look at the items for sale at Mesa Toys on
Student Activity Book page 30. Ask a student to read
aloud problem 1. Use **Step-by-Step at the Board** and
choose four students to come to the board to
demonstrate how to solve the problem. As each student
performs the addition, he or she describes the steps. The
class performs the same steps at their seats.

 Math Talk in Action

Kyra: Jeremy bought the dog for $8.95 and the cat for $9.29.
There is a pause while Kyra writes the problem on the board. I
first need to add the ones (pennies). 5 plus 9 is 14. I need to
make a new ten. I'll write a 1 for the new ten under the tens
column. The new ten will wait until the tens are added. I'll write
4 for the leftover ones in the ones column under the line.

James: I'll add the tens (dimes). 9 tens plus 2 tens plus the new
ten is 12 tens. I can make a new hundred (dollar). I'll write 1 for
the new hundred under the hundreds column. There are 2
leftover tens. I'll write 2 in the tens column under the line.

Lucero: The last column is the hundreds (dollars). I need to add 8
hundreds and 9 hundreds plus the hundred that has been
waiting. 8 plus 9 plus 1 is 18. There are 18 hundreds. That's the
same as 1 thousand and 8 hundreds. I'll put the 8 in the hundreds
place and the 1 in the thousands place. The total amount for the
dog and the cat is 18 dollars and 24 cents.

As students discuss each step, make sure that students
understand the grouping that is involved. Also point out
that students may use any of the three addition methods
to solve the problems. Ask the following questions:

● **What happens when you add the tens (dimes)?**
   Sample response: When I add the new ten (dime), 9
   tens (dimes), and 2 tens (dimes), I get 1 new hundred
   (dollar) and 2 tens (dimes).

● **Explain what happens when you add the hundreds.**
   Sample response: I get 1 new thousand and 8 hundreds and that's the same as $18.00.

● **Where do you place the 1 for the new thousand (ten
   dollars)?** Sample response: It goes to the left of
   the 8.

Ask students to complete problems 2–5 independently.
Then ask for volunteers to come to the board to show
their work.

Activities for Individualizing

Intervention
for students having difficulty

PAIRS

Cash Only

Materials: Restaurant menus, play money

Give each pair of students a restaurant menu. Have one partner select two items from the menu. The other partner adds to find the total cost. The first partner then uses play money to show the costs and total. Encourage students to trade pennies for dimes and dimes for dollars. Partners check that the totals match.

Have partners switch roles and repeat the activity.

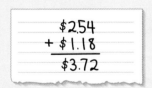

$$\begin{array}{r} \$2.54 \\ + \$1.18 \\ \hline \$3.72 \end{array}$$

On Level
for students having success

INDIVIDUALS

Missing Numbers

Materials: MathBoard materials

Have students copy the puzzles below onto their MathBoards.

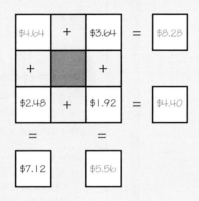

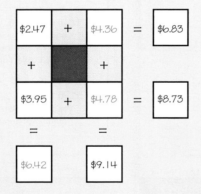

Students should work together to find the missing numbers in the puzzles.

Challenge
for students seeking a challenge

PAIRS

What's Next?

Have students copy the following onto a sheet of paper. Have them find the rule and complete the pattern.

1, 3, 6, 10, <u>15</u>, <u>21</u>, <u>28</u>,
add 1, add 2, add 3, etc.

$.75, $1.25, $1.75, <u>$2.25</u>, <u>$2.75</u>,
add $0.50.

1,500, 2,900, 4,200, <u>5,400</u>, <u>6,500</u>,
add 1,400, add 1,300, add 1,200, etc.

450, 575, 800, 1,125, <u>1,550</u>, <u>2,075</u>,
add 125, add 225, add 325, etc.

$7.37, $7.62, $7.97, <u>$8.42</u>, <u>$8.97</u>,
add $0.25, add $0.35, add $0.45, etc.

Then tell students to make their own patterns and have their partner complete it.

Also Use
Challenge Master for 1-9

 Math Writing Prompt

Intervention

Explain Your Thinking
Explain to a friend how you know when to group pennies as dimes and dimes as dollars.

 Math Writing Prompt

On Level

Summarize
Explain how you know without adding that $6.59 and $4.29 will total more than $10.00.

 Math Writing Prompt

Challenge

Investigate Math
Explain how to find the next number in the pattern $0.01, $0.06, $0.16, $0.17, $0.22, $0.32, $0.33, $0.38, $0.48, $0.49, _____.

③ Homework and Spiral Review

Goal: Additional Practice

This Homework page provides practice in solving addition problems involving money.

1-9
Homework

Name _____ Date _____

Use the menu from Carmen's Cafe on Student Activity Book page 29 to solve each problem.

Check student's work.

1. Randy ordered a peanut butter and jelly sandwich and cinnamon apple rings. How much did he spend? _____ $4.81_

2. Jamie and her dad went to lunch. He ordered the chili and cornbread. She ordered the black-eyed peas and rice. What was their bill? _$8.10_

3. Rafael ordered the ham and bean delight and a mango shake. What was the total cost?
_____$6.64_____

4. Teri ordered raspberry ice cream and a melon bowl. How much was her bill? _$3.83_

5. Yao gave the saleswoman $3.88 for 2 melon bowls. Is $3.88 the correct amount? If not, explain the error Yao made.

   Possible answer: Yao did not make a new
   ten when he added $1.99 and $1.99. The
   correct amount is $3.98.

UNIT 1 LESSON 9   Practice Addition **17**

Homework and Remembering page 17

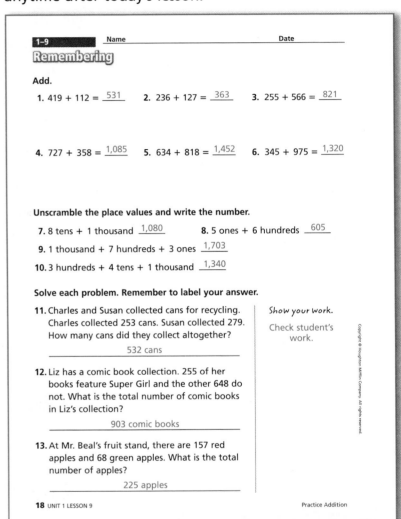

Goal: Spiral Review

This Remembering page would be appropriate anytime after today's lesson.

1-9
Remembering

Name _____ Date _____

Add.

1. 419 + 112 = _531_   2. 236 + 127 = _363_   3. 255 + 566 = _821_

4. 727 + 358 = _1,085_   5. 634 + 818 = _1,452_   6. 345 + 975 = _1,320_

Unscramble the place values and write the number.

7. 8 tens + 1 thousand _1,080_   8. 5 ones + 6 hundreds _605_

9. 1 thousand + 7 hundreds + 3 ones _1,703_

10. 3 hundreds + 4 tens + 1 thousand _1,340_

Solve each problem. Remember to label your answer.

11. Charles and Susan collected cans for recycling. Charles collected 253 cans. Susan collected 279. How many cans did they collect altogether?
    _____532 cans_____

    Show your work.
    Check student's work.

12. Liz has a comic book collection. 255 of her books feature Super Girl and the other 648 do not. What is the total number of comic books in Liz's collection?
    _____903 comic books_____

13. At Mr. Beal's fruit stand, there are 157 red apples and 68 green apples. What is the total number of apples?
    _____225 apples_____

18 UNIT 1 LESSON 9   Practice Addition

Homework and Remembering page 18

Home or School Activity

 Multicultural Connection

Foods from Around the World Explain to students that countries and cultures have their own special foods. Ask students to share some of the special foods their families prepare and eat on holidays and at celebrations. Have students create a menu and then role play customers and servers ordering meals and finding total costs.

Chicken Curry	$4.95
Corn Kabobs	$1.75
Fruit Chaat	$1.15
Spinach Parathas	$2.25

Ungroup to Subtract

Lesson Objectives

- Explore methods for subtracting multi-digit numbers.
- Discuss a common subtraction error.

The Day at a Glance

Today's Goals	Materials	Math Talk
Quick Practice Subtract larger numbers.	Quick Practice materials	In today's activities, the students are involved in discussion as they:
1 Teaching the Lesson A1: Solve problems using subtraction methods. A2: Discuss ways to avoid a common subtraction error.	MathBoard materials Base ten blocks Game Cards Index Cards	▶ show ways to subtract with regrouping ▶ present and explain subtraction drawings
2 Extending the Lesson ▶ Differentiated Instruction	Student Activity Book pages 31–32	
3 Homework and Spiral Review	Homework and Remembering pages 19–20 Math Journals	

Quick Practice

 5 MINUTES   **Goal:** Subtract larger numbers.
Materials: Demonstration Secret Code Cards
(Copymasters M3–M18)

Class Management

Consider choosing two Student Leaders. As one leads the class, the other can be selecting cards for the next exercise.

Subtract Tens From the Demonstration Secret Code Cards, have a Student Leader select the 100 card and two tens cards. The Student Leader assembles the cards so the class can see a 3-digit number on the left and a number of tens on the right.

The leader then gives students a few seconds to mentally subtract the numbers, and says "Subtract." The class says the subtraction equation aloud. The leader then selects one student to illustrate the Make a Hundred strategy (See page 49). Repeat this for several pairs of cards.

① Teaching the Lesson

Share Different Subtraction Methods

 20 MINUTES

Goal: Solve problems using different subtraction methods.

Materials: Student Activity Book page 31, MathBoard materials

 NCTM Standards:
Number and Operations
Algebra
Problem Solving

Teaching Note

What to Expect from Students
Some students may not be skilled with a particular subtraction method at this point. They will have many opportunities to develop subtraction understanding and skill over the next several lessons. Encourage students having difficulty to listen closely as other students present their methods and to ask questions when they do not understand.

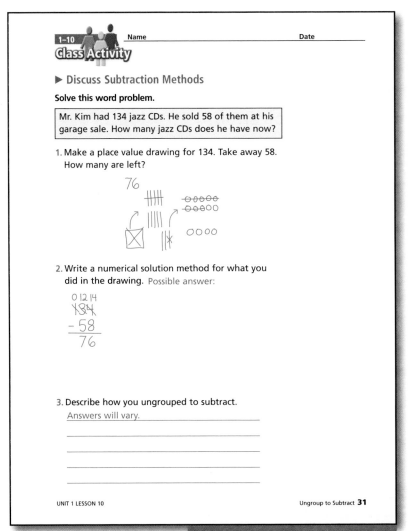

Student Activity Book page 31

▶ Discuss Subtraction Methods [WHOLE CLASS]

Ask a student to read aloud the word problem on Student Activity Book page 31. Work with the class to make a place value drawing for exercise 1.

Have a student volunteer explain their place value drawing. Make sure students use correct place value language when explaining their subtraction.

As the student volunteer explains their drawing and subtraction, encourage the other students to ask questions so they understand how they can "get" more ones to subtract if they do not have enough.

Correct drawings should show a ten ungrouped to form 10 ones and the hundred ungrouped to show 10 tens. Students can ungroup from the left or from the right. Here are two ways students might show this.

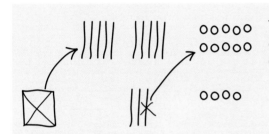

This student crossed out the hundred-box and 1 ten-stick and then redrew the tens and ones.

This student drew the 10 tens inside the hundred-box and drew the 10 ones on the ten-stick.

After ungrouping, students should cross out 5 tens and 8 ones. This leaves 7 tens and 6 ones, or 76. They can subtract from the left or from the right.

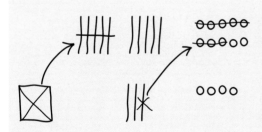

It is helpful to cross out within the ten. This helps support the Make a Ten method. Here 14 − 8 can be seen to be 2 (left in the 10) + 4 (over 10) = 6.

The student drew lines through the 5 tens and 8 ones.

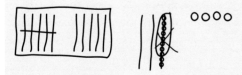

The student drew the line through the 5 tens and circled the 8 ones before crossing them out.

Activity continued ▶

Teaching Note

Another Common Method: This method is widely used in other countries and so may be used by some of your students. The method is somewhat confusing because the way a small 1 written next to a digit is interpreted depends on whether it is in the top number or the bottom number. Allow your students to use this method if they understand it and can explain why it works.

$$
\begin{array}{r}
134 \\
-58 \\
\end{array}
$$

1. There are not enough ones to subtract from, so give 10 ones to the 4 ones to get 14 ones. To compensate, give 1 ten to the 5 tens in the bottom number. (In essence, you are adding 10 to both the top and bottom numbers, which does not affect the difference.) **Note:** The 1 next to the 5 is 1 ten, not 10 tens. So the ¹5 represents 6 tens, not ¹5 tens.

2. Subtract the ones.

$$
\begin{array}{r}
13^{1}4 \\
-{}^{1}58 \\
\hline
6 \\
\end{array}
$$

3. There are not enough tens to subtract from, so give 10 tens to the 3 tens to get 13 tens. To compensate, give 1 hundred to the 0 hundreds in the bottom number. (So, you have added 100 to both the top and bottom numbers, which does not affect the difference.)

4. Subtract the tens, keeping in mind that ¹5 represents 6 tens.

5. Subtract the hundreds. (The result is 0.)

$$
\begin{array}{r}
{}^{1}13^{1}4 \\
-{}^{1}58 \\
\hline
76 \\
\end{array}
$$

Now have students use a numerical solution method to solve the word problem. Have student volunteers present their different solution methods.

Students who used *Math Expressions* in a previous grade may use the Expanded method or the Ungroup First method. Other students are likely to use the common U.S. method. These methods are shown below for your reference. Please *do not* "teach" any of these methods at this time. Allow students to show and explain the methods they are already using.

Expanded Method

Ungroup right to left

$$
\begin{array}{r}
134 = \overset{0}{\cancel{100}} + \overset{120}{\cancel{30}} + \overset{14}{4} \\
-58 \quad - \quad 50 + 8 \\
\hline
70 + 6 = 76 \\
\end{array}
$$

Ungroup left to right

$$
\begin{array}{r}
134 = \overset{0}{\cancel{100}} + \overset{\overset{120}{\cancel{130}}}{\cancel{30}} + \overset{14}{4} \\
-58 \quad - \quad 50 + 8 \\
\hline
70 + 6 = 76 \\
\end{array}
$$

1. Expand 134 as 100 + 30 + 4 and 58 as 50 + 8.

2. Start with the ones. There are not enough ones to subtract from, so take 10 ones from 30 and give them to the 4 ones to make 14.

3. Go to the tens. There are not enough tens to subtract from, so take 10 tens from 100 and give them to the 20 to make 120.

4. Subtract each place. Add the differences.

Ungroup First Method

Ungroup left to right

$$
\begin{array}{ccccc}
134 & & \overset{0\ 13}{\cancel{134}} & & \overset{0\ \overset{12}{\cancel{13}}\ 14}{\cancel{134}} \\
-58 & \rightarrow & -58 & \rightarrow & -58 \\
& & & & \hline \\
& & & & 76 \\
\end{array}
$$

Ungroup right to left

$$
\begin{array}{ccccc}
134 & & \overset{2\ 14}{134} & & \overset{0\ \overset{12}{\cancel{2}}\ 14}{\cancel{134}} \\
-58 & \rightarrow & -58 & \rightarrow & -58 \\
& & & & \hline \\
& & & & 76 \\
\end{array}
$$

Note: The ungrouping in this method can be done in either direction. Here we ungroup from left to right.

1. Starting with the hundreds, see if you can subtract at each place.

2. There are not enough tens, so ungroup 1 hundred to get 10 tens. Give these new tens to the 3 tens to get 13 tens.

3. There are not enough ones, so ungroup 1 ten to get 10 ones. Give these new ones to the 4 ones to give 14 ones.

4. Subtract in either direction.

Common U.S. Method

$$
\begin{array}{ccccc}
134 & & \overset{2}{13^{1}4} & & \overset{0\ {}^{1}2}{\cancel{13}^{1}4} \\
-58 & \rightarrow & -58 & \rightarrow & -58 \\
& & \hline & & \hline \\
& & 6 & & 76 \\
\end{array}
$$

This method alternates ungrouping and subtracting:

1. Start with ones. There are not enough ones to subtract from, so ungroup 1 ten to get 10 ones. Give these new ones to the 4 ones to get 14 ones.

2. Subtract the ones.

3. Look at the tens. There are not enough tens, so ungroup 1 hundred to get 10 tens. Give these new tens to the 2 tens to get 12 tens.

4. Subtract the tens. There are no hundreds. With this alternating method, students in the middle step are more likely to make the common top from bottom error:

$$
\begin{array}{r}
\overset{2}{13^{1}4} \\
-58 \\
\hline
136 \\
\end{array}
\quad \text{or} \quad
\begin{array}{r}
134 \\
-58 \\
\hline
124 \\
\end{array}
$$

Avoid Subtracting the Wrong Way

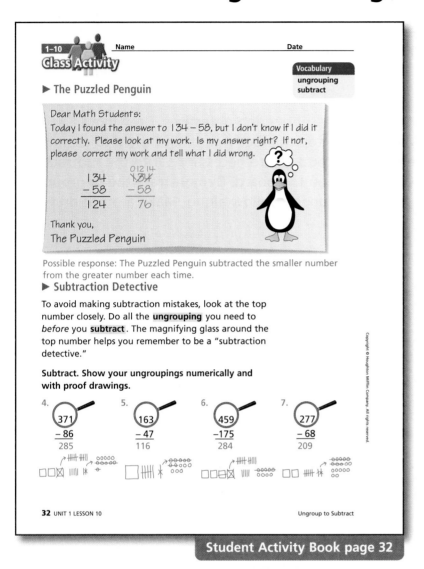

Student Activity Book page 32

35 MINUTES

Goal: Discuss ways to avoid common subtraction errors.

Materials: Student Activity Book page 32, MathBoard materials

 NCTM Standards:
Number and Operations
Algebra
Problem Solving

 Class Management

Depending on your class, you can work through some or all of the exercises together. The focus here is on understanding that the bottom number is *always* subtracted from the top number.

▶ The Puzzled Penguin | WHOLE CLASS |

Direct students' attention to the letter from the Puzzled Penguin on Student Activity Book page 32. Ask them to look closely at the penguin's work and try to figure out what he did wrong. Then, do the subtraction correctly. Students should notice that he subtracted the top number from the bottom number in the tens and ones places.

Students should check that the bottom number is always subtracted from the top in their own work and the work of their classmates.

Activity continued ▶

▶ **Subtraction Detective** WHOLE CLASS

Explain that students can avoid subtracting the wrong way by examining the problem carefully *before* they start subtracting. They should look at each place and determine where they need to ungroup. It is also a good idea to do all of the ungrouping where needed *first* and *then* do all the subtracting.

Tell students that they can be subtraction detectives. Drawing a magnifying glass around the top number will remind them to examine the number closely and ungroup where necessary. Write the subtraction and magnifying glass below on the board. Demonstrate the ungrouping and subtracting process as students follow along. Make a proof drawing as you work.

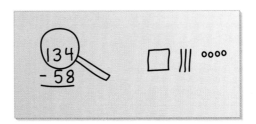

Step 1

First, have students focus on the hundreds column.

● The hundreds column is OK. We can subtract 0 hundreds from 1 hundred.

Step 2

Have students look at the tens column.

● Are there enough tens to subtract from? no

● How do we get more tens? Ungroup the 1 hundred to get 10 more tens.

● How can you show this in your drawing? Cross out the hundred-box and draw 10 ten-sticks.

● How many hundreds do you have after you ungroup the 1 hundred? none How can you show this? By crossing out the 1 in the hundreds column and writing 0.

● How many tens do you have? 13 How can you show this? By crossing out the 3 in the tens column and writing 13.

Step 3

Now look at the ones column.

- Are there enough ones to subtract from? no, 8 is more than 4

- How do we get more ones? Ungroup 1 ten to get 10 more ones.

- How can you show this in my drawing? Cross out a ten-stick and draw 10 circles.

- How many tens do you have after you ungroup 1 ten? 12
  How can you show this? By crossing out the 13 in the tens column and writing 12.

- How many ones do you have? 14
  How can you show this? By crossing out the 4 in the ones column and writing 14.

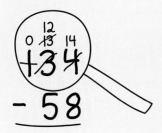 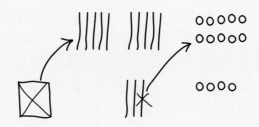

Step 4

- Is there anything left to ungroup? no

- What is the next step? Now that I have ungrouped everything, I can subtract.

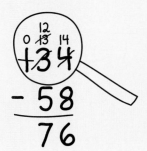 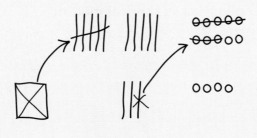

Activity continued ▶

Teaching Note

Watch For! As students make proof drawings for the subtraction, watch for those who make place value drawings for *both* the top number and the bottom number. Emphasize that they should start with a drawing for the top number and then find a way to "take away" the bottom number. Show an example with small numbers: 8 − 2.

- Do we draw 8 and draw 2? No, draw 8 and take away 2.

Suggest that students who have trouble remembering this, should draw a circle around the minus sign. The circle can remind them to draw the magnifying glass around the top number.

The Learning Classroom

Building Concepts Notice how taking the first objects from the ten shows the Make-a-Ten strategy:

14 − 8 is 2 + 4 = 6 ones

12 − 5 is 5 + 2 = 7 tens

Explain that, once everything is ungrouped, you can subtract the place value columns in any order. You might demonstrate by first subtracting from left to right, and then erasing your answer and subtracting from right to left.

Point out to students that, before ungrouping, the top number has 1 hundred, plus 3 tens, plus 4 ones. Write the following expression on the board:

1 hundred + 3 tens + 4 ones

● How many hundreds, tens, and ones does the top number have *after* ungrouping? 0 hundreds, 12 tens, 14 ones

Write the following expression under the first expression:

O hundreds + 12 tens + 14 ones

● Why do the expressions represent the same number? 12 tens is 120 and 14 ones is 14. When you add these together, you get 134, which is 1 hundred + 3 tens + 4 ones.

Emphasize that, when we ungroup, we are not changing the value of the top number, we are just writing it in a different way. The magnifying glass can help you see and remember this.

Have students find the answer to exercise 4 on Student Activity Book page 32 and then discuss the steps for subtracting as a class. Tell students that, if it is easier, they can make their proof drawing first and then use the picture to decide how to write the subtraction numerically.

Use the **Solve and Discuss** structure to solve the exercises 5–7. Have presenters show how each step in their proof drawing relates to each step in their numerical method.

Ongoing Assessment

Write 364 − 187 on the board. Have students write the subtraction vertically, find the answer, and make a proof drawing.

② Extending the Lesson

Differentiated Instruction — Activities for Individualizing

Intervention
for students having difficulty

PAIRS

Modeling Subtraction

Materials: Base ten blocks

Have pairs use base ten blocks to explain the subtraction exercises below.

348 − 159 = _____

235 − 88 = _____

As one partner moves the blocks, the other partner describes the modeling using math language.

Have students switch roles and find the answer to the second exercise.

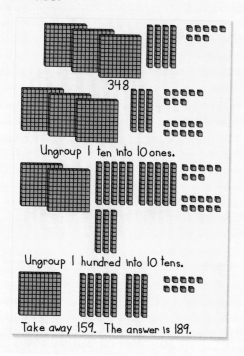

348

Ungroup 1 ten into 10 ones.

Ungroup 1 hundred into 10 tens.

Take away 159. The answer is 189.

On Level
for students having success

INDIVIDUALS

Plan Ahead to Ungroup

Materials: Game Cards (Copymaster M25) (1 set per student)

Have students mix the Game cards and choose any 6 at random. Students then arrange the cards to form two 3-digit numbers that, when subtracted, require ungrouping. Remind them that the number they subtract must be less than the number they subtract from. Have students write the numbers on paper, and subtract in any way they choose.

Have students mix the Game cards and repeat the activity.

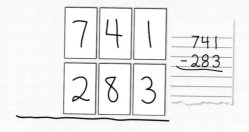

741
−283

Challenge
for students seeking a challenge

INDIVIDUALS

How Old Are They?

Display the table shown below. Have students subtract to determine the age of these movies.

Once students are finished, have a classmate check their work to look for any errors.

Students should discuss their errors and how to avoid them.

Name of Movie	Year Made
Cinderella	1950
ET: The Extra-Terrestrial	1982
King Kong (original)	1933
The Sound of Music	1965
Star Wars	1977
The Wizard of Oz	1939

        1 9 9
        2̶0̶0̶5
      − 1 9 3 9
          6 6

The Wizard of Oz was made 66 years ago.

Also Use
Challenge Master for 1-10

🖊 Math Writing Prompt
Intervention
Explain Your Thinking
Explain what a "subtraction detective" does.

🖊 Math Writing Prompt
On Level
Write a Rule
Write a rule about when to ungroup for subtracting.

🖊 Math Writing Prompt
Challenge
Investigate Math
Michelle knew that 134 − 58 was less than 100 without subtracting. Explain how Michelle may have known this.

③ Homework and Spiral Review

 **1-10**
Homework **Goal:** Additional Practice

✓ Include students' completed Homework page as part of their portfolios.

1-10
Remembering **Goal:** Spiral Review

This Remembering page would be appropriate anytime after today's lesson.

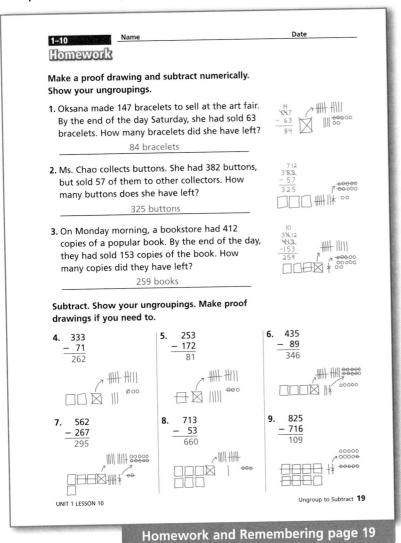

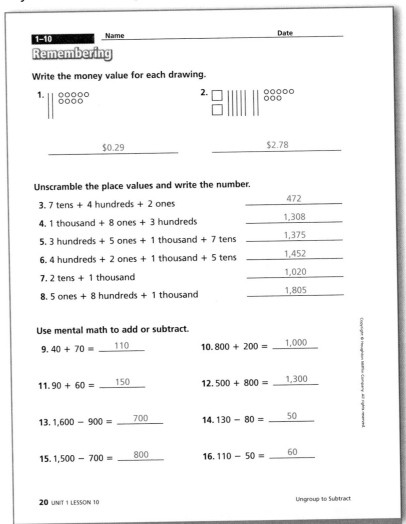

Home or School Activity

 Science Connection

Subtracting Sunny Days Have students gather statistics and create a chart about the average number of sunny days per year in some American cities. Then have them find the average number of days per year that are *not* sunny by subtracting the number of sunny days from 365 (days per year).

Name of City	Number of Sunny Days
Austin, TX	219 days
Seattle, WA	156 days
Chicago, IL	197 days
Orlando, FL	328 days
Philadelphia, PA	204 days

Subtract Across Zeros

Lesson Objectives

- Subtract with zeros in the top number.
- Solve subtraction problems involving money.

Vocabulary
ungrouping

The Day at a Glance

Today's Goals	Materials	Math Talk
Quick Practice Subtract larger numbers. **1 Teaching the Lesson** **A1:** Solve subtraction problems with zeros in the top number. **A2:** Subtract from whole-dollar amounts. **A3:** Practice subtraction with zeros in the top number. **2 Extending the Lesson** ▶ Differentiated Instruction **3 Homework and Spiral Review**	Quick Practice materials MathBoard materials Play money Paper bags Student Activity Book pages 33–36 Homework and Remembering pages 21–22 Math Journals	In today's activities, the students are involved in discussion as they ▶ describe how to subtract from top number zeros ▶ present and explain subtraction drawings

Quick Practice

 5 MINUTES   **Goal:** Subtract larger numbers.
Materials: Demonstration Secret Code Cards
(Copymasters M3–M18)

Subtract Tens From the Demonstration Secret Code Cards, have a Student Leader select the 100 card and two tens cards. The Student Leader assembles the cards so the class can see a 3-digit number on the left and a number of tens on the right.

The leader then gives students a few seconds to mentally subtract the numbers, and says "Subtract." The class says the subtraction equation aloud. The leader then selects one student to illustrate the Make a Hundred strategy (See page 49). Repeat this for several pairs of cards.

Class Management

Consider choosing two student leaders. As one leads the class, the other can be selecting cards for the next problem.

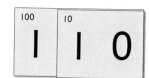 

Teaching the Lesson

Ungroup for Subtraction

 20 MINUTES

Goal: Solve subtraction problems with zeros in the top number.

Materials: Student Activity Book page 33, MathBoard materials

✓ **NCTM Standards:**
Number and Operations
Problem Solving

Teaching Note

What to Expect from Students
Subtraction with zeros in the top number is especially challenging for students. *Math Expressions* has had success introducing this type of subtraction early on, rather than waiting until students have spent lots of time with other types of subtractions. Once students master the ungrouping required with top-number zeros, they can solve other multi-digit subtraction exercises with less difficulty.

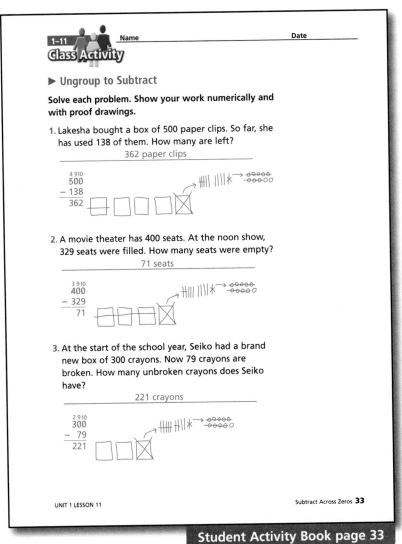

Student Activity Book page 33

▶ Ungroup to Subtract WHOLE CLASS

Read aloud problem 1 on Student Activity Book, page 33. Work through the problem with students, discussing each step of the solution.

● **What do we need to do to solve the problem?** Subtract 138 from 500.

Have students draw a magnifying glass to remember to look closely at the 500 and ungroup before subtracting.

● **To make a proof drawing, what should you draw first?** 5 hundred boxes

Have students focus on the hundreds column.

● Are there enough hundreds to subtract from? yes

Then move to the tens column:

● Are there enough tens to subtract from? no

● How can we get more tens? Ungroup one of the hundreds to get 10 tens.

● How do you show this in your proof drawing? Cross out 1 hundreds-box and draw 10 ten-sticks

● How do you show this with numbers? Cross out the 5 in the hundreds column and write 4. Cross out the 0 in the tens column and write 10.

● Now, how many hundreds and tens are there? 4 hundreds and 10 tens.

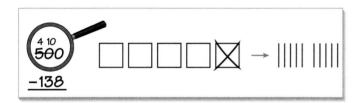

Now look at the ones column and ask if there are enough ones to subtract from. no Elicit responses from students on how to get more ones. Ungroup one of the tens to get 10 ones.

● How do you show this in your proof drawing? Cross out 1 ten-stick and draw 10 circles.

● How do you show this with numbers? Cross out the 10 in the tens column and write 9. Cross out the 0 in the ones column and write 10.

● How many tens and ones do you now have? 9 tens and 10 ones.

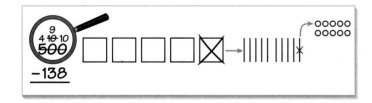

Students who start from the right will have to go clear over the hundreds place to get more ones. They will need to ungroup 1 hundred to get 10 tens so they can get 10 ones from 1 ten. They do not want to get 100 ones in the ones column.

Activity continued ▶

Teaching Note

What to Expect from Students
Students who are used to using the common subtraction method may be skeptical about the fact that, once everything is ungrouped, they can subtract the place value columns in any order. To demonstrate that you get the same answer either way, you might subtract in the order hundreds, tens, ones; erase your answer (just the answer, not the regrouping at the top); and then select a volunteer to subtract in the order ones, tens, hundreds.

Two Ways to Ungroup Zeros

1. Step-by-Step

$$\begin{array}{c} 9 \\ 4 \; \cancel{10} \; 10 \\ \cancel{5\,0\,0} \end{array}$$

Know 100 = 90 + 10

2. Ungroup All at Once

$$\begin{array}{c} 4 \; 9 \; 10 \\ \cancel{5\,0\,0} \end{array}$$

① Teaching the Lesson (continued)

Teaching Note

Watch For! Some students who try to "borrow" both more tens and more ones from the hundreds column, as illustrated below.

Encourage students who make this mistake to ungroup one place at a time and to think about the place-value of each number. Remind them that ungrouping 1 hundred gives 100 ones, not 10 ones. If they want to get 10 ones, they need to ungroup a ten, not a hundred.

Now that everything has been ungrouped, ask students what to do next. Subtract

● Does it matter which place value column you subtract first? no

● How do you show the subtraction in your proof drawing? Cross out 1 hundred, 3 tens, and 8 ones.

● Does your final drawing match your answer? yes

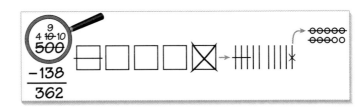

Use the **Solve and Discuss** structure for problems 2 and 3. As students work, walk around to monitor progress and provide help. Make note of the kinds of errors students are making. When you select presenters, include students who made common errors so these errors can be discussed and corrected.

Math Talk in Action

Cameron: Problem 2 says that a movie theater has 400 seats and there were 329 filled. We need to find out how many were empty.

Justine: We have to subtract 400 – 329 to do that.

Cameron: Let's try this without a proof drawing.

Justine: Ok. There are 4 hundreds, 0 tens, and 0 ones in 400. I think that we have to ungroup something so that we can subtract 329.

Cameron: We can ungroup the 4 hundreds into 3 hundreds and 10 tens. I'll cross out the 4 in the hundreds column and write 3. I'll cross out the 0 in the tens column and write 10.

Justine: We've got 3 hundreds and 10 tens. We can't subtract the nine ones yet though because there aren't any ones to subtract from. Let's ungroup the 10 tens into 9 tens and 10 ones.

Cameron: Now we can subtract! 10 ones minus 9 ones is 1 one. 9 tens minus 2 tens is 7 tens.

Justine: And 3 hundreds minus 3 hundreds is 0 hundreds. We have 7 tens and 1 one left. The answer is 71!

Cameron: Don't forget that we have to answer the question. There are 71 empty seats.

✓ Ongoing Assessment

▶ Ask students to explain to a younger student how to subtract 800 − 324.

Subtract from Whole-Dollar Amounts

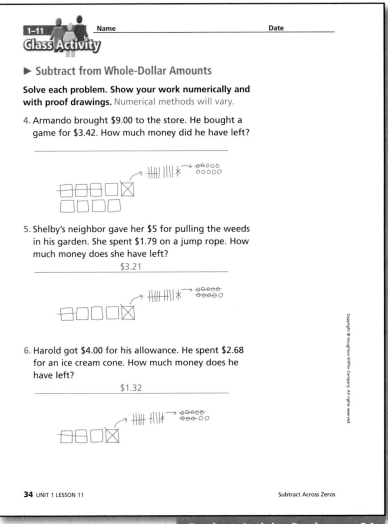

Student Activity Book page 34

15 MINUTES

Goal: Subtract from whole-dollar amounts.

Materials: Student Activity Book page 34, MathBoard materials

NCTM Standards:
Number and Operations
Problem Solving

The Learning Classroom

Math Talk To continue to keep students in their seats engaged and to move this engagement to a deeper level, challenge them to listen carefully so that they might say the explainers' statements. Ask several students to *repeat* what has been explained by the student explainer in their own words.

▶ Subtract from Whole-Dollar Amounts WHOLE CLASS

Read aloud problem 4 on Student Activity Book, page 34. Using the **Solve and Discuss** structure, have students complete the problem. If students have difficulty solving subtraction problems involving money, work together to set up and start solving the problem:

● What do we need to do to solve the problem? Subtract $3.42 from $9.00

● How do you line up the two numbers? Line up the decimal point, so dollars are lined up with dollars, dimes with dimes, and pennies with pennies.

Activity continued ▶

Class Management

Suggested Groups You may want to divide the class into partners rather than using the **Solve and Discuss** structure with the entire class. Partners can work together to discuss how subtracting money amounts is similar to subtracting whole numbers. As partners work, check to be sure that each partner understands the method used to solve the subtraction problems.

Have students draw a magnifying glass to remember to do all of their ungrouping before subtracting.

● **What should you draw first?** 9 hundred-boxes

● **What does each hundred-box represent?** 1 dollar, or 100 pennies

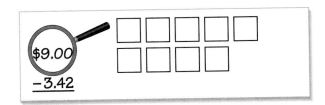

Have students focus on the dollars column.

● **Are there enough dollars to subtract from?** yes Then, look at the dimes column.

● **Are there enough dimes to subtract from?** no

● **How can you get more dimes?** Ungroup a dollar to get 10 new dimes.

● **How do you show this in the drawing?** Cross out a hundred-box and make 10 ten-sticks.

● **How many dollars and dimes will you have after you ungroup?** 8 dollars and 10 dimes

● **How do you show this with numbers?** Cross out the 9 in the dollars column and write 8. Cross out the 0 in the tens column and write 10.

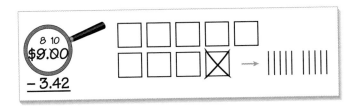

Have students finish subtracting. Then use the **Solve and Discuss** structure for problems 5 and 6. Explain in problem 5 that $5 can also be written as $5.00.

Practice Subtraction Across Zeros

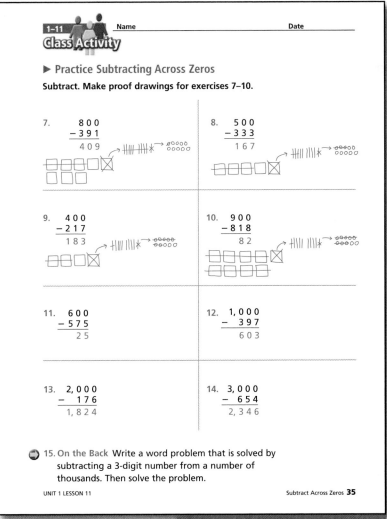

Student Activity Book page 35

Inside the student book page:

1-11 Class Activity   Name _____ Date _____

▶ Practice Subtracting Across Zeros

Subtract. Make proof drawings for exercises 7–10.

7.
```
   8 0 0
 - 3 9 1
   4 0 9
```

8.
```
   5 0 0
 - 3 3 3
   1 6 7
```

9.
```
   4 0 0
 - 2 1 7
   1 8 3
```

10.
```
   9 0 0
 - 8 1 8
     8 2
```

11.
```
   6 0 0
 - 5 7 5
     2 5
```

12.
```
   1, 0 0 0
 -    3 9 7
       6 0 3
```

13.
```
   2, 0 0 0
 -    1 7 6
    1, 8 2 4
```

14.
```
   3, 0 0 0
 -    6 5 4
    2, 3 4 6
```

15. On the Back Write a word problem that is solved by subtracting a 3-digit number from a number of thousands. Then solve the problem.

UNIT 1 LESSON 11   Subtract Across Zeros **35**

⏱ **20 MINUTES**

Goal: Practice subtraction with zeros in the top number.

Materials: Student Activity Book page 35, MathBoard materials

✔ **NCTM Standards:**
Number and Operations
Problem Solving

Teaching Note

Watch For! Some students may discover a shortcut that allows them to ungroup only once. For example, the problem below shows that we can ungroup 1 hundred all at once to get 9 tens and 10 ones.

```
   3 9 10
   4̶0̶0̶
 - 3 2 9
      7 1
```

▶ Practice Subtracting Across Zeros [WHOLE CLASS]

Have students focus on exercise 7 on Student Activity Book page 35. Ask students to suggest some word problems this subtraction might represent. Listen to a few suggestions. Then have students complete the page.

Walk around, monitoring progress and noting common errors. Provide individual help for students who are struggling or pair these students with Student Helpers. If a large number of students are having difficulties, stop after a few minutes and work through the first problem or two as a class. Then, let students try the remaining problems on their own.

Activity continued ▶

Differentiated Instruction

Extra Help For students who have difficulty ungrouping 3- and 4-digit top numbers with zeros, have them practice ungrouping with 2-digit top numbers. For example, rewrite exercise 1 as 80 − 39, rather than 800 − 391. Once students are comfortable with ungrouping single top number zeros, then move them on to larger numbers.

When most students have completed Student Activity Book page 35, discuss any problems that caused difficulty for students and talk about the common errors you observed as you walked around the room. Students may have trouble with exercise 12, which requires them to subtract from thousands. You might ask students to present solutions and proof drawings.

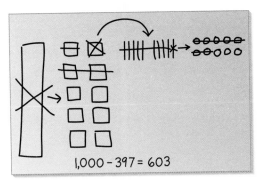

$$1,000 - 397 = 603$$

If time allows, have students present the On the Back problems they wrote. Have students write their problems on the board and then ask for volunteers to solve the problems.

Subtraction with Larger Numbers If your district's goals require subtracting from numbers greater than 3,000, you might spend some time today having your students solve exercises such as:

$$\begin{array}{r} 9{,}205 \\ -\ 6{,}437 \end{array}$$

The methods for solving such exercises are simple extensions of the methods for solving subtraction exercises involving smaller numbers. Students may need to make place value drawings to help them visualize the subtraction.

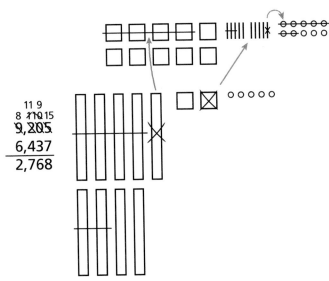

Include subtraction problems like this in future lessons.

② Extending the Lesson

Activities for Individualizing

Intervention
for students having difficulty
PAIRS

Ungrouping Money

Materials: Play money (pennies, dimes, and dollar bills)

Have students use play money to model subtracting the money amounts below.

$3.00 − $1.48

$5.00 − $2.61

Have one student subtract by describing what to do and asking for trades, such as 10 dimes for 1 dollar, or 10 pennies for 1 dime. The other student acts as a banker to make any trades required and checks his or her partner's work.

Students then switch roles and complete the second exercise.

On Level
for students having success
PAIRS

What is the Change?

Materials: Paper bags (1 per pair)

Have students write $2.00 through $7.00 on separate slips of paper. Put them into a paper bag.

Give students a list of items they can buy at a store, such as the following:

Arts and Crafts Supplies	
Water color paints	$4.65
Set of brushes	$3.84
Sketch paper	$5.79
Crayons	$2.58
Art chalk	$1.90

One student pulls a slip of paper from the bag and chooses an item from the list to buy. The partner subtracts to find out how much change to give or how much more money is needed to buy the item.

Students switch roles and continue the activity.

Challenge
for students seeking a challenge
PAIRS

Target Practice

Materials: Math Journals

Have students copy the targets below in their Math Journal. Have pairs use the digits around the outside of each target to write subtraction sentences with three-digit numbers whose difference is the number in the center.

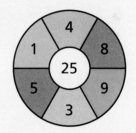

$$518 - 493 = 25$$

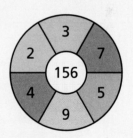

$$453 - 297 = 156$$

Also Use
Challenge Master for 1-11

 Math Writing Prompt

Intervention

Explain Your Thinking
Rico says that it is impossible to subtract from a zero in the top number, so the answer to 200 − 158 is 158. Explain the error in his thinking.

 Math Writing Prompt

On Level

Find the Error
Chen used $6.00 to buy a game that cost $5.45. The store clerk gave Chen $1.55 in change. Is this the correct amount of change? Explain.

 Math Writing Prompt

Challenge

Mental Math
Explain how to find the answer to $10.00 − $3.98 using mental math.

③ Homework and Spiral Review

1–11
Homework **Goal:** Additional Practice

✓ Include students' completed Homework page as part of their portfolios.

1–11
Remembering **Goal:** Spiral Review

This Remembering page would be appropriate anytime after today's lesson.

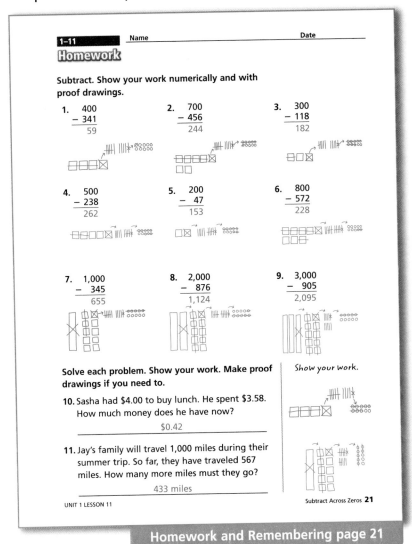

1–11 Name   Date
Homework

Subtract. Show your work numerically and with proof drawings.

1. 400
 − 341
 59

2. 700
 − 456
 244

3. 300
 − 118
 182

4. 500
 − 238
 262

5. 200
 − 47
 153

6. 800
 − 572
 228

7. 1,000
 − 345
 655

8. 2,000
 − 876
 1,124

9. 3,000
 − 905
 2,095

Solve each problem. Show your work. Make proof drawings if you need to.

Show your work.

10. Sasha had $4.00 to buy lunch. He spent $3.58. How much money does he have now?
 $0.42

11. Jay's family will travel 1,000 miles during their summer trip. So far, they have traveled 567 miles. How many more miles must they go?
 433 miles

UNIT 1 LESSON 11

Subtract Across Zeros **21**

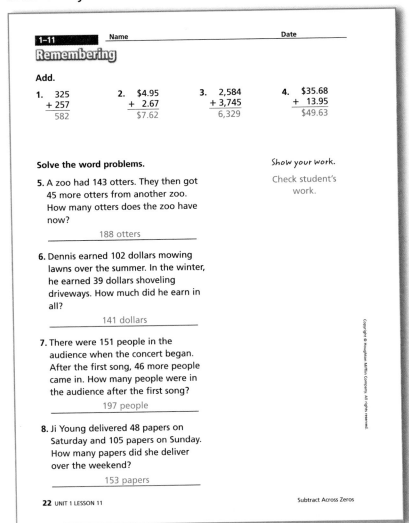

1–11 Name   Date
Remembering

Add.

1. 325
 + 257
 582

2. $4.95
 + 2.67
 $7.62

3. 2,584
 + 3,745
 6,329

4. $35.68
 + 13.95
 $49.63

Solve the word problems.

Show your work.
Check student's work.

5. A zoo had 143 otters. They then got 45 more otters from another zoo. How many otters does the zoo have now?
 188 otters

6. Dennis earned 102 dollars mowing lawns over the summer. In the winter, he earned 39 dollars shoveling driveways. How much did he earn in all?
 141 dollars

7. There were 151 people in the audience when the concert began. After the first song, 46 more people came in. How many people were in the audience after the first song?
 197 people

8. Ji Young delivered 48 papers on Saturday and 105 papers on Sunday. How many papers did she deliver over the weekend?
 153 papers

22 UNIT 1 LESSON 11

Subtract Across Zeros

Homework and Remembering page 21

Homework and Remembering page 22

Home and School Activity

 Social Studies Connection

Inventions Help students research and create a list of items that were invented years ago. Then, have them make a chart to show five inventions and the year in which they were developed in chronological order. Students can then subtract from the current year to find out how long the invention has been around.

For example, Thomas Edison patented the light bulb in 1879. If the current year is 2007, students will use 2007 − 1879 to discover that the light bulb has been around for 128 years.

Invention	Year
Paper	105
Pencil	1565
Telescope	1608
Ear Muffs	1873
Television	1927

90 UNIT 1 LESSON 11

UNIT 1 LESSON 12

Discuss Methods of Subtracting

Lesson Objectives

- Subtract using two different methods.
- Explain when and how to ungroup when subtracting multi-digit numbers.

Vocabulary
ungroup

The Day at a Glance

Today's Goals	Materials	Math Talk
Quick Practice Subtract tens.	Quick Practice materials	In today's activities, the students are involved in discussion as they
① Teaching the Lesson **A1:** Compare two subtraction methods— ungrouping from the left and ungrouping from the right. **A2:** Determine whether to ungroup when solving a subtraction problem. **A3:** Choose items from a price list, find the total cost for the items, and determine how much money will be left from a given amount.	MathBoard materials Base ten blocks Number cubes Student Activity Book pages 37–38 Homework and Remembering pages 23–24 Math Journals	▶ compare two subtraction methods ▶ determine when and how to ungroup when solving a subtraction problem
② Extending the Lesson ▶ Differentiated Instruction		
③ Homework and Spiral Review		

Quick Practice

 5 MINUTES **Goal:** Subtract tens from numbers that are greater than 100.
Materials: Demonstration Secret Code Cards (Copymasters M3–M18)

Subtract Tens Have a Student Leader select the 100 card and two tens cards from the Demonstration Secret Code Cards. The Student Leader assembles the cards so the class can see a three-digit number on the left and a number of tens on the right. The leader then gives students a few seconds to mentally subtract the numbers, and says "Subtract." (See Unit 1 Lesson 10)

 Class Management

You may want to choose two student leaders. As one leads the class, the other can be selecting cards for the next exercise.

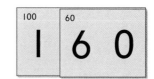

① Teaching the Lesson

Activity 1

Two Methods for Subtraction

 20 MINUTES

Goal: Compare two subtraction methods—ungrouping from the left and ungrouping from the right.

Materials: Student Activity Book page 37, MathBoard Materials

 NCTM Standards:
Number and Operations
Communication
Problem Solving

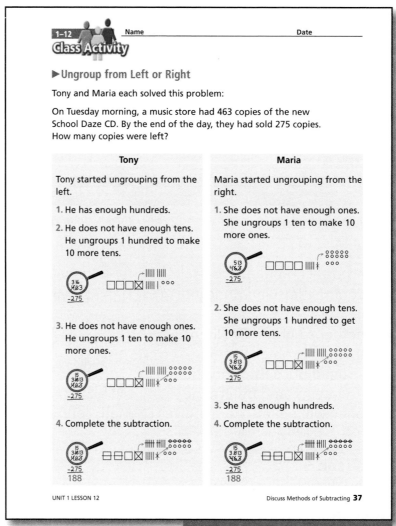

Student Activity Book page 37

The content of the Student Activity Book page:

1–12 **Class Activity**   Name _____ Date _____

▶ Ungroup from Left or Right

Tony and Maria each solved this problem:

On Tuesday morning, a music store had 463 copies of the new School Daze CD. By the end of the day, they had sold 275 copies. How many copies were left?

Tony

Tony started ungrouping from the left.

1. He has enough hundreds.

2. He does not have enough tens. He ungroups 1 hundred to make 10 more tens.

3. He does not have enough ones. He ungroups 1 ten to make 10 more ones.

4. Complete the subtraction.

188

Maria

Maria started ungrouping from the right.

1. She does not have enough ones. She ungroups 1 ten to make 10 more ones.

2. She does not have enough tens. She ungroups 1 hundred to get 10 more tens.

3. She has enough hundreds.

4. Complete the subtraction.

188

UNIT 1 LESSON 12   Discuss Methods of Subtracting **37**

▶ Ungroup from Left or Right [WHOLE CLASS]

Read aloud the word problem on Student Activity Book page 37. Ask students how they would solve the problem. Subtract 275 from 463.

Tell students that Tony and Maria subtracted in different ways. Tony started on the left, with the hundreds place. Work through Tony's method as students follow along. Ask volunteers to explain what Tony did in each step and why he did it.

Next, tell students that Maria started from the right, with the ones place. Work through Maria's method, asking a volunteer to explain each step.

Ask students to compare the two methods, explaining what is different and what is the same.

Then, have students complete the subtraction.

Write 617 − 159 on the board in vertical form. Ask students to subtract by ungrouping from the right and then by ungrouping from the left on their MathBoards. Have some students work at the board. Have one student explain each method.

▶ A Special Case When Ungrouping From the Left

WHOLE CLASS

Write the following subtraction example and place value drawing on the board.

$$\begin{array}{r} 435 \\ -138 \\ \end{array}$$ □□ ||| °°°°°
  □□

Tell students that you will subtract by ungrouping from the left.

- Are there enough hundreds to subtract? yes

- Are there enough tens to subtract? yes

- Are there enough ones to subtract? no. How can you get enough ones to subtract? Ungroup 1 ten to make 10 more ones.

Draw the ungrouping on the board. Then have a volunteer explain what happens when you subtract the ones. Write the result on the board.

$$\begin{array}{r} 2\ 15 \\ \cancel{435} \\ -138 \\ \hline 7 \end{array}$$ □□ ||⧣   °°°°°
                        °°°°°
                       °°°°°
  □□

- Are there enough tens to subtract? no Why aren't there enough tens to subtract? because we ungrouped 1 ten

- How can you get enough tens to subtract? Go back and ungroup 1 hundred to make 10 more tens.

Draw the ungrouping on the board. Have volunteers subtract the tens and the hundreds. Write the results on the board.

$$\begin{array}{r} 12 \\ 3\ \cancel{2}\ 15 \\ \cancel{435} \\ -138 \\ \hline 297 \end{array}$$ □⊠ ||⧣   °°°°°
                      °°°°°
                     °°°°°
  □⊟

Activity continued ▶

The Learning Classroom

Building Concepts Students' understanding of each step that is taken in subtraction is reinforced through the process of starting at the left (hundreds), and going to the right without ungrouping, then going back to ungroup a hundred when this becomes necessary. Moreover, this process can give students added confidence in their ability to complete any addition or subtraction example. This is an opportunity for students to realize that if they pay attention to place value, they can create their own procedures for computation, and can go back and correct steps that they have already taken.

Write the following examples on the board. Have volunteers come to the board and subtract starting at the left.

$$
\begin{array}{r}
865 \\
- 368 \\
\hline 497
\end{array}
\qquad
\begin{array}{r}
453 \\
- 257 \\
\hline 196
\end{array}
$$

Have students discuss how the examples are alike, and describe the patterns they see.

● When will you need to go back and ungroup a hundred in order to subtract tens? When there are the same number of tens in each number and there are not enough ones to subtract.

Activity 2

Decide When to Ungroup

 15 MINUTES

Goal: Decide whether to ungroup when solving a subtraction problem.

Materials: MathBoard materials

 NCTM Standards:
Number and Operations
Communication

Teaching Note

Watch For! To address common errors, such as failing to record ungrouping, solve a few problems yourself on the board, purposely making errors you have seen your students make. Ask students to observe and watch for mistakes. Students should identify the errors you make and offer suggestions for avoiding such errors.

▶ **Discuss Ungrouping** WHOLE CLASS

Ask students a few general questions about ungrouping:

● When you need to subtract, how can you tell if you will need to ungroup? If the top number in any column is smaller than the bottom number, you will need to ungroup.

● What do you do if there are not enough ones to subtract from? Ungroup 1 ten to make 10 more ones.

● What do you do if there are not enough tens to subtract from? Ungroup 1 hundred to make 10 new tens.

Write the four subtraction exercises below on the board. Have students copy them on their MathBoards or paper.

$$
\begin{array}{llll}
1.\ \begin{array}{r} 912 \\ -265 \\ \hline 647 \end{array} &
2.\ \begin{array}{r} 323 \\ -147 \\ \hline 176 \end{array} &
3.\ \begin{array}{r} 280 \\ -136 \\ \hline 44 \end{array} &
4.\ \begin{array}{r} 489 \\ -263 \\ \hline 226 \end{array}
\end{array}
$$

● Which of these involves ungrouping 1 hundred to make 10 more tens? 1 and 2

● Which will involve ungrouping 1 ten to make 10 more ones? 1, 2, and 3

● What is different about exercise 4? You don't need to ungroup.

As students are working, walk around the room to monitor progress and look for common errors. Have student helpers walk around the room to provide help to students experiencing some difficulty. Discuss the common errors students made.

Activity 3

Andy's Arts and Crafts Store

1–12 **Class Activity** Name ______________________ Date __________

ANDY'S ARTS AND CRAFTS STORE
SALE!

TOOLS
Paintbrush $0.29
Set of Cookie Cutters $2.42
Roller $1.17
Set of Stampers $2.89

PAINTS, INKS, AND CLAY
Set of Paints $2.37
Ink Pad $0.68
Clay $1.75

OTHER SUPPLIES
Marker $0.83
Glue $1.45
Construction Paper $1.25
Posterboard $1.26
Set of Large Blank Buttons $1.57

▶ **Solve and Discuss**

Imagine that you have the amount of money shown to spend at Andy's Arts and Crafts Store each day.

Monday	$8.00
Tuesday	$7.25
Wednesday	$6.50
Thursday	$6.95
Friday	$6.20

Here's what to do for each day:

- Choose two, three, or four different items you want to buy.
- Find the total cost for the items.
- Figure out how much money you will have left for that day.

Show your work on a separate sheet of paper.

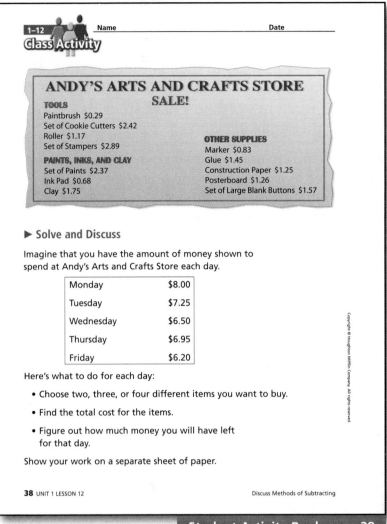

Student Activity Book page 38

▶ Solve and Discuss WHOLE CLASS

Direct students' attention to the ad for Andy's Arts and Crafts Store on Student Activity Book page 38.

Read aloud the directions for the activity. Then, ask a volunteer to choose three or four different items from the price list. Remind students that they only have a set amount of money each day. Have them begin with Monday's budget of $8.00. Using the **Solve and Discuss** structure, have students find the total price for the items.

Students may use different strategies for adding the prices. Some may add all of the prices at once. Some may add two prices, then add the total to the next price, and so on. If there are four prices, some students may add them in pairs and then add the two totals. Try to choose students who used different strategies to present their methods of solving.

Be sure that students understand how to figure out how much money they will have left over for the day. They should subtract the total

Activity continued ▶

20 MINUTES

Goal: Choose items from a price list, find the total cost for the items, and determine how much money will be left from a given amount

Materials: Student Activity Book page 38

NCTM Standards:
Number and Operations
Problem Solving
Communication

The Learning Classroom

Math Talk You can create math conversations by eliciting multiple strategies for solving problems. When you ask, "Did anyone do this problem differently?" your students will pay greater attention to the work on the board because they will be comparing and contrasting it with their own math strategies. The comparisons and contrasts that result can naturally springboard to significant math talk.

Differentiated Instruction

Extra Help Some students may have difficulty discovering a way to add more than two numbers. Suggest that students choose two of the prices, find the sum, and then add another price to the sum. If there is a fourth number, they can add this number to the second sum that they found.

Differentiated Instruction

English Learners Be sure that students understand that "change" means the amount of money you get back when you give the cashier more money than the cost of the item.

amount for the art supplies they wish to buy from the amount of money they have listed for each day.

▶ Subtract from $10.00 PAIRS

Now, tell the class that they have $10.00 to spend at the art store. Have students calculate the change they would receive if they bought $6.06 worth of art supplies. Elicit students' methods. Have students who used different methods explain their thinking with the class.

Students may have some difficulty because they have not worked with money amounts of $10.00 or more. If necessary, point out that the leftmost column can be thought of as the $10-bill column. Students can trade one $10 bill for ten $1 bills. It may be helpful to have a volunteer make a proof drawing. The original amount $10.00, can be represented by a thousand bar, which must be ungrouped into 10 hundred-boxes, and so on.

✓ Ongoing Assessment

Ask students the following questions:

▶ Did you ungroup a dime to make ten pennies? Why?

▶ Why did you ungroup a dollar?

▶ How can you get more dollars to subtract?

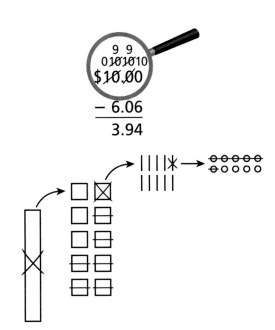

② Extending the Lesson

Differentiated Instruction Activities for Individualizing

Intervention
for students having difficulty

PAIRS

Decide Before You Subtract

Materials: Base ten blocks (20 hundreds, 20 tens, 20 ones per pair), MathBoard materials

Write the following exercises on the board or on chart paper.

$$
\begin{array}{r} 842 \\ -562 \end{array}
\qquad
\begin{array}{r} \$2.77 \\ -\$1.36 \end{array}
$$

$$
\begin{array}{r} 500 \\ -212 \end{array}
\qquad
\begin{array}{r} 963 \\ -269 \end{array}
$$

Students work in pairs and use base ten blocks to find the answer. While they work, they should talk about what ungrouping is necessary to find the answer. Students should be recording their work on their MathBoards as they ungroup using the base ten blocks.

On Level
for students having success

SMALL GROUPS

Race to Two Digits

Materials: 3 number cubes per pair (labeled 0–5, 1–6, 2–7), MathBoard materials

For this activity, students work in groups of three. Have all students copy this place value chart with the number 999 on their MathBoards. Explain the H stands for hundreds, the T for tens, and the O for ones.

H	T	O
9	9	9

Players roll the number cubes and form any 3-digit number and subtract it from 999. Players roll the number cubes again, and subtract the new number formed from the last difference. Players continue until a player reaches a 2-digit difference.

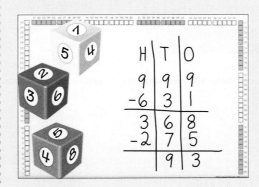

Challenge
for students seeking a challenge

PAIRS

What's the Difference?

Materials: MathBoard materials

Write the following sets of four numbers on the board or chart paper.

115, 129, 141, 155

122, 138, 210, 226

Tell students that each set of numbers can be arranged in a square so that each row in the square has the same difference and each column in the square has the same difference. Students should work in pairs to place the numbers.

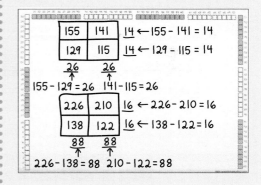

Also Use
Challenge Master for 1-12

 Math Writing Prompt

Intervention

Choose a Method
Write a rule about when to ungroup to subtract.

 Math Writing Prompt

On Level

Think Critically
Ben solved this as: 548 − 322 = 256. Explain the error that he made.

 Math Writing Prompt

Challenge

Number Sense
Will 572 − 352 be more or less than 200? Explain how you know.

③ Homework and Spiral Review

Homework **Goal:** Additional Practice

This Homework page gives students practice in addition and subtraction.

1–12
Remembering **Goal:** Spiral Review

This Remembering page would be appropriate any time after today's lesson.

1–12 Name _____ Date _____
Homework

Solve each problem. Use the ad for Andy's Arts and Crafts Store on Student Activity Book page 38.

Check student's work.

1. You have $5.00. If you buy a set of paints, how much will you have left? ___$2.63___

2. You have $3.75. If you buy construction paper, how much will you have left? ___$2.50___

3. You have $1.00. If you buy a marker, how much will you have left? ___$0.17___

4. You have $6.00. If you buy a set of cookie cutters and glue, how much will you have left?
___$2.13___

Subtract.

5.	972	6.	300	7.	1,278
	− 129		− 276		− 426
	843		24		852

8.	1,336	9.	1,398	10.	997
	− 207		− 528		− 218
	1,129		870		779

11. Write a word problem for one of the subtraction exercises above.
Answers will vary.
_____
_____

UNIT 1 LESSON 12   Discuss Methods of Subtracting **23**

Homework and Remembering page 23

1–12 Name _____ Date _____
Remembering

Add.

1.	972	2.	309	3.	1,278	4.	449
	+ 129		+ 276		+ 426		+ 88
	1,101		585		1,704		537

Use mental math to add or subtract.

5. 800 + 800 = ___1,600___   6. 70 + 70 = ___140___   7. 900 + 300 = ___1,200___

8. 40 + 70 = ___110___   9. 1,800 − 900 = ___900___   10. 120 − 60 = ___60___

11. 1,500 − 500 = ___1,000___   12. 170 − 80 = ___90___   13. 1,600 − 900 = ___700___

Solve. Label your answer.

Show your work.
Check student's work.

14. At a meeting of the third, fourth, and fifth grades, there are 58 third-graders, 62 fourth-graders, and 59 fifth-graders. How many students are at the meeting?
_____179 students_____

15. Jen sells 125 raffle tickets. Jen's sister sells 89 raffle tickets. Melanie sells 119 raffle tickets. How many raffle tickets did the three girls sell in all?
_____214 tickets_____

24 UNIT 1 LESSON 12   Discuss Methods of Subtracting

Homework and Remembering page 24

Home or School Activity

 Literature Connection

Some Favorite Books Give students a copy of this reading list. Ask students how many more pages the book with the greatest number of pages has than the book with the least number of pages. Have students write and solve some other subtraction problems that compare the number of pages in the books.

The Hoboken Chicken Emergency	112 pages
Nate the Great	80 pages
I Was a Third Grade Science Project	96 pages
Charlotte's Web	192 pages
The Best School Year Ever	128 pages
Mr. Popper's Penguins	139 pages

UNIT 1 LESSON 13

Relate Addition and Subtraction

Lesson Objective

● Relate grouping in addition and ungrouping in subtraction.

The Day at a Glance

Today's Goals	Materials	Math Talk
Quick Practice Subtract hundreds.	Quick Practice materials	In today's activities, the students are involved in discussion as they
1 Teaching the Lesson **A1:** Relate grouping in addition to ungrouping in subtraction and discuss that addition and subtraction undo one another. **A2:** Explore different ways of expressing the ideas of ungrouping and grouping.	Base ten blocks Chart paper MathBoard materials Index cards Sticky notes	▶ relate grouping for addition to ungrouping for subtraction ▶ explain the relationship between addition and subtraction
2 Extending the Lesson ▶ Going Further: Subtract Larger Numbers ▶ Differentiated Instruction	Student Activity Book pages 39–40 Homework and Remembering pages 25–26	▶ talk about different ways of expressing the ideas of ungrouping and grouping
3 Homework and Spiral Review	Math Journals	

Quick Practice

🕐 **5 MINUTES**   **Goal:** Subtract hundreds.
Materials: Demonstration Secret Code Cards
(Copymasters M3–M18)

Class Management

You may want to choose two Student Leaders. As one leads the class, the other can be selecting cards for the next problem.

Subtract Hundreds Have a Student Leader select the 1,000 card and the 200 card from the Demonstration Secret Code Cards. The Student Leader assembles the cards so the class can see a 4-digit number on the left and a number of hundreds on the right.

The leader then gives students a few seconds to mentally subtract the numbers, and says "Subtract." The class says the equation aloud. The leader then selects one student to illustrate the Make a Thousand strategy (see page 49). Repeat this activity several times, subtracting different hundreds from combinations of cards between 1,100 and 1,900.

① Teaching the Lesson

Relate Addition and Subtraction Methods

 30 MINUTES

Goal: Relate grouping in addition to ungrouping in subtraction.

Materials: Student Activity Book page 39–40, base ten blocks

✓ **NCTM Standards:**
Number and Operations
Problem Solving
Communication

✋ Alternate Approach

Base Ten Blocks Some students may find it interesting to use base ten blocks to model addition and subtraction problems.

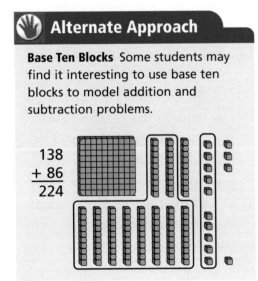

$$\begin{array}{r} 138 \\ + 86 \\ \hline 224 \end{array}$$

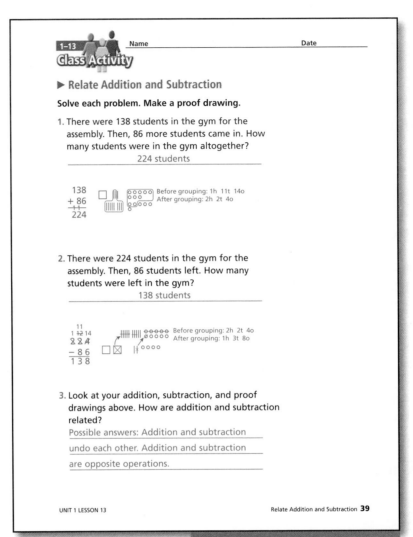

1-13
Class Activity
Name   Date

▶ **Relate Addition and Subtraction**

Solve each problem. Make a proof drawing.

1. There were 138 students in the gym for the assembly. Then, 86 more students came in. How many students were in the gym altogether?

    224 students

$$\begin{array}{r} 138 \\ + 86 \\ \hline 224 \end{array}$$
Before grouping: 1h 11t 14o
After grouping: 2h 2t 4o

2. There were 224 students in the gym for the assembly. Then, 86 students left. How many students were left in the gym?

    138 students

$$\begin{array}{r} 224 \\ - 86 \\ \hline 138 \end{array}$$
Before grouping: 2h 2t 4o
After grouping: 1h 3t 8o

3. Look at your addition, subtraction, and proof drawings above. How are addition and subtraction related?

Possible answers: Addition and subtraction undo each other. Addition and subtraction are opposite operations.

UNIT 1 LESSON 13   Relate Addition and Subtraction **39**

Student Activity Book page 39

▶ Relate Addition and Subtraction WHOLE CLASS

Using the **Solve and Discuss** structure, have students solve problem 1 on Student Activity Book page 39. Tell them to make a proof drawing, even if they don't need to. Choose a student who made a clear drawing to present the addition and proof drawing. Next to the drawing, record the number of hundreds, tens, and ones the drawing showed before grouping and after grouping. Remind students they can use the abbreviation H, T, and O for hundreds, tens, and ones to save time. Leave the drawing and labels on the board.

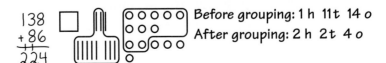

$$\begin{array}{r} 138 \\ + 86 \\ \hline 224 \end{array}$$
Before grouping: 1 h 11t 14 o
After grouping: 2 h 2t 4 o

Read aloud problem 2. Ask students how they can figure out the answer without doing any work. Allow several students to share their ideas. Students should see that:

- In problem 1, they combined 138 students and 86 students to get a total of 224 students.

- In problem 2, they start with the total from problem 1, which is 224 students. Then they take away 86 students, so there must be 138 students left.

Math Mountains Review or introduce the idea of a Math Mountain. A Math Mountain shows the relationship between a *total* and two *partners* of the total; that is, two numbers that add to make the total. Make a Math Mountain for problem 1. You might tell students that they can visualize the total at the top breaking into two pieces, one of which rolls down one side and one of which rolls down the other side.

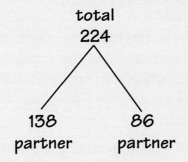

total
224

138   86
partner   partner

Explain to students that they can write an addition equation that shows that the two partners in the Math Mountain add to make the total. Write the following on the board:

138   +   86   =   224
partner   partner   total

Explain that they can also write a subtraction equation that shows that when one of the partners is taken away from the total, the result is the other partner. Write the following on the board:

224   −   86   =   138
total   partner   partner

Point out that addition and subtraction undo each other.

Activity continued ▶

1 Teaching the Lesson (continued)

Teaching Note

Watch For! Watch for students who do not record the results of ungrouping above each place in the subtraction example.

The Learning Classroom

Math Talk One part of helping students to listen to one another is to make sure that the explainers are talking loudly enough, and that they are talking to the whole class, not just to you.

To achieve this goal, you may wish to have presenters pick up a pen or other object and pretend it is a microphone. This imaginary situation frees students to talk more loudly than they usually do and to look directly at their audience.

Tell students that, even though they know the answer to problem 2, they will work through the subtraction and make a proof drawing to show how grouping in addition and ungrouping in subtraction are related. Ask students what subtraction you should write. Then, ask them how to start the proof drawing.

$$\begin{array}{r} 224 \\ -86 \end{array}$$ ☐ ☐ || ○ ○ ○ ○

Give students a few minutes to complete the subtraction and the proof drawing. Choose a student who made a clear drawing to present the subtraction and proof drawing. Next to the proof drawing, have the presenter record the number of hundreds, tens, and ones before and after ungrouping, eliciting what to record from students.

Have the presenter continue with the subtraction.

Before ungrouping: 2 h 2 t 4 o
After ungrouping: 1 h 11 t 14 o

Direct students' attention to the labels next to both the addition and subtraction proof drawings that show the number of hundreds, tens, and ones before and after grouping, and before and after ungrouping. Ask them what they notice. After grouping matches before ungrouping and before grouping matches after ungrouping.

Talk about how ungrouping and grouping are related. Make sure the following key points are made:

● When adding, we sometimes need to *group* 10 ones to make a new ten or *group* 10 tens to make a new hundred.

● When subtracting, we sometimes need to *ungroup* a ten to make 10 new ones or *ungroup* a hundred to make 10 new tens.

● Grouping and ungrouping are opposites.

Have students complete exercise 3. Then, discuss their conclusions. Make sure these points are made:

● Addition and subtraction undo each other.

● Addition and subtraction are opposite operations.

Ask students how they can use addition to check the answer to a subtraction. Add the answer to the other partner. The sum should be the total.

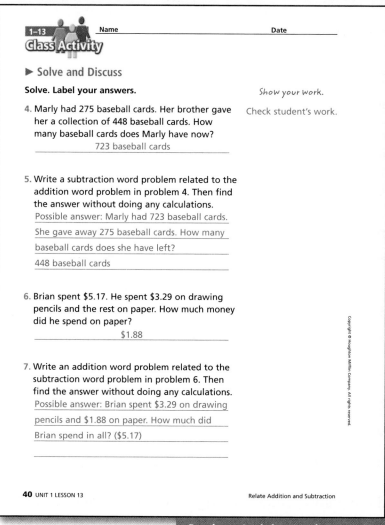

▶ Solve and Discuss

Solve. Label your answers.

Show your work.

Check student's work.

4. Marly had 275 baseball cards. Her brother gave her a collection of 448 baseball cards. How many baseball cards does Marly have now?

723 baseball cards

5. Write a subtraction word problem related to the addition word problem in problem 4. Then find the answer without doing any calculations.

Possible answer: Marly had 723 baseball cards. She gave away 275 baseball cards. How many baseball cards does she have left?

448 baseball cards

6. Brian spent $5.17. He spent $3.29 on drawing pencils and the rest on paper. How much money did he spend on paper?

$1.88

7. Write an addition word problem related to the subtraction word problem in problem 6. Then find the answer without doing any calculations.

Possible answer: Brian spent $3.29 on drawing pencils and $1.88 on paper. How much did Brian spend in all? ($5.17)

Student Activity Book page 40

▶ **Solve and Discuss** ⎡WHOLE CLASS⎤

Problems 4–7 give students practice relating addition and subtraction. Have students solve these problems. Walk around the room to monitor progress and provide help. If students have trouble writing the subtraction word problem in problem 5, guide them by asking questions such as:

● When we subtract, we start with a total and take away one of the parts. What is the total in this situation? 723 baseball cards

● What are the parts? 275 baseball cards and 448 baseball cards

● Try to think of a problem where you start with the total and take away one of the two parts. How might your problem start? Possible answer: Marly had 723 cards.

● Now you need something about taking away one of the parts. What could you say next? Possible answer: Her brother took 448 of her cards.

● What question do you want to ask? Possible question: How many cards did Marly have left?

Using **Solve and Discuss**, have students present their answers.

Relate Addition and Subtraction   **103**

Activity 2

Relate Grouping and Ungrouping Language

 20 MINUTES

Goal: Explore different ways of expressing the ideas of ungrouping and grouping.

Materials: Chart paper (2 sheets)

 NCTM Standards:
Number and Operations
Communication

Differentiated Instruction

English Learners Use this activity to introduce a number of new words to English learners that can be used to express grouping in addition and ungrouping in subtraction — pack, package, trade, regroup, unpack, borrow, and so on. After the words are on the chart paper, have students use the charts to act out what the words mean using base ten blocks.

▶ **Grouping in Addition** WHOLE CLASS

Begin by briefly reviewing when and how to group when adding.

Write **Grouping in Addition** on the top of a sheet of chart paper and have students brainstorm different ways to express grouping in addition. Record students' suggestions. Here are some examples:

Grouping in Addition
Make a new ten from 10 ones or a new hundred from 10 tens.
Package 10 ones into a ten or 10 tens into a hundred.
Pack 10 ones into a ten or 10 tens into a hundred.
Trade 10 ones for a new ten or 10 tens for a new hundred.
Regroup 10 ones into a new ten or 10 tens as a new hundred.

▶ **Ungrouping in Subtraction** WHOLE CLASS

Next, briefly review when and how to ungroup when subtracting.

Write **Ungrouping in Subtraction** on the top of a second sheet of chart paper and have students brainstorm ways to express ungrouping in subtraction. Record the phrases students suggest. Here are some examples:

Ungrouping in Subtraction
Unpack a ten to get 10 ones or a hundred to get 10 tens.
Open a ten to get 10 ones or a hundred to get 10 tens.
Break a ten into 10 ones or a hundred into 10 tens.
Trade a ten for 10 ones or a hundred for 10 tens.
Borrow 10 ones from a ten or 10 tens from a hundred.
Get 10 more ones from a ten or 10 more tens from a hundred.

Post both sheets of chart paper where everyone can see them.

Choose one of the addition exercises below and write it on the board.

Addition and Subtraction Exercises			
159 + 267 426	576 − 358 218	382 + 295 677	892 − 712 180
493 + 377 870	932 − 485 447	549 + 214 763	712 − 428 284

Select a student to come to the board. Ask him or her to choose one of the sayings from the **Grouping in Addition** list. Ask the student to complete the addition, explaining the grouping using the chosen saying. Ask other students to listen and point out any mistakes. See sample dialogue in the Math Talk in Action at the bottom of the page.

Next, write one of the subtraction exercises on the board. Repeat the process above with a different student. This time have the student select an expression from the **Ungrouping in Subtraction** list.

Repeat this process a few more times, alternating addition and subtraction exercises. Have the student choose a different phrase each time.

 Math Talk in Action

Jason: We have to add 159 + 267. What should we do first?

Jonelle: We add 9 ones plus 7 ones. That gives us 16 ones.

Kurt: 16 ones is the same as 10 ones and 6 ones. We can trade the 10 ones for a new ten.

Jason: I'm going to write the new 10 above the tens column and I'm going to write the 6 ones under the line in the ones column.

Jonelle: Now we add the 5 tens plus the 6 tens to get 11 tens.

Kurt: Don't forget to add the new ten! 11 tens plus 1 more makes 12 tens.

Jonelle: Now we can trade 10 tens for a new hundred and we have 2 tens left.

Jason: That's right. I'll write the 1 for the new hundred above the hundreds column and the 2 in the tens column under the line.

Jonelle: 1 hundred plus 2 hundreds plus the new hundred make 4 hundreds. I'll write the 4 in the hundreds column under the line.

Kurt: So 159 + 267 equals 426.

② Extending the Lesson

Going Further: Subtract Larger Numbers

Goal: Find differences involving numbers up to 10,000.

Materials: MathBoard materials

✔ **NCTM Standards:**
Number and Operations
Problem Solving
Communication

▶ Introduce Regrouping Thousands

WHOLE CLASS

Write 6,239 − 2,468 vertically on the board. Tell students to copy the subtraction on their MathBoards and make a proof drawing.

Give students a few minutes to complete the subtraction and proof drawing. Ask for two students to present their work. As they discuss their solutions, point out that they had to ungroup 1 thousand into 10 hundreds to find the answer.

▶ Subtract Larger Numbers PAIRS

Write the following word problems on the board.

A hippopotamus weighs 5,265 pounds. A giraffe weighs 3,418 pounds. How much heavier is the hippopotamus than the giraffe? 1,847 pounds

A great white shark weighs 7,684 pounds. A tiger shark weighs 1,990 pounds. How much heavier is the great white shark than the tiger shark? 5,694 pounds

A school district has 10,000 students. 2,385 were absent today. How many were at school? 7,615

Math Talk Have student pairs work together to complete the first problem. Give them a few minutes to complete the problem independently. Remind them to include a proof drawing.

Invite a student pair to the board to explain how they solved the problem.

As students discuss each step, make sure they understand the ungrouping that is involved.

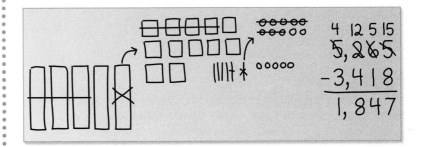

Have student pairs complete the two remaining problems. Then have volunteers come to the board to explain their work.

Teaching Note

Watch For! Walk around the room and observe students as they subtract. Watch for students who do not understand when to ungroup, or who forget to record the ungrouping. Use questioning to help students decide when to ungroup and to record regrouping. For example:

▶ Can you subtract the hundreds? Why not?

▶ How can you get more hundreds to subtract?

▶ What happens to the number of thousands when you ungroup 1 thousand and make 10 hundreds? How can you record this?

Intervention
for students having difficulty

PAIRS

Relate Partners and Totals

Materials: index cards (6 per pair), sticky notes

Write the following numbers on separate index cards:

217	226	443
180	465	645

Have pairs arrange the cards so that they show these two Math Mountains with partners and totals labeled on sticky notes.

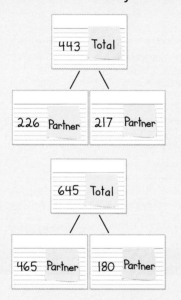

Next, students write the related addition and subtraction sentences for the Math Mountain.

On Level
for students having success

PAIRS

Related Stories

Materials: index cards (8 per pair)

Have each student write two 3-digit numbers on separate index cards. Have one student mix all of the cards and place them face down. Each student then selects two cards and uses the numbers on the cards to write an addition or subtraction word problem on another index card. Students exchange problems to solve. After they have solved the problem, students use the same numbers to write a related word problem using the opposite operation on another index card. Students exchange their problems again and check each other's work.

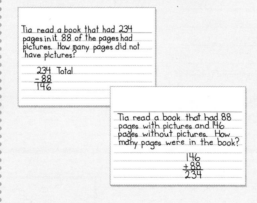

Challenge
for students seeking a challenge

PAIRS

Find the Partners

Write the following on the board:

- TOTAL = 875

  Rule: Make one partner odd, the other even

- TOTAL = 314

  Rule: Make a 2-digit and 3-digit partner

- TOTAL = 769

  Rule: Make partners with a difference of at least 300.

Using the rules on the board, have pairs work together to find partners for each total.

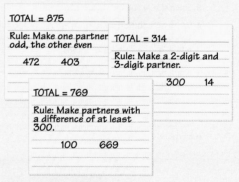

Students than find other partners for the total.

Also Use
Challenge Master for 1-13

 **Math Writing Prompt**

Intervention

Make Connections
How can you use addition to check subtraction? Use an example to explain your answer.

 Math Writing Prompt

On Level

Summarize
Explain how a Math Mountain can be used to show both adding and subtracting.

Math Writing Prompt

Challenge

What Are the Partners?
The total is $7.71 and the rule for the partners is that they have a difference of at least $2.00. Explain how you can find three different pairs of partners.

③ Homework and Spiral Review

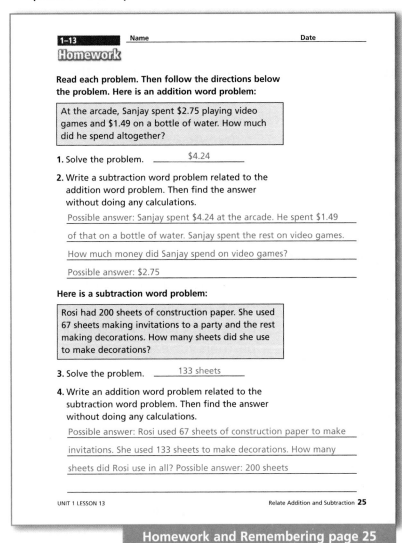

Homework Goal: Additional Practice

✔ Include students' completed Homework page as part of their portfolios.

1–13 Name _____ Date _____
Homework

Read each problem. Then follow the directions below the problem. Here is an addition word problem:

> At the arcade, Sanjay spent $2.75 playing video games and $1.49 on a bottle of water. How much did he spend altogether?

1. Solve the problem. _____ $4.24 _____

2. Write a subtraction word problem related to the addition word problem. Then find the answer without doing any calculations.

   Possible answer: Sanjay spent $4.24 at the arcade. He spent $1.49

   of that on a bottle of water. Sanjay spent the rest on video games.

   How much money did Sanjay spend on video games?

   Possible answer: $2.75

Here is a subtraction word problem:

> Rosi had 200 sheets of construction paper. She used 67 sheets making invitations to a party and the rest making decorations. How many sheets did she use to make decorations?

3. Solve the problem. _____ 133 sheets _____

4. Write an addition word problem related to the subtraction word problem. Then find the answer without doing any calculations.

   Possible answer: Rosi used 67 sheets of construction paper to make

   invitations. She used 133 sheets to make decorations. How many

   sheets did Rosi use in all? Possible answer: 200 sheets

UNIT 1 LESSON 13   Relate Addition and Subtraction **25**

Homework and Remembering page 25

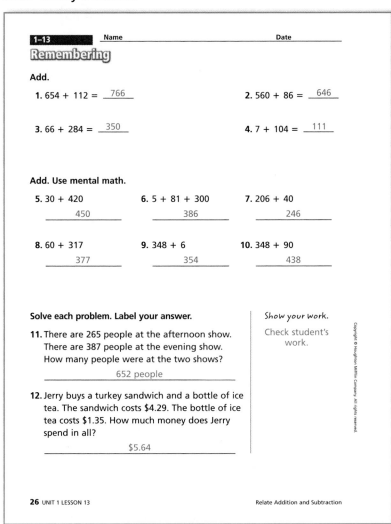

Remembering Goal: Spiral Review

This Remembering page would be appropriate anytime after today's lesson.

1–13 Name _____ Date _____
Remembering

Add.

1. 654 + 112 = ___766___   2. 560 + 86 = ___646___

3. 66 + 284 = ___350___   4. 7 + 104 = ___111___

Add. Use mental math.

5. 30 + 420   6. 5 + 81 + 300   7. 206 + 40
   ___450___   ___386___   ___246___

8. 60 + 317   9. 348 + 6   10. 348 + 90
   ___377___   ___354___   ___438___

Solve each problem. Label your answer.   *Show your work.*

11. There are 265 people at the afternoon show. There are 387 people at the evening show. How many people were at the two shows?
    _____ 652 people _____

12. Jerry buys a turkey sandwich and a bottle of ice tea. The sandwich costs $4.29. The bottle of ice tea costs $1.35. How much money does Jerry spend in all?
    _____ $5.64 _____

Check student's work.

26 UNIT 1 LESSON 13   Relate Addition and Subtraction

Homework and Remembering page 26

Home and School Activity

Science Connection

Migration Some birds live in Canada and in the United States during the summer. They travel south to Central and South America for the winter. This is called *migration*.

Display the migration distances table shown at the right. Explain that a Painted Bunting may fly anywhere from 300 to 3,000 miles when migrating. Have students write and solve addition and subtraction exercises based on the information in the table.

One-Way Migration Distances	
Bird	**Distance (miles)**
Lucy's Warbler	500 to 1,500
Painted Bunting	300 to 3,000
Wood Thrush	600 to 3,750

UNIT 1
LESSON
14

Subtraction Practice

Lesson Objective
- **Practice and discuss subtraction methods.**

Vocabulary
ungroup

The Day at a Glance

Today's Goals	Materials	Math Talk
Quick Practice Subtract hundreds. **1 Teaching the Lesson** **A1:** Solve and discuss subtraction word problems. **A2:** Create toy store ads and use them to practice addition and subtraction of money amounts. **2 Extending the Lesson** ▶ Differentiated Instruction **3 Homework and Spiral Review**	Quick Practice materials Crayons, colored pencils, or markers Index cards Game Cards Chart paper Student Activity Book pages 41–42 Homework and Remembering pages 27–28 Math Journals	In today's activities, the students are involved in discussion as they ▶ explore subtraction word problems ▶ practice addition and subtraction of money amounts

Quick Practice

⏱ **5 MINUTES** **Goal:** Subtract hundreds.
Materials: Demonstration Secret Code Cards
(Copymasters M3–M18)

Subtract Hundreds Have a Student Leader select the 1,000 card and the 300 card from the Demonstration Secret Code Cards. The Student Leader assembles the cards so the class can see a 4-digit number on the left and a number of hundreds on the right.

The leader then gives students a few seconds to mentally subtract the numbers, and says "Subtract." The class says the equation aloud. The leader then selects one student to illustrate the Make a Thousand strategy (see page 49). Repeat this activity several times, subtracting different hundreds from combinations of cards between 1,100 and 1,900.

Class Management

You may want to choose two Student Leaders. As one leads the class, the other can be selecting cards for the next exercise.

Teaching the Lesson

Discuss Subtraction Methods

 20 MINUTES

Goal: Solve and discuss subtraction word problems.

Materials: Student Activity Book pages 41–42

 NCTM Standards:
Number and Operations
Problem Solving
Communication

Class Management

If you would like to work with students needing extra help, use the **Solve and Discuss** structure for the first problem only. Then, work with the students experiencing difficulty at the board, while the remainder of the class completes the problems independently or in helping pairs.

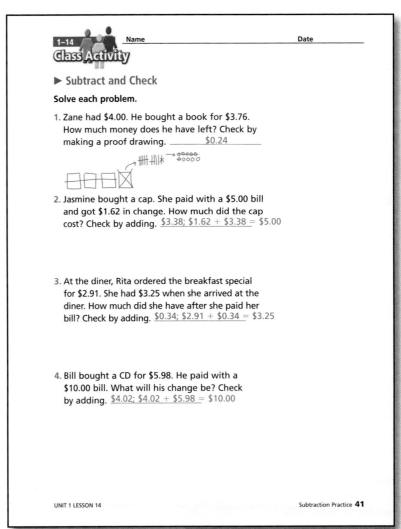

Student Activity Book page 41

▶ Subtract and Check WHOLE CLASS

Using the **Solve and Discuss** structure, have students solve the problems on Student Activity Book page 41. As presenters explain their work, tell other students to watch that students subtract the bottom number from the top number and to listen to the way the presenter uses place value language to describe the subtraction.

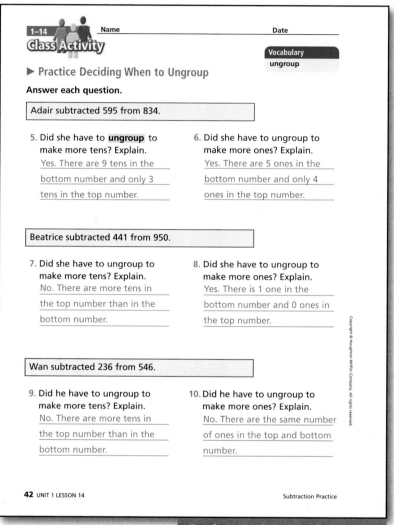

Student Activity Book page 42

▶ Practice Deciding When to Ungroup [WHOLE CLASS]

Direct students' attention to questions 5 and 6 on Student Activity Book page 42. Write the 834 − 595 on the board in vertical form. Ask a volunteer to answer questions 5 and 6. Student explanations should cover the following points:

● There are not enough tens to subtract 9 tens. So, students need to ungroup a hundred to make 10 tens.

● There are not enough ones to subtract 5 ones. So, students need to ungroup a ten to make 10 more ones.

Have students work independently to answer the rest of the questions. Invite volunteers to explain their answers.

Differentiated Instruction

Extra Help To help students focus on the subtraction process in each place, have students write each problem in a place value grid. Then tell them to use any method to subtract. Ask students who subtracted right to left the following questions:

▶ Are there enough ones to subtract? Do you need to ungroup a ten to make more ones?

▶ Are there enough tens to subtract? Do you need to ungroup a hundred to make more tens?

Ask students who subtracted left to right the following questions.

▶ Are there enough tens to subtract? Do you need to ungroup a hundred to make more tens?

▶ Are there enough ones to subtract? Do you need to ungroup a ten to make more ones?

Activity 2

Create and Use an Ad

 35 MINUTES

Goal: Create toy store ads and use them to practice addition and subtraction of money amounts.

Materials: Crayons, colored pencils, or markers for each pair of students, Homework and Remembering page 27

 NCTM Standards:
Number and Operations
Problem Solving

 Class Management

Looking Ahead Collect the students' completed toy store ads for use in Lesson 15.

 Ongoing Assessment

Discuss one day's toy store purchases with student pairs. Have students explain how they determined the change they would receive. Make sure students explain how they knew whether or not they needed to ungroup.

▶ **Create and Use a Toy Store Ad** PAIRS

Divide the class into pairs. Explain that each pair should pretend they run a toy store. Students will create an ad for a toy sale. The ad should have the name of the store at the top and a list of at least six different toys and their prices. Tell students that the sale price of each item should be between $1.00 and $6.00.

If time allows, have students decorate their ads using crayons, markers, or colored pencils (or have them do this for homework). If you do not want students to make their own ads, they can use the ad for Ted's Toy Town, which appears on the homework page for this lesson. See Homework and Remembering page 27.

▶ **Use an Ad** PAIRS

Tell students that they have a different amount to spend each day at the toy store. Write the amounts on the board.

Monday	$8.00
Tuesday	$7.00
Wednesday	$9.50
Thursday	$8.50
Friday	$9.00

Explain that for each day, the partners should choose at least two items they want to buy. They should add the prices for the items and figure out if they can afford another item or two. If so, they should add the item(s) to the list of items they already chose. When the list is complete, they should calculate the total cost and the amount of money they would have left after paying for all of the items.

As students work, walk around the room and provide help if needed.

Have pairs save their advertisements for use in the next lesson.

```
        K and L Toy Store
            Specials

Puzzles    $2.25 each
Block Set  $3.49
Pony       $3.97
Puppets    $2.89
Marker Set $1.88
Crayon Set $1.79
```

```
Have $9.50 to spend
              1 1
marker set  $1.88
   puppet +$2.89
            $4.77
     pony +$3.97
            $8.74
           8 4 10
Change  $9.50   Change is $.76
      - $8.74
        $0.76
```

② Extending the Lesson

Differentiated Instruction   Activities for Individualizing

Intervention
for students having difficulty

INDIVIDUALS

Compare Home Run Hitters

Materials: Chart paper

Display the following table on chart paper.

Some Famous Home Run Hitters	
Name	Home Runs
Hank Aaron	755
Hector Espino	484
Josh Gibson	962
Mickey Mantle	536
Sadaharu Oh	868
Babe Ruth	714

Tell students that no one knows exactly how many home runs Josh Gibson hit because records were not kept early in his career. So we will use the estimate of 962 home runs for the number of home runs he hit. People agree that he has the most home runs ever recorded over a career.

Have students use the data to determine how many more home runs Josh Gibson hit than four other players listed.

On Level
for students having success

PAIRS

Less is More

Materials: Index cards (4 per pair), Game Cards, (Copymaster M25)

Write the numbers 500, 476, 319, and 248 on separate index cards. One student mixes the index cards and places them in a stack face down. The other student mixes the game cards and deals 4 to each student.

To play, students turn over the top index card in the stack. Pairs then choose two of their game cards to form a 2-digit number. Pairs subtract the number they made from the 3-digit number. The student with the smallest difference wins the round and gets one point.

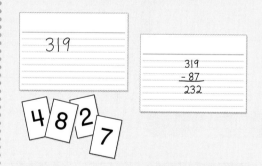

Students mix the game cards and repeat the activity until one student earns 5 points.

Challenge
for students seeking a challenge

PAIRS

Magic Square

Materials: Index cards (1 per pair)

Explain to students that in a magic square, the numbers in each row, column, and diagonal have the same sum. This is called the *magic sum*. Write on the board:

Magic Square		
276	115	
161		253
184	299	

Tell students to copy the magic square onto an index card and find the missing numbers.

Magic Square		
276	115	230
161	207	253
184	299	138

Also Use

Challenge Master for 1-14

 Math Writing Prompt

Intervention

How Do You Know?
Explain how you know when to ungroup in a subtraction problem.

 Math Writing Prompt

On Level

Summarize
Explain how you would solve $5.45 - $1.79. You may add a proof drawing to help you.

Math Writing Prompt

Challenge

Looking Back
Jerry took 162 pictures on his train trip to Florida and 128 pictures on the way back. Can he make two collages that each use 150 pictures? Explain.

③ Homework and Spiral Review

Homework **Goal:** Additional Practice

The Homework page gives students practice adding and subtracting money amounts.

1–14
Remembering **Goal:** Spiral Review

This Remembering page would be appropriate anytime after today's lesson.

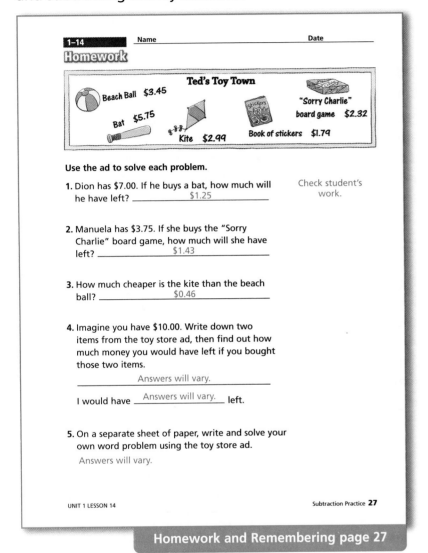

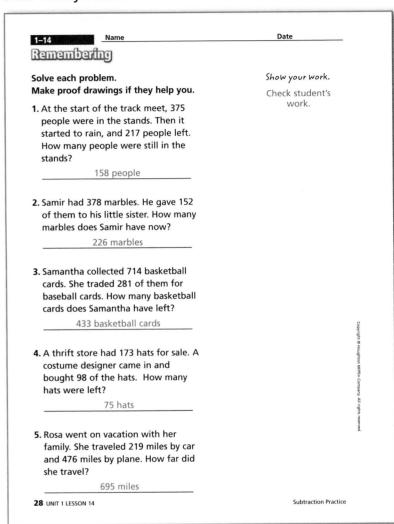

Home and School Activity

 Sports Connection

Baseball Ticket Prices Display the price list shown at the right. Explain that it shows the ticket prices for baseball games at Wrigley Field in Chicago in 1952. Discuss the difference between those prices and what tickets would cost today. In a recent year, tickets for a regular Chicago Cubs game at Wrigley Field cost between $14 and $40.

Have students use the price list to create and solve several addition and subtraction problems based on the price list.

Ticket Prices at Wrigley Field in 1952	
Adults	
Box Seats	$2.50
Grandstand	$1.25
Bleachers	$0.60
Children under 14	
Box Seats	$1.85
Grandstand	$0.60
Bleachers	$0.60

Addition and Subtraction Practice

Lesson Objectives
● **Practice and discuss addition and subtraction methods.**

The Day at a Glance

Today's Goals	Materials	Math Talk
Quick Practice Subtract hundreds.	Quick Practice materials	In today's activities, the students are involved in discussion as they
① Teaching the Lesson **A1:** Create and solve addition and subtraction word problems. **A2:** Use ads to practice addition and subtraction of money amounts.	Toy store ads from Lesson 14 Play money Index cards Paper bags	▶ talk about addition and subtraction problems
② Extending the Lesson ▶ Going Further: Choose a Computation Method. ▶ Differentiated Instruction	Calculators MathBoard materials Game Cards Student Activity Book pages 43–44	
③ Homework and Spiral Review	Homework and Remembering pages 29–30 Math Journals Quick Quiz 3 (Assessment Guide)	

Quick Practice

⏱ **5 MINUTES** **Goal:** Subtract hundreds.
Materials: Demonstration Secret Code Cards
(Copymasters M3–M18)

Subtract Hundreds Have a Student Leader select the 1,000 card and the 500 card from the Demonstration Secret Code Cards. The Student Leader assembles the cards so the class can see a 4-digit number on the left and a number of hundreds on the right.

The leader then gives students a few seconds to mentally subtract the numbers, and says "Subtract." The class says the equation aloud. The leader then selects one student to illustrate the Make a Thousand strategy. Repeat this activity several times, subtracting different hundreds from combinations of cards between 1,100 and 1,900.

Activity 1

Create and Solve Problems

 25 MINUTES

Goal: Create and solve addition and subtraction word problems.

✔ **NCTM Standards:**
Number and Operations
Problem Solving
Communication

The Learning Classroom

Math Talk When students discuss how they can solve an addition problem or a subtraction problem without doing any calculations, encourage them to use the words *partner* and *total* in their explanations. For example:

▶ The total is 900. When I subtract the partner 672, I get the other partner, 228.

▶ I start with the partner 717. When I add the other partner, 655, I get the total, 1,372.

 Class Management

Students will continue to solve problems using multi-digit addition and subtraction for the next two units. Give the unit test to see where your students are and what you might need to address in the next two units, but move on to Unit 2. Less-advanced students will begin to pull their place value and multi-digit concepts together over the next two units so that they are accurate and fluent. Be sure to discuss the top-from-bottom error if any students are making it, and be sure that those students are making the magnifying glass to inhibit that error in subtraction.

▶ **Use Math Mountains to Relate Addition and Subtraction** WHOLE CLASS

Write the numbers 672 and 228 on the board. Ask students to think of an addition word problem that has these numbers.

 Math Talk Choose a volunteer to share his or her word problem. Have students solve the problem, using the **Solve and Discuss** structure. Make a Math Mountain for the problem on the board, eliciting the partners and total from students. Then, have a volunteer write an addition and subtraction equation from the Math Mountain.

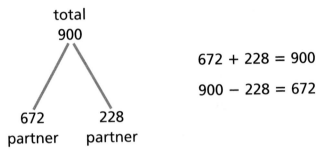

Ask students to think of a subtraction word problem that can be written based on this Math Mountain. Choose a volunteer to share his or her word problem. Then have a student explain how you can find the answer without doing any calculations.

Next, write the numbers 1,372 and 717 on the board. Ask if anyone can think of a subtraction word problem that has these numbers. Choose a volunteer to share his or her problem. Have students solve the problem, using the **Solve and Discuss** structure. Make a Math Mountain for the problem on the board, eliciting the partners and total from students. Then have a volunteer write a subtraction and addition equation from the Math Mountain.

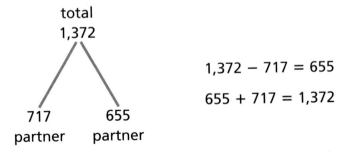

Ask students to think of an addition word problem that can be written based on this Math Mountain. Choose a volunteer to share his or her problem. Then have a student explain how you can find the answer without doing any calculations.

Repeat this process for two more pairs of numbers.

Use Ads to Practice Addition and Subtraction

▶ Add and Subtract Money Amounts PAIRS

Ask students to take out the toy store ads they made in Lesson 14. Have each pair trade ads with another pair.

Explain that, as before, students have a different amount to spend each day at the toy store. Write the following amounts on the board.

Monday	$10.00
Tuesday	$15.25
Wednesday	$16.00
Thursday	$18.50
Friday	$20.00

Explain that, just as they did in the previous lesson, partners should choose at least two items they want to buy each day. They should add the prices for the items and figure out if they can afford another item or two. If so, they should add the item(s) to the list of items that they already chose. When the list is complete, they should calculate the total cost and the amount of money they would have left after paying for all of the items.

As students work, walk around the room and provide help if needed.

🕐 **30 MINUTES**

Goal: Use ads to practice addition and subtraction of money amounts.

Materials: Toy store ads from Lesson 14

✔ **NCTM Standards:**
Number and Operations
Problem Solving

✋ Alternate Approach

Use Play Money Some students may benefit from using play money to check their computation. Provide students with play money. Review the value of each coin and bill before having students model the computation.

✓ Ongoing Assessment

Ask students to explain how addition and subtraction are related.

✓ Quick Quiz

See Assessment Guide for Unit 1 Quick Quiz 3.

Going Further: Choose a Computation Method

Goal: Choose a computation method to add or subtract.

Materials: Student Activity Book pages 43–44, calculators (1 per group of three students), index cards (6 per group) paper bags (1 per group)

 NCTM Standards:
Number and Operations
Problem Solving

▶ Add or Subtract Larger Numbers

WHOLE CLASS

Write the following exercises on the board.

516,219	326,324
+ 314,845	− 77,456
831,064	248,868

123 Math Talk Using the **Solve and Discuss** structure, have students solve the examples. Make sure volunteers explain the computation place-by-place, noting and recording all grouping and ungrouping.

Ask students if they had a choice of using a calculator or pencil and paper to add or subtract these exercises, which they would use. Sample response: A calculator. Why? It's faster.

Compare Computation Methods Discuss the uses of the three computation methods (mental math, pencil and paper, and calculator) by asking students the following questions.

● When would you use mental math to find the answer to an exercise? Give an example. Sample response: When you add two numbers that are easy to add such as 150 + 20.

● Would you use pencil and paper or a calculator to find the answer to 428,965 − 325,941? Why? Sample response: A calculator because the numbers are large.

● When would you use pencil and paper instead of a calculator to find the answer? Give an example. Sample response: When the numbers are in the tens, hundreds, or thousands such as 267 + 986.

▶ Choose Mental Math, Pencil and Paper, or Calculator INDIVIDUALS

Direct students' attention to Student Activity Book page 43. Read aloud the directions. Make sure students understand that for problems 1–12, they are to record the method they will use, then complete the computation.

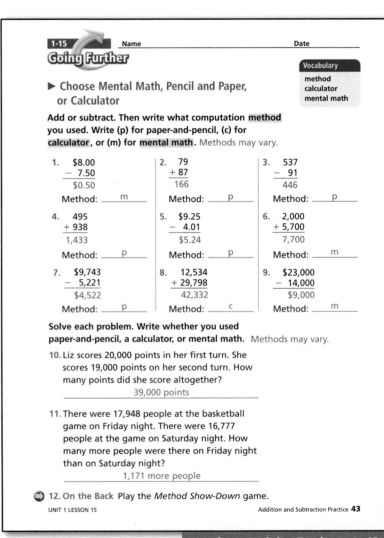

Student Activity Book page 43

Intervention
for students having difficulty

PAIRS

Help Yourself!

Materials: MathBoard materials

Have students write a 4-digit number on their MathBoards. Pairs add the two numbers and compare totals. If the totals do not match, have students work together to find the error.

Next, have students subtract the smaller number from the larger number to find the difference. If the differences do not match, students work together to find the error.

On Level
for students having success

SMALL GROUPS

Pass the Arithmetic

Materials: Index cards (1 per student), paper bags (1 per group)

Each student writes a 5-digit addition or subtraction on an index card. Then they place the cards in a paper bag.

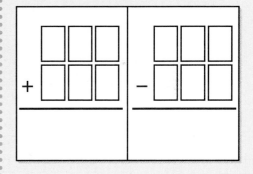

Each student picks a card from the bag and then adds or subtracts the ones place (or subtracts the ten-thousands place). Then each student passes the card to the student on the right so that the next student in the group can add or subtract the next place. Students continue in this manner until each exercise is completed. Pass the card once more so that students can check the completed exercise.

Challenge
for students seeking a challenge

PAIRS

Use Only Once!

Materials: Game Cards (Copymaster M25)

Have students use the Game Cards to make addition and subtraction exercises. Students may use each number card only one time per exercise. The goal is to form two 3-digit numbers that will result in:

- the least sum
- the greatest sum
- the least difference
- the greatest difference

Also Use
Challenge Master for 1-15

 Math Writing Prompt

Intervention

You Decide
Write an addition word problem for this equation:
$315 + 277 = 592$.

 Math Writing Prompt

On Level

Real Life Experience
Think of a time outside of school when you or someone you were with needed to add or subtract. Describe the situation.

 Math Writing Prompt

Challenge

Find the Rule
What is the next number in the pattern? 25, 51, 77, 93, ____. Explain how you know.

③ Homework and Spiral Review

1–15 Homework Goal: Additional Practice

This Homework page provides practice in addition and subtraction.

1–15 Homework

Name _____ Date _____

Solve.

1. Write and solve an addition word problem that has the numbers 268 and 487.

   _____ Answers will vary. _____

   _____

   _____

2. Write and solve a subtraction word problem that has the numbers 194 and 526.

   _____ Answers will vary. _____

   _____

   _____

3. The yearbook staff took a total of 1,005 photographs. They used 487 of the photographs in the yearbook. How many of the photographs were not used?

   _____ 518 photographs _____

4. Mr. Pinsky has to read a 362-page book for his book club. He read the first 129 pages last week. This week he has read 153 pages. How many pages does he have left to read?

   _____ 80 pages _____

5. Josh had $9.00 in his pocket when he left the house this morning. He spent $1.75 on bus fare and $3.48 on lunch. How much does he have left?

   _____ $3.77 _____

UNIT 1 LESSON 15   Addition and Subtraction Practice **29**

Homework and Remembering page 29

1–15 Remembering Goal: Spiral Review

This Remembering page would be appropriate anytime after today's lesson.

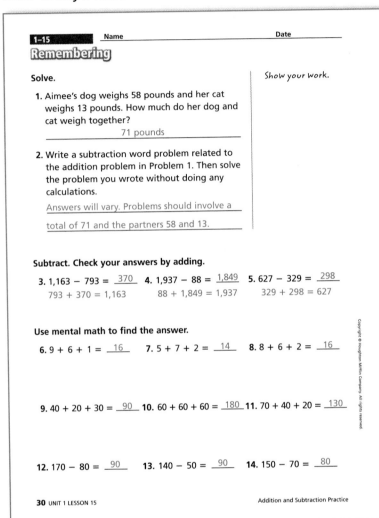

1–15 Remembering

Name _____ Date _____

Solve.   Show your work.

1. Aimee's dog weighs 58 pounds and her cat weighs 13 pounds. How much do her dog and cat weigh together?

   _____ 71 pounds _____

2. Write a subtraction word problem related to the addition problem in Problem 1. Then solve the problem you wrote without doing any calculations.

   Answers will vary. Problems should involve a

   total of 71 and the partners 58 and 13.

Subtract. Check your answers by adding.

3. $1,163 - 793 = \underline{370}$ 4. $1,937 - 88 = \underline{1,849}$ 5. $627 - 329 = \underline{298}$

   $793 + 370 = 1,163$ $88 + 1,849 = 1,937$ $329 + 298 = 627$

Use mental math to find the answer.

6. $9 + 6 + 1 = \underline{16}$ 7. $5 + 7 + 2 = \underline{14}$ 8. $8 + 6 + 2 = \underline{16}$

9. $40 + 20 + 30 = \underline{90}$ 10. $60 + 60 + 60 = \underline{180}$ 11. $70 + 40 + 20 = \underline{130}$

12. $170 - 80 = \underline{90}$ 13. $140 - 50 = \underline{90}$ 14. $150 - 70 = \underline{80}$

30 UNIT 1 LESSON 15   Addition and Subtraction Practice

Homework and Remembering page 30

Home and School Activity

Social Studies Connection

Where Can You Find 100? Have students list places and situations where they might see more than 100 people at a time. Have students write a short paragraph that describes one of these places or situations. Then ask students to write and solve an addition or subtraction word problem using the paragraph they wrote.

> Places with More than 100 People
>
> circus
> basketball game
> airplane
> concert
> train

Unit Review and Test

Lesson Objective

● **Assess student progress on unit objectives.**

The Day at a Glance

Today's Goals	Materials
Quick Practice Review any skills you choose to meet the needs of your students.	Unit 1 Test, Student Activity Book pages 45–46
1 Assessing the Unit ▶ Assess student progress on unit objectives. ▶ Use activities from unit lessons to reteach content.	Unit 1 Test, Form A or B, Assessment Guide (optional)
2 Extending the Assessment ▶ Use remediation for common errors.	Unit 1 Performance Assessment, Assessment Guide (optional)
There is no homework assignment on a test day.	

Quick Practice

 5 MINUTES   **Goal:** Review any skills you choose to meet the needs of your students

If you are doing a unit review day, use any of the Quick Practice activities that provide support for your students. If this is a test day, omit Quick Practice.

 Class Management

Review and Test Day You may want to choose a quiet game or other activity (reading a book or working on homework for another subject) for students who finish early.

Assessing the Unit

Assess Unit Objectives

45 MINUTES (more if schedule permits)

Goal: Assess student progress on unit objectives.

Materials: Student Activity Book pages 45–46; Assessment Guide Unit 1 Test Form A or B (optional), Assessment Guide Unit 1 Performance Assessment (optional)

▶ Review and Assessment

If your students are ready for assessment on the unit objectives, you may use either the test on the Student Activity Book pages or one of the forms of the Unit 1 Test in the Assessment Guide to assess student progress.

If you feel that students need some review first, you may use the test on the Student Activity Book pages as a review of unit content, and then use one of the forms of the Unit 1 Test in the Assessment Guide to assess student progress.

To assign a numerical score for all of these test forms, use 5 points for each question.

You may also choose to use the Unit 1 Performance Assessment. Scoring for that assessment can be found in its rubric in the Assessment Guide.

▶ Reteaching Resources

The chart at the right lists the test items, the unit objectives they cover, and the lesson activities in which the objective is covered in this unit. You may revisit these activities with students who do not show mastery of the objectives.

Unit Test

Name _____ Date _____

Make a place value drawing for each number.

1. 57

2. 392

Unscramble the place values and write the number.

3. 9 ones + 6 hundreds + 4 tens _____ 649

4. 5 hundreds + 2 ones + 3 tens _____ 532

5. 5 ones + 7 hundreds + 1 thousand + 6 tens _____ 1,765

6. 8 tens + 4 ones + 0 hundreds + 1 thousand _____ 1,084

Write the number for the words.

7. eight hundred seventy-two _____ 872

8. five hundred four _____ 504

9. one thousand fifty _____ 1,050

Add or subtract.

10. 435 + 283 = _____ 718

11. 962 − 87 = _____ 875

UNIT 1   Test **45**

Student Activity Book page 45

Unit Test Items	Unit Objectives Tested	Activities to Use for Reteaching
1–9, 20	**1.1** Read, write, identify, and represent the place value of whole numbers.	Lesson 1, Activity 2 Lesson 4, Activity 1 Lesson 3, Activity 2
10–14	**1.2** Add and subtract whole numbers.	Lesson 5, Activity 2 Lesson 6, Activity 2 Lesson 8, Activity 1 Lesson 10, Activity 1 Lesson 11, Activity 1 Lesson 12, Activities 1 and 2

Student Activity Book page 46

Unit Test

Name _____ Date _____

Add or subtract. Use extra paper if you need it.

12.	13.	14.
972	617	800
+ 129	− 549	− 684
1,101	68	116

15.	16.	17.
$3.29	$5.31	$10.00
+ 5.98	− 0.32	− 7.54
$9.27	$4.99	$2.46

18. Gordon baked 346 blueberry muffins and 287 bran muffins. How many muffins did he bake in all?

633 muffins

19. Write a subtraction word problem related to the addition word problem in problem 18. Then find the answer without doing any calculations.

Possible answer: Gordon baked 633 muffins. He baked 346 blueberry muffins and the rest were bran muffins. How many were bran muffins? (287 bran muffins)

20. **Extended Response** Veronica has 423 baseball cards. She put them in piles of 10 cards each.

How many piles of 10 cards did she make? 42 piles

How many extra cards did she have? 3 cards

Explain your reasoning. Possible answer: Four hundreds is the same as 40 tens. 40 tens plus 2 tens make 42 tens. There are 3 ones in 423, so there are 3 cards left over.

46 UNIT 1   Test

Unit Test Items	Unit Objectives Tested	Activities to Use for Reteaching
15–17	**1.3** Add and subtract money amounts.	Lesson 7, Activity 2
18, 19	**1.4** Write a related subtraction word problem for an addition problem and vice versa.	Lesson 13, Activity 1

▶ Assessment Resources

Free Response Tests
Unit 1 Test, Student Activity Book pages 45–46
Unit 1 Test, Form A, Assessment Guide

Extended Response Item
The last item in the Student Activity Book test and in the Form A test will require an extended response as an answer.

Multiple Choice Test
Unit 1 Test, Form B, Assessment Guide

Performance Assessment
Unit 1 Performance Assessment, Assessment Guide
Unit 1 Performance Assessment Rubric, Assessment Guide

▶ Portfolio Assessment

Teacher-Selected Items for Student Portfolios:

- Homework, Lessons 3, 4, 10, 11, and 13
- Class Activity work, Lessons 6, 7, and 14

Student-Selected Items for Student Portfolios:

- Favorite Home or School Activity
- Best Writing Prompt

② Extending the Assessment

Unit Objective 1.1
Read, write, identify, and represent the place value of whole numbers.

Common Error: Omits Zeros

Given the word form of a number, students may sometimes omit one or more zeros when writing the standard form of the number.

Remediation Use Secret Code Cards to make numbers including numbers with zeros.

Unit Objective 1.2
Add and subtract whole numbers.

Common Error: Incorrect Alignment

When writing an addition or subtraction exercise vertically, some students may not align the places correctly; for example:

$$\begin{array}{r} 267 \\ +\ 32 \\ \hline \end{array} \quad \text{instead of} \quad \begin{array}{r} 267 \\ +\ 32 \\ \hline \end{array}$$

Remediation Have students complete their computations in a place value chart or on grid paper.

Common Error: Does Not Group or Ungroup Correctly

Some students make errors when forming new groups in addition or ungrouping in subtraction.

Remediation Distribute base ten blocks and ask students to act out the grouping or ungrouping in each place. Assign a helping partner to help with the student's chosen method. Use proof drawings (Step-by-Step) with the numerical method.

Unit Objective 1.3
Add and subtract money amounts.

Common Error: Difficulty Grouping or Ungrouping

Some students make grouping or ungrouping errors when adding or subtracting money amounts.

Remediation Remind students that even though they are adding and subtracting money amounts, the computations are completed in the same way as whole number computations. For some students, computations with money may be simpler if the numbers are aligned vertically by place value and the decimal point is written in the answer before the answer is found.

Common Error: Does Not Align Decimals

Students may add or subtract money amounts incorrectly because they have misaligned decimal points and place values.

Remediation Have students align the decimals and digits using a place value chart or grid paper.

Common Error: Does Not Record the Decimal Point in the Answer

Students may neglect to write the decimal point when adding money amounts.

Remediation Encourage students to write the decimal point first, before completing the computation.

Unit Objective 1.4
Write a related subtraction word problem for an addition problem and vice versa.

Common Error: Difficulty Deciding Whether to Add or to Subtract

Students may have difficulty determining if a word problem involves addition or subtraction.

Remediation Have students use blocks to act out a problem. As they take various actions, work with them to make the connection to addition or to subtraction by asking questions such as,

- Are you putting groups together? Putting groups together means you are adding.
- Are you separating a group into parts? Separating groups means you are subtracting.
- Are you taking some away? Taking away means you are subtracting.
- Are you comparing numbers? Comparing means you are subtracting.

Common Error: Cannot Explain Why an Operation was Chosen

Students may have difficulty explaining why a word problem involves addition or subtraction

Remediation Have students make up addition and subtraction problems. Reinforce the language of operations by posing questions similar to the questions above. Have students make lists of words that mean to add or to subtract.

Lines, Line Segments, and Quadrilaterals

UNIT A BUILDS UPON the conceptual understanding of linear measurement and the properties of quadrilaterals students developed in previous grade levels. In this unit, students name, sort, and classify quadrilaterals using quadrilateral names and describe them using geometric terms. Students are expected to apply their understanding of attributes of quadrilaterals to find perimeters of squares and rectangles without measuring all four sides.

Planning Unit A

See pages xvii and xviii for a list of unit materials and manipulatives that are available in the *Math Expressions* Kit.

Lesson Title	Lesson Resources	Materials and Manipulatives	
		Math Expressions	Other
1 Measure Line Segments and Perimeters of Figures	Family Letter Student Activity Book pages 47–52 Homework and Remembering pages 31–32	MathBoard materials, Centimeter rulers or Centimeter Rulers (Copymaster M26), Pattern Blocks (Copymaster M27)	Scissors, blank transparency (optionals), transparent ruler (optional), overhead projector (optional), overhead transparency of Student Activity Book page 47 (optional), Math Journals
2 Parallel and Perpendicular Lines and Line Segments	Student Activity Book pages 53–56 Homework and Remembering pages 33–34	Centimeter rulers, Centimeter Dot Paper (Copymaster M28), MathBoard materials, Pattern Blocks (Copymaster M27), Venn Diagram (Copymaster M29)	Geoboards and rubber bands, Math Journals
3 Parallelograms, Rectangles, Squares, and Rhombuses	Student Activity Book pages 57–64 Homework and Remembering pages 35–36	Centimeter rulers, Tangrams (Copymaster M30)	Scissors, Math Journals, *Grandfather Tang's Story* by Ann Tompert (Bantam Doubleday Dell Books for Young Readers, 1997)
4 Draw Parallelograms and Rectangles	Student Activity Book pages 65–66 Homework and Remembering pages 37–38	Centimeter rulers, Centimeter Grid Paper, (Copymaster M31), Pattern Blocks (Copymaster M27)	Scissors, Math Journals, paper
5 Classify Quadrilaterals	Student Activity Book pages 67–68 Homework and Remembering pages 39–40	Centimeter rulers, Venn Diagram (Copymaster M29), Quadrilaterals (Copymaster M32), Mathboard materials	Scissors, sheet protectors, dry-erase markers, geoboards and rubber bands, pencils, straws, Math Journals, *Squares and Cubes* by Sally Morgan (Thomson Learning, 1994)
Unit Review and Test	Student Activity Book pages 69–70 Assessment Guide		

Unit A Assessment

✓ Unit Objectives Tested	Unit Test Items	Lessons
A.1 Measure and draw line segments to the nearest centimeter and find the perimeter of geometric figures.	1, 2	1, 3
A.2 Identify lines and line segments.	3, 4, 9, 10	2
A.3 Identify and classify quadrilaterals.	5–8	3, 5

Formal Assessment	Informal Assessment	Review Opportunities
Open or Free Response Tests • Unit Review and Test (Student Activity Book pages 69–70, Teacher's Guide pages 159–162) • Unit A Test Form A (Assessment Guide) • Unit A Open Response Test (Test Generator) • Test Bank Items for Unit A (Test Generator) **Multiple Choice Tests** • Unit A Test Form B (Assessment Guide) • Unit A Multiple Choice Test (Test Generator) • Test Bank Items for Unit A (Test Generator) **Performance Tasks** • Unit A Performance Assessment (Assessment Guide)	**Ongoing Assessment** • In every Teacher's Guide lesson **Performance Assessment** • Class discussions • Small-group work • Individual work on teacher-selected tasks **Portfolios** • See Unit A Review and Test for suggestions for selecting items for portfolios. • Some Homework pages are noted as suitable for portfolio inclusion.	**Homework and Remembering** • Homework pages provide review of recently taught topics. • Remembering pages provide spiral review. **Teacher's Guide** • Unit Review and Test (pages 159–162) **Test Generator CD-ROM** • Test Bank Items can be used to create custom review sheets.

Unit A Teaching Resources

Differentiated Instruction

Reaching All Learners

English Learners
Lesson 2, page 134

Extra Help
Lesson 1, page 128
Lesson 4, page 149

Individualizing Instruction

Activities
• Intervention (in every lesson)
• On Level (in every lesson)
• Challenge (in every lesson)

Math Writing Prompts
• Intervention (in every lesson)
• On Level (in every lesson)
• Challenge (in every lesson)

Challenge Masters
• (for every lesson)

Cross-Curricular Links • Home or School Activities

 Sports Connection
Lines Around You (Lesson 2, page 138)

 Art Connection
Picture Frames (Lesson 4, page 152)

 Social Studies Connection
Quadrilaterals in Architecture (Lesson 5, page 158)

 Literature Connection
Grandfather Tang's Story (Lesson 3, page 146)

Teaching Unit A

Putting Research into Practice for Unit A

From Current Research: Properties of Quadrilaterals

Learning mathematics involves accumulating ideas and building successively deeper and more refined understanding. A school mathematics curriculum should provide a road map that helps teachers guide students to increasing levels of sophistication and depths of knowledge. Such guidance requires a well-articulated curriculum so that teachers at each level understand the mathematics that has been studied by students at the previous level and what is to be the focus at successive levels. For example, in grades K–2 students typically explore similarities and differences among two-dimensional shapes. In grades 3–5 they can identify characteristics of various quadrilaterals. In grades 6–8 they may examine and make generalizations about properties of particular quadrilaterals. In grades 9–12 they may develop logical arguments to justify conjectures about particular polygons. As they reach higher levels, students should engage more deeply with mathematical ideas and their understanding and ability to use the knowledge is expected to grow.

National Council of Teachers of Mathematics. *Principles and Standards for School Mathematics.* Reston: NCTM, 2000. p. 15.

The Use of Tools

The study of geometry in grades 3–5 requires thinking *and* doing. As students sort, build, draw, model, trace, measure, and construct, their capacity to visualize geometric relationships will develop. At the same time they are learning to reason and to make, test, and justify conjectures about these relationships. This exploration requires access to a variety of tools, such as graph paper, rulers, pattern blocks, geoboards, and geometric solids, and is greatly enhanced by electronic tools that support exploration, such as dynamic geometry software.

National Council of Teachers of Mathematics. *Principles and Standards for School Mathematics.* Reston: NCTM, 2000. p. 165.

Other Useful References: Measurement, 2-D Shapes, Perimeter

Batista, Michael. T. "Learning Geometry in a Dynamic Computer Environment." *Teaching Children Mathematics.* 8.6 (Feb. 2002): p. 333.

National Council of Teachers of Mathematics. *Principles and Standards for School Mathematics* (Number and Operations Standard for Grades 3–5). Reston: NCTM, 2000. pp. 97, 103–105.

Math Background

Concept Building Activities

Linear Measurement In this unit, students are provided with an opportunity to further develop their skills in linear measurement. Using centimeter rulers, students will measure line segments and draw line segments with specified lengths. In the previous grade, the idea that linear measurement involves counting the number of times a standard unit fits along a length was developed. In this unit, students draw a collection of line segments from 1 cm to 6 cm marked in 1-cm lengths and then compare the line segments to a ruler to reinforce this idea.

Attributes of Quadrilaterals In previous grades, students investigated the properties of rectangles, squares, and parallelograms, with students primarily using their own vocabulary to describe the properties of these quadrilaterals. In this unit, the rhombus is added to the list of quadrilaterals and students see, hear, and use specialized vocabulary like *parallel, perpendicular, opposite,* and *adjacent* in descriptions of quadrilaterals. To help clarify the relationships between the different quadrilaterals, students draw, name, sort, and classify them. Activities include using a Venn diagram as a graphic organizer to sort quadrilaterals according to attributes or names or both. In this grade, students are expected to increase their knowledge about how geometric shapes are related to one another and begin to articulate geometric arguments about the properties of these shapes.

Perimeter In lessons 1, 3, and 4 of Unit A, students will calculate the perimeter of quadrilaterals and triangles using informal methods. In the previous grades, class discussion identified that only one side measure is needed to find the perimeter of a square. In this unit, students identify that opposite sides of a rectangle are equal, and students are expected to apply this knowledge to find the perimeter of a rectangle with only two side measures. Calculating perimeters of squares and rectangles with the least number of side measures is a goal of this unit, providing the conceptual foundation for formula development in subsequent years.

In lesson 4, students will draw rectangles for given perimeters and begin to look at the relationships between dimensions and perimeter of rectangles.

MINI UNIT A

LESSON

1

Measure Line Segments and Perimeters of Figures

Lesson Objectives

- Measure lengths to the nearest centimeter.
- Draw line segments of given lengths.
- Find perimeters of triangles and quadrilaterals.

Vocabulary

centimeter
line segment
horizontal
vertical
perimeter
triangle
quadrilateral

The Day at a Glance

Today's Goals	Materials	123 Math Talk
1 Teaching the Lesson A1: Measure and draw line segments of given lengths. A2: Find the perimeters of triangles and quadrilaterals. **2 Extending the Lesson** ▶ Differentiated Instruction **3 Homework and Spiral Review**	Centimeter rulers or Centimeter Rulers (Copymaster M26) Scissors Blank transparency, transparent ruler, and overhead projector (optional) Overhead transparency of Student Activity Book page 47 (optional) MathBoard materials Pattern blocks or Pattern Blocks (Copymaster M27) Student Activity Book pages 47–52 Homework and Remembering pages 31–32 Math Journals Family Letter	In today's activities, the students are involved in discussion as they ▶ use rulers to measure and draw line segments ▶ measure the perimeter of a geometric figure

① Teaching the Lesson

Draw and Measure Line Segments

 20 MINUTES

Goal: Measure and draw line segments of given lengths.

Materials: Centimeter rulers (2 per student) or Centimeter Rulers (Copymaster M26) printed on card stock, scissors (1 pair per student), blank transparency, transparent ruler, and overhead projector (optional), overhead transparency of Student Activity Book pages 47–48 (optional)

 NCTM Standard:
Measurement

▶ Discuss Measuring with a Ruler

WHOLE CLASS

Distribute rulers to each student. If you do not have centimeter rulers, use Copymaster M26 and give students 2 horizontal and 2 vertical rulers. Students can keep 2 rulers in school and take 2 rulers home. Emphasize that they should find a safe place to keep their rulers at home, as they will need them throughout the year.

● For what do we use rulers for? to draw straight lines; to measure things

Tell students that these rulers are used to measure lengths in centimeters. Explain that the distance between any two numbered marks is 1 cm.

 Class Management

If you have access to the *Math Expressions* Materials Kit, the Centimeter Rulers are included, so you will not have to prepare these materials.

On a blank transparency or the board, draw 1-cm, 2-cm, 3-cm, 4-cm, 5-cm, and 6-cm horizontal lengths directly beneath one another. At the end of each line segment, write its length. Have students do the same on a sheet of paper at their desks.

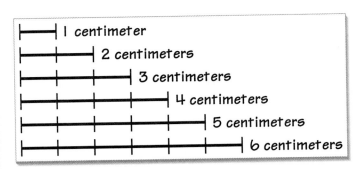

Ask students to imagine what it would look like if they could draw these line segments right on top of one another (they would create a ruler). Emphasize that each number on the ruler refers to the number of 1-cm lengths from the left edge of the ruler to that point.

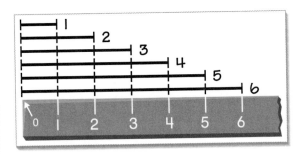

Teaching Note

Language and Vocabulary When you discuss the exercises in this section, use the term *line segment* rather than *line*. Students will learn the difference between a line and a line segment in Lesson 2.

▶Measure Line Segments [WHOLE CLASS]

Display a transparency of Student Activity Book page 47. Invite a volunteer to demonstrate how to find the length of the line segment in exercise 1 while other students follow on their pages. Emphasize that the 0-cm mark on the ruler should be lined up with one end of the line segment. The other end of the line segment will be at the 10-cm mark, so the line segment is about 10 cm long.

Not to scale

Have students look at the line segment in exercise 2.

● How is this line segment different from the one in exercise 1? It goes up and down; the first one went side to side.

Review the terms *horizontal* (a line segment that goes straight "across," like the line segment in exercise 1) and *vertical* (a line segment that goes straight "up and down," like the one in exercise 2).

Have a volunteer demonstrate how to measure the line segment in exercise 2. Remind students to line up the 0-cm mark on the ruler with one end of the line segment.

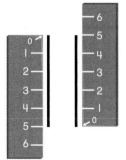

Not to scale

Have the student volunteer report the length. 5 cm

Invite another volunteer to measure the line segment in exercise 3 for the class, while other students

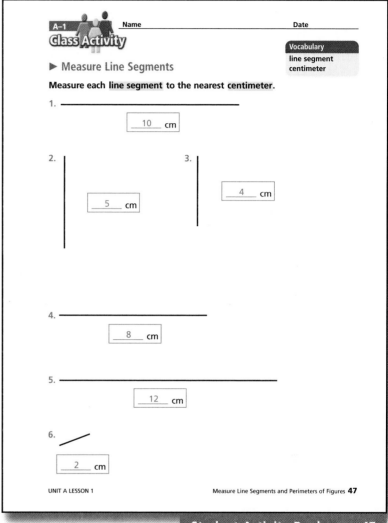

measure on their page. Point out that the right end of the line segment falls between the 8-cm mark and the 9-cm mark on the ruler.

● The directions say to measure to the nearest centimeter. What do you think this means? Find the centimeter measurement the length is closest to.

● Is the right end of the line segment closer to the 8-cm mark or the 9-cm mark? the 8-cm mark

● So, what is the length of the line segment to the nearest centimeter? 8 cm

Have students complete page 47, and discuss their answers.

Activity continued ▶

Measure Line Segments and Perimeters of Figures **127**

❶ Activity 1 (continued)

▶ Draw Line Segments of Given Lengths [INDIVIDUALS]

Have students look at Student Activity Book page 48. Invite a volunteer to come to the overhead or the board to draw the line segment in exercise 7, while the rest of the students work at their desks. Tell students not to worry if their line segments are not exactly horizontal. Emphasize that students should start at the 0-cm mark and draw, with their pencils against the ruler, until they get to the 7-cm mark. Provide assistance if necessary.

Have students complete exercises 8–11. Students' line segments do not need to be exactly horizontal or vertical.

Differentiated Instruction

Extra Help If students have trouble drawing and measuring at the same time, suggest that they start by drawing a line segment longer than the specified length. They can then mark off the correct length and erase the extra length.

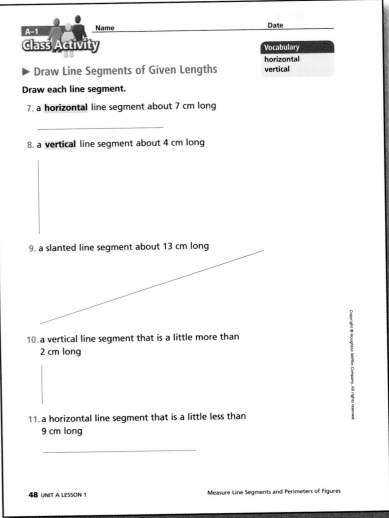

Student Activity Book page 48

 Ongoing Assessment

Have students work in pairs to measure and record the lengths of common small objects in the classroom, such as pencils, books, and erasers. If two students get different measurements, ask them to measure again and explain why their measurements were different.

Find Perimeters

 25 MINUTES

Goal: Find the perimeters of triangles and quadrilaterals.

Materials: Student Activity Book pages 49–50, centimeter rulers (1 per student)

 NCTM Standards:
Measurement
Geometry

▶ Measure the Perimeter of a Triangle

WHOLE CLASS

Ask a volunteer to explain what the perimeter of a figure is. Make sure students understand that the perimeter is the distance around a figure. Refer students to Student Activity Book page 49 and have them focus on the triangle in exercise 12.

● This figure is a triangle. What is a triangle? a figure with three sides

● How many line segments will you have to measure to find the perimeter of a triangle? 3

● How can you find the perimeter of this triangle? Find the length of each side and then add the three lengths.

Give students a few minutes to find the perimeter. Suggest that they label each side with its length so they can keep track of their measurements. Invite a student to the board to explain how he or she found the perimeter.

Have students find the perimeter of the other triangles on the page and encourage them to discuss the results.

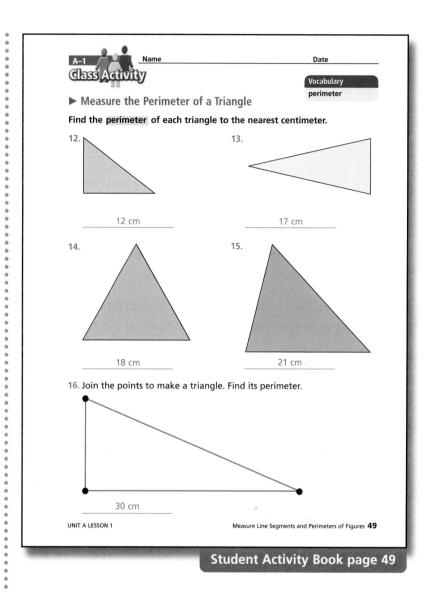

Student Activity Book page 49

Language and Vocabulary

Perimeter—"rim" of the shape—compare to rim of glass as being distance around the opening.

Activity continued ▶

▶ Measure the Perimeter of a Quadrilateral WHOLE CLASS

Direct students' attention to the figures on Student Activity Book page 50. Point out that these figures are quadrilaterals.

● What is a quadrilateral? a figure with 4 sides

● Look at exercise 17. What is another name for this quadrilateral? a rectangle

● A rectangle is a special kind of quadrilateral. Look at exercise 18. What is another name for this quadrilateral? a square

● A square is also a special kind of quadrilateral. Does the figure in exercise 19 have a special name? no

Have students find the perimeter of the quadrilaterals, and then discuss the results. As part of the discussion, you might ask questions like the following:

● When you measured the sides of the square, what did you notice? All the sides are the same length.

● When you measured the sides of the rectangle, what did you notice? The opposite sides are the same length.

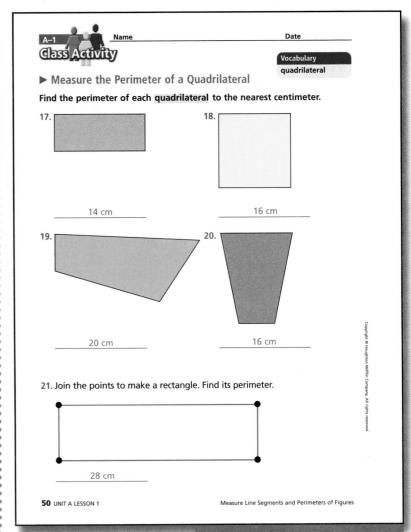

Student Activity Book page 50

The Learning Classroom

Building Concepts Students will look more closely at squares and rectangles in Lesson 3. In that lesson, students learn the important attributes of parallelograms, rectangles, and squares, and explore the relationships among these figures.

② Extending the Lesson

Activities for Individualizing

Intervention
for students having difficulty

INDIVIDUALS

Draw New Line Segments

Materials: Student Activity Book page 48, centimeter rulers (1 per student), MathBoard materials

Students read the instructions on Student Activity Book page 48. On their Mathboards, they draw new line segments of the same lengths, but in different positions.

For example:

- Draw a vertical line segment the same length as the line segment in exercise 1.

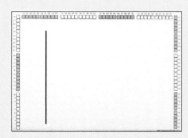

Next, students compare their line segments with the ones they drew on the Student Activity Book page to make sure they are the same length.

On Level
for students having success

PAIRS

Estimate Perimeter

Materials: centimeter rulers (1 per student), pattern blocks or Pattern Blocks (Copymaster M27)

Students examine each of the blocks in a set of pattern blocks and estimate which has the greatest perimeter and which has the smallest perimeter. Students measure the perimeters to check their answers.

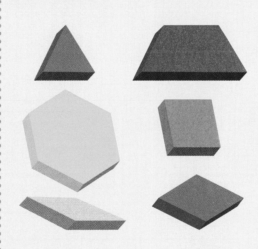

Challenge
for students seeking a challenge

PAIRS

Draw a Triangle

Materials: centimeter rulers (1 per student), MathBoard materials

Students draw at least four triangles with one side 7 cm long and one side 9 cm long.

- How long is the third side to the nearest centimeter?
- What is the perimeter of the triangle?

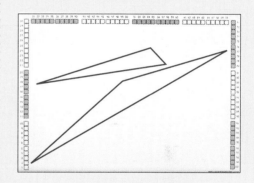

Also Use
Challenge Master for A-1

 Math Writing Prompt

Intervention

Define Perimeter
How can the word *rim* inside the word *perimeter* help you to remember what perimeter means?

 Math Writing Prompt

On Level

Explain Your Thinking
How can you use a single piece of string to measure the perimeter of a figure?

 Math Writing Prompt

Challenge

Investigate Math
Try to draw a triangle with sides that are 5 cm, 5 cm, and 15 cm long. Describe what happens.

③ Homework and Spiral Review

Homework **Goal:** Additional Practice

On this Homework page, students find the perimeters of triangles and quadrilaterals.

Remembering **Goal:** Spiral Review

This Remembering activity is appropriate anytime after today's lesson.

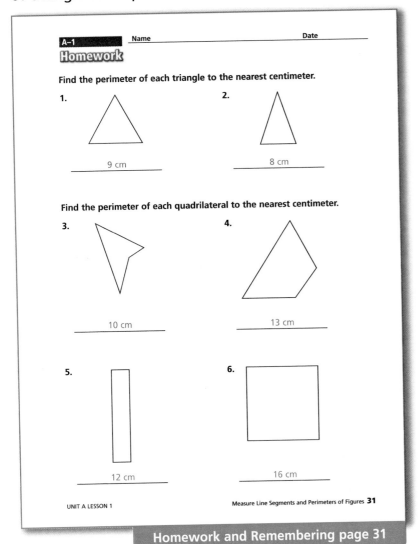

A-1 Name _____ Date _____
Homework

Find the perimeter of each triangle to the nearest centimeter.

1.

9 cm

2.

8 cm

Find the perimeter of each quadrilateral to the nearest centimeter.

3.

10 cm

4.

13 cm

5.

12 cm

6.

16 cm

UNIT A LESSON 1   Measure Line Segments and Perimeters of Figures **31**

Homework and Remembering page 31

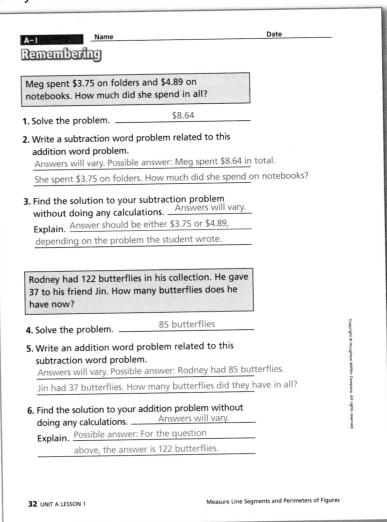

A-1 Name _____ Date _____
Remembering

Meg spent $3.75 on folders and $4.89 on notebooks. How much did she spend in all?

1. Solve the problem. _____ $8.64

2. Write a subtraction word problem related to this addition word problem.
   Answers will vary. Possible answer: Meg spent $8.64 in total.
   She spent $3.75 on folders. How much did she spend on notebooks?

3. Find the solution to your subtraction problem without doing any calculations. _____ Answers will vary.
   Explain. _____ Answer should be either $3.75 or $4.89,
   depending on the problem the student wrote.

Rodney had 122 butterflies in his collection. He gave 37 to his friend Jin. How many butterflies does he have now?

4. Solve the problem. _____ 85 butterflies

5. Write an addition word problem related to this subtraction word problem.
   Answers will vary. Possible answer: Rodney had 85 butterflies.
   Jin had 37 butterflies. How many butterflies did they have in all?

6. Find the solution to your addition problem without doing any calculations. _____ Answers will vary.
   Explain. _____ Possible answer: For the question
   above, the answer is 122 butterflies.

32 UNIT A LESSON 1   Measure Line Segments and Perimeters of Figures

Homework and Remembering page 32

Home and School Connection

Family Letter Have students take home the Family Letter on Student Activity Book page 51. A Spanish translation of this letter is on the following page in the Student Activity Book. This letter explains how the concept of quadrilaterals is developed in *Math Expressions*. It gives parents and guardians a better understanding of the learning that goes on in math class and creates a bridge between school and home.

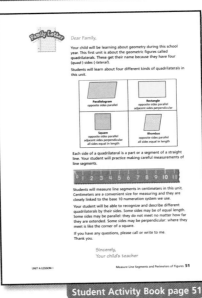

Student Activity Book page 51

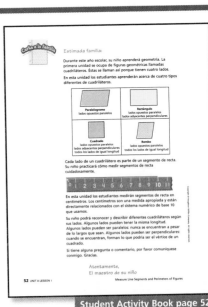

Student Activity Book page 52

Parallel and Perpendicular Lines and Line Segments

Lesson Objectives

- Identify and find examples to illustrate the terms *line, line segment, parallel,* and *perpendicular.*

- Identify opposite and adjacent sides of quadrilaterals.

The Day at a Glance

Today's Goals	Materials	🔢 Math Talk
1 **Teaching the Lesson** **A1:** Demonstrate understanding of the meanings of *line, line segment, parallel,* and *perpendicular* and find examples of each. **A2:** Identify opposite and adjacent sides of quadrilaterals. **A3:** Identify types of lines and line segments. **2** **Extending the Lesson** ▶ Differentiated Instruction **3** **Homework and Spiral Review**	MathBoard materials Centimeter rulers Geoboards and rubber bands Centimeter Dot Paper (Copymaster M28) Pattern blocks or Pattern Blocks (Copymaster M27) Venn Diagram (Copymaster M29) Student Activity Book pages 53–56 Homework and Remembering pages 33–34 Math Journals	In today's activities, the students are involved in discussion as they ▶ analyze what makes two lines parallel or perpendicular ▶ talk about what makes two lines opposite or adjacent

Teaching the Lesson

Learn about Parallel Lines and Perpendicular Lines

 30 MINUTES

Goal: Demonstrate understanding of the meanings of *line, line segment, parallel,* and *perpendicular* and find examples of each.

Materials: Student Activity Book pages 53–54

✓ **NCTM Standards:**
Geometry
Representation

▶ **Define Lines and Line Segments**

WHOLE CLASS

Have students look at the examples of lines on Student Activity Book page 53. Discuss the following key ideas:

● Lines go on forever in both directions.

● When we draw a line, we put arrows on the ends to show the line continues on and on.

Next, have students look at the line segments. Discuss the key ideas about line segments:

● A line segment is part of a line.

● A line segment has two ends, which are called endpoints.

Remind students that they measured line segments in the previous lesson.

Continue the discussion with exercise 1.

Draw examples like those below.

 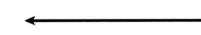

Explain that even though the line on the left looks shorter, it is not shorter. All lines go on forever. Tell students that when they look at a drawing of a line, they need to use their imagination to picture the line extending forever in both directions.

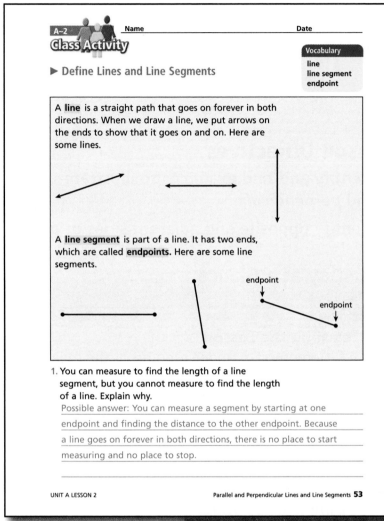

Student Activity Book page 53

Differentiated Instruction

English Learners Remind students that many words in English have more than one meaning. For example, a *line* besides being a straight path that goes on forever may also refer to a fishing line, clothes line, a line of poetry, a railroad line, line of work, and boundary line.

▶ Define Parallel Lines [WHOLE CLASS]

Direct students' attention to Student Activity Book page 54. Ask them to examine the parallel lines and the lines that are not parallel. Then ask:

● What do you think it means for two lines to be parallel?

Give students a few minutes to respond in writing, then invite two or three students to share their ideas. Answers will vary, but should include at least these two possibilities:

● Two lines are parallel if they are everywhere the same distance apart.

● Two lines are parallel if they never cross each other.

Note that the drawings of the first two pairs of lines that are not parallel do not cross each other, but because the lines go on forever, they will eventually cross. Students can extend the lines in each pair to check.

Ask students to look at the parallel line segments. Explain that line segments are parallel if the lines they are part of are parallel.

● What examples of parallel line segments do you see in the classroom? Possible answers: opposite sides of the board, lines on notebook paper, opposite sides of a window or door

▶ Define Perpendicular Lines [WHOLE CLASS]

Ask students to look at the perpendicular and non-perpendicular lines on Student Activity Book page 54. Then ask:

● What do you think it means for two lines to be perpendicular?

Give students a few minutes to respond in writing. Then invite two or three students to share their ideas.

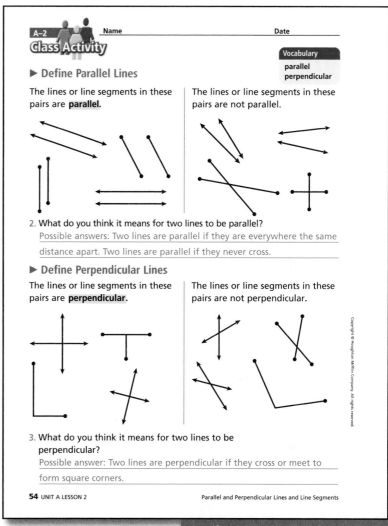

Student Activity Book page 54

Possible answer: Perpendicular lines cross each other to form square corners (some students may use the term *right angles*).

Have students look at the perpendicular line segments. Explain that line segments are perpendicular if they meet to form square corners.

● What examples of perpendicular line segments do you see in the classroom? Possible answers: the edges that form a corner of a desk, door, window, or the cover of a book

✓ Ongoing Assessment

Ask students to think of examples of parallel lines and perpendicular lines in their home or neighborhood or school.

❶ Teaching the Lesson (continued)

Activity 2

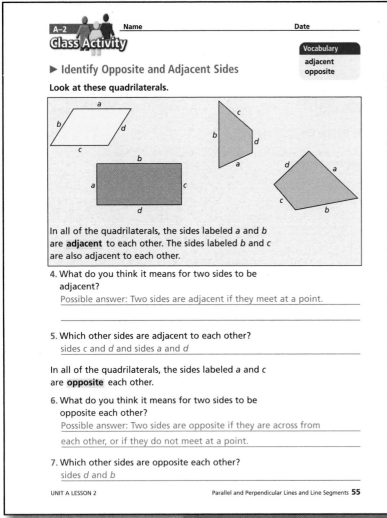

Student Activity Book page 55

Define Opposite and Adjacent Sides

 15 MINUTES

Goal: Identify opposite and adjacent sides of quadrilaterals.

Materials: Student Activity Book page 55

 NCTM Standard:
Geometry

▶ Identify Opposite and Adjacent Sides
| WHOLE CLASS |

Have students identify the opposite sides and adjacent sides in each figure and describe opposite sides and adjacent sides in their own words. Then have them complete the page.

Activity 3

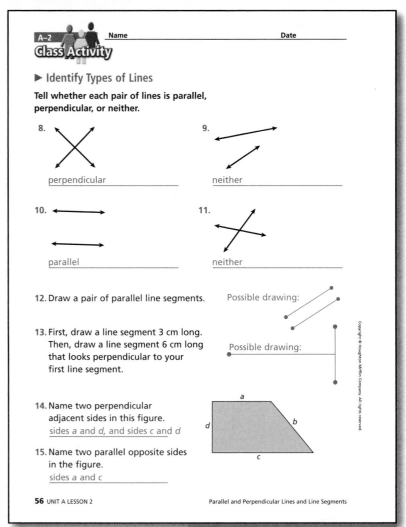

Student Activity Book page 56

Practice with New Ideas

 15 MINUTES

Goal: Identify types of lines and line segments.

Materials: Student Activity Book page 56, centimeter rulers (1 per student)

 NCTM Standards:
Geometry
Measurement

▶ Identify Types of Lines | INDIVIDUALS |

Elicit from students how to check if two lines are parallel, perpendicular, or neither. Then have them complete the exercises.

② Extending the Lesson

Activities for Individualizing

Intervention
for students having difficulty

`PAIRS`

Make a Quadrilateral

Materials: geoboards and rubber bands or Centimeter Dot Paper (Copymaster M28)

Students work in pairs to create quadrilaterals on geoboards. One partner makes a quadrilateral. The other partner draws the quadrilateral on Copymaster M28.

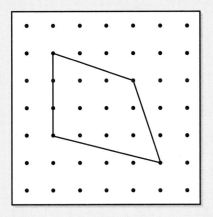

Encourage students to make figures with parallel sides and figures with perpendicular sides. They mark parallel and perpendicular sides. If no sides are parallel or perpendicular, students change the quadrilateral to include such sides.

On Level
for students having success

`PAIRS`

Sort Pattern Blocks

Materials: pattern blocks or Pattern Blocks (Copymaster M27), Venn Diagram (Copymaster M29)

Students use a Venn diagram to sort pattern blocks by parallel sides and perpendicular sides.

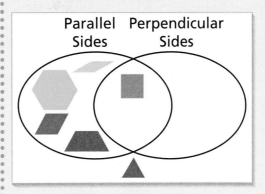

They then draw a new quadrilateral to go in the empty part of the diagram.

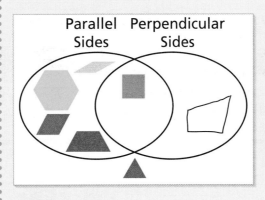

Challenge
for students seeking a challenge

`INDIVIDUALS`

Investigate Math

Materials: MathBoard materials

Students draw a vertical line segment. They explain whether it is possible to draw two lines perpendicular to the vertical line segment and have them not be parallel.

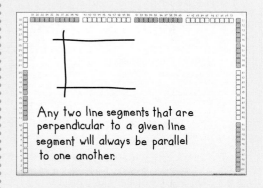

Any two line segments that are perpendicular to a given line segment will always be parallel to one another.

Also Use
Challenge Master for A-2

 Math Writing Prompt

Intervention

Check Your Answer
Explain how you can use lined paper or grid paper to check whether two lines are parallel or perpendicular.

 Math Writing Prompt

On Level

Use Reasoning
Why are opposite sides of a quadrilateral not perpendicular? Why are adjacent sides not parallel?

 Math Writing Prompt

Challenge

Draw a Picture
Draw a quadrilateral with no parallel sides and no perpendicular sides. Explain how you can show that the opposite sides are not parallel.

③ Homework and Spiral Review

Homework **Goal:** Additional Practice

On this Homework page, students can apply their understanding of the following terms: *adjacent, opposite, parallel,* and *perpendicular.*

Remembering **Goal:** Spiral Review.

This Remembering activity is appropriate anytime after today's lesson.

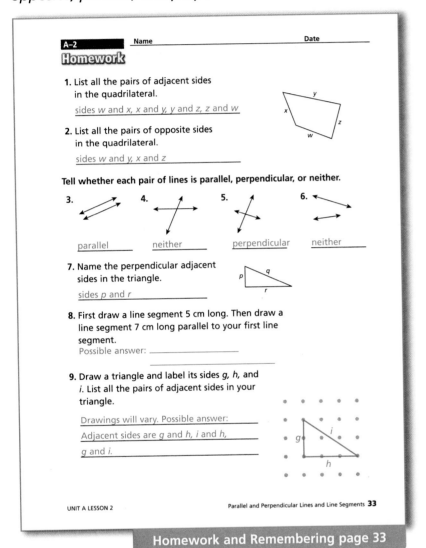

A-2 **Name** ___ **Date** ___
Homework

1. List all the pairs of adjacent sides in the quadrilateral.
   sides *w* and *x, x* and *y, y* and *z, z* and *w*

2. List all the pairs of opposite sides in the quadrilateral.
   sides *w* and *y, x* and *z*

Tell whether each pair of lines is parallel, perpendicular, or neither.

3. parallel 4. neither 5. perpendicular 6. neither

7. Name the perpendicular adjacent sides in the triangle.
   sides *p* and *r*

8. First draw a line segment 5 cm long. Then draw a line segment 7 cm long parallel to your first line segment.
   Possible answer: ___

9. Draw a triangle and label its sides *g, h,* and *i.* List all the pairs of adjacent sides in your triangle.
   Drawings will vary. Possible answer:
   Adjacent sides are *g* and *h, i* and *h,*
   g and *i.*

UNIT A LESSON 2   Parallel and Perpendicular Lines and Line Segments **33**

Homework and Remembering page 33

Remembering

Add or subtract. Use a separate sheet of paper.
1. 505 − 277 __228__   2. 1,237 + 692 __1,929__   3. 1,060 − 487 __573__
4. 478 + 642 __1,120__   5. 340 − 62 __278__   6. 1,389 + 57 __1,446__
7. 1,005 − 996 __9__   8. 1,637 + 92 __1,729__   9. 1,541 − 2 __1,539__
10. 69 + 953 __1,022__   11. 1,500 − 89 __1,411__   12. 935 + 165 __1,100__

13. Write a word problem for one of the addition exercises above.
    Answers will vary.

14. Write a word problem for one of the subtraction exercises above.
    Answers will vary.

34 UNIT A LESSON 2   Parallel and Perpendicular Lines and Line Segments

Homework and Remembering page 34

Home or School Activity

 Sports Connection

Lines Around You Have students list examples of parallel and perpendicular lines you might find in a gym or a playing field.

Possible answers: bars on the climber in a playground, uprights and crossbars on a football or soccer field, lines on the gym floor, strings on a racket

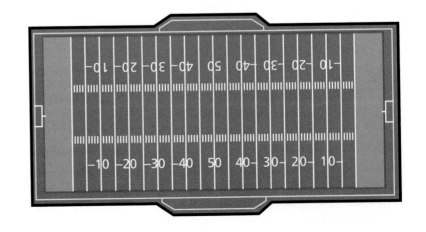

138 UNIT A LESSON 2

Parallelograms, Rectangles, Squares, and Rhombuses

Lesson Objectives

- Develop definitions for *parallelogram, rectangle, square,* and *rhombus.*
- Explore the relationships among parallelograms, rectangles, squares, and rhombuses.
- Find the perimeters of rectangles and squares without measuring all four sides.

The Day at a Glance

Today's Goals	Materials	123 Math Talk
1 Teaching the Lesson **A1:** Define *parallelogram* and observe, by measuring, that opposite sides of a parallelogram are the same length. **A2:** Define *rectangles, squares,* and *rhombuses* and explain the relationships among them. **A3:** Find perimeters of rectangles and squares by measuring as few sides as possible. **A4:** Identify all the names for given quadrilaterals.	Centimeter rulers Tangrams or Tangrams (Copymaster M30) Scissors Student Activity Book pages 57–64 Homework and Remembering pages 35–36 Math Journals *Grandfather Tang's Story* by Ann Tompert (Bantam Doubleday Dell Books for Young Readers, 1997)	In today's activities, the students are involved in discussion as they ▶ develop definitions of geometric figures ▶ identify and classify figures with proper geometric names ▶ share designs and patterns created with tangrams
2 Extending the Lesson ▶ Going Further: Visualize Figures with Tangrams ▶ Differentiated Instruction		
3 Homework and Spiral Review		

Teaching the Lesson

Define and Measure Parallelograms

 15 MINUTES

Goal: Define *parallelogram* and observe, by measuring, that opposite sides of a parallelogram are the same length.

Materials: Student Activity Book page 57, centimeter rulers (1 per student)

✔ **NCTM Standards:**
Geometry
Measurement

▶ Define a Parallelogram WHOLE CLASS

Refer students to the first two rows of figures on Student Activity Book page 57. Ask them to look at the examples of parallelograms and the figures that are not parallelograms. Ask students what they think a parallelogram is. If necessary, suggest that they think about the word *parallel*. (You might write the word *parallelogram* on the board and underline "parallel.") Help students refine and clarify their answers. For example:

- If a student says that a parallelogram is a quadrilateral with parallel sides, point out that figure G is a quadrilateral with parallel sides, but it is not a parallelogram.

- If a student says that a parallelogram is a figure with two pairs of parallel sides, point out that figure J has two pairs of parallel sides, but it is not a parallelogram.

Work as a class to complete the definition: A parallelogram is a quadrilateral in which both pairs of opposite sides are parallel. Record the definition on the board or on a sheet of chart paper and leave it posted for the remainder of the lesson.

Teaching Note

Language and Vocabulary Some students may suggest the following definition: A parallelogram is a quadrilateral in which both pairs of opposite sides are the same length. This definition is also correct. If it is mentioned, record it as well. If not, you do not need to bring it up. This point will be made later.

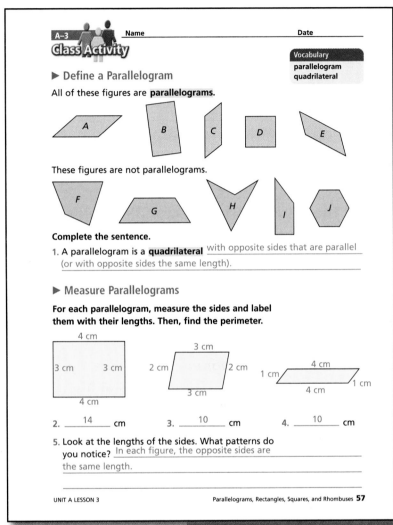

Student Activity Book page 57

▶ Measure Parallelograms INDIVIDUALS

Read aloud the directions in the Measure Parallelograms section and make sure everyone knows what to do. Give students a few minutes to complete exercises 2–5 as you circulate and provide assistance. Then, discuss the answers. Students should notice that in all the parallelograms the opposite sides are the same length.

Rectangles, Squares, and Rhombuses

 15 MINUTES

Goal: Define *rectangles, squares,* and *rhombuses* and explain the relationships among them.

Materials: Student Activity Book page 58

 NCTM Standard:
Geometry

▶ Define a Rectangle WHOLE CLASS

Have students look at the rectangles, and read and discuss Adel's statement. If necessary, refer them to the posted definition of *parallelogram.*

- Is Adel right? Are rectangles parallelograms? yes
- How do you know? They are quadrilaterals and both pairs of opposite sides are parallel.
- Adel said that rectangles are special parallelograms. What makes them special?

Allow several students to share their answers and encourage them to use any new words. Work as a class to write at least one of the following definitions:

- A rectangle is a parallelogram with four square corners.
- A rectangle is a parallelogram in which adjacent sides are perpendicular.

Record the definition(s) on the board or chart paper.

▶ Explore Squares and Rhombuses

WHOLE CLASS

Refer students to the squares and read aloud Takeshi's statement.

- Is Takeshi right? Are squares rectangles? yes
- How do you know? They are parallelograms and they have four square corners.
- What makes squares special rectangles? All the sides are the same length.

Work as a class to complete the definitions of a square and a rhombus. A square is a rectangle in which all four

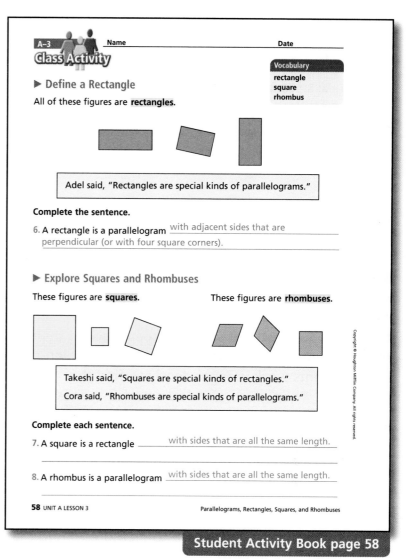

A-3
Class Activity

Name _____ Date _____

Vocabulary
rectangle
square
rhombus

▶ Define a Rectangle
All of these figures are **rectangles**.

Adel said, "Rectangles are special kinds of parallelograms."

Complete the sentence.

6. A rectangle is a parallelogram with adjacent sides that are perpendicular (or with four square corners).

▶ Explore Squares and Rhombuses
These figures are **squares**.   These figures are **rhombuses**.

Takeshi said, "Squares are special kinds of rectangles."
Cora said, "Rhombuses are special kinds of parallelograms."

Complete each sentence.

7. A square is a rectangle _____ with sides that are all the same length.

8. A rhombus is a parallelogram with sides that are all the same length.

58 UNIT A LESSON 3   Parallelograms, Rectangles, Squares, and Rhombuses

Student Activity Book page 58

sides are the same length. A rhombus is a parallelogram in which all four sides are the same length. Record the definitions under the previous one(s).

▶ Explore Trapezoids (Optional)
WHOLE CLASS

Draw three different trapezoids on the board.

- These quadrilaterals are called trapezoids. What do you notice about them? Each has one pair of parallel sides.

Ask students to complete this sentence.

- A trapezoid is a quadrilateral _____ with just one pair of parallel sides.

Activity 3

Perimeters of Rectangles and Squares

 15 MINUTES

Goal: Find perimeters of rectangles and squares by measuring as few sides as possible.

Materials: Student Activity Book page 59, centimeter rulers (1 per student)

 NCTM Standards:
Geometry
Measurement

▶ Find the Perimeters of Rectangles and Squares   INDIVIDUALS

Read aloud the directions at the top of Student Activity Book page 59 and emphasize that students should only measure the sides they need to, not all four sides. Suggest that students keep track of their measurements by labeling the sides with their lengths. Have students work independently to find the perimeters. Then, discuss and summarize the results.

● How many sides do you have to measure to find the perimeter of a rectangle? 2

● How do you know? The opposite sides are the same length, so you just have to measure the two adjacent sides, and you know the length of the other sides.

● How many sides do you have to measure to find the perimeter of a square? 1

● How do you know? All the sides are the same length, so if you know the length of one side, you know the length of all four.

Have each student write an answer to exercise 13 and then ask volunteers to share their answers with the class.

 Alternate Approach

Act it Out Vocabulary words such as *adjacent* and *perpendicular* may be hard for students to understand. If students can't visualize paper and pencil drawings, have small groups create human rectangles and squares. When students create these figures, they will clearly see how the opposite or parallel sides are different from the adjacent, perpendicular sides.

A-3
Class Activity   Name _____ Date _____

Vocabulary
rectangle
square

▶ Find the Perimeters of Rectangles and Squares

Find the perimeter of each figure *without* measuring all four sides.

These figures are **rectangles**.

9. ___10___ cm   10. ___14___ cm

These figures are **squares**.

11. ___12___ cm   12. ___4___ cm

13. Write About It How are rectangles and squares the same? How are they different?
   Answers will vary.
   _____
   _____
   _____
   _____

UNIT A LESSON 3   Parallelograms, Rectangles, Squares, and Rhombuses **59**

Student Activity Book page 59

The Learning Classroom

Helping Community Have students work in pairs to complete Student Activity Book page 59. Together, students measure and add to find the perimeter. Students can try to work out the problem independently first, and then check with their partner to see if they both found the same measurements and perimeter.

Name Quadrilaterals

 15 MINUTES

Goal: Identify all the names for given quadrilaterals.

Materials: Student Activity Book page 60

 NCTM Standard:
Geometry

▶ Describe Quadrilaterals

Refer students to Student Activity Book 60. Discuss the different names a quadrilateral can have. You may have to ask specific questions to get students to realize that there are other possible names for quadrilaterals. For example:

- Are there words in the box that describe the figure in exercise 14? What about the word *quadrilateral*? Can someone remind us what a quadrilateral is? a figure with four sides

- Does this figure have four sides? yes

- So, is it a quadrilateral? yes

- Is this figure a parallelogram? yes

- How do you know? Both pairs of opposite sides are parallel.

- Is this shape a square? no

- Why not? because not all of the sides are the same length

- So, this figure is a quadrilateral, a parallelogram, and a rectangle, but not a square.

Have students complete the page and discuss their answers.

Teaching Note

Watch For! Students may have difficulty understanding the inclusive nature of some of these figures. A square is a kind of rectangle, which is a kind of parallelogram, which is a kind of quadrilateral. This should become clearer as students continue to explore these quadrilaterals in the next geometry unit. To help students understand inclusive relationships, you might mention some examples that are more familiar to them. For example, a beagle is a kind of dog, which is a kind of animal. Point out that we would not say, "This can't be a dog because it is a beagle" or "This can't be an animal because it is a dog." Relate this to the idea that we would not say, "This can't be a parallelogram because it is a rectangle."

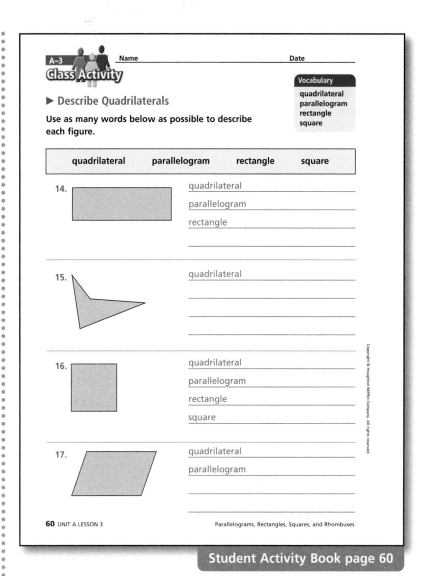

Student Activity Book page 60

✔ Ongoing Assessment

Draw any quadrilateral on the board. Then, have students classify the quadrilateral by writing its name on their MathBoards. Have students hold their MathBoards up so the class can see the different names for one quadrilateral.

Extending the Lesson

Going Further: Visualize Figures with Tangrams

Goal: Visualize figures with tangrams.

Materials: Student Activity Book pages 61–64, tangrams or Tangrams (Copymaster M30)

✓ **NCTM Standard:**
Geometry

▶ Tangram Figures

Have students cut out the tangram pieces on Student Activity Book page 61. Then use these critical thinking questions to help familiarize students with the tangram pieces.

● **How can two tangram pieces become one figure?** line up 2 sides to make 1 figure

● **Look at the cat pattern on Student Activity Book page 63. What tangram pieces can you use to make the tail?** the parallelogram or the 2 small triangles

● **What different figures can you make with the two small triangles?** a square, a larger triangle, and a parallelogram

● **How many small triangles can fit inside the largest triangle?** 4

● **Two small triangles fit into the square and the medium size triangle. Does that mean that the square fits into the medium size triangle?** No; the square has 4 sides and the triangle only has 3 sides.

● **Which combination of figures can you use to make the largest triangle?** 1 medium size triangle and 2 small triangles; a square and 2 small triangles; a parallelogram and 2 small triangles

Explain that tangram puzzles came from ancient China. Have students try to make the cat puzzle shown on Student Activity Book page 63 using the tangram pieces they cut out from Student Activity Book page 61. If time permits, have students try to create the other tangram patterns on the page and complete the On the Back activity.

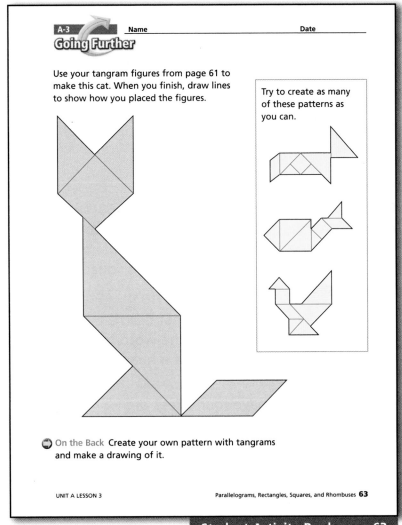

Student Activity Book page 63

🖐 **Alternate Approach**

Tangrams Students can also use foam or plastic tangrams if available. Such materials will be of a precise size and will help students create patterns more accurately.

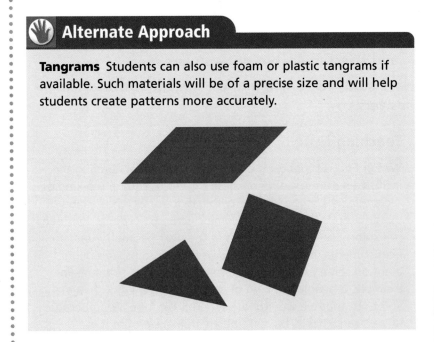

Intervention
for students having difficulty
INDIVIDUALS

Just Two Triangles

Materials: tangrams (Student Activity Book page 61)

Have students use the two small triangle tangrams to create each figure.

a square

a parallelogram

a larger triangle

On Level
for students having success
INDIVIDUALS

Two or More Pieces

Materials: tangrams (Student Activity Book page 61)

Have students use any of the tangram pieces to create each figure.

a square

a rectangle

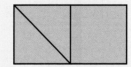

a parallelogram

a triangle twice as big as the medium size triangle

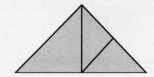

Challenge
for students seeking a challenge
INDIVIDUALS

All Seven Pieces

Materials: tangram (Student Activity Book page 61)

Have students recreate the original square using all the tangram pieces.

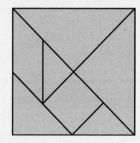

If time allows, challenge students to use all seven tangram pieces to create other quadrilaterals.

a rectangle

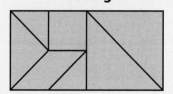

a parallelogram

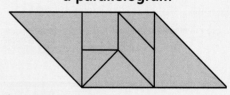

Also Use
Challenge Master for A-3

 **Math Writing Prompt**

Intervention

Explain Your Answer
Isaac wants to find the perimeter of a square. He measures each side with his ruler and adds the measurements together. Explain to Isaac another way to calculate the perimeter.

 Math Writing Prompt

On Level

Explain Your Thinking
Takeshi said that squares are special rectangles. Do you think he is correct? Explain your thinking.

Math Writing Prompt

Challenge

Draw a Picture
Cora said that rhombuses are special kinds of parallelograms. Do you think she is correct? Include a drawing in your answer.

③ Homework and Spiral Review

Homework **Goal:** Additional Practice

✔ Include students' completed Homework page as part of their portfolios.

Remembering **Goal:** Spiral Review

This Remembering activity is appropriate anytime after today's lesson.

A-3	Name		Date

Homework

Solve.

1. A square has sides 3 cm in length.

   What is the perimeter of the square? ___12 cm___

2. The adjacent sides of a parallelogram have lengths of 12 cm and 18 cm.

   Adjacent   Opposite

   Adjacent   Opposite

   What is the perimeter of the parallelogram? ___60 cm___

3. Draw a rectangle that has sides 5 cm and 2 cm in length.

   5 cm

   2 cm

   What is the perimeter of your rectangle? ___14 cm___

4. Draw a square with a perimeter of 8 cm.

   2 cm

5. Draw a parallelogram with a perimeter of 12 cm.

UNIT A LESSON 3   Parallelograms, Rectangles, Squares, and Rhombuses **35**

Homework and Remembering page 35

A-3	Name		Date

Remembering

Read each sentence and write whether it is true or false.

1. All squares are rectangles. ___true___
2. All parallelograms are squares. ___false___
3. All quadrilaterals are parallelograms. ___false___
4. The opposite sides of a square are always parallel. ___true___
5. If you know the lengths of two opposite sides of a parallelogram, you can find its perimeter. ___false___

Use the word problem below to complete exercises 6–8.

> Ms. Molina has 148 paperback books and 82 hardcover books. How many books does she have in all?

6. Solve the problem. ___230 books___

7. Write a subtraction word problem related to this addition word problem.

   Possible answer: Ms. Molina has 230 books. 148 of her books are paperback books. How many of her books are hardcover books?

8. Find the answer to your subtraction problem without doing any calculations.

   Answers will vary: For the question above the answer is 82 hardcover books.

36 UNIT A LESSON 3   Parallelograms, Rectangles, Squares, and Rhombuses

Homework and Remembering page 36

Home or School Activity

Literature Connection

Grandfather Tang's Story Have students read Ann Tompert's book, *Grandfather Tang's Story* (Bantam Doubleday Dell Books for Young Readers, 1997). As they read along, have them create the animals in the story with tangrams. As an extension, have students create their own animal pattern out of tangrams and write and illustrate an animal story. If students would like to color their own tangram pattern, they can use Copymaster M30.

MINI UNIT A
LESSON
4

Draw Parallelograms and Rectangles

Lesson Objectives

- Draw parallelograms and rectangles.
- Observe the relationship between the dimensions of a rectangle and its perimeter.

Vocabulary

parallel
parallelogram
rectangle
square

The Day at a Glance

Today's Goals	Materials	123 Math Talk
1 Teaching the Lesson **A1:** Review the attributes of and draw parallelograms. **A2:** Review the attributes of rectangles and draw all possible rectangles with a given perimeter and sides with whole-number lengths. **2 Extending the Lesson** ▶ Differentiated Instruction **3 Homework and Spiral Review**	Rulers Centimeter Grid Paper (Copymaster M31) Pattern blocks or Pattern Blocks (Copymaster M27) Scissors Paper Student Activity Book pages 65–66 Homework and Remembering pages 37–38 Math Journals	In today's activities, the students are involved in discussion as they ▶ tell what they know about parallelograms and rectangles ▶ describe patterns in the dimensions of rectangles

Teaching the Lesson

Draw Parallelograms

 25 MINUTES

Goal: Review the attributes of and draw parallelograms.

Materials: Student Activity Book page 65, rulers (one per student)

✓ **NCTM Standards:**
Geometry
Representation

▶ **Explore Parallelograms** | INDIVIDUALS |

Review what students learned about parallel line segments. Then, have students look at Student Activity Book page 65.

● Look at the parallelogram on the page. Which sides are opposite sides? sides *a* and *c; b* and *d*

● What can you say about the opposite sides of a parallelogram? The opposite sides are parallel.

● What can you say about the length of the opposite sides of a parallelogram? The opposite sides are the same length.

● If you wanted to find the perimeter of this parallelogram, would you have to measure all four sides? no

● Why not? If you know the length of one side, you automatically know the length of the opposite side.

● Which sides would you have to measure? any two adjacent sides: *a* and *b; b* and *c; c* and *d; d* and *a*

Have students complete exercise 1.

Ask students to draw parallelograms of different sizes, shapes, and orientations on the grid provided. Students can use the lines on the grid to draw one pair of parallel sides and draw the other sides by "eyeballing."

Examples of possible drawings are in the following column.

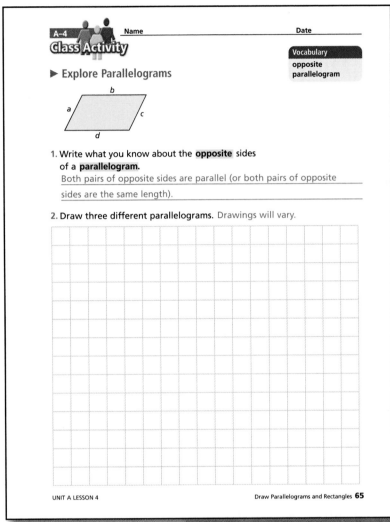

Student Activity Book page 65

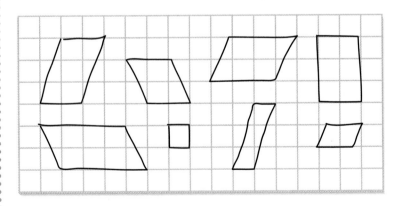

Ask volunteers to share some of the parallelograms they drew. Ask about special parallelograms.

● Did anybody draw a rectangle? Did anybody draw a square? How do you know that a rectangle and a square are parallelograms? In both figures, both pairs of opposite sides are parallel.

Draw Rectangles

35 MINUTES

Goal: Review the attributes of rectangles and draw all possible rectangles with a given perimeter and sides with whole-number lengths.

Materials: Student Activity Book page 66, rulers (1 per small group), Centimeter Grid Paper (Copymaster M31)

 NCTM Standards:
Geometry
Measurement

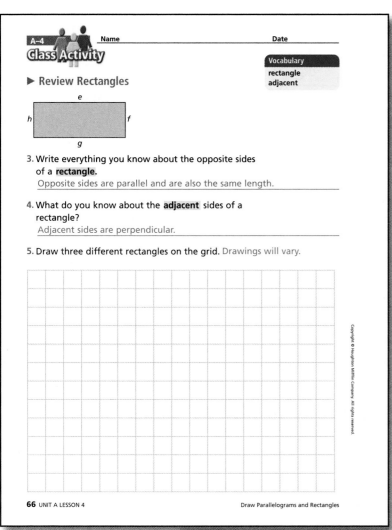

Student Activity Book page 66

▶ Review Rectangles [SMALL GROUPS]

Review rectangles by discussing the rectangle on Student Activity Book page 66.

● Rectangles are special kinds of parallelograms. What makes them special? They have four square corners.

● What do you know about the lengths of the sides of a rectangle? The opposite sides are the same length.

● If you wanted to find the perimeter of the rectangle on Student Activity Book page 66, which sides would you have to measure? any two adjacent sides

You might mention that some people refer to the two adjacent sides of a rectangle as the length and the width. These measurements are called the *dimensions* of the rectangle. Have students complete exercises 3–5.

Rectangles with Specific Side Lengths Divide the class into groups of two or three. Assign one of the perimeters below to each group.

10 cm	12 cm
14 cm	16 cm
18 cm	20 cm
22 cm	24 cm

Have each group draw, on Copymaster M31, all the possible rectangles with the given perimeter (and sides with whole-number lengths). Ask students to label the lengths of a pair of adjacent sides for each rectangle. Suggest that groups figure out the lengths and widths of all the possible rectangles before they begin drawing.

Differentiated Instruction

Extra Help You may want to have your struggling students work together. Assign the smaller perimeters, which have fewer possible rectangles, to these students. Assist these groups as they draw their rectangles.

Activity continued ▶

① Teaching the Lesson (continued)

On the board, make a chart with a row for each perimeter. Select a spokesperson for each group to come to the board and list the lengths of two adjacent sides for each rectangle the group drew. Students can list just the numbers. They don't need to write "centimeters."

Teaching Note

Watch For! Students may write each pair of dimensions twice. For example, they may write both 3 and 5, and 5 and 3. You can either allow them to do this or point out that these rectangles are really the same; one is simply a rotated copy of the other.

Perimeter (centimeters)	Possible Lengths of Sides (centimeters)					
10	1 and 4	2 and 3				
12	1 and 5	2 and 4	3 and 3			
14	1 and 6	2 and 5	3 and 4			
16	1 and 7	2 and 6	3 and 5	4 and 4		
18	1 and 8	2 and 7	3 and 6	4 and 5		
20	1 and 9	2 and 8	3 and 7	4 and 6	5 and 5	
22	1 and 10	2 and 9	3 and 8	4 and 7	5 and 6	
24	1 and 11	2 and 10	3 and 9	4 and 8	5 and 7	6 and 6

After all groups have recorded their work, ask students to look closely at the chart.

● Which rectangles are also squares? 3 and 3; 4 and 4; 5 and 5; 6 and 6

● How do you know that a square is also a rectangle? Its opposite sides are the same length.

Then, ask students if they see any patterns in the chart. If no one mentions the fact that the total for each pair of lengths is half the perimeter, ask specific questions:

● Look at the row for a rectangle with a perimeter of 16 cm. If you add each pair of lengths of sides, what do you get? 8 cm

● How does this compare to the perimeter? It is half the perimeter.

Challenge students to find similar patterns in other rows of the chart.

Examine several rows as a class to help convince students that this relationship is always true. Ask whether anyone can explain why this relationship makes sense, but don't worry if no one can at this point. Students will continue to explore this relationship in the homework for this lesson and the next. You might ask this question again after students have completed both of these assignments.

 Ongoing Assessment

Ask students to explain, in writing and by drawing a picture, why all rectangles are also parallelograms, but not all parallelograms are rectangles.

② Extending the Lesson

Activities for Individualizing

Intervention
for students having difficulty
PAIRS

Geometric Designs

Materials: parallelograms and squares from a set of pattern blocks or from Pattern Blocks (Copymaster M27)

Students use the parallelogram and square pattern blocks to make a geometric design. They describe their design to a partner using the names of the figures.

On Level
for students having success
INDIVIDUALS

Make Parallelograms

Materials: scissors, rectangular sheets of paper

Students cut a rectangular sheet of paper along a straight, slanted line near the middle of the sheet, forming two pieces. They then show how to fit the two pieces together again to make a parallelogram that is not a rectangle.

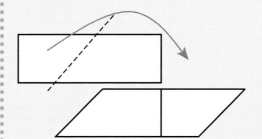

Challenge
for students seeking a challenge
INDIVIDUALS

Investigate Math

Materials: 10 squares from a set of pattern blocks or from Pattern Blocks (Copymaster M27)

Students start with a square pattern block.

They add three more square pattern blocks to make a larger square.

Next, they decide how many more pattern blocks they need to make the next larger square, and how many more they would need to make the next larger square after this one.

Students describe the pattern they see.

Also Use
Challenge Master for A-4

 Math Writing Prompt
Intervention
Organize Data
What do you know about the sides and corners of rectangles, squares, and parallelograms? Use a chart to organize your thinking.

 Math Writing Prompt
On Level
Explain Your Thinking
Draw a quadrilateral that is not a parallelogram. Explain how you can prove that it is not a parallelogram.

 Math Writing Prompt
Challenge
Investigate Possibilities
How many different rectangles can you make with twelve 1-cm squares? Explain your answer.

③ Homework and Spiral Review

Goal: Additional Practice

For homework, students draw all possible rectangles that have a given perimeter and whole-number lengths of sides.

Goal: Spiral Review

This Remembering activity is appropriate anytime after today's lesson.

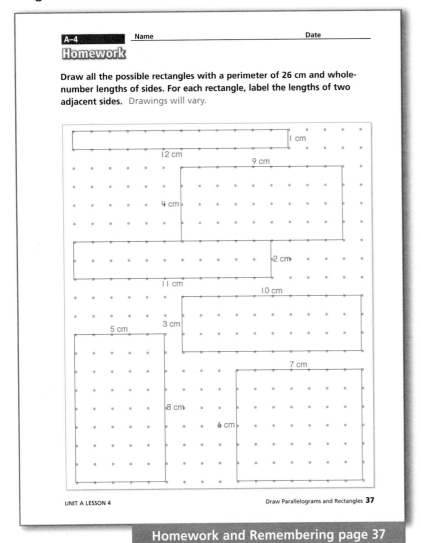

A-4   Name _____ Date _____

Homework

Draw all the possible rectangles with a perimeter of 26 cm and whole-number lengths of sides. For each rectangle, label the lengths of two adjacent sides. Drawings will vary.

(rectangles labeled: 12 cm, 1 cm; 9 cm, 4 cm; 11 cm, 2 cm; 10 cm, 3 cm; 5 cm, 8 cm; 7 cm, 6 cm)

UNIT A LESSON 4   Draw Parallelograms and Rectangles **37**

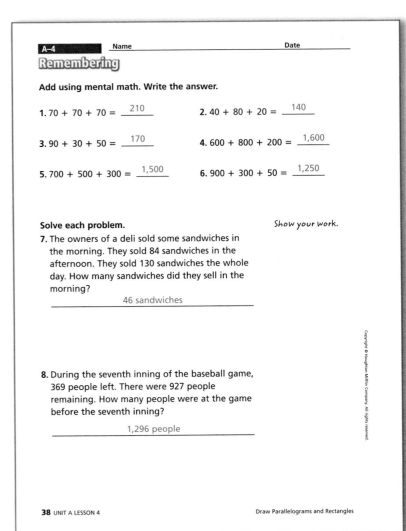

A-4   Name _____ Date _____

Remembering

Add using mental math. Write the answer.

1. 70 + 70 + 70 = 210

2. 40 + 80 + 20 = 140

3. 90 + 30 + 50 = 170

4. 600 + 800 + 200 = 1,600

5. 700 + 500 + 300 = 1,500

6. 900 + 300 + 50 = 1,250

Solve each problem.   *Show your work.*

7. The owners of a deli sold some sandwiches in the morning. They sold 84 sandwiches in the afternoon. They sold 130 sandwiches the whole day. How many sandwiches did they sell in the morning?

   46 sandwiches

8. During the seventh inning of the baseball game, 369 people left. There were 927 people remaining. How many people were at the game before the seventh inning?

   1,296 people

38 UNIT A LESSON 4   Draw Parallelograms and Rectangles

Homework and Remembering page 37

Homework and Remembering page 38

Home or School Activity

 Art Connection

Picture Frames Pose this problem to students: A picture measures 8 inches by 10 inches.

The wooden frame around the picture is one inch wide.

What is the shortest total length of wood you will need to make the frame?

10 + 10 + 12 + 12 = 44 inches

MINI UNIT A
LESSON
5

Classify Quadrilaterals

Lesson Objectives

- Review the features of quadrilaterals, parallelograms, rectangles, and squares.
- Describe the relationships among various types of quadrilaterals.

Vocabulary

quadrilateral
parallelogram
rhombus
rectangle
square

The Day at a Glance

Today's Goals	Materials	123 Math Talk
1 Teaching the Lesson **A1:** Classify quadrilaterals and review the key attributes of quadrilaterals, parallelograms, rectangles, and squares. **A2:** Draw quadrilaterals that match given descriptions. **2 Extending the Lesson** ▶ Differentiated Instruction **3 Homework and Spiral Review**	Centimeter rulers Quadrilaterals (Copymaster M32) Scissors Venn Diagram (Copymaster M29) Sheet protectors Dry erase markers MathBoard materials Geoboards and rubber bands Pencils Straws Student Activity Book pages 67–68 Homework and Remembering pages 39–40 Math Journals *Squares and Cubes* by Sally Morgan (Thomson Learning, 1994)	In today's activities, the students are involved in discussion as they ▶ describe the attributes of quadrilaterals ▶ classify quadrilaterals ▶ explain the possibilities of drawing different types of quadrilaterals

Teaching the Lesson

Different Types of Quadrilaterals

 40 MINUTES

Goal: Classify quadrilaterals and review the key attributes of quadrilaterals, parallelograms, rectangles, and squares.

Materials: Student Activity Book pages 67–68, centimeter rulers (1 per student), Quadrilaterals (Copymaster M32), scissors (1 pair per student), Venn Diagram (Copymaster M29), sheet protector, dry erase markers

✔️ **NCTM Standard:**
Geometry

▶ Describe Quadrilaterals WHOLE CLASS

Read aloud the directions on Student Activity Book page 67 and make sure students know what to do. Have them work independently to complete the page. Review the results, asking students to provide explanations for their answers. For example, for exercise 1:

● Is it a quadrilateral? yes

● How do you know? It has four sides.

● Is it a parallelogram? yes

● How do you know? Both pairs of opposite sides are parallel.

● Is it a rhombus? yes

● How do you know? All sides are the same length.

● Is it a rectangle? no

● How do you know? It doesn't have four square corners.

● How do you know it isn't a square? It's not a rectangle, so it can't be a square.

Have students look at all of their answers and ask whether they see any patterns. Students may notice that the word *quadrilateral* is marked for all the figures. They might also notice that when a name is marked, every name above it is also marked, with the exception of number 4.

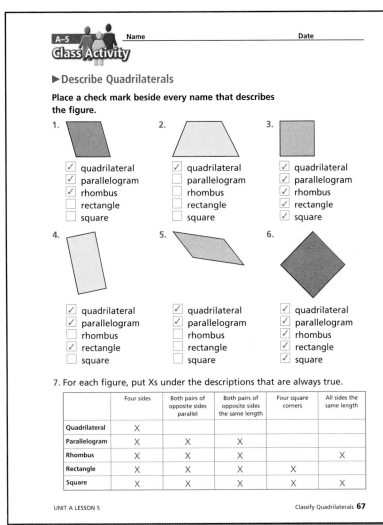

Student Activity Book page 67

Continue eliciting information from students until they have completed the chart together. Ask students what they notice about the completed chart. Make sure they see that each category of figures has all the features of the category above plus some other feature(s). For example, rectangles have all the features of quadrilaterals plus two pairs of parallel opposite sides, two pairs of opposite sides of the same length, and four square corners.

Work as a class and use the information on the chart to complete statements 8–12 on Student Activity Book page 68.

Student Activity Book page 68

▶ **Classify Quadrilaterals** [WHOLE CLASS]

Give each pair a copy of Copymaster M32. The first quadrilateral has two perpendicular adjacent sides of the same length. If you haven't taught trapezoids, they may not know the name of the sixth quadrilateral, but they can still use it for sorting. It is an isosceles trapezoid. Make sure students notice that it has two sides of equal length and one pair of parallel sides.

Have students cut out the six quadrilaterals from Copymaster M32.

Ask students to note the sides of the quadrilaterals and mark sides of equal length, opposite parallel sides, and adjacent perpendicular sides.

● How can you sort the quadrilaterals using the lengths of their sides? equal lengths and different lengths

● How else can you sort the quadrilaterals using descriptions of their sides? parallel sides, perpendicular sides

Give each pair of students a copy of Copymaster M29, a sheet protector, and dry-erase markers. Students should slip their Venn diagram in the sheet protector and write labels for their Venn diagram on it. Then, they should sort the six quadrilaterals on the Venn diagram. Challenge students to find two rules that will put figures inside all three parts of the circles. Suggest that students can also sort quadrilaterals by name; for example, those that are parallelograms.

Some possible sorting rules are:

● parallelograms/all sides of equal length

● at least one pair of parallel sides/exactly two sides of equal length

● at least one pair of perpendicular sides/at least one pair of sides of equal length

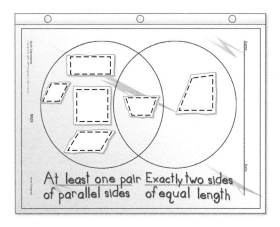

Classify Quadrilaterals   **155**

Activity 2

Draw Quadrilaterals

 20 MINUTES

Goal: Draw quadrilaterals that match given descriptions.

Materials: Student Activity Book page 68, centimeter rulers (1 per student), MathBoard materials, geoboards and rubber bands

 NCTM Standard:
Geometry

▶ Draw Quadrilaterals if Possible

WHOLE CLASS

Re-direct students' attention to Student Activity Book page 68 and read aloud the direction for exercises 13–17. Have students complete these exercises using the **Solve and Discuss** structure. If necessary, students can refer to the chart you completed on the board.

Make sure presenters explain the reasoning they used to draw the figure or to decide that drawing it is impossible. For a sample of classroom dialogue, see Math Talk in Action.

 Math Talk in Action

Can you draw the figure in exercise 13?

Aretha: Yes. A parallelogram is a quadrilateral where both pairs of opposite sides are parallel. You can draw a quadrilateral that isn't a parallelogram by drawing a quadrilateral with opposite sides that are not parallel.

What about the figure in exercise 14?

Jeffrey: A square is a rectangle with four square corners, so it is impossible to draw a square that is not a rectangle.

Can you draw the figure in exercise 15?

Diego: Yes. A rectangle is a parallelogram with four square corners. You can draw a parallelogram that isn't a rectangle by drawing a parallelogram that does not have four square corners.

Is the figure in exercise 16 possible?

Alison: Yes. A square is a rectangle with all sides the same length. You can draw a rectangle that is not a square if you draw a rectangle that does not have four sides of the same length.

What about the last figure?

Hoy: It's impossible. The table we completed shows that a rhombus is a parallelogram with some other features. You can't draw a rhombus that is not a parallelogram.

 Alternate Approach

Geoboards Have students use rubber bands to make quadrilaterals on geoboards.

 Ongoing Assessment

Ask students to draw a quadrilateral that is not a parallelogram and then to explain why the quadrilateral cannot be a square or a rectangle.

Extending the Lesson

Intervention
for students having difficulty

PAIRS

Make a Quadrilateral

Materials: 2 short straws or pencils of the same length, 2 long straws or pencils of the same length

Students show and name the quadrilaterals that they can make using the four straws (or pencils).

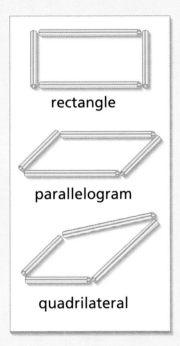

rectangle

parallelogram

quadrilateral

On Level
for students having success

PAIRS

Fold Figures

Materials: Quadrilaterals (Copymaster M32), scissors (1 pair per student)

Students cut out a square, a rhombus that isn't a square, a rectangle that isn't a square, and a parallelogram that isn't a rectangle or a rhombus from Copymaster M32. They test each figure to see if they can fold it in half so that each half exactly covers the other half.

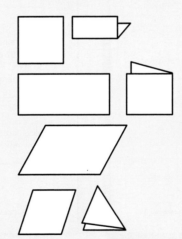

Challenge
for students seeking a challenge

PAIRS

Investigate Math

Pose the following question to students and have them draw a picture to explain their answer: Can you extend the opposite sides of a quadrilateral so that they are perpendicular?

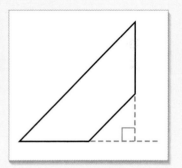

Also Use
Challenge Master for A-5

 Math Writing Prompt

Intervention

Draw a Picture
Draw a parallelogram that is not a rectangle. Explain why it is not a rectangle.

 Math Writing Prompt

On Level

You Decide
Write as many true sentences as possible by filling the blanks with the words *quadrilateral, parallelogram, rhombus, square,* or *rectangle.*

A _____ is a special kind of _____ .

 Math Writing Prompt

Challenge

Explain Your Thinking
Draw a trapezoid (a quadrilateral with two sides parallel and two sides not parallel). In a trapezoid, can two sides of the same length be parallel?

Explain how a trapezoid can have three sides of the same length.

③ Homework and Spiral Review

Homework **Goal:** Additional Practice

✓ Include students' completed Homework page as part of their portfolios.

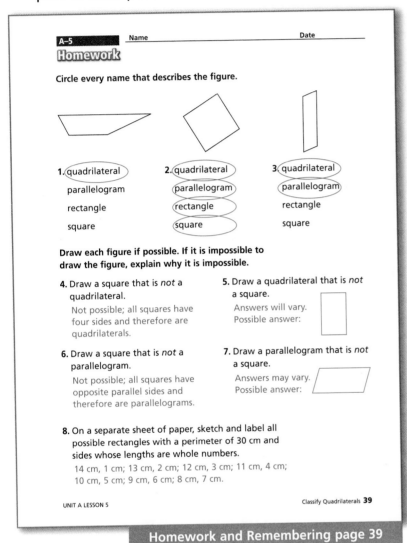

Remembering **Goal:** Spiral Review

This Remembering activity is appropriate anytime after today's lesson.

A–5 Name _____ Date _____
Homework

Circle every name that describes the figure.

1. (quadrilateral)
   parallelogram
   rectangle
   square

2. (quadrilateral)
   (parallelogram)
   (rectangle)
   (square)

3. (quadrilateral)
   (parallelogram)
   rectangle
   square

Draw each figure if possible. If it is impossible to draw the figure, explain why it is impossible.

4. Draw a square that is *not* a quadrilateral.
   Not possible; all squares have four sides and therefore are quadrilaterals.

5. Draw a quadrilateral that is *not* a square.
   Answers will vary.
   Possible answer:

6. Draw a square that is *not* a parallelogram.
   Not possible; all squares have opposite parallel sides and therefore are parallelograms.

7. Draw a parallelogram that is *not* a square.
   Answers may vary.
   Possible answer:

8. On a separate sheet of paper, sketch and label all possible rectangles with a perimeter of 30 cm and sides whose lengths are whole numbers.
   14 cm, 1 cm; 13 cm, 2 cm; 12 cm, 3 cm; 11 cm, 4 cm; 10 cm, 5 cm; 9 cm, 6 cm; 8 cm, 7 cm.

UNIT A LESSON 5   Classify Quadrilaterals **39**

Homework and Remembering page 39

A–5 Name _____ Date _____
Remembering

Add or subtract.

1.	682	2.	$6.94	3.	600
	+ 245		+ 1.29		− 187
	927		$8.23		413

4.	877	5.	2,784	6.	4,562
	− 491		+ 3,725		− 784
	386		6,509		3,778

Solve each problem.   *Show your work.*

7. Waleed barbecued some turkey burgers. He had 16 buns. He put a burger on each bun and had 5 buns left over. How many burgers did he cook?
   11 burgers

8. The drama club sold too many tickets to the play. 782 people bought tickets. 37 people had to stand because there were not enough seats. How many seats are in the auditorium?
   745 seats

9. Sara had $5.00 to buy lunch. She spent $3.49. How much does she have left?
   $1.51

40 UNIT A LESSON 5   Classify Quadrilaterals

Homework and Remembering page 40

Home or School Activity

Social Studies Connection

Quadrilaterals in Architecture Have students look for and list examples of quadrilaterals in buildings. They can look first in books like Sally Morgan's *Squares and Cubes* (Thomson Learning, 1994) and then in their community.

> Quadrilaterals in my Neighborhood
>
> The windows at the community center are squares.
>
> The bricks on my house are rectangles.
>
> The border on the carpet at the library has a pattern made of parallelograms.

Unit Review and Test

Lesson Objective

● **Assess student progress on unit objectives.**

The Day at a Glance

Today's Goals	Materials
1 Assessing the Unit ▶ Assess student progress on unit objectives. ▶ Use activities from unit lessons to reteach content. **2 Extending the Assessment** ▶ Use remediation for common errors. There is no homework assignment on a test day.	Unit A Test, Student Activity Book pages 69–70 Unit A Test, Form A or B, Assessment Guide (optional) Unit A Performance Assessment, Assessment Guide (optional)

 Class Management

Review and Test Day You may want to choose a quiet game or other activity (reading a book or working on homework for another subject) for students who finish early.

Assessing the Unit

Assess Unit Objectives

45 MINUTES (more if schedule permits)

Goal: Assess student progress on unit objectives

Materials: Student Activity Book pages 69–70; Assessment Guide (optional)

▶ Review and Assessment

If your students are ready for assessment on the unit objectives, you may use either the test on the Student Activity Book pages or one of the forms of the Unit A Test in the Assessment Guide to assess student progress.

If you feel that students need some review first, you may use the test on the Student Activity Book pages as a review of unit content, and then use one of the forms of the Unit A Test in the Assessment Guide to assess student progress.

To assign a numerical score for all of these test forms, use 10 points for each question.

You may also choose to use the Unit A Performance Assessment. Scoring for that assessment can be found in its rubric in the Assessment Guide.

▶ Reteaching Resources

The chart lists the test items, the unit objectives they cover, and the lesson activities in which the objective is covered in this unit. You may revisit these activities with students who do not show mastery of the objectives.

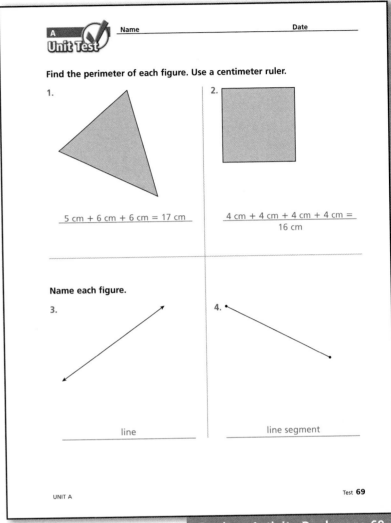

Student Activity Book page 69

Unit Test Items	Unit Objectives Tested	Activities to Use for Reteaching
1, 2	**A.1** Measure and draw line segments to the nearest centimeter and find the perimeter of geometric figures.	Lesson 1, Activities 1 and 2
3, 4, 9, 10	**A.2** Identify lines and line segments.	Lesson 2, Activity 1
5–8	**A.3** Identify and classify quadrilaterals.	Lesson 3, Activity 4 Lesson 5, Activity 1

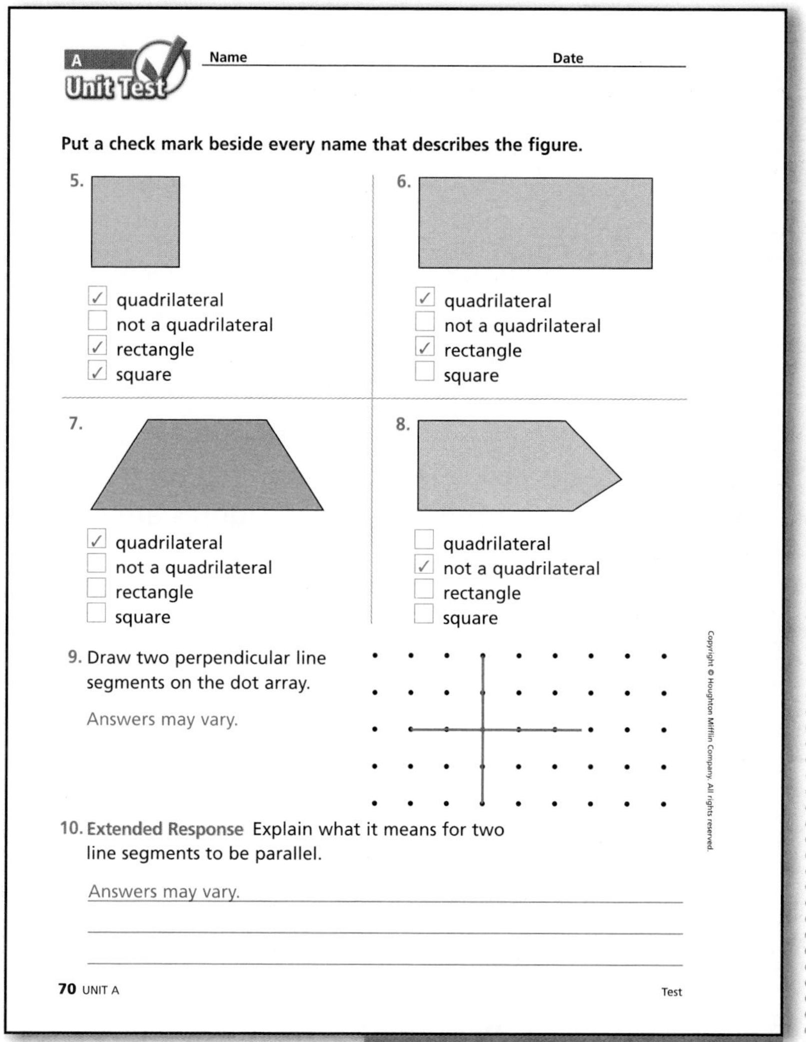

A Unit Test

Name _____ Date _____

Put a check mark beside every name that describes the figure.

5.

☑ quadrilateral
☐ not a quadrilateral
☑ rectangle
☑ square

6.

☑ quadrilateral
☐ not a quadrilateral
☑ rectangle
☐ square

7.

☑ quadrilateral
☐ not a quadrilateral
☐ rectangle
☐ square

8.

☐ quadrilateral
☑ not a quadrilateral
☐ rectangle
☐ square

9. Draw two perpendicular line segments on the dot array.

Answers may vary.

10. **Extended Response** Explain what it means for two line segments to be parallel.

Answers may vary.

_____
_____
_____

70 UNIT A   Test

Student Activity Book page 70

▶ Assessment Resources

Free Response Tests
Unit A Test, Student Activity Book pages 69–70
Unit A Test, Form A, Assessment Guide

Extended Response Item
The last item in the Student Activity Book test and in the Form A test will require an extended response as an answer.

Multiple Choice Test
Unit A Test, Form B, Assessment Guide

Performance Assessment
Unit A Performance Assessment, Assessment Guide
Unit A Performance Assessment Rubric, Assessment Guide

▶ Portfolio Assessment

Teacher-selected Items for Student Portfolios:

- Homework, Lessons 3, 5
- Class Activity work, Lessons 2, 4

Student-selected Items for Student Portfolios

- Favorite Home or School Activity
- Best Writing Prompt

② Extending the Assessment

Unit Objective A.1

Measure and draw line segments to the nearest centimeter and find the perimeter of geometric figures.

Common Error: Uses a Ruler Incorrectly

Students may not line up 0 on the ruler with the endpoint of a line to be measured.

Remediation The exact location of 0 may vary from one ruler to another. Make sure students know where the 0 indicator of their ruler is. If necessary, have them write a 0 on the ruler itself.

Common Error: Doesn't Use All Measurements

In finding perimeter, students may fail to use the lengths of all sides of a polygon.

Remediation Remind students that the number of addends used to find the perimeter must equal the number of sides of the polygon. Suggest that it may help to count the sides and the addends as a check that all sides have been included.

Unit Objective A.2

Identify lines and line segments.

Common Error: Confuses Lines and Line Segments

Students may say line segments are lines, especially if the endpoints are not specifically marked.

Remediation Explain to students that lines are of infinite (or endless) length. You can't draw a whole line, so you represent a line on paper by putting an arrowhead at each end of a line segment. The arrowheads show that the line continues without end in each direction. Also point out that line segments have endpoints and have length (the distance between the endpoints). Endpoints do not have to be marked, but they are sometimes shown as points at each end or tick marks at each end.

Line segment AB

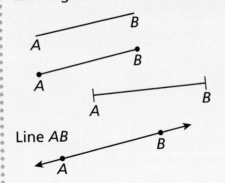

Line AB

Unit Objective A.3

Identify and classify quadrilaterals.

Common Error: Doesn't Identify Irregular 4-Sided Figures as Quadrilaterals

Students usually recognize 4-sided figures such as squares, rectangles (that are not squares), parallelograms, trapezoids, and rhombuses. These routine figures may lead them to believe that irregular 4-sided figures are not quadrilaterals.

Remediation Remind students that "quad" means "four" and that any closed 4-sided figure is a quadrilateral.

Common Error: Doesn't Differentiate Types of Figures

Students may not classify a square or a rectangle as a parallelogram, or classify a square as a rhombus.

Remediation Make side-by-side lists comparing the properties of the different figures, including the kinds of line segments used to make each figure. Remind them that all the basic properties of parallelograms are shared by squares and rectangles, and that the properties of rhombuses are shared by squares.

Addition and Subtraction Word Problems

THE GOAL FOR UNIT 2 is for students to develop effective strategies to solve many types of addition and subtraction word problems involving both single and multi-digit numbers. Students will solve addition and subtraction word problems that involve a total and two partners. One of these three numbers will be unknown. The lessons present a number of math tools that are useful for organizing information in word problems to find the solution.

Unit 2 Assessment

✓ Unit Objectives Tested	Unit Test Items	Lessons
2.1 Solve a variety of word problems involving addition and subtraction.	1–7	1–8
2.2 Write equations and use comparison bars to represent and solve word problems.	8–10	2–5

Formal Assessment

Open or Free Response Tests

- Quick Quizzes (Assessment Guide)
- Unit Review and Test (Student Activity Book pages 97–98, Teacher's Guide pages 225–228.
- Unit 2 Test Form A (Assessment Guide)
- Unit 2 Open Response Test (Test Generator)
- Test Bank Items for Unit 2 (Test Generator)

Multiple Choice Tests

- Unit 2 Test Form B (Assessment Guide)
- Unit 2 Multiple Choice Test (Test Generator)
- Test Bank Items for Unit 2 (Test Generator)

Performance Tasks

- Unit 2 Performance Assessment (Assessment Guide)

Informal Assessment

Ongoing Assessment

- In every Teacher's Guide lesson

Performance Assessment

- Class discussions
- Small-group work
- Quick Practice (in every lesson)
- Individual work on teacher-selected tasks

Portfolios

- See Unit 2 Review and Test for suggestions for selecting items for portfolios.
- Some Homework pages are noted as suitable for portfolio inclusion.

Review Opportunities

Homework and Remembering

- Homework pages provide review of recently taught topics.
- Remembering pages provide spiral review.

Teacher's Guide

- Unit Review and Test (page 225)

Test Generator CD-ROM

- Test Bank Items can be used to create custom review sheets.

Planning Unit 2

that are available in the *Math Expressions* kit.

Lesson Title	Lesson Resources	Materials and Manipulatives	
		Math Expressions	Other
1 Addition and Subtraction Situations	Family Letter Student Activity Book pages 71–76 Teacher's Resource Book Problem Bank 1 Homework and Remembering pages 41–42	MathBoard materials	Pointer, chart paper, number cubes (0–5, 1–6, 4–9), Math Journals
2 Word Problems with Unknown Partners	Student Activity Book pages 77–78 Teacher's Resource Book Problem Bank 2 Homework and Remembering pages 43–44	MathBoard materials, Centimeter Grid Paper (Copymaster M31)	Chart paper, number cubes (1–6, 4–9), Chart from Lesson 1, markers, *A Bundle of Beasts* by Mark Steele and Patricia Hooper (Houghton Mifflin, 1987), Math Journals
3 Word Problems with Unknown Starts	Student Activity Book pages 79–80 Teacher's Resource Book Problem Bank 3 Homework and Remembering pages 45–46	MathBoard materials	Index cards, Math Journals
4 Comparison Problems	Student Activity Book pages 81–82 Teacher's Resource Book Problem Bank 4 Homework and Remembering pages 47–48	MathBoard materials, Spinner B (Copymaster M35), Game Cards (Copymaster M25), Hundred Chart (Copymaster M34)	Number cubes (0–5, 4–9), two-color counters, paper clips, Math Journals
5 Comparison Problems with Misleading Language	Student Activity Book pages 83–84 Teacher's Resource Book Problem Bank 5 Homework and Remembering pages 49–50 **Quick Quiz 1**	MathBoard materials, Game Cards (Copymaster M25)	Two-color counters, Math Journals
6 Multi-Digit Unknown Partner and Unknown Start Problems	Student Activity Book pages 85–88 Teacher's Resource Book Problem Banks 6–8 Homework and Remembering pages 51–52	MathBoard materials	Sentence strips, calculators, Math Journals
7 Multi-Digit Comparison Problems	Student Activity Book pages 89–92 Teacher's Resource Book Problem Banks 9–10 Homework and Remembering pages 53–54	MathBoard materials, Multi-Digit Addition Race (Copymaster M36), Cross-Number Puzzle (Copymaster M37)	Two-color counters, calculators (optional), Math Journals
8 Mixed Multi-Digit Word Problems	Student Activity Book pages 93–96 Teacher's Resource Book Problem Banks 11 and 12 Homework and Remembering pages 55–56 **Quick Quiz 2**	MathBoard materials	Math Journals
Unit Review and Test	Student Activity Book pages 97–98 Assessment Guide		

163D UNIT 2 Overview

Unit 2 Teaching Resources

Differentiated Instruction

Reaching All Learners

Extra Help

Lesson 2, page 175
Lesson 4, page 191
Lesson 5, page 197
Lesson 7, page 211
Lesson 7, page 214

English Learners

Lesson 1, page 166
Lesson 1, page 170
Lesson 2, page 175
Lesson 2, page 176
Lesson 3, page 180
Lesson 4, page 187
Lesson 6, page 203

Individualizing Instruction

Activities
• Intervention (in every lesson)
• On Level (in every lesson)
• Challenge (in every lesson)

Math Writing Prompts
• Intervention (in every lesson)
• On Level (in every lesson)
• Challenge (in every lesson)

Challenge Masters
• (for every lesson)

Cross-Curricular Links • Home or School Activities

 Sports Connection
Sports Problems (Lesson 3, page 184)

 Science Connections
Many Moons (Lesson 4, page 194)
Compare Pulse Rates (Lesson 7, page 216)

 Language Arts Connection
Tall Tales (Lesson 6, page 208)

 Real-World Connection
Local Comparisons (Lesson 5, page 200)

 Art Connection
Create an Advertisement (Lesson 8, page 224)

 Literature Connection
A Bundle of Beasts (Lesson 2, page 178)

Teaching Unit 2

Putting Research into Practice for Unit 2

From Our Curriculum Research Project:
The Underlying Meaning and Structure of Word Problems

Word problems form an essential part of the *Math Expressions* curriculum. They reinforce one of the program's main goals: the integration of student's real-world experiences with math concepts. In this unit, students are encouraged to analyze the meaning and structure of different types of addition and subtraction word problems. When analyzing word problems, students are encouraged to look for patterns in the structure of the problems in order to find solution methods.

Research has found that students approach word problems in different ways, and they use various strategies to solve word problems. Some students will use tools such as Math Mountains, equations, and Comparison bars, while others invent methods to solve the word problem.

Because students may use various methods to solve word problems, it is important to use the **Solve and Discuss** structure to have students explain their strategies and solution methods. If students have difficulty explaining their work or are prone to error, others can model other accessible methods for students to use

Fuson, Karen C. *Children's Math World Video Research Report,* 2005

Fuson, Karen C. *Children's Math World Field Test Teacher's Guide Grade 3*

From Current Research:
Word Problems: Different Types of Problems

Four basic classes of addition and subtraction problems can be identified: problems involving (a) joining, (b) separating, (c) part-part-whole relations, and (d) comparison relations. Problems within a class involve the same type of action or relation, but within each class several distinct types of problems can be identified depending on which quantity is the unknown.

. . . Children's proficiency [in solving problems] gradually develops in two significant directions. One is from having a different solution method for each type of problem to developing a single general method that can be used for classes of problems with a similar mathematical structure. Another direction is toward more efficient calculation procedures. . . . For word problems, these procedures are essentially abstractions of direct modeling that continue to reflect the actions and relations in the problems.

National Research Council. "Developing Proficiency with Whole Numbers." *Adding It Up: Helping Children Learn Mathematics.* Washington, D.C.: National Academy Press, 2001. pp. 184, 186.

Other Useful References: Addition and Subtraction Word Problems

Carpenter, Thomas P., Fennema, E., Franke, M.L., Empson, S.B., & Levi, L.W. *Children's Mathematics: Cognitively Guided Instruction.* Portsmouth, NH: Heinemann, 1999.

Carpenter, Thomas P. "Learning to add and subtract: An exercise in problem solving." *Teaching and learning mathematical problem solving: Multiple research perspectives,* E.A. Silver (Ed.). Hillsdale, NJ: Erlbaum, 1985. pp. 17–40.

Math Background

Some Types of Word Problems

Unknown Partner Problems

• In "unknown partner" problems, one of the partners is not given—it is unknown. Unknown partner problems can involve *put together, take apart, change plus,* and *change minus* situations. *Change plus* and *change minus* problems provide a quantity which is modified by a change—something is added or subtracted—which results in a new quantity.

Unknown Partner: Put Together

Stacy invited 9 girls and some boys to her party. 16 children were invited in all. How many boys were invited?

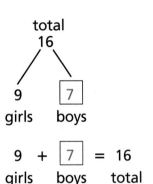

$$9 \; + \; \boxed{7} \; = \; 16$$
girls   boys   total

Unknown Partner: Take Apart

There were 15 people at the park. 7 were playing soccer. The others were playing softball. How many people were playing softball?

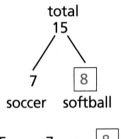

$$15 \; - \; 7 \; = \; \boxed{8}$$
total   soccer   softball

Unknown Start Problems

• In "unknown start" problems, the starting number is the unknown number.

Unknown Start: Change Plus

Greta's chicken laid some eggs. Then the chicken laid 7 more. Now Greta has 13 eggs. How many eggs did the chicken lay at the start?

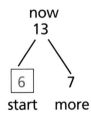

situation equation:

$$\boxed{6} \; + \; 7 \; = \; 13$$
start   more   now

solution equations:

$$7 + \boxed{6} = 13$$

$$13 - 7 = \boxed{6}$$

Unknown Start: Change Minus

Patricia was carrying some books. Her friend took 3 of them. Patricia has 8 books left. How many books was she carrying at first?

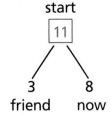

situation equation:

$$\boxed{11} \; - \; 3 \; = \; 8$$
start   friend   now

solution equations:

$$8 \; + \; 3 \; = \; \boxed{11}$$

Patterns in Unknown Partner Problems

As students explore the different problem structures described above, they begin to see the following general patterns:

• If the total is unknown, it can be found by adding the partners.
• If one of the partners is unknown, it can be found by subtracting the known partner from the total, or adding on from the known partner to the total.

Representation

Using Math Tools to Represent Word Problems

Students should be encouraged to use a variety of solution strategies for the word problems in this unit. However, the lessons do present math tools that are useful for organizing the information in the problems and finding the solution. These tools become especially important when the focus shifts later in this unit, from word problems with single-digit numbers to those with multi-digit numbers.

Math Tool: Math Mountains

Students use Math Mountains to show a total and two partners. The total is written at the top of the mountain, and the partners are written at the bottom. Students can imagine that the total splits into two parts that roll down opposite sides of the mountain. Eight equations can be written for a given Math Mountain.

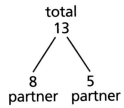

$13 = 8 + 5$	$8 + 5 = 13$
$13 = 5 + 8$	$5 + 8 = 13$
$8 = 13 - 5$	$13 - 5 = 8$
$5 = 13 - 8$	$13 - 8 = 5$

Math Tool: Comparison Bars

Comparison problems involve one quantity that is more than or less than another quantity. The unknown in a comparison problem may be the smaller quantity, the larger quantity, or the difference between quantities. Making Comparison Bars can help students organize the information in the problem and figure out how to find the unknown.

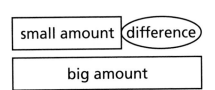

To solve a particular comparison problem, students must ask themselves: *Who has more* (or *fewer*)? and *How many more* (or *fewer*)? They can use this information to label a set of Comparison Bars. For example, consider the problem:

Louis ate 14 crackers.
Walt ate 5 fewer crackers than Louis.
How many crackers did Walt eat?

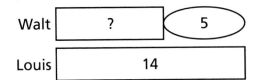

Addition and Subtraction Situations

Lesson Objectives

- Represent and solve a variety of word problems.
- Review the relationship between addition and subtraction.

Vocabulary

unknown partner	addend
equation	change plus
total	change minus
sum	put together
partner	take apart

The Day at a Glance

Today's Goals	Materials	Math Talk
Quick Practice Find the unknown partner. **1 Teaching the Lesson** A1: Discuss Math Mountains. A2: Review word problems. A3: Explore the relationship between addition and subtraction. A4: Explore math language for addition and subtraction equations. **2 Extending the Lesson** ▶ Differentiated Instruction **3 Homework and Spiral Review**	Quick Practice materials MathBoard materials Chart paper Number cubes Student Activity Book pages 71–76 Homework and Remembering pages 41–42 Math Journals Family Letter	In today's activities, the students are involved in discussion as they ▶ talk about Math Mountains ▶ review word problems ▶ explore math language ▶ review the relationship between addition and subtraction

Quick Practice

5 MINUTES **Goal:** Find the unknown partner.
Materials: pointer

Unknown Partner Addition: Write these equations on the board:

$$9 + \boxed{} = 15 \qquad 90 + \boxed{} = 150 \qquad 900 + \boxed{} = 1{,}500$$

$$9 + \boxed{} = 17 \qquad 90 + \boxed{} = 170 \qquad 900 + \boxed{} = 1{,}700$$

Have the Student Leader direct the class to complete the equations. Then one student explains the Make a Ten, Make a Hundred, or Make a Thousand strategies.

Leader: (pointing to the first equation) Equation
Class: 9 plus 6 equals 15.
Student: 9 plus 1 is 10 plus 5 more is 15.

Teaching Note

Language and Vocabulary When reading an equation that has a box representing an unknown number, such as $9 + \square = 15$, read the equation as "Nine plus what number equals 15," rather than "Nine plus box equals 15."

Teaching the Lesson

Discuss Math Mountains

 10 MINUTES

Goal: Discuss Math Mountains.

Materials: MathBoard materials, Student Activity Book page 71

 NCTM Standards:
Number and Operations
Algebra
Communication

Class Management

Math Mountains Students who used *Math Expressions* in a previous grade will be very familiar with Math Mountains. If most of your students understand Math Mountains, you can move through this activity quickly. If they are unfamiliar with them, you may need to spend more than one day on this lesson. Math Mountains are important for solving more complex types of word problems.

The Learning Classroom

Building Concepts To foster algebraic understanding, we associate eight equations, rather than four, with a Math Mountain. It is important for students to see equations with only one number on the left (for example, $11 = 7 + 4$ and $4 = 11 - 7$) as early as possible. In *Math Expressions*, students are introduced to equations such as $5 = 2 + 3$ beginning in kindergarten.

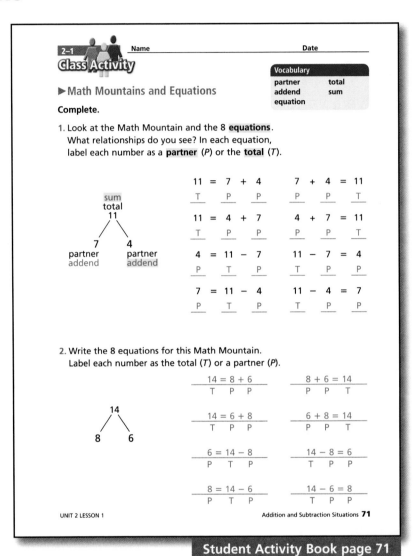

Student Activity Book page 71

▶ Math Mountains and Equations [WHOLE CLASS]

Have students look at the Math Mountain in exercise 1 on Student Activity Book page 71. Explain that a Math Mountain shows the relationship between a total (sum) and its two partners (addends)—that is, the two partners or addends when added equal the total or sum. Eight equations are associated with every Math Mountain.

Discuss the vocabulary associated with Math Mountains.

- **What does the word *partner* or *addend* mean?** one of two numbers that add to make a total

- **How do the two smaller numbers in the Math Mountain work as partners?** They add to make a total.

- **What does *sum* mean?** the result of adding

Discuss the formal math words *addend* and *sum,* relating them to the words *partner* and *total.* Explain that partner and total are used to make the relationships easier to remember.

Ask students how the equations in exercise 1 are related to the Math Mountain and how they are related to one another. Have students label the total and partners in each equation, using the labels *T* and *P.* Then ask students what patterns they notice when they look at where the totals and partners are in the equations.

Have students look at the Math Mountain in exercise 2. Using the **Solve and Discuss** structure, ask them to generate the eight equations associated with it. Tell them to label the partners and total in each equation.

If students need more practice, create additional Math Mountains and have students write the corresponding equations.

123 **Math Talk** Ask questions to check students' understanding of Math Mountains and the corresponding equations:

- **How many numbers does a Math Mountain always have?** 3 numbers

- **Where do we find the total in a Math Mountain?** at the top

- **Where do we find the two partners?** at the bottom

- **Where do we find the total and partners in an addition equation?** The total is on one side of the equals sign, and the two partners are on the other side.

- **Where do we find the total and partners in a subtraction equation?** The total and one partner are on one side, with the total given first, and the other partner is on the other side.

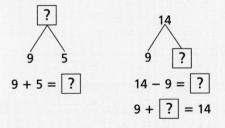

Teaching the Lesson (continued)

Introduction to Word Problems

 15 MINUTES

Goal: Review word problems.

Materials: MathBoard materials, Student Activity Book pages 72–74

 NCTM Standards:
Number and Operations
Algebra
Problem Solving
Communication

Class Management

Observing Students Most of the problem types introduced today will be familiar to your students. These activities will give you a chance to observe how your students approach word problems and the strategies they use. This lesson should focus more on discussion than on instruction.

Differentiated Instruction

English Learners Word problems generally present a challenge for English learners. The Solve and Discuss classroom structure provides the opportunity for students to communicate their strategies aloud. This enables students to not only check their understanding, but also their ability to communicate effectively to others. Be sure that English learners are an integral part of this activity.

2-1 **Class Activity**   Name _____ Date _____

▶ Solve and Discuss

Solve each problem. Label your answers.

Show your work.

Check student's work.

3. **Change Plus** Chris picked 8 apples. His mother picked 6 more. How many apples do they have now?

14 apples

4. **Change Minus** Chris had 14 apples. He ate 8 of them. How many apples does he have now?

6 apples

5. **Put Together** Alison has 7 juice boxes. Taylor has 5 juice boxes. How many juice boxes do they have altogether?

12 juice boxes

6. **Take Apart** There are 12 juice boxes at the picnic. Alison puts 7 on the table and leaves the rest in the cooler. How many juice boxes are in the cooler?

5 juice boxes

72 UNIT 2 LESSON 1   Addition and Subtraction Situations

Student Activity Book page 72

▶ Solve and Discuss [WHOLE CLASS]

Read problem 3 on Student Activity Book page 72. Using **Solve and Discuss,** have students solve the problem by making simple drawings on their MathBoards. Although students may not need to make drawings to solve this problem, the drawings can help explain their thinking to their classmates. See sample drawings on the next page.

Here are some drawings students might make.

Math Mountain	Count All
now T 14 / \\ 8 6 P P Chris Mom	14 now [OOOOOOO] [OOOOOO] Chris Mom
Equation	**Count On**
8 + 6 = 14 P P T	8 [OOOOOO] 14 had count on now 6 more

Repeat this process for problem 4.

Here are some drawings students might make.

Math Mountain	Count On to Student
T Chris 14 / \\ 8 6 Ate Now	14 – 8 = ? 8 + ? = 14 8 oooooo 8 + 6 = 14 14 – 8 = 6
Equation	**Use a Drawing**
14 – 8 = 6 T P P	⊗⊗⊗⊗⊗⊗⊗⊗ooooooo 14 – 8 = 6

Next, direct students' attention to the labels for problems 3 and 4. Ask students why they think these problems are labeled *Change Plus* and *Change Minus.* A group of things changes over time because something is either added (*Change Plus*) or taken away (*Change Minus*).

Repeat **Solve and Discuss** for problems 5 and 6. Point out to the class the various solution methods students use (making drawings, writing equations, and so on). Discuss the different ways students labeled their work. Ask students why these problems are labeled *put together* and *take apart.* Two groups of things are put together or a total is taken apart to form two groups.

Activity continued ▶

The Learning Classroom

Building Concepts When solving word problems, it is important that students label their drawings and equations so that they can follow their own thinking and so that others can understand their work. In Change Plus and Change Minus problems, they may want to write action words such as *first, then,* and *now* to help represent the problem situation.

Teaching Note

Watch For! When some students subtract, they start with the total and try to count backward to find the difference. This method is awkward and prone to error. Once students see that subtraction involves finding an unknown partner, they can find the unknown partner by counting on from the known partner to the total. Counting on for subtraction should be encouraged because it is much easier and it makes the connection between subtraction and addition clearer. (The last activity in Unit 1 Lesson 3 reviews subtracting by counting on.)

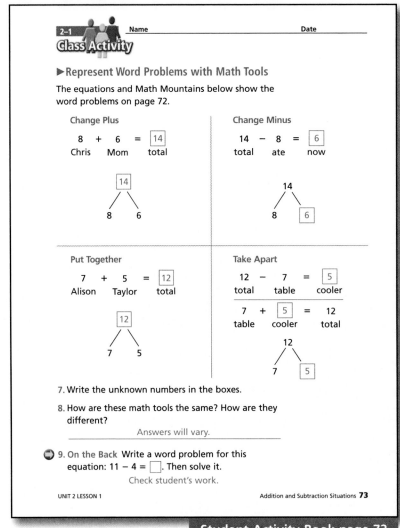

Student Activity Book page 73

►Represent Word Problems with Math Tools

WHOLE CLASS

Direct students' attention to the equations and Math Mountains on the top of Student Activity book page 73. Have students relate these math tools to problems 3–6 on Student Activity Book page 72. Compare the patterns students see in the Math Mountains and the problems. Discuss how they are alike and how they are different.

Be sure students understand that they are finding the unknown partner when they subtract. Have them look at the math tools for a Take Apart problem. Discuss the fact that it is possible to think about this as either an addition or a subtraction problem. Students should understand these points.

● Take Apart as Subtraction: There are a total of 12 juice boxes, and we need to figure out how many are left after we *take away,* or *subtract,* 7.

● Take Apart as Addition: There are 7 juice boxes on the table, and we need to figure out how many boxes we need to *add* to get the total of 12.

Have students complete the page to reinforce the relationships between addition and subtraction problems and between Math Mountains and equations.

Relate Addition and Subtraction

▶ Discuss Related Addition and Subtraction Problems [WHOLE CLASS]

Have students look back at problems 3 and 4 on Student Activity Book page 72. Ask them how these problems are related. Discuss that in problem 3 we start with 8 and add 6 to get a total of 14. In problem 4 we start with a total of 14 and take away 8, leaving 6. These problems undo each other.

Next, ask students how the Math Mountains for problems 3 and 4 shown under Change Plus and Change Minus on Student Activity Book page 73 are related. They should notice that in the Math Mountain for problem 3, the total is unknown. In problem 4, a partner is unknown. However, with the unknown numbers filled in, the Math Mountains are the same.

Finally, ask how the equations for problems 3 and 4 shown under Change Plus and Change Minus on Student Activity Book page 73 are related. Discuss the fact that addition and subtraction equations undo each other. In the addition equation, we add two partners to get a total. In the subtraction equation, we start with the total and take away one of the partners to get the other partner. Point out that now that the unknown numbers in the equations are filled in, the partners and totals in the equations are identical.

Have students look back at problems 5 and 6 on Student Activity page 72. Discuss how the problems undo each other.

- In problem 5, we start with 7 and add 5 to get a total of 12. In problem 6, we start with a total of 12 and take away 7, leaving 5.

Ask how the Math Mountains shown under Put Together and Take Apart on Student Activity page 73 are related.

- In the Math Mountain for problem 5, the total is unknown. In the Math Mountain for problem 6, a partner is unknown.

- With the numbers filled in, the Math Mountains are the same.

Ask how the equations for problems 5 and 6 undo each other.

- In the addition equation, we add two partners to get a total.

- In the subtraction equation, we start with a total and take away one of the partners.

 20 MINUTES

Goal: Explore the relationship between addition and subtraction.

Materials: Student Activity Book pages 72–74

 NCTM Standards:
Number and Operations
Algebra
Problem Solving
Communication

 Class Management

If your students still direct their explanations to you rather than to the other students, move to the side or the back of the room and direct the class from there. Try to keep from giving answers and filling in explanations so that the students will learn to do this themselves.

Explore Math Language

 10 MINUTES

Goal: Explore math language for addition and subtraction equations.

Materials: Student Activity Book page 72, chart paper

 NCTM Standards:
Number and Operations
Problem Solving
Communication

 Ongoing Assessment

Present the following problem, question, and instructions to the students.

Russ had 12 grapes. He ate 4 of them. How many grapes does he have now?

▶ Is the problem a change plus or a change minus problem?

Then have students:

▶ draw a Math Mountain for the problem,

▶ write an equation for the problem, and

▶ give the solution

 Class Management

Looking Ahead This chart will be used over the next few days, so leave it posted and add new ideas as they emerge.

▶ **Discuss Math Language** WHOLE CLASS

Divide a sheet of chart paper into four sections labeled *Change Plus, Change Minus, Put Together,* and *Take Apart.*

Have students look again at problem 3 on Student Activity Book, page 72. Ask students to restate the question in different ways. Possible questions students might generate are:

● What is the total number of apples that they have?

● How many apples do they have altogether?

● How many apples do they have in all?

● How many apples do they have now?

Create a chart like the one below on chart paper. Then fill in the chart with new ways to ask a *change plus* question that were suggested by students. Repeat this process for the other three types of problems. This chart shows some common math questions for each problem type:

Change Plus	Change Minus
What is the total number?	How many are left?
How many altogether?	How many now?
How many in all?	How many remain?
How many now?	How many are still there?

Put Together	Take Apart
How many altogether?	How many remain?
How many in all?	How many are left?
How many total?	How many are (the other kind)?

Be sure that **English learners** participate in this important language exercise.

② Extending the Lesson

Intervention
for students having difficulty

PAIRS

Roll a Math Mountain

Materials: Number cubes (2 per pair, labeled 0-5 and 1-6); MathBoard materials

One student rolls two number cubes and uses the numbers in a Math Mountain. Then the student writes an addition equation on the MathBoard. The other student writes the related subtraction equation under the addition equation. Students switch roles and repeat the activity.

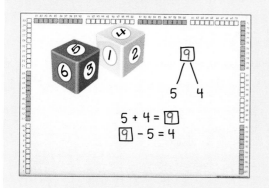

On Level
for students having success

PAIRS

Math Mountain Equations

Materials: Number cubes (4 per pair, 2 labeled 1-6, 2 labeled 4-9), MathBoard materials

Each student rolls two number cubes and uses the numbers to write as many unknown addition and subtraction equations on the MathBoard as possible. Students switch MathBoards and solve the equations. If time allows, repeat the activity.

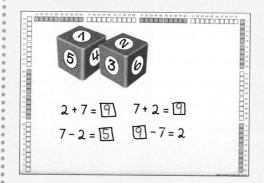

Challenge
for students seeking a challenge

PAIRS

Math Mountain Puzzles

Materials: Number cubes (2 per pair, labeled 1-6 and 4-9)

Each student sets up three blank Math Mountains on their MathBoards. One of the students rolls both cubes. Each student uses those numbers to fill in Math Mountains on their own board.

For example, if a 2 and a 5 are rolled, students can fill any blank spaces with those two numbers. Or, students can add the numbers together and fill in one blank space (7) or subtract the numbers and fill in one blank space (3).

The first student to complete all three Math Mountains wins.

Also Use
Challenge Master for 2-1

 Math Writing Prompt

Intervention

Explain How You Know
Explain how you can find a missing number in a Math Mountain.

 Math Writing Prompt

On Level

Compare and Contrast
How are a Change Plus problem and a Change Minus problem different? How are they alike?

 Math Writing Prompt

Challenge

Explain Your Thinking
Joni said, "I can either add or subtract to solve a Take Apart problem." Write an explanation of what Joni means.

③ Homework and Spiral Review

This Homework page gives students additional practice in solving problems and relating addition and subtraction.

This Remembering page would be appropriate anytime after today's lesson.

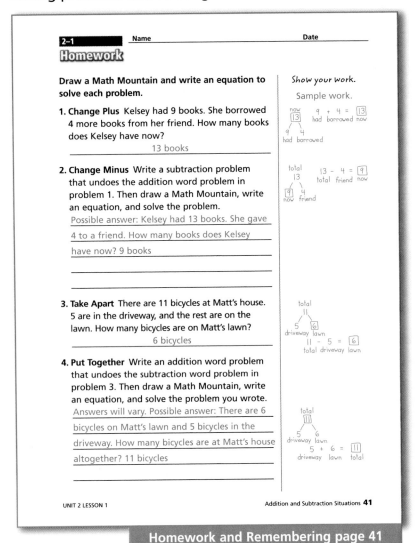

Homework and Remembering page 41

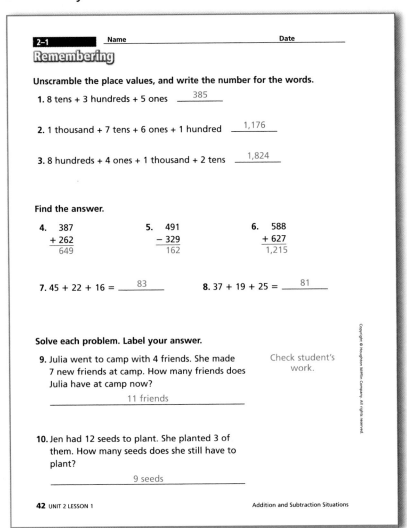

Homework and Remembering page 42

Home and School Connection

Family Letter Have students take home the Family Letter on Student Activity Book page 75. This letter explains how the concept of solving addition and subtraction word problems is developed in *Math Expressions*. It gives parents and guardians a better understanding of the learning that goes on in math class and creates a bridge between school and home. A Spanish translation of this letter is on the following page in the Student Activity Book.

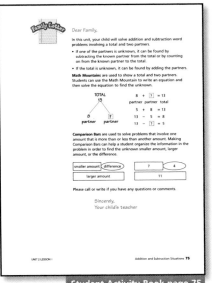

Student Activity Book page 75

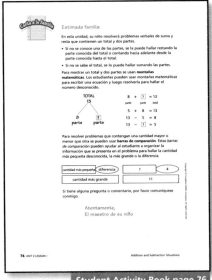

Student Activity Book page 76

Word Problems with Unknown Partners

Lesson Objectives

- Represent and solve a variety of word problems.
- Review the relationship between addition and subtraction.

Vocabulary

put together	change plus
take apart	change minus

The Day at a Glance

Today's Goals	Materials	123 Math Talk
Quick Practice Find the unknown partner.	MathBoard materials	In today's activities, the students are involved in discussion as they
1 Teaching the Lesson **A1:** Review the relationship between addition and subtraction. **A2:** Solve word problems with unknown partners.	Chart from Lesson 1 Chart paper Equation Challenge (Copymaster M33) Number cubes	▶ solve word problems involving addition and subtraction
2 Extending the Lesson ▶ Differentiated Instruction	Markers Math Journals	▶ review the relationship between addition and subtraction
3 Homework and Spiral Review	Student Activity Book pages 77–78 Homework and Remembering pages 41, 43–44 *A Bundle of Beasts* by Mark Steele and Patricia Hooper (Houghton Mifflin, 1987)	

Quick Practice

 5 MINUTES   **Goal:** Find the unknown partner in addition equations.

Unknown Partner Addition: Write these equations on the board. A Student Leader directs the class to complete the equations and to explain the Make a Ten, Make a Hundred, or Make a Thousand Strategies. (See Unit 2 Lesson 1.)

$$9 + \boxed{} = 13 \qquad 90 + \boxed{} = 130 \qquad 900 + \boxed{} = 1{,}300$$
$$9 + \boxed{} = 16 \qquad 90 + \boxed{} = 160 \qquad 900 + \boxed{} = 1{,}600$$

① Teaching the Lesson

Activity 1

Review Addition and Subtraction Relationships

 15 MINUTES

Goal: Review the relationship between addition and subtraction.

Materials: MathBoard materials, Homework and Remembering page 41, chart from Lesson 1

 NCTM Standards:
Number and Operations
Problem Solving
Communication

 Math Talk in Action

Write 5 + 7 on the board.

What is the sum?

Clarisse: The sum is 12.

How can you use subtraction to undo the addition?

Gregory: Subtract 7 from 12

Evita: You can also subtract 5 from 12.

Now write 11 − 8 on the board.

What is the difference?

Yuri: 3

How can you use addition to undo the subtraction?

Berta: You can add 3 + 8 or you can add 8 + 3.

▶ **Review How Addition and Subtraction Undo Each Other** | WHOLE CLASS |

Review problems 1–4 from Lesson 1 Homework and Remembering page 41. Have two or three students present their answers for problems 1 and 2. They should share the Math Mountain and equation for problem 1, the word problem written for problem 2, and the equation and Math Mountain for problem 2.

Here are possible examples of students' answers.

Problem 1: Kelsey had 9 books. She borrowed 4 more books from her friend. How many books does Kelsey have now?

$$\text{now} \boxed{13}$$
$$9 + 4 = \boxed{13} \qquad 9 + 4 = \boxed{13}$$
$$\text{K} \quad \text{f} \quad \text{now} \qquad \text{K} \quad \text{f} \quad \text{total}$$
$$9 \quad 4$$
$$\text{Kelsey} \quad \text{friend}$$

Possible problem for problem 2: Kelsey had 13 books. She gave 4 of the books to a friend. How many books does Kelsey have now?

$$\text{had} \quad 13$$
$$13 - 4 = \boxed{9}$$
$$\text{had} \quad \text{gave} \quad \text{now}$$
$$\text{away}$$
$$4 \quad \boxed{9}$$
$$\text{gave} \quad \text{now}$$
$$\text{away}$$

Discuss whether the problem written for problem 2 actually undoes problem 1. Compare the equations and Math Mountains for the two problems. Then repeat the process for problems 3 and 4.

Next, review problem 5. Have students share their new ways of asking the questions. Add any new questions or terms students suggest to the chart your class started in Lesson 1.

 Math Talk Lead students to describe and summarize the relationship between addition and subtraction. See **Math Talk in Action** in side column for a sample of classroom discussion.

Introduce Word Problems with Unknown Partners

2-2
Class Activity

Name _____ Date _____

▶ Solve Unknown Partner Word Problems

Draw a Math Mountain and write and label an
equation to solve each problem.

Show your work.
Check student's
work.

1. **Put Together: Unknown Partner** Stacy invited
   9 girls and some boys to her party. 16 children
   were invited in all. How many boys were
   invited?

   _____ 7 boys

2. **Take Apart: Unknown Partner** There were
   15 people at the park. 7 were playing soccer.
   The others were playing softball. How many
   people were playing softball?

   _____ 8 people

3. **Change Plus: Unknown Partner** Jan planted
   8 tulips last week. Today she planted some lilies.
   Now she has 17 flowers. How many lilies did she
   plant?

   _____ 9 lilies

4. **Change Minus: Unknown Partner** Tim had
   14 tennis balls. Then his brother borrowed
   some. Now Tim has 6 tennis balls. How many
   did his brother borrow?

   _____ 8 tennis balls

UNIT 2 LESSON 2   Word Problems with Unknown Partners **77**

Student Activity Book page 77

▶ Solve Unknown Partner Word Problems | WHOLE CLASS

Using the **Solve and Discuss** structure, have students solve problem 1 on
Student Activity Book page 77. Some students will think of this as an
addition, while others will think of it as a subtraction.

$$9 \quad + \quad \square \quad = \quad 16 \qquad or \qquad 16 \quad - \quad 9 \quad = \quad \square$$
girls   boys   children   children   girls   boys

Ask students why we might call problem 1 an *unknown partner
problem.* We don't know one of the partners. It is unknown.

Use **Solve and Discuss** for problems 2–4. Students usually write addition
equations for change plus situations (for example, 8 + ☐ = 17 for
problem 3) and subtraction equations for change minus situations (for
example, 14 − ☐ = 6 for problem 4). Some students may make math
drawings. Leave the equations and Math Mountains on the board.

Activity continued ▶

40 MINUTES

Goal: Solve word problems with
unknown partners.

Materials: MathBoard materials,
chart paper, Student Activity Book
pages 77–78

 NCTM Standards:
Number and Operations
Algebra
Problem Solving
Communication

Differentiated Instruction

Extra Help The level of difficulty
your students experience with word
problems with unknown partners will
depend on their familiarity with
Math Expressions, their reading
ability, their English proficiency, and
their understanding of addition and
subtraction. Help your students,
particularly **English Learners,** focus
on understanding the situations in
the word problems. The math may be
easy, but the situations and language
may be unfamiliar. Retelling, acting
out, or drawing problem situations
might be helpful.

 Ongoing Assessment

Circulate around the room as
students complete the Math
Mountains and equations. Be sure
they match the situations described
in the word problems. Determine
whether student errors stem from
misinterpretation of a situation or
from incorrect computation.

❶ Teaching the Lesson (continued)

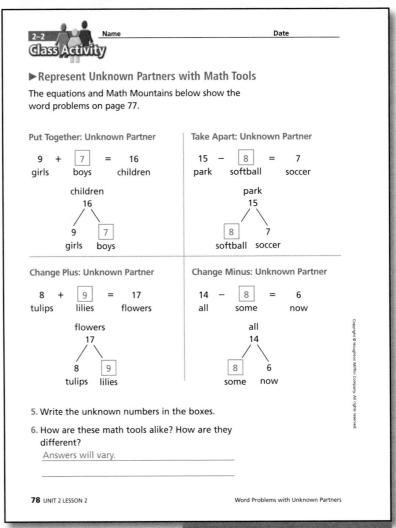

Student Activity Book page 78

▶ Represent Unknown Partners with Math Tools

WHOLE CLASS

Direct students attention to the equations and Math Mountains shown on Student Activity Book page 78, which correspond to problems 1–4. Discuss the relationships students see between these math tools and problems 1–4. Some relationships they might mention are that the Put Together and Change Plus problems both have addition equations and the Take Apart and Change Minus problems both have subtraction equations.

Have students discuss any differences between the Math Mountains and equations they wrote on the board and those on page 78. For example, the order of the partners in the Math Mountains may be different.

If a Math Mountain or equation on the page is not on the board, have a student explain how it models the problem situation. Ask students how they would solve some of the equations.

Have students complete the page to reinforce the relationships between addition and subtraction and between Math Mountains and equations.

② Extending the Lesson

Differentiated Instruction — Activities for Individualizing

Intervention
for students having difficulty

PAIRS

Picture It

Materials: Chart paper, Math Journals

Write these two unknown start problems on the board or on chart paper. Have students draw a comic strip, cartoon, diagram, or other visual aid to show they grasp the main idea of each problem. Have them include a labeled Math Mountain for each problem.

> Liz just mailed some party invitations. She'll mail the other 9 after she gets more stamps. She will send 17 invitations in all. How many did Liz already mail?
>
> Liz got a bag of balloons. 7 of them are round. The other 5 are long. How many balloons are in the bag?

On Level
for students having success

INDIVIDUALS

Find the Errors

Materials: Math Journals

Write the following equations on the board. Tell students that each equation has an error in it.

$$16 = 8 - \boxed{8}$$
$$7 - 9 = \boxed{16}$$
$$14 = \boxed{7} + 6$$
$$15 + \boxed{7} = 8$$

Have students copy the equation as given, and then write a true equation by changing **one** number or symbol. Tell students to first circle the part they want to change, and then write the true equation below or beside the original one.

$$16 = 8 \ominus 8$$
$$16 = 8 + 8$$

Challenge
for students seeking a challenge

PAIRS

Equation Challenge

Materials: Equation Challenge (Copymaster M33), number cubes (labeled 1–6, 4–9, 2 per pair), markers in two different colors (2 per pair)

One student rolls both cubes and tries to use the numbers to fill in missing partners or totals, or to write new equations on the grid. If both numbers cannot be used, just one number can be selected. If neither number can be used, the student loses his or her turn, and play continues on with the other student.

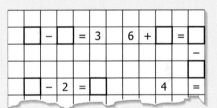

Students can play as long as time allows or until they run out of room on the sheet. The student who has filled in the most squares wins.

Also Use
Challenge Master for 2-2

 Math Writing Prompt

Intervention

Explain Your Thinking
Identify the partners and the total in this equation: $12 = 5 + 7$. Explain how you know which numbers are the partners and which is the total.

 Math Writing Prompt

On Level

Check for Errors
Sonia wrote $15 - 8 = 6$. Explain how you can check if she is correct.

 Math Writing Prompt

Challenge

Relate
Use a subtraction equation to solve $22 = \boxed{} + 10$. Explain your thinking.

 # Homework and Spiral Review

2–2 Homework **Goal:** Additional Practice

✓ Include students' completed Homework page as part of their portfolios.

2–2 Remembering **Goal:** Spiral Review

This Remembering page would be appropriate anytime after today's lesson.

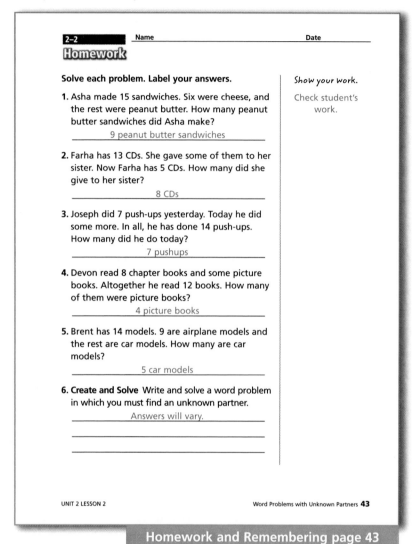

2–2 Homework

Name _____ Date _____

Solve each problem. Label your answers.

Show your work.

Check student's work.

1. Asha made 15 sandwiches. Six were cheese, and the rest were peanut butter. How many peanut butter sandwiches did Asha make?
   _____ 9 peanut butter sandwiches _____

2. Farha has 13 CDs. She gave some of them to her sister. Now Farha has 5 CDs. How many did she give to her sister?
   _____ 8 CDs _____

3. Joseph did 7 push-ups yesterday. Today he did some more. In all, he has done 14 push-ups. How many did he do today?
   _____ 7 pushups _____

4. Devon read 8 chapter books and some picture books. Altogether he read 12 books. How many of them were picture books?
   _____ 4 picture books _____

5. Brent has 14 models. 9 are airplane models and the rest are car models. How many are car models?
   _____ 5 car models _____

6. **Create and Solve** Write and solve a word problem in which you must find an unknown partner.
   _____ Answers will vary. _____
   _____
   _____

UNIT 2 LESSON 2 — Word Problems with Unknown Partners **43**

Homework and Remembering page 43

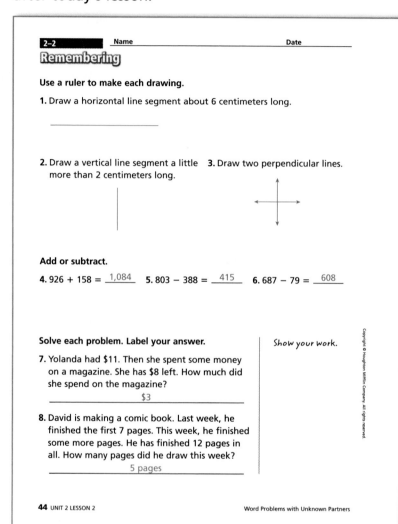

2–2 Remembering

Name _____ Date _____

Use a ruler to make each drawing.

1. Draw a horizontal line segment about 6 centimeters long.
   _____

2. Draw a vertical line segment a little more than 2 centimeters long.

3. Draw two perpendicular lines.

Add or subtract.

4. $926 + 158 = $ _1,084_   5. $803 - 388 = $ _415_   6. $687 - 79 = $ _608_

Solve each problem. Label your answer.

Show your work.

7. Yolanda had $11. Then she spent some money on a magazine. She has $8 left. How much did she spend on the magazine?
   _____ $3 _____

8. David is making a comic book. Last week, he finished the first 7 pages. This week, he finished some more pages. He has finished 12 pages in all. How many pages did he draw this week?
   _____ 5 pages _____

44 UNIT 2 LESSON 2 — Word Problems with Unknown Partners

Homework and Remembering page 44

Home or School Activity

 ### Literature Connection

A Bundle of Beasts In the collection of poems titled A *Bundle of Beasts,* Mark Steele and Patricia Hooper use unusual collective nouns to describe groups of animals. For example, Hooper describes "a *skein* of wildfowl," "a *cast* of hawks," and "an *army* of frogs." Use these poems and group words to initiate a discussion of more common group words for animals, such as a *pride* of lions, *a school* of fish, or a *flock* of geese. Then have students write an unknown partner problem in which they use group words for animals.

Word Problems with Unknown Starts

Lesson Objectives
- Represent and solve word problems with unknown starts.
- Convert situation equations to solution equations.

Vocabulary

unknown start
situation equation
solution equation

The Day at a Glance

Today's Goals	Materials	Math Talk
Quick Practice Find the unknown partner. **1** **Teaching the Lesson** A1: Review word problems with unknown partners. A2: Solve and discuss unknown start problems. **2** **Extending the Lesson** ▶ Differentiated Instruction **3** **Homework and Spiral Review**	MathBoard materials Index cards Student Activity Book pages 79–80 Homework and Remembering pages 43, 45–46 Math Journals	In today's activities, the students are involved in discussion as they ▶ solve word problems involving addition and subtraction

Quick Practice

 5 MINUTES   **Goal:** Find the unknown partner.

Unknown Partner Addition: Write these equations on the board:

$8 + \square = 12$ $80 + \square = 120$ $800 + \square = 1{,}200$

$8 + \square = 15$ $80 + \square = 150$ $800 + \square = 1{,}500$

The Student Leader directs the class to complete the equations and to explain the Make a Ten, Make a Hundred, or Make a Thousand strategies. (See Unit 2 Lesson 1.)

Teaching the Lesson

Review Word Problems with Unknown Partners

 15 MINUTES

Goal: Review word problems with unknown partners.

Materials: Homework and Remembering page 43

✔ **NCTM Standards:**
Number and Operations
Algebra
Problem Solving
Communication

Differentiated Instruction

English Learners Students having difficulty generating word problems may choose to draw or diagram their problems first and then work with a partner to find the best words to communicate the problems and their solution strategies.

Teaching Note

Watch For! When discussing students' word problems, watch for students who write word problems in which the answer is the total rather than a partner. Remind students that in a unknown partner problem, the answer is one of the partners.

▶ **Review How to Represent Problems with Unknown Partners** [WHOLE CLASS]

Review the first section of the Homework and Remembering page 43, from Lesson 2. Briefly discuss the solutions for problems 1–4 and the ways students represented the problems. Discuss how the various equations and other representations of each problem are related to the same Math Mountain.

Here are the Math Mountains and some possible equations students may present:

Problem 1:
Asha made 15 sandwiches. Six were cheese and the rest were peanut butter. How many peanut butter sandwiches did Asha make?

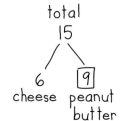

Problem 2:
Farha has 13 CDs. She gave some of them to her sister. Now Farha has 5 CDs. How many did she give to her sister?

had
13
/   \
[8]   5
gave   left
away

13 − [8] = 5
5 + [8] = 13
13 = 5 + [8]
13 − 5 = [8]

Problem 3:
Joseph did 7 push-ups yesterday. Today he did some more. In all, he has done 14 push-ups. How many did he do today?

in all
14
/   \
7   [7]
yesterday today

7 + [7] = 14
14 − 7 = [7]
14 − [7] = 7

Problem 4:
Devon read 8 chapter books and some picture books. Altogether he read 12 books. How many of them were picture books?

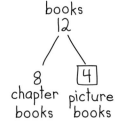

Invite some students to share the word problems they wrote at the bottom of the page. Talk about whether the word problems they wrote are really problems with unknown partners. Make a Math Mountain and write an equation for each problem.

Unknown Starts in Addition and Subtraction

Student Activity Book page 79

> **2-3**
> **Class Activity**
> Name _____ Date _____
>
> ▶ Solve Unknown Start Problems
>
> **Solve each problem. Label your answers.**
>
> *Show your work.*
> Check student's work.
>
> 1. **Change Plus: Unknown Start** Greta puts some beads on a string. Then she puts on 7 more beads. Now there are 13 beads on the string. How many beads did she put on the string to start?
>   _____ 6 beads _____
>
> 2. **Change Minus: Unknown Start** Greta puts some beads on a string. Seven of the beads fell off the string. Six beads are still on the string. How many beads were there at first?
>   _____ 13 beads _____
>
> 3. **Change Plus: Unknown Start** Patrick was carrying some books. His teacher asked him to carry 3 more books. Now he has 11 books. How many books did he start with?
>   _____ 8 books _____
>
> 4. **Change Minus: Unknown Start** Patricia was carrying some books. Her friend took 3 of them. Patricia has 8 books left. How many books was she carrying at first?
>   _____ 11 books _____
>
> UNIT 2 LESSON 3   Word Problems with Unknown Starts **79**

---

 40 MINUTES

Goal: Solve unknown start problems.

Materials: MathBoard materials, Student Activity Book page 79

 NCTM Standards:
Number and Operations
Algebra
Problem Solving
Communication

Teaching Note

Math Background A Change Plus or Change Minus problem in which the starting number is the unknown number is called an *unknown start problem*. A *situation equation* for an unknown start problem is an equation based directly on the word problem. It shows the unknown number first. Students often find it difficult to solve such equations because it is not obvious how to count on to find the answer. However, a situation equation can be rewritten as a *solution equation* that is easier to solve. For example, students can rewrite the situation equation $\square + 6 = 10$ as $6 + \square = 10$ by switching the partners, or students can use the fact that addition and subtraction undo each other to rewrite $\square + 6 = 10$ as $10 - 6 = \square$.

Do not expect all students to master unknown start problems in this lesson. They will get practice with these types of problems throughout the year.

▶ Solve Unknown Start Problems WHOLE CLASS

Have the class look at problem 1. Why is the problem called an unknown start problem? The number of beads Greta started with is the unknown number.

Have students solve the problem. Point out different solution methods as students present their work on the board. Here are some possibilities:

● **Switch the Partner:** Students can solve the situation equation $\square + 7 = 13$ by switching the partners to make the solution equation $7 + \square = 13$. This can be solved by counting on or by making a ten.

● **Math Mountain:** Students can draw a Math Mountain to help them see that they need to find the unknown partner.

Activity continued ▶

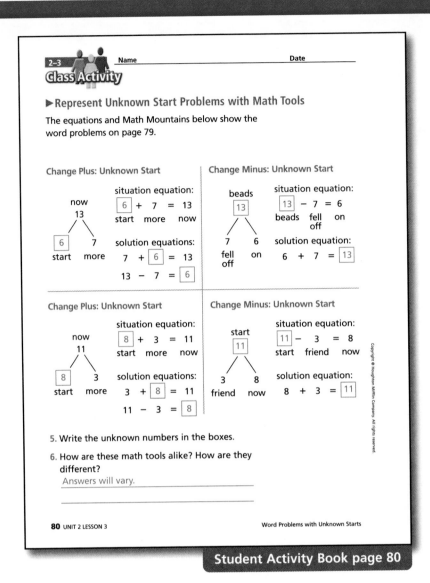

Student Activity Book page 80

The content shown on Student Activity Book page 80:

2–3
Class Activity
Name _____ Date _____

▶ **Represent Unknown Start Problems with Math Tools**

The equations and Math Mountains below show the word problems on page 79.

Change Plus: Unknown Start

now
13

6   7
start more

situation equation:
6 + 7 = 13
start more now

solution equations:
7 + 6 = 13
13 − 7 = 6

Change Minus: Unknown Start

beads
13

7   6
fell   on
off

situation equation:
13 − 7 = 6
beads fell on
off

solution equation:
6 + 7 = 13

Change Plus: Unknown Start

now
11

8   3
start more

situation equation:
8 + 3 = 11
start more now

solution equations:
3 + 8 = 11
11 − 3 = 8

Change Minus: Unknown Start

start
11

3   8
friend now

situation equation:
11 − 3 = 8
start friend now

solution equation:
8 + 3 = 11

5. Write the unknown numbers in the boxes.

6. How are these math tools alike? How are they different?
   Answers will vary.

80 UNIT 2 LESSON 3   Word Problems with Unknown Starts

▶ **Represent Unknown Start Problems with Math Tools** [WHOLE CLASS]

Have students look at the equations and Math Mountains shown on Student Activity Book page 80, which correspond to the word problems on Student Activity Book page 79. Discuss the relationships between each situation equation and the solution equation(s). Ask why the solution equations might be easier to solve.

Discuss the fact that the Math Mountains show that there are only two kinds of problems to solve: unknown total (for which you must add the partners) and unknown partner (for which you need to subtract, count on, or make a ten). Discuss any differences in the Math Mountains and equations on this page and those students wrote on the board.

If most students understand unknown start problems, ask them to write their own. Solve their problems as a class, or have students exchange problems with a partner and solve their partner's problems.

 **Ongoing Assessment**

Write the following problem on the board:

Ned had some stickers. Susan gave Ned 5 more stickers. Now Ned has 11 stickers.

▶ What situation equation could you use to represent the problem?

▶ What solution equation could you use to solve the problem?

② Extending the Lesson

Differentiated Instruction   Activities for Individualizing

Intervention
for students having difficulty

PAIRS

Equation Practice

Materials: Homework and Remembering page 45, MathBoard materials

Have students practice writing situation and solution equations using the word problems on Homework and Remembering page 45.

Pairs take turns reading aloud the word problem. Then students draw Math Mountains and write situation and solution equations on their MathBoards. Students check their partner's equations. Remind students to use the words from the word problems when writing the situation equations and drawing the Math Mountains.

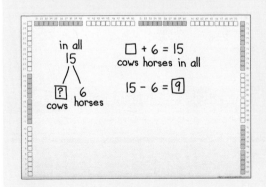

On Level
for students having success

PAIRS

Make Up Unknown Starts

Materials: index cards (3 per student)

On separate index cards, students should write:

- an unknown start equation that uses the number 17.
- a change minus equation with an unknown start and all even numbers
- a change plus equation in which the unknown start is an odd number.

Students then exchange index cards and solve each other's equations.

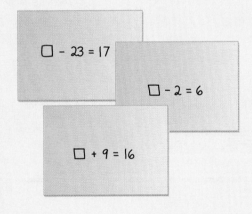

Challenge
for students seeking a challenge

INDIVIDUALS

Make Up Unknown Starts

Materials: MathBoard materials

Create an unknown start equation that fits all these clues:

- One partner is greater than 6.
- The total is an odd number.
- The second partner is a doubles number.

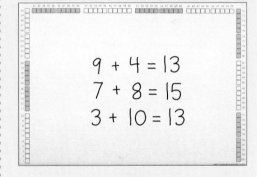

If time allows, have students write clues to an unknown start equation.

Also Use
Challenge Master for 2-3

 Math Writing Prompt

Intervention

Summarize
How is an unknown start problem different from an unknown partner problem? Explain.

 Math Writing Prompt

On Level

Compare and Contrast
Explain how you can use a situation equation and a solution equation to solve unknown start problems.

 Math Writing Prompt

Challenge

Multiple Answers
Neeraj says, "There are only two kinds of problems. Some have an unknown total. Others have an unknown partner." Do you agree or disagree with Neeraj? Explain.

# ③ Homework and Spiral Review

2-3
Homework **Goal:** Additional Practice

This Homework page gives students additional practice in solving problems using methods of their choice.

2-3
Remembering **Goal:** Spiral Review

This Remembering page would be appropriate anytime after today's lesson.

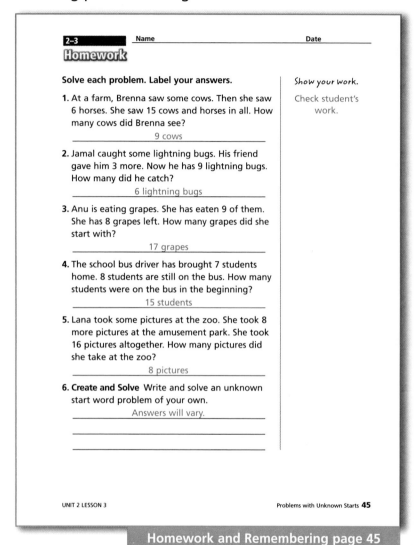

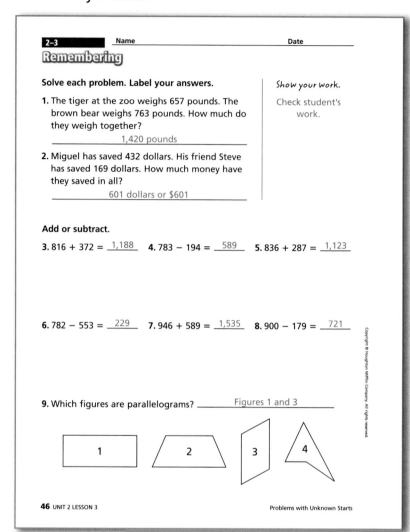

Homework and Remembering page 45

Homework and Remembering page 46

Home or School Activity

 Sports Connection

Sports Problems Have students think about how numbers are used in their favorite sport. For example, in baseball:

● There are 3 outs in an inning.

● There are usually 9 innings in a game.

● Numbers are used to tell how many runs are scored.

Then have students write an unknown start problem about their favorite sport.

Ryan had some hits in the first game of the doubleheader. He had 4 hits in the second game of the doubleheader. Ryan had 6 hits in the two games. How many hits did Ryan have in the first game?

Comparison Problems

Lesson Objectives

- Interpret and use comparison language such as the words *more* and *fewer* to solve word problems.
- Represent and solve comparison word problems.

Vocabulary
situation equation
difference
solution equation
comparison problem
comparison bars

The Day at a Glance

Today's Goals	Materials	123 Math Talk
Quick Practice Find the unknown partner.	MathBoard materials	In today's activities, the students are involved in discussion as they
1 **Teaching the Lesson** A1: Represent and solve comparison problems with unknown differences. A2: Represent and solve comparison problems with unknown larger or smaller amounts. A3: Use comparison bars to represent unknown larger or smaller amounts.	Number cubes Hundred Chart (Copymaster M34) Spinner B (Copymaster M35) Paper clips Two-color counters Game Cards (Copymaster M25)	▶ solve word problems involving subtraction ▶ use comparison bars to model situations
2 **Extending the Lesson** ▶ Differentiated Instruction	Student Activity Book pages 81–82	
3 **Homework and Spiral Review**	Homework and Remembering pages 47–48 Math Journals	

Quick Practice

 5 MINUTES   **Goal:** Find the unknown partner.

Unknown Partner Addition: Write these equations on the board:

$$7 + \boxed{} = 13 \qquad 70 + \boxed{} = 130 \qquad 700 + \boxed{} = 1,300$$

$$7 + \boxed{} = 11 \qquad 70 + \boxed{} = 110 \qquad 700 + \boxed{} = 1,100$$

The Student Leader directs the class to complete the equations and to explain the Make a Ten, Make a Hundred, or Make a Thousand strategies. (See Unit 2 Lesson 1.)

Teaching the Lesson

Introduction to Comparison Problems

 20 MINUTES

Goal: Represent and solve comparison problems with unknown differences.

Materials: MathBoard materials, Student Activity Book page 81

✔ **NCTM Standards:**
Number and Operations
Problem Solving
Communication

Teaching Note

Language and Vocabulary Focus instruction on helping students understand the language in comparison word problems. Comparison problems involve one quantity that is more or less than another quantity. The comparing statement or question has two key pieces of information: *Who has more?* and *How many more?* Asking themselves these two key questions will help students understand the situation. Most students need to show the quantities with a drawing in order to decide whether to add or subtract to solve the problem.

Another needed skill is being able to reverse the comparison statement, which may lead students to an easier solution method. With most comparison problems, the comparison can be stated in two ways:

▶ How many more does B have than A?

▶ How many fewer does A have than B?

Comparison bars such as the ones introduced on Student Activity Book page 81 can help students see and solve such problems.

2-4

Class Activity

Name _____ Date _____

▶ Discuss Comparison Problems

Solve each problem. Label your answers.

David has 5 marbles. Ana has 8 marbles.

1. How many more marbles does Ana have than David? ___3 marbles___

2. How many fewer marbles does David have than Ana? ___3 marbles___

Here are two ways to represent the comparison situation.

Comparison Drawing

David OOOOO
Ana OOOOOOOO

Comparison Bars

David | 5 | ? |
Ana | 8 |

Claire has 8 marbles. Sasha has 15 marbles.

Show your work.

3. How many more marbles does Sasha have than Claire? ___7 marbles___

4. How many fewer marbles does Claire have than Sasha? ___7 marbles___

Rocky has 7 fishing lures. Megan has 12 fishing lures.

5. How many fewer fishing lures does Rocky have than Megan? ___5 fishing lures___

UNIT 2 LESSON 4

Comparison Problems **81**

Student Activity Book page 81

▶ Discuss Comparison Problems [WHOLE CLASS]

Math Talk Read aloud the situation on Student Activity Book page 81, and have students answer questions 1 and 2 using the **Solve and Discuss** structure.

Have students look at the matching drawing and comparison bars for questions 1 and 2 on Student Activity Book page 81.

● How does each drawing show who has more marbles and who has fewer? In the matching drawing, the person with the longer row of circles has more, and the person with the shorter row has fewer. In the comparison bars, the person with the longer bar has more, and the person with the shorter bar has fewer. Both drawings show that Ana has more.

- The amount more or fewer one person has than the other is called the *difference*. **How does each drawing show the difference?** In the first drawing, the difference is the number of circles in Ana's row that do not have matches in David's row. In the second drawing, the oval shows the difference.

Point out that the difference is the number of marbles David would need to get to have the same number as Ana.

Discuss how the drawings compare to drawings students may have made when they solved the problem.

Have students read problems 3 and 4.

- **Which type of drawing is easier to make for this situation? Why?** Possible answer: Comparison bars are easier because you don't have to draw each marble.

Using **Solve and Discuss,** have students solve problems 3 and 4. Encourage them to make comparison bars, but allow them to use any method they understand and can explain.

Following are some methods that students might use to solve problems 3 and 4. If none of the presenters draws comparison bars, draw them as a class.

- Students might think, "How many more would Claire need to have 15 like Sasha?" and write $8 + \square = 15$.

- Students might think, "How many would Sasha have to give away to have as many as Claire?" and write $15 - \square = 8$.

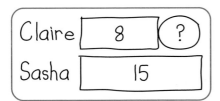

- Students might make comparison bars and write either $8 + \square = 15$ or $15 - \square = 8$.

Using **Solve and Discuss,** have students solve problem 5. Then ask students to restate the question in problem 5 using the word *more* instead of *fewer.* How many more fishing lures does Megan have than Rocky?

Teaching the Lesson (continued)

Activity 2

Comparison Problems with an Unknown Amount

 15 MINUTES

Goal: Represent and solve comparison problems with unknown larger or smaller amounts.

Materials: Student Activity Book page 82

✓ **NCTM Standards:**
Number and Operations
Problem Solving
Communication

Teaching Note

What to Expect from Students
Problems in which unknown amounts must be found may be tricky for some students. Now students will be finding *amounts* instead of *differences*. Students will still need to determine who has more and who has fewer as they did with the comparison problems in Activity 1. This knowledge will help them decide what numbers must be added or subtracted.

2–4

Class Activity

Name _____ Date _____

▶ **Find an Unknown Larger or Smaller Amount**

Solve each problem. Label your answers.

Show your work.

Check student's work.

6. **Unknown Larger Amount** Maribel has 8 stickers. Arnon has 3 more stickers than Maribel. How many stickers does Arnon have?

_____ 11 stickers _____

7. **Unknown Smaller Amount** Arnon has 11 stickers. Maribel has 3 fewer stickers than Arnon. How many stickers does Maribel have?

_____ 8 stickers _____

8. **Unknown Larger Amount** Ivan has 9 goldfish. Milo has 5 more goldfish than Ivan. How many goldfish does Milo have?

_____ 14 goldfish _____

9. **Unknown Smaller Amount** Milo has 14 goldfish. Ivan has 5 fewer goldfish than Milo. How many goldfish does Ivan have?

_____ 9 goldfish _____

82 UNIT 2 LESSON 4   Comparison Problems

Student Activity Book page 82

▶ Find an Unknown Larger or Smaller Amount

WHOLE CLASS

123 **Math Talk** Using **Solve and Discuss,** have students solve problem 6 on Student Activity Book page 82. Students might write the equation $8 + 3 = \square$ or use comparison bars. If students do not mention comparison bars, work as a class to draw them. Start with the basic comparison bar structure, which is shown below.

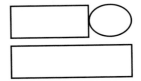

Tell students they can start with this arrangement and then fill in the details.

Elicit the information needed to label the bars.

- Which part of the problem tells us who has more or fewer? Arnon has 3 more stickers than Maribel.

- Who has more? Arnon

- Which bar should I write "Arnon" next to? the longer bar Why? Arnon has more stickers than Maribel.

Write *Arnon* next to the longer bar and *Maribel* next to the shorter bar.

- How many more does Arnon have? 3 more stickers

- Where can we write the "3" to show this difference? in the oval

- What other information does the problem tell us? Maribel has 8 stickers.

- How do we show this in our drawing? Write "8" in Maribel's bar.

- What do we need to find? how many stickers Arnon has

Explain that you can write a question mark in Arnon's bar to show that this is the number that needs to be found.

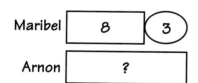

- How do we find out how many stickers Arnon has? We can add 8 and 3.

- How many stickers does Arnon have? 11 stickers

Leave the comparison bars for problem 6 on the board.

Next, use **Solve and Discuss** for problem 7. Encourage students to make comparison bars.

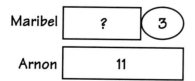

Activity continued ▶

The Learning Classroom

Building Concepts Some students may prefer to draw comparison bars like this:

Maribel 8

Arnon ? 3

Teaching Note

Language and Vocabulary In English, we say that one person has *less* than the other for a continuous quantity like water. But if we are talking about a discrete, countable quantity, we say *fewer* (for example, "less juice" but "fewer cookies"). We also say *less* for numbers (for example, "5 is less than 7").

Try to use these terms correctly. However, do not tell students they are incorrect for using *less* instead of *fewer*. The distinction is often difficult even for adults. Students will begin to understand the distinction better as they hear the words used correctly.

Ongoing Assessment

Circulate around the room as students complete problems 8 and 9. For each problem, have students explain how their comparison bars represent the situation.

Ask students to compare problems 6 and 7 and the comparison bars for the two problems.

Problem 6

Maribel | 8 | 3

Arnon | ?

Problem 7

Maribel | ? | 3

Arnon | 11

● **How are the situations in the two problems the same? How are they different?** The situations and the amounts are the same, but the unknown number is different. In problem 6, the larger amount (how many Arnon has) is unknown. In problem 7, the smaller amount (how many Maribel has) is unknown.

● **Are the comparison statements in the two problems the same or different?** They are different. Problem 6 says, "Arnon has 3 more stickers than Maribel." Problem 7 says, "Maribel has 3 fewer stickers than Arnon." These two statements give us the same information but in different ways.

● **How are the comparison bars the same and different?** They look the same, but the question mark is in a different place. For problem 6, it is in Arnon's bar. For problem 7, it is in Maribel's bar.

Ask students to restate the comparison statement in problem 6 using the word *fewer,* and the comparison statement in problem 7 using the word *more.*

Using **Solve and Discuss,** have students solve problems 8 and 9. Have students compare the situations and comparison bars for these problems as they did for problems 6 and 7.

Practice with Comparison Bars

▶ Use Comparison Bars to Represent an Unknown Amount INDIVIDUALS

Draw the diagram on the board, and ask students to draw it on their MathBoards.

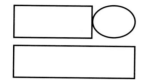

Ask students to listen as you read this comparison statement:

● George has 5 more stamps than Lillian.

Have students ask themselves, *Who has more (or fewer)?* and *How many more or fewer does that person have?* Students should use the answers to these questions to label the bars with the names and to write the difference in the oval. (If you prefer, have students label the bars using just the first letter of each name.) Tell them not to worry about the numbers for the larger and smaller amounts right now.

Have students hold up their MathBoards when they are done so you can check their work.

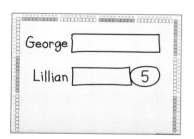

Now have students erase the labels from their comparison bars. Read the statement below, and have them label the bars to represent it. Check their work as before.

● Michael has 6 fewer pencils than Lucia.

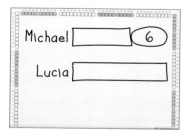

 15 MINUTES

Goal: Use comparison bars to represent unknown larger or smaller amounts.

Materials: MathBoard materials

 NCTM Standards:
Number and Operations
Problem Solving
Communication

Differentiated Instruction

Extra Help Use questioning to help students make the link between the terms *more* and *fewer* and the lengths of the comparison bars. For example:

▶ Which shows more items, the long bar or the short bar?

▶ Which shows fewer items, the long bar or the short bar?

▶ If George has more stamps than Lillian, should his bar be longer or shorter than Lillian's bar?

Activity continued ▶

Repeat this process for the statements below.

- Grace has 4 more comic books than Myles.

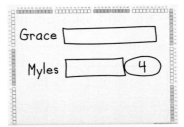

- Kim has 3 fewer grapes than Ramish.

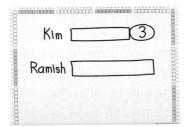

Have students make up and represent additional statements if they need more practice. Now draw the comparison bars below on the board.

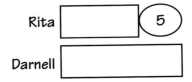

Ask students to give two comparison statements that match the drawing, one using the word *more* and one using the word *fewer*. Here is one possible answer:

- Darnell has 5 more baseball cards than Rita.

- Rita has 5 fewer baseball cards than Darnell.

Replace the names and the difference, and have students make up comparison statements for the new drawing. Do this several more times.

② Extending the Lesson

Intervention
for students having difficulty

`PAIRS`

More or Fewer

Materials: 2 number cubes (labeled 0–5 and 4–9), Spinner B (Copymaster M35), paper clips, Hundred Chart (Copymaster M34), two-color counters (50 per pair) Math Journals

One student rolls two number cubes and spins the More or Fewer spinner. Then the students arrange the cubes into any 2-digit number (for example, 45 or 54) and cover a number on the hundred chart that is *more than* or *fewer than* the rolled number. Students switch roles and repeat the activity. The person with the most counters on the chart wins.

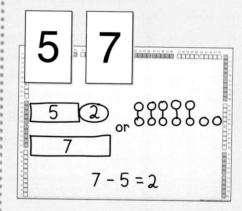

43	44	45	●
○	54	55	56

On Level
for students having success

`INDIVIDUALS`

Start with Bars

Materials: Game Cards (Copymaster M25), MathBoard materials

Students shuffle the game cards and randomly pick two at a time. Students use comparison drawings or comparison bars to represent the two numbers on their MathBoards. They should also write an equation.

$$7 - 5 = 2$$

Challenge
for students seeking a challenge

`SMALL GROUPS`

Create Comparison Problems

Materials: Math Journals

On the board, draw these comparison bars and write the equation.

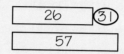

$$57 - 26 = 31$$

Ask students to predict what would happen to the difference (31) if you add the same amount to the number on each comparison bar. Students should discuss and draw examples with their groups.

$$26 + 3 = 29 \quad \boxed{31}$$
$$57 + 3 = 60$$

Students will discover that the difference remains the same when you add the same amount to the numbers on each bar.

Also Use
Challenge Master for 2-4

 Math Writing Prompt

Intervention

Make a Plan
Explain how to draw comparison bars for this equation 8 + 5 = 13.

 Math Writing Prompt

On Level

Compare and Contrast
Explain how comparison drawings and comparison bars are alike and how they are different. Which do you prefer and why?

 Math Writing Prompt

Challenge

Explain Your Thinking
Would you solve a comparison problem with an unknown difference the same way you solve a comparison problem with an unknown larger or smaller amount? Explain your thinking.

3 Homework and Spiral Review

2-4
Homework Goal: Additional Practice

✓ Include students' completed Homework page as part of their portfolios.

2-4
Remembering Goal: Spiral Review

This Remembering page would be appropriate anytime after today's lesson.

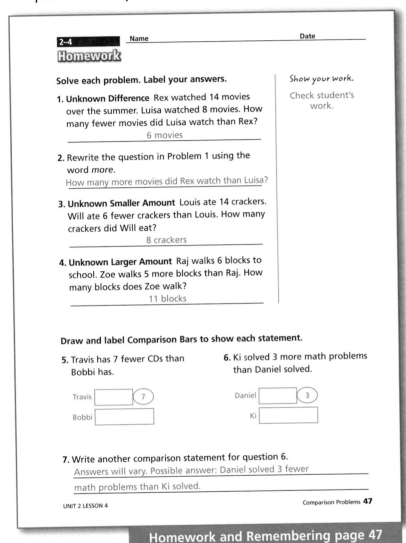

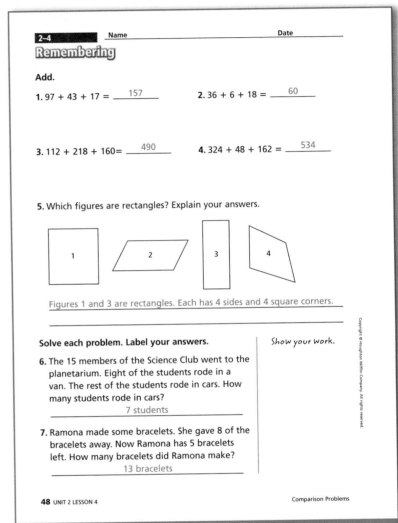

2-4 Name _____ Date _____
Homework

Solve each problem. Label your answers.

Show your work.
Check student's work.

1. Unknown Difference Rex watched 14 movies over the summer. Luisa watched 8 movies. How many fewer movies did Luisa watch than Rex?
6 movies

2. Rewrite the question in Problem 1 using the word *more*.
How many more movies did Rex watch than Luisa?

3. Unknown Smaller Amount Louis ate 14 crackers. Will ate 6 fewer crackers than Louis. How many crackers did Will eat?
8 crackers

4. Unknown Larger Amount Raj walks 6 blocks to school. Zoe walks 5 more blocks than Raj. How many blocks does Zoe walk?
11 blocks

Draw and label Comparison Bars to show each statement.

5. Travis has 7 fewer CDs than Bobbi has.
Travis [ ] (7)
Bobbi [ ]

6. Ki solved 3 more math problems than Daniel solved.
Daniel [ ] (3)
Ki [ ]

7. Write another comparison statement for question 6.
Answers will vary. Possible answer: Daniel solved 3 fewer math problems than Ki solved.

UNIT 2 LESSON 4   Comparison Problems **47**

2-4 Name _____ Date _____
Remembering

Add.

1. $97 + 43 + 17 =$ ___157___

2. $36 + 6 + 18 =$ ___60___

3. $112 + 218 + 160 =$ ___490___

4. $324 + 48 + 162 =$ ___534___

5. Which figures are rectangles? Explain your answers.

[1] [2] [3] [4]

Figures 1 and 3 are rectangles. Each has 4 sides and 4 square corners.

Solve each problem. Label your answers.
Show your work.

6. The 15 members of the Science Club went to the planetarium. Eight of the students rode in a van. The rest of the students rode in cars. How many students rode in cars?
7 students

7. Ramona made some bracelets. She gave 8 of the bracelets away. Now Ramona has 5 bracelets left. How many bracelets did Ramona make?
13 bracelets

48 UNIT 2 LESSON 4   Comparison Problems

Homework and Remembering page 47

Homework and Remembering page 48

Home or School Activity

Science Connection

Many Moons Provide students with the table shown at the right. Ask students to create comparison problems based on the data in the table. Have students solve each other's problems.

Planet	Moons
Mercury	0
Venus	0
Earth	1
Mars	2
Jupiter	28
Saturn	30
Uranus	21
Neptune	8
Pluto	1

Comparison Problems with Misleading Language

Lesson Objectives

- Interpret and apply comparison language.
- Represent and solve comparison word problems with misleading language.

Vocabulary

unknown partner problem	comparison problem
make a ten	comparison bars
make a hundred	unknown amount
make a thousand	

The Day at a Glance

Today's Goals	Materials	Math Talk
Quick Practice Find the unknown partner.	MathBoard materials	In today's activities, the students are involved in discussion as they
1 Teaching the Lesson **A1:** Represent and solve comparison problems that have misleading language. **A2:** Solve comparison problems that do not include the words *more* or *fewer*.	Two-color counters Game Cards (Copymaster M25) Student Activity Book pages 83–84	▶ solve word problems involving subtraction ▶ explore comparison language
2 Extending the Lesson ▶ Differentiated Instruction	Homework and Remembering pages 49–50	
3 Homework and Spiral Review	Math Journals Quick Quiz 1 (Assessment Guide)	

Quick Practice

🕐 **5 MINUTES   Goal:** Find the unknown partner.

Unknown Partner Addition: Write these equations on the board:

$$6 + \boxed{} = 11 \qquad 60 + \boxed{} = 110 \qquad 600 + \boxed{} = 1{,}100$$

$$6 + \boxed{} = 14 \qquad 60 + \boxed{} = 140 \qquad 600 + \boxed{} = 1{,}400$$

The Student Leader directs the class to complete the equations and to explain the Make a Ten, Make a Hundred, or Make a Thousand strategies. (See Unit 2 Lesson 1.)

Teaching the Lesson

Solve Problems with Misleading Language

 30 MINUTES

Goal: Represent and solve comparison problems that have misleading language.

Materials: MathBoard materials, Student Activity Book page 83

✔ **NCTM Standards:**
Number and Operations
Problem Solving
Communication

Teaching Note

Language and Vocabulary
Sometimes comparison problems are stated in a way that is misleading for students. For example, when students read the problem below, they may see the word *fewer* and assume they should subtract 5 from 8.

> Lyle has 8 pencils. Lyle has 5 fewer pencils than Jess. How many pencils does Jess have?

When students are faced with such a problem, they can do one of the following:

▶ Use the problem as it is stated to determine who has more (or fewer) and how many more (or fewer) that person has. Use this information to label comparison bars, and use the bars to decide whether to add or subtract to find the answer.

▶ Find the comparison statement in the problem and state it in terms of the other person in the problem. For example, restating *Lyle has 5 fewer pencils than Jess* as *Jess has 5 more pencils than Lyle* makes it clear that you should start with Lyle's 8 pencils and add 5 to find the number Jess has.

Make sure both methods are mentioned during this activity.

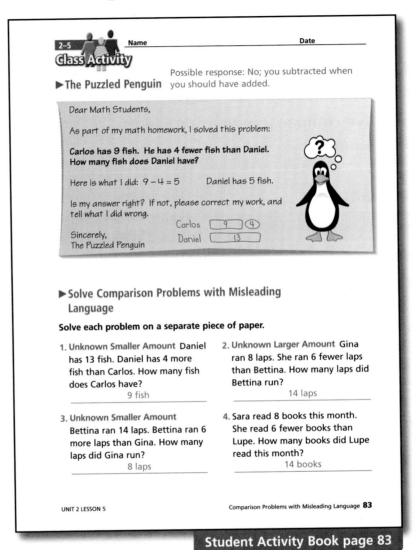

Student Activity Book page 83

▶ The Puzzled Penguin WHOLE CLASS

Have students read the problem the Puzzled Penguin solved. As a class, discuss the steps the Puzzled Penguin took to solve the problem.

● **Did the Puzzled Penguin do something wrong?** yes

● **What did he do wrong?** He subtracted when he should have added.

● **Why do you think he did this?** He probably saw the word *fewer* and thought that meant he should subtract.

(123) **Math Talk** Have the class reread the letter and draw comparison bars on their MathBoards to help them solve the problem.

- Which statement is the comparison statement? He [Carlos] has 4 fewer fish than Daniel.

- Who has fewer fish? Carlos

- Which bar should we label "Carlos"? the shorter one

- How many fewer fish does he have? 4 fewer fish

- Where do we put the number 4? in the oval

- Who has more fish? Daniel

- Where do we put Daniel's name? next to the longer bar

- What else does this problem tell us? that Carlos has 9 fish

- Where do we put the number 9? in the bar for Carlos

Daniel ▢

Carlos ▢ 9 ◯ 4

Differentiated Instruction

Extra Help Use questions to help students who have difficulty identifying the smaller amount and the larger amount in comparison problems. For example, for problem 4, ask questions such as the following:

▶ How many books did Sara read?

▶ Did Sara read more books or fewer books than Lupe? How do you know?

▶ How many more books did Lupe read than Sara?

▶ How can you find the number of books that Lupe read?

Have students look at the comparison bars and discuss how to find the missing number.

- How can we find out how many fish Daniel has? by adding 9 and 4

Have students look back at the original problem.

- How could we restate the comparison statement "He had 4 fewer fish than Daniel" using the word more? Daniel has 4 more fish than Carlos.

- Does saying the statement this way make the problem easier to solve? Why? Answers will vary. Possible response: Yes; it makes it clear that we start with Carlos' 9 fish and add 4 more fish.

▶ Solve Comparison Problems WHOLE CLASS

Have students solve problems 1–3. Discuss the relationship between The Puzzled Penguin problem and problem 1, and between problems 2 and 3. In each pair of problems, the situation is the same but the unknown numbers are different. In one problem, you have to find the larger amount. In the other problem, you have to find the smaller amount.

Have students solve problem 4 and discuss how the comparison statement can be restated using the word *more*.

① Teaching the Lesson (continued)

Activity 2

Other Comparison Language

 20 MINUTES

Goal: Solve comparison problems that do not include the words *more* or *fewer.*

Materials: MathBoard materials, Student Activity Book page 84

 NCTM Standards:
Number and Operations
Problem Solving
Communication

 Ongoing Assessment

Write this problem on the board:

Diego went on 12 rides at the fair. Janie went on 5 fewer rides. How many rides did Janie go on?

Ask students to:

▶ solve the problem

▶ rewrite the problem using *more* instead of *fewer.*

 Quick Quiz

See Assessment Guide for Unit 2 Quick Quiz 1.

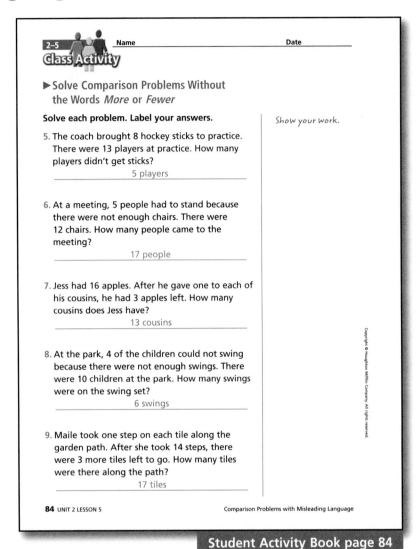

Student Activity Book page 84

▶ Solve Comparison Problems Without the Words *More* or *Fewer*

Discuss problems 5–9 and explain that sometimes comparison problems do not use the words *more* or *fewer.* Students can solve these problems by carefully thinking about which is more and which is fewer. For example, in problem 5, there are fewer hockey sticks than players.

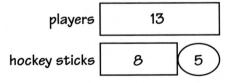

For some students, the comparison may be easier to see with a comparison drawing.

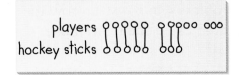

198 UNIT 2 LESSON 5

② Extending the Lesson

Differentiated Instruction · Activities for Individualizing

Intervention
for students having difficulty

`PAIRS`

Another Way

Materials: Two-color counters, (20 per pair), Homework and Remembering page 49, Math Journals

Have students use counters to make comparison drawings that represent the problems on Homework and Remembering page 49. Write the first problem on the board. Have students use two-color counters to represent the number of pictures drawn by each girl in the problem.

> Lucia drew 13 pictures. Lucia drew 6 more pictures than Chelsea. How many pictures did Chelsea draw?

> Lucia ●●●●●●●●● ●●●●
> Chelsea ○○○○○○○
> Chelsea has 7 pictures.

Then have students work on the rest of the homework problems using the counters.

On Level
for students having success

`PAIRS`

More or Fewer Fishing

Materials: 2 sets of Game Cards (per pair) (Copymaster M25)

A student in each pair shuffles the 20 game cards. They randomly pass out 5 cards to each player and put the remaining cards face down in a pile. Students take turns trying to collect cards from their partners by asking *more* and *fewer* questions. When a *more/fewer* match is made, both cards are added to the student's pile of matches. When a match is not made, the student loses a turn and picks up another card from the pile.

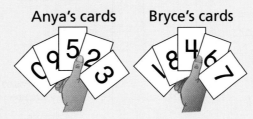

Anya's cards   Bryce's cards

Anya: Do you have a card that's 1 fewer than 5?

Bryce: Yes, I have a 4. (He hands the 4 card to Anya to add to her pile of matches.)

Challenge
for students seeking a challenge

`INDIVIDUALS`

Fill in the Blanks

Materials: Math Journals

Write the following problem on the board.

Jack has _____ more books than Judy. They have a total of 12 books.

Have students fill in the blank with at least 3 different numbers to complete the comparison statement. They should draw all the possible comparison bars to represent that statement.

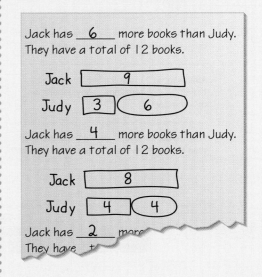

Also Use
Challenge Master for 2-5

 Math Writing Prompt

Intervention

Explain Your Thinking
How can you use counters to solve comparison problems? Use an example to explain your thinking.

 Math Writing Prompt

On Level

Draw a Picture
Jeff has 15 pencils. He has 5 fewer than Jan. Draw comparison bars to show the relationship. Explain how you decided which person had the larger amount.

 Math Writing Prompt

Challenge

Choose a Strategy
May has 15 pens. She has 4 more than Kim and 4 fewer then Lynn. Explain what strategy you would use to find how many pencils Kim and Lynn have.

③ Homework and Spiral Review

2–5
Homework **Goal:** Additional Practice

This Homework page provides additional practice in solving comparison problems.

2–5
Remembering **Goal:** Spiral Review

This Remembering page would be appropriate anytime after today's lesson.

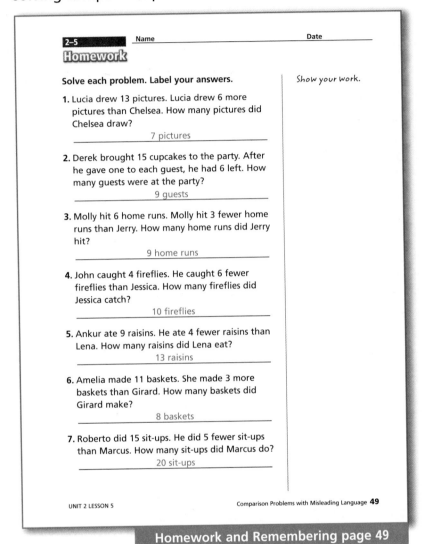

2–5
Homework
Name _____ Date _____

Solve each problem. Label your answers.   Show your work.

1. Lucia drew 13 pictures. Lucia drew 6 more pictures than Chelsea. How many pictures did Chelsea draw?
   _____ 7 pictures

2. Derek brought 15 cupcakes to the party. After he gave one to each guest, he had 6 left. How many guests were at the party?
   _____ 9 guests

3. Molly hit 6 home runs. Molly hit 3 fewer home runs than Jerry. How many home runs did Jerry hit?
   _____ 9 home runs

4. John caught 4 fireflies. He caught 6 fewer fireflies than Jessica. How many fireflies did Jessica catch?
   _____ 10 fireflies

5. Ankur ate 9 raisins. He ate 4 fewer raisins than Lena. How many raisins did Lena eat?
   _____ 13 raisins

6. Amelia made 11 baskets. She made 3 more baskets than Girard. How many baskets did Girard make?
   _____ 8 baskets

7. Roberto did 15 sit-ups. He did 5 fewer sit-ups than Marcus. How many sit-ups did Marcus do?
   _____ 20 sit-ups

UNIT 2 LESSON 5   Comparison Problems with Misleading Language **49**

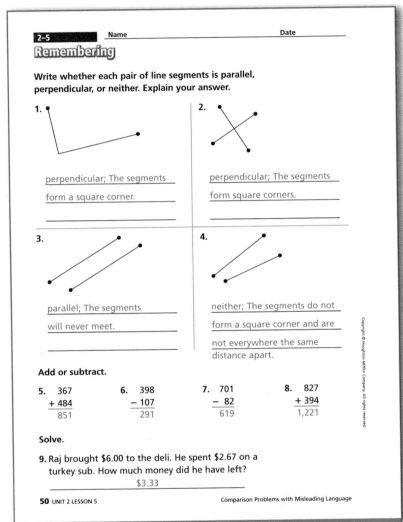

2–5
Remembering
Name _____ Date _____

Write whether each pair of line segments is parallel, perpendicular, or neither. Explain your answer.

1.
perpendicular; The segments form a square corner.

2.
perpendicular; The segments form square corners.

3.
parallel; The segments will never meet.

4.
neither; The segments do not form a square corner and are not everywhere the same distance apart.

Add or subtract.

5. 367
   + 484
   ‾‾‾‾‾
    851

6. 398
   − 107
   ‾‾‾‾‾
    291

7. 701
   − 82
   ‾‾‾‾‾
    619

8. 827
   + 394
   ‾‾‾‾‾
   1,221

Solve.

9. Raj brought $6.00 to the deli. He spent $2.67 on a turkey sub. How much money did he have left?
   _____ $3.33

50 UNIT 2 LESSON 5   Comparison Problems with Misleading Language

Homework and Remembering page 49

Homework and Remembering page 50

Home or School Activity

Real-World Connection

Local Comparisons Have students write pairs of comparison statements in which they compare things in their town or neighborhood. In each pair of statements, students use two different ways to make the same comparison. For example:

- There are more apartment buildings than houses.
- There are fewer houses than apartment buildings.
- The school is farther than the library.
- The library is closer than the school.

The high school has more students than the middle school.

The middle school has fewer students than the high school.

Multi-Digit Unknown Partner and Unknown Start Problems

Lesson Objectives
- Represent and solve multi-digit word problems with unknown partners.
- Represent and solve multi-digit word problems with unknown starts.

Vocabulary

situation equation
solution equation

The Day at a Glance

Today's Goals	Materials	Math Talk
Quick Practice Find the unknown partner. **1 Teaching the Lesson** A1: Represent and solve multi-digit word problems with unknown partners. A2: Represent and solve multi-digit word problems with unknown starts. A3: Represent and solve multi-digit unknown partners and unknown start problems. **2 Extending the Lesson** ▶ Differentiated Instruction **3 Homework and Spiral Review**	MathBoard materials Sentence Strips Calculators Student Activity Book pages 85–88 Homework and Remembering pages 51–52 Math Journals	In today's activities, the students are involved in discussion as they ▶ solve and discuss word problems involving multi-digit unknown partners and multi-digit unknown starts ▶ justify their answers in problem solving

Quick Practice

🕐 **5 MINUTES**   **Goal:** Find the unknown partner.

Unknown Partner Subtraction: Write these equations on the board.

$$14 - \boxed{} = 9 \qquad 140 - \boxed{} = 90 \qquad 1,400 - \boxed{} = 900$$

$$17 - \boxed{} = 9 \qquad 170 - \boxed{} = 90 \qquad 1,700 - \boxed{} = 900$$

The Student Leader directs the class to complete the equations. Then one student explain the Make a Ten, Make a Hundred, or Make a Thousand strategies.

Leader: (pointing to the first equation) Equation

Class: 14 minus 5 equals 9.

Student: 9 plus 1 is 10 plus 4 more is 14. I added 5 in all, so $14 - 9 = 5$.

Teaching the Lesson

Multi-Digit Problems with Unknown Partners

 15 MINUTES

Goal: Represent and solve multi-digit word problems with unknown partners.

Materials: MathBoard materials, Student Activity Book page 85

✔ **NCTM Standards:**
Number and Operations
Problem Solving
Representation

Teaching Note

Math Tools Students will now use the math tools introduced in Lessons 1–5 of Unit 2 to solve problems with multi-digit numbers. Some students may still be modeling word problems by drawing and labeling circles. Because the problems in Lessons 6–8 have larger numbers, this method will no longer be practical. For these problems, students may find it helpful to use place value drawings. However, most students should be able to use numerical methods without math drawings to solve. With these larger numbers students may need to write a solution equation after writing a situation equation or they may be able to decide on the computational operation without writing a situation equation. Have any students, who make top-from-bottom errors in subtraction, draw the magnifying glass around the top number to remind them to ungroup where needed before subtracting.

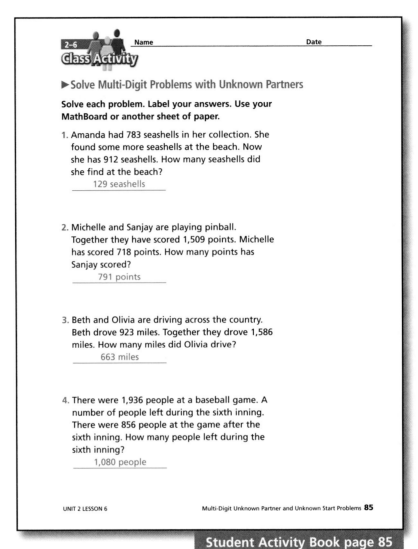

Student Activity Book page 85

▶ **Solve Multi-Digit Problems with Unknown Partners** WHOLE CLASS

Using the **Solve and Discuss** structure, have students solve problem 1 on Student Activity Book page 85. Emphasize that they should identify the partners and the total, and label them in their equations and drawings. Make sure a variety of methods are presented. Some possible strategies are presented on the following page.

Add on with a Drawing

783 + ☐ = 912
 P   P   T

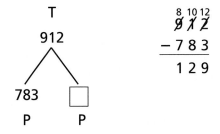

783 ⭕⭕⭕⭕⭕ | ☐ | ⭕⭕ ← 129 added on
    ⭕⭕   to get to 912
      790   800 900 910 912

Add on Numerically

783 + ☐ = 912
 P   P   T

783   +   7 is 790

       + 10 is 800

       + 112 is 912
        129

Use a Math Mountain to Subtract.

       T   8 10 12
                  9̶ 1̶ 2̶
    912   − 7 8 3
     /\   1 2 9

783   ☐
 P   P

Using **Solve and Discuss,** have students solve problems 2–4 on Student Activity Book page 85. Remind them to identify and label the partners and the total when showing their work.

Activity 2

Other Comparison Language

 20 MINUTES

Goal: Represent and solve multi-digit word problems with unknown starts.

Materials: MathBoard materials, Student Activity Book page 86

✓ **NCTM Standards:**
Number and Operations
Problem Solving
Representation

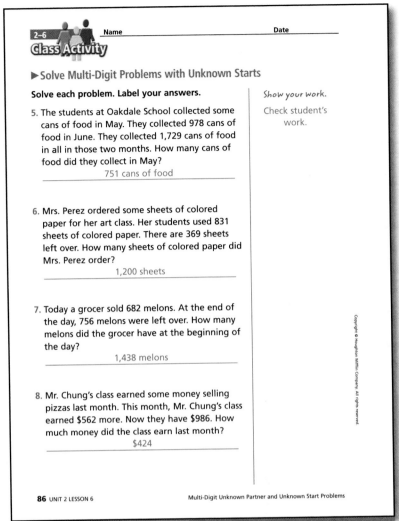

2-6
Class Activity   Name _____ Date _____

▶ Solve Multi-Digit Problems with Unknown Starts

Solve each problem. Label your answers.   *Show your work.*

Check student's work.

5. The students at Oakdale School collected some cans of food in May. They collected 978 cans of food in June. They collected 1,729 cans of food in all in those two months. How many cans of food did they collect in May?
                751 cans of food

6. Mrs. Perez ordered some sheets of colored paper for her art class. Her students used 831 sheets of colored paper. There are 369 sheets left over. How many sheets of colored paper did Mrs. Perez order?
                1,200 sheets

7. Today a grocer sold 682 melons. At the end of the day, 756 melons were left over. How many melons did the grocer have at the beginning of the day?
                1,438 melons

8. Mr. Chung's class earned some money selling pizzas last month. This month, Mr. Chung's class earned $562 more. Now they have $986. How much money did the class earn last month?
                $424

86 UNIT 2 LESSON 6   Multi-Digit Unknown Partner and Unknown Start Problems

Student Activity Book page 86

▶ Solve Multi-Digit Problems with Unknown Starts INDIVIDUALS

Using the **Solve and Discuss** structure, have students solve problem 5 on Student Activity Book page 86. If students struggle, suggest they use Math Tools like they used in Lesson 3. The Math Mountain and situation equation for problem 5 are shown below.

Math Mountain	Situation Equation
two months T 1,729 ☐ 978 P P May June	May June both ☐ + 978 = 1,729 P P T

The following are some other possible solution strategies for problem 5.

- **Reversing the Situation:** Write a solution equation by thinking about the operation that undoes addition. The number 978 is *added* to the unknown partner to get 1,729. So, if 978 is *taken away* from 1,729, the result will be the unknown partner.

  Solution equation: 1,729 − 978 = ☐

- **Math Mountain:** Use the Math Mountain to write and solve a subtraction.

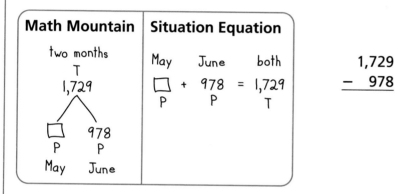

- **Switch the Partner:** Write a solution equation by switching the partners in the situation equation. Add on to find the solution.

  Solution equation: 978 + ☐ = 1,729

  978 + 22 is 1,000   Add on to get to the next hundred.

  + 729 is 1,729   Add on to get to 1,729.
  ___
  751

Have students use **Solve and Discuss** to solve problem 6 on Student Activity Book page 86. The Math Mountain, situation equation, and solution equation for problem 6 are shown below.

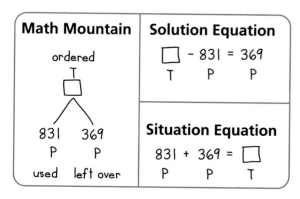

Using **Solve and Discuss,** have students solve problems 7 and 8 on Student Activity Book page 86.

Activity 3

Mixed Problems

 20 MINUTES

Goal: Represent and solve multi-digit unknown partner and unknown start word problems.

Materials: MathBoard materials, Student Activity Book pages 87–88

 NCTM Standards:
Number and Operations
Problem Solving
Representation

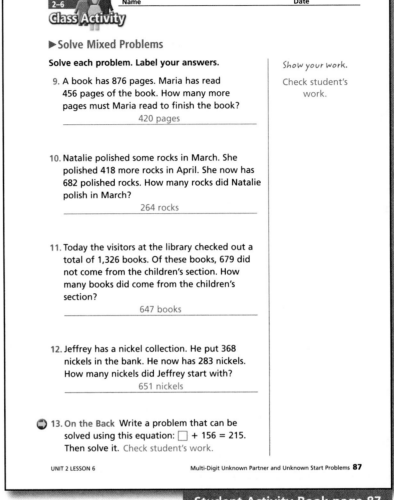

Student Activity Book page 87

Within the activity book image:

2–6
Class Activity

Name _____ Date _____

▶ Solve Mixed Problems

Solve each problem. Label your answers.

Show your work.
Check student's work.

9. A book has 876 pages. Maria has read 456 pages of the book. How many more pages must Maria read to finish the book?
   _____ 420 pages

10. Natalie polished some rocks in March. She polished 418 more rocks in April. She now has 682 polished rocks. How many rocks did Natalie polish in March?
   _____ 264 rocks

11. Today the visitors at the library checked out a total of 1,326 books. Of these books, 679 did not come from the children's section. How many books did come from the children's section?
   _____ 647 books

12. Jeffrey has a nickel collection. He put 368 nickels in the bank. He now has 283 nickels. How many nickels did Jeffrey start with?
   _____ 651 nickels

13. On the Back Write a problem that can be solved using this equation: □ + 156 = 215. Then solve it. Check student's work.

UNIT 2 LESSON 6   Multi-Digit Unknown Partner and Unknown Start Problems **87**

 **Ongoing Assessment**

As students solve problem 12, ask questions such as:

▶ How do you know whether 386 is a partner or the total? What about 283?

▶ How did you decide whether to add or subtract the numbers?

▶ Solve Mixed Problems WHOLE CLASS

Using the **Solve and Discuss** structure, have students solve problems 9–12 on Student Activity Book page 87–88. The problems are not labeled by type, so students must think carefully about the situation before deciding how to solve the problem. Remind them to label the total and partners. Talk about the Math Mountains and equations students write.

On the Back If time allows, have students share the problems they created in exercise 13. Have students who used different solution methods present and explain their work.

② Extending the Lesson

Intervention
for students having difficulty

SMALL GROUPS

Solve a Simpler Problem

Materials: sentence strips, Math Journals, Homework and Remembering page 51, MathBoard materials

Write these equations from Homework and Remembering page 51 on sentence strips.

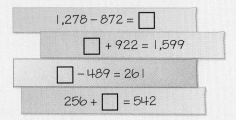

$$1,278 - 872 = \square$$
$$\square + 922 = 1,599$$
$$\square - 489 = 261$$
$$256 + \square = 542$$

Post the equations and have students solve them. Suggest that students write an equation with smaller numbers to help them decide what operation to use to solve the equation. Then use that operation to solve the original equation with the larger numbers.

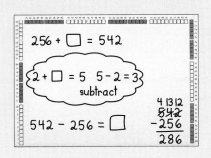

On Level
for students having success

PAIRS

Dial a Number

Materials: Math Journals, calculators (1 per pair)

Copy a telephone key pad onto the board.

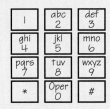

Have students create as many words as they can from the telephone key pad using at least three letters. Then they can use the corresponding digits to make multi-digit numbers and use them in equations. Have partners check each other's work with a calculator.

$$THE = 843 \qquad FAR = 327$$
$$843 + 327 = 1,170$$

Challenge
for students seeking a challenge

PAIRS

Break the Code

Materials: Math Journals

Copy a telephone key pad on the board.

Have students create as many words as they can from the telephone key pad. Then, have them write different kinds of equations for other students to solve using multi-digit numbers and the words they created.

$$NOW + HI = \square$$
$$228 + \square = DOG$$
$$\square + \bigcirc = LOW$$

Also Use
Challenge Master for 2-6

 Math Writing Prompt

Intervention

Simpler Problem
How could you use smaller numbers to help you decide how to solve $524 - \square = 312$.

 Math Writing Prompt

On Level

Compare and Contrast
In what way is solving a multi-digit problem just like solving a problem with 1-digit numbers? In what ways is it different? Explain your thinking.

 Math Writing Prompt

Challenge

Real-World Application
Describe a real-life situation where you might need to solve a math problem involving 3-digit numbers.

③ Homework and Spiral Review

 **Goal:** Additional Practice

✓ Include students' completed Homework page as part of their portfolios.

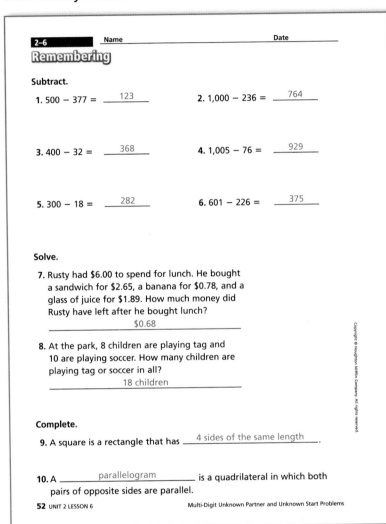 **Goal:** Spiral Review

This Remembering page would be appropriate anytime after today's lesson.

2–6
Homework

Name _____ Date _____

Solve each problem. Label your answers.

1. Trista used 872 beads to make some necklaces. There were 1,278 beads in the package to start. How many beads are left over?
   _____ 406 beads _____

2. Ali is building a model boat from toothpicks. Yesterday, Ali used some toothpicks to start her model. Today, she added 398 toothpicks to finish the model. The finished model has 1,123 toothpicks. How many toothpicks did Ali use yesterday? _____ 725 toothpicks _____

3. Collin received some hits on his new website yesterday. Today, he got 922 more hits. He now has 1,599 hits. How many hits did Collin get yesterday? _____ 677 hits _____

4. John went on a trip. The first day he traveled 489 miles. He traveled 261 miles the second day. How many miles did he travel? _____ 750 miles _____

5. Ronald and Tonya planted 542 flowers in all. Ronald planted 256 flowers. How many flowers did Tonya plant? _____ 286 flowers _____

UNIT 2 LESSON 6   Multi-Digit Unknown Partner and Unknown Start Problems **51**

Homework and Remembering page 51

2–6
Remembering

Name _____ Date _____

Subtract.

1. $500 - 377 =$ _____ 123 _____   2. $1,000 - 236 =$ _____ 764 _____

3. $400 - 32 =$ _____ 368 _____   4. $1,005 - 76 =$ _____ 929 _____

5. $300 - 18 =$ _____ 282 _____   6. $601 - 226 =$ _____ 375 _____

Solve.

7. Rusty had $6.00 to spend for lunch. He bought a sandwich for $2.65, a banana for $0.78, and a glass of juice for $1.89. How much money did Rusty have left after he bought lunch?
   _____ $0.68 _____

8. At the park, 8 children are playing tag and 10 are playing soccer. How many children are playing tag or soccer in all?
   _____ 18 children _____

Complete.

9. A square is a rectangle that has _____ 4 sides of the same length _____.

10. A _____ parallelogram _____ is a quadrilateral in which both pairs of opposite sides are parallel.

52 UNIT 2 LESSON 6   Multi-Digit Unknown Partner and Unknown Start Problems

Homework and Remembering page 52

Home or School Activity

 Language Arts Connection

Tall Tales Explain to students that a *tall tale* is a story in which exaggerations are used. Remind students of tall tales they may know, such as the stories of Paul Bunyan, Johnny Appleseed, and Pecos Bill.

Have students write tall tales in which they are the main characters. The tall tales should involve large numbers. Students should give a title to the tall tale and draw a picture that illustrates the situation described in the story. Then they should write and solve an unknown partner or an unknown start problem that is based on their tall tale.

Multi-Digit Comparison Problems

Lesson Objectives

- Represent and solve multi-digit comparison problems.
- Represent and solve multi-digit comparison problems with misleading language.

Vocabulary
comparison problem
comparison bars

The Day at a Glance

Today's Goals	Materials	Math Talk
Quick Practice Find the unknown partner. **1 Teaching the Lesson** A1: Solve multi-digit comparison word problems using different strategies. A2: Represent and solve multi-digit comparison problems with misleading language. **2 Extending the Lesson** ▶ Going Further: Logical Reasoning ▶ Differentiated Instruction **3 Homework and Spiral Review**	MathBoard materials Multi-Digit Addition Race (Copymaster M36) Two-Color counters Calculators (optional) Cross-Number Puzzle (Copymaster M37) Student Activity Book pages 89–92 Homework and Remembering pages 53–54 Math Journals	In today's activities, the students are involved in discussion as they ▶ solve word problems involving multi-digit number comparisons ▶ justify their answers in problem solving

Quick Practice

🕐 **5 MINUTES**   **Goal:** Find the unknown partner.

Unknown Partner Subtraction: Write the following equations on the board.

$$15 - \square = 8 \qquad 150 - \square = 80 \qquad 1{,}500 - \square = 800$$

$$12 - \square = 8 \qquad 120 - \square = 80 \qquad 1{,}200 - \square = 800$$

The Student Leader directs the class to complete the equations and to explain the Make a Ten, Make a Hundred, or Make a Thousand strategies. (See Unit 2 Lesson 6 Quick Practice.)

① Teaching the Lesson

Multi-Digit Comparison Problems

 20 MINUTES

Goal: Solve multi-digit comparison problems using different strategies.

Materials: MathBoard materials, Student Activity page 89

 NCTM Standards:
Number and Operations
Problem Solving
Representation

The Learning Classroom

Helping Community Students at the board may get stuck at some point. They usually welcome help from another student at that point. Allowing other students to help instead of you will help them to assume responsibility for one another's learning. Ask who they would like to come up to help them. You can move on to another explainer while they redo their work. Of course, sometimes it is fine just to go ahead and have the whole class help the student with you leading with questions.

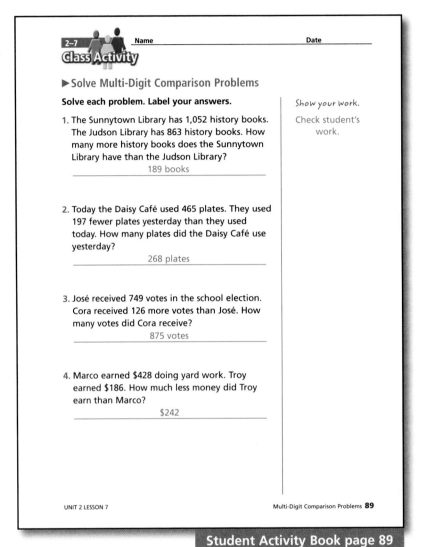

Student Activity Book page 89

▶ Solve Multi-Digit Comparison Problems

WHOLE CLASS

Using the **Solve and Discuss** structure, have students solve problem 1 on Student Activity Book page 89. Select students who used different strategies to present their solutions.

A variety of strategies are presented on the following page.

Comparison Bars

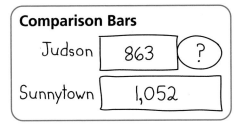

Judson | 863 | ?
Sunnytown | 1,052

Numerical Methods

$$\begin{array}{r} 1,052 \\ -\ 863 \\ \hline 189 \end{array}$$

863 + 7 is 870
+ 30 is 900
+152 is 1,052

Equation

863 + ☐ = 1,052

Place Value Drawings

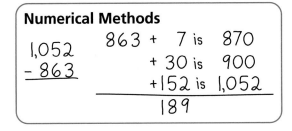

863 ooooo ||| ☐ ||||| oo ←189 added
            870 900 1,000 1,050 1,052 on to get 1,052

Using **Solve and Discuss**, have students solve problem 2 on Student Activity Book page 89. Select students who used different strategies to present their solutions. Here are the comparison bars for problem 2.

yesterday | ? | 197
today | 465

Students may also write and solve one of the following equations to solve the problem.

☐ + 197 = 465   197 + ☐ = 465   465 − 197 = ☐

Using **Solve and Discuss,** have students solve problems 3 and 4 on Student Activity Book page 89.

 Math Talk in Action

Jonah: The problem says that the Daisy Café used 465 plates today and yesterday they used 197 fewer plates than they did today.

Carrie: We have to find out how many plates were used yesterday. I think we have to add 465 + 197.

Alexa: No we don't, the word *fewer* means *less than.* They used fewer plates yesterday than they did today. That means they used more plates today.

Carrie: I still don't understand.

Jonah: When we draw the comparison bars, we fill in the bars for the larger amount, 465 and the difference, 197. We can subtract 465 − 197 to find out the smaller amount. That stands for how many plates they used yesterday.

Alexa: 465 − 197 = 268. They used 268 plates yesterday.

Carrie: And that's fewer than they used today. Now I understand!

Differentiated Instruction

Extra Help If you think students need practice restating *more* comparisons using *fewer,* and *fewer* comparisons using *more,* go through problems 1–4 on Student Activity Book page 89, asking students to restate each comparison.

Activity 2

Multi-Digit Comparison Problems with Misleading Language

 20 MINUTES

Goal: Represent and solve multi-digit comparison problems with misleading language.

Materials: MathBoard materials, Student Activity Book page 90

✔ **NCTM Standards:**
Number and Operations
Problem Solving
Representation

Teaching Note

Critical Thinking Encourage students to review their answers to make sure that the answer makes sense and is reasonable.

2-7
Class Activity

Name _____ Date _____

▶ **Solve Multi-Digit Comparison Problems with Misleading Language**

Solve each problem. Draw comparison bars to help you. Label your answers.

5. Billy has 679 pennies. He has 278 more pennies than Lee. How many pennies does Lee have?
   _____ 401 pennies _____

6. Rebecca drove 362 miles. She drove 439 fewer miles than Fiona. How many miles did Fiona drive? _____ 801 miles _____

7. The baseball team gave 250 caps to people who came to the game today. There were 569 people at the game. How many people did not get a cap? _____ 319 people _____

8. The principal bought 975 pencils at the beginning of the school year. Each student in the school received one pencil. The principal had 123 pencils left over. How many students are in the school? _____ 852 students _____

90 UNIT 2 LESSON 7   Multi-Digit Comparison Problems

Student Activity Book page 90

▶ Solve Multi-Digit Comparison Problems with Misleading Language WHOLE CLASS

Using the **Solve and Discuss** structure, have students solve problem 5 on Student Activity Book page 90. Here are the comparison bars for problem 5.

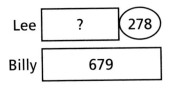

Discuss the common error many people make when solving this type of problem.

- The Puzzled Penguin might solve this problem by adding 679 and 278. Why do you think he might make this mistake? He sees the word *more* and thinks he should add.

- How can you avoid this error? Answers will vary. Possible answers: Think carefully about who has more and who has fewer, and draw comparison bars, or say the comparison the other way to see if it makes the problem clearer.

Have students solve problem 6 on Student Activity Book page 90, using the **Solve and Discuss** structure. Here are the comparison bars for problem 6.

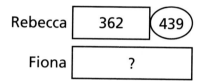

Rebecca | 362 | (439)

Fiona | ?

Using **Solve and Discuss,** have students solve problems 7 and 8 on Student Activity Book page 90. Make sure a variety of solution methods are presented, including the use of comparison bars, which are shown below.

caps | 250 | ?

people | 569

pencils | ? | (123)

students | 975

If time allows, have students brainstorm and write more comparison problems.

Extending the Lesson

Going Further: Logical Reasoning

Goal: Use logical reasoning to solve problems.

Materials: MathBoard materials, Student Activity Book pages 91–92

✔ **NCTM Standards:**
Number and Operations
Problem Solving

Teaching Note

Math Background The problem-solving strategy, *Use Logical Reasoning,* can be applied to many different types of situations. On this page, students organize the facts given and use logical reasoning to find unknown facts to solve the problem.

▶ Use Logical Reasoning to Solve Problems   WHOLE CLASS

Have students read problem 1 on Student Activity Book page 91. Lead students through the logical reasoning process by asking the following questions.

- You know the exact amount that one person spent. Who is it? Darnell How much did he spend? $11

- Whose amount is compared to Darnell's? Mark's What is the comparison? Mark spent $3 less than Darnell. How much did Mark spend? $8

- Whose amount is compared to Marks? Rita's What is the comparison? Rita spent $7 more than Mark. What amount did Rita spend? $15

Have a student read aloud problem 2. Help students start to solve the problem by asking:

- You know one person's house number. Who is it? Lily What is it? 251

Give students a few minutes to finish. Then ask a volunteer to present their method of solving.

Using the **Solve and Discuss** structure, have students solve problems 3–5 on Student Activity Book page 91. As time allows, have students share their strategies for the On the Back problem.

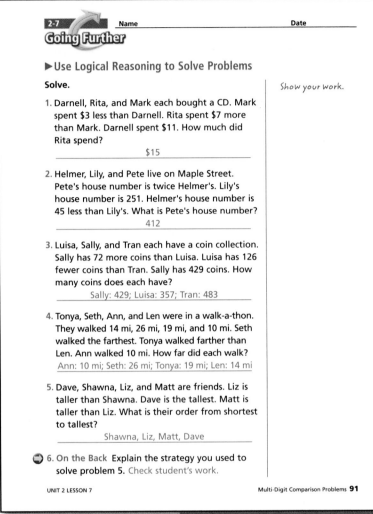

Student Activity Book page 91

Differentiated Instruction

Extra Help Some students may find it helpful to write each sentence of a problem on a separate strip of paper. Then they can identify a logical order for the given information by rearranging the strips of paper.

Darnell, Rita and Mark each bought a CD.

Darnell spent $11.

Mark spent $3 less than Darnell.

Rita spent $7 more than Mark.

How much did Rita spend?

Intervention
for students having difficulty

PAIRS

Multi-Digit Addition Race

Materials: Two-color counters (handful), Multi-Digit Addition Race (Copymaster M36), calculators (optional), Math Journal

Students take turns picking two numbers from the Partner Pool, finding the sum of the numbers, and then covering that sum with their color counter. Students can check their totals with a calculator. If the sum has already been covered by another player, the student loses their turn. The first player to cover five squares (across, down, or diagonally) wins.

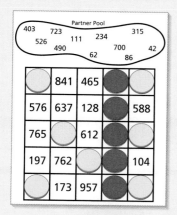

On Level
for students having success

INDIVIDUALS

Cross-Number Puzzle

Materials: Cross-Number Puzzle (Copymaster M37), calculators (optional), Math Journals

Have students find the missing numbers for each equation clue to complete the puzzle. Students can use a calculator to check their math.

¹3	4	1		²2	³7	6	
7				⁴3	4	5	
⁵4	2	⁶5		⁷5	1	2	
		8		8		⁸1	
	9	3	¹⁰2	7		5	
¹¹8	9		5		¹²2	7	4

Across

1. $254 + 87 = \square$
2. $751 - \square = 475$
4. $172 + \square = 517$
5. $\square - 186 = 239$
7. $819 - \square = 307$
9. $416 - 89 = \square$
11. $\square + 224 = 313$
12. $\square - 123 = 151$

Down

1. $523 - 149 = \square$
2. $\square + 172 = 413$
3. $921 - \square = 169$
4. $511 - 153 = \square$
6. $723 - \square = 141$
8. $\square + 98 = 252$
9. $125 - 86 = \square$
10. $689 + \square = 764$

Challenge
for students seeking a challenge

SMALL GROUPS

Pattern Rule Search

Materials: Math Journals

Display these patterns on the board and have students copy them down. Students work in small groups to find the missing numbers and write the rule for each pattern. Remind students that there may be more than one correct number that fits the pattern. Once they've completed the patterns and written the rules, each group can create their own number patterns for other groups to solve.

1. 123, 345, 567, ____
2. 115, 350, 585, ____
3. 152, 251, 323, ____, 701, 800

1. 789; each 3-digit number is in consecutive order

2. 821; add 235

3. Possible answer: 440; each of the three digits adds up to 8

Also Use
Challenge Master for 2-7

 Math Writing Prompt
Intervention

Understand the Problem
What questions can you ask yourself after you read a comparison problem to help you label the comparison bars?

 Math Writing Prompt
On Level

Say It Another Way
Don has 5 more books than Sarah. What is another way to write this comparison? Which one is clearer? Explain.

 Math Writing Prompt
Challenge

Explain Your Thinking
Is the word *more* a clue word to add? Explain.

③ Homework and Spiral Review

2-7
Homework **Goal:** Additional Practice

The Homework page provides additional practice in solving comparison problems using any method.

2-7
Remembering **Goal:** Spiral Review

This Remembering page would be appropriate anytime after today's lesson.

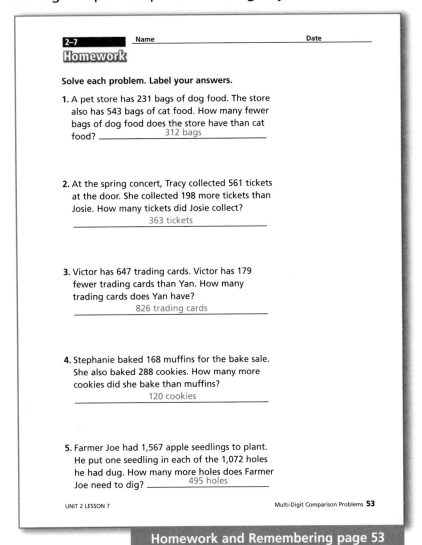

2-7
Homework

Name _____ Date _____

Solve each problem. Label your answers.

1. A pet store has 231 bags of dog food. The store also has 543 bags of cat food. How many fewer bags of dog food does the store have than cat food? _____312 bags_____

2. At the spring concert, Tracy collected 561 tickets at the door. She collected 198 more tickets than Josie. How many tickets did Josie collect?
   _____363 tickets_____

3. Victor has 647 trading cards. Victor has 179 fewer trading cards than Yan. How many trading cards does Yan have?
   _____826 trading cards_____

4. Stephanie baked 168 muffins for the bake sale. She also baked 288 cookies. How many more cookies did she bake than muffins?
   _____120 cookies_____

5. Farmer Joe had 1,567 apple seedlings to plant. He put one seedling in each of the 1,072 holes he had dug. How many more holes does Farmer Joe need to dig? _____495 holes_____

UNIT 2 LESSON 7   Multi-Digit Comparison Problems **53**

Homework and Remembering page 53

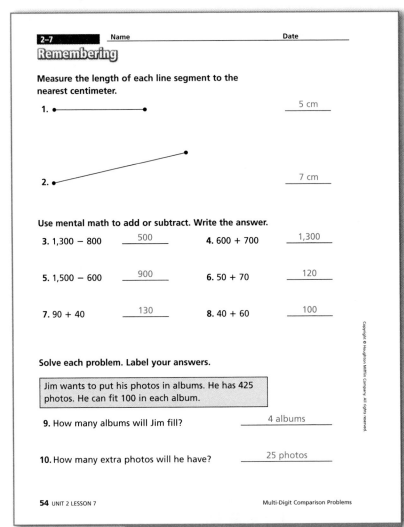

2-7
Remembering

Name _____ Date _____

Measure the length of each line segment to the nearest centimeter.

1. •————————•   _____5 cm_____

2. •————————•   _____7 cm_____

Use mental math to add or subtract. Write the answer.

3. 1,300 − 800 _____500_____   4. 600 + 700 _____1,300_____

5. 1,500 − 600 _____900_____   6. 50 + 70 _____120_____

7. 90 + 40 _____130_____   8. 40 + 60 _____100_____

Solve each problem. Label your answers.

> Jim wants to put his photos in albums. He has 425 photos. He can fit 100 in each album.

9. How many albums will Jim fill? _____4 albums_____

10. How many extra photos will he have? _____25 photos_____

54 UNIT 2 LESSON 7   Multi-Digit Comparison Problems

Homework and Remembering page 54

Home or School Activity

Science Connection

Compare Pulse Rates Explain to students that the number of times the heart beats per minute is called the *pulse rate.* Show students how to take their pulses by pressing two fingers to the side of the neck and counting the number of beats. Then have students do the following:

• Take their resting pulse rate for 1 minute and record the number.

• Run in place for 1 minute and record the number.

• Find the difference between the two pulse rates.

216 UNIT 2 LESSON 7

Mixed Multi-Digit Word Problems

Lesson Objective
- Represent and solve a variety of multi-digit word problems.

The Day at a Glance

Today's Goals	Materials	123 Math Talk
Quick Practice Find the unknown partner.	MathBoard materials	In today's activities, the students are involved in discussion as they
❶ **Teaching the Lesson** **A1:** Represent and solve multi-digit word problems of various types.	Student Activity Book pages 93–96 Homework and Remembering pages 55–56	▶ solve mixed multi-digit word problems and explain their solutions
❷ **Extending the Lesson** ▶ Going Further: Missing Digits ▶ Differentiated Instruction	Math Journals Quick Quiz 2 (Assessment Guide)	▶ justify their answers in problem solving
❸ **Homework and Spiral Review**		

Quick Practice

 5 MINUTES   Goal: Find the unknown partner.

Unknown Partner Subtraction Write the following equations on the board.

$$11 - \boxed{} = 7 \qquad 110 - \boxed{} = 70 \qquad 1{,}100 - \boxed{} = 700$$
$$15 - \boxed{} = 7 \qquad 150 - \boxed{} = 70 \qquad 1{,}500 - \boxed{} = 700$$

The Student Leader directs the class to complete the equations and to explain the Make a Ten, Make a Hundred, or Make a Thousand strategies. (See Unit 2 Lesson 6.)

Teaching the Lesson

Mixed Multi-Digit Word Problems

 45 MINUTES

Goal: Represent and solve multi-digit word problems of various types.

Materials: MathBoard materials, Student Activity Book pages 93–94

✔ **NCTM Standards:**
Number and Operations
Problem Solving
Representation

Math Mountain	**Situation Equation**
T 347 / 219 P ☐ P	219 + ☐ = 347 P P T

Add on with a Drawing

219 o ☐ ‖ 00000 ← 128 added
220 320 340 347   on to get 347

Add on Numerically

219 + 1 is 220
    +100 is 320
    + 20 is 340
    + 7 is 347
        128

2–8
Class Activity

Name _____ Date _____

▶ Solve Mixed Multi-Digit Word Problems

Solve each problem. Label your answers.

1. Jacob had 219 bottle caps in his collection. Then he found some more. Now he has 347 bottle caps. How many bottle caps did Jacob find?
    128 bottle caps

    Check student's work.

2. Yesterday Tamara stamped some invitations. Today she stamped 239 invitations. She stamped 427 invitations in all. How many invitations did she stamp yesterday? _____188 invitations_____

3. Batai made 122 calls in the phone-a-thon. Gina made 261 calls. How many more calls did Gina make than Batai? _____139 calls_____

4. Greta has 449 feet of fencing for her dog run. Mitch has 110 fewer feet of fencing for his dog run. How many feet of fencing does Mitch have? _____339 feet_____

UNIT 2 LESSON 8 | Mixed Multi-Digit Word Problems **93**

Student Activity Book page 93

▶ Solve Mixed Multi-Digit Word Problems [WHOLE CLASS]

Have students use **Solve and Discuss** to solve problems 1–8 on Student Activity Book pages 93–94. For each problem, select two or three students who used different strategies to present their solutions. The following examples are some of the ways students might solve each problem.

Problem 1 is a Change Plus unknown partner problem. Other students may rewrite the equation as 347 − 219 = ☐ and solve it by subtracting. Others may solve 219 + ☐ = 347 by adding on. See the left side column for sample student work.

Problem 2 is a Change Plus unknown start problem. Students might write the situation equation ☐ + 239 = 427 and change it to the solution equation 427 − 239 = ☐.

Math Mountain	Solution Equation
T 427 ☐ 239 P P	427 − 239 = ☐ T P P

Problem 3 is a comparison problem with an unknown difference. Students might draw comparison bars and then write and solve the equation 261 − 122 = ☐ or 122 + ☐ = 261.

Comparison Bars

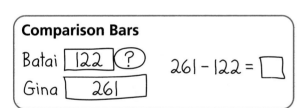

Batai ☐122☐ (?)   261 − 122 = ☐
Gina ☐ 261 ☐

Problem 4 is a comparison problem with an unknown smaller amount. Students might draw comparison bars and then write and solve the equation 449 − 110 = ☐.

Comparison Bars

Mitch ☐ ? ☐(110)   449 − 110 = ☐
Greta ☐ 449 ☐

Students might also write the addition equation ☐ + 110 = 449, rewrite it as 110 + ☐ = 449, and solve by adding on.

Activity continued ▶

2-8
Class Activity

Name _____   Date _____

Solve each problem. Label your answers.

Show your work.

Check student's work.

5. The Grove Street bus carried 798 passengers today. The Elm Street bus carried 298 more passengers today than the Grove Street bus. How many passengers did the Elm Street bus carry today?

_____ 1,096 passengers _____

6. Park City Cycle has 876 bicycles in stock. This is 134 more bicycles than Bentley's Bike Shop has in stock. How many bicycles does Bentley's Bike Shop have in stock?

_____ 742 bicycles _____

7. At Sunflower Bakery's grand opening, the first 250 customers received a free bagel. There were 682 customers at the grand opening. How many customers did not get a free bagel?

_____ 432 customers _____

8. There were some chairs set up for a concert. Then Shantel set up 256 more chairs. Now 610 chairs are set up. How many chairs were set up to start with?

_____ 354 chairs _____

94 UNIT 2 LESSON 8

Mixed Multi-Digit Word Problems

Student Activity Book page 94

Problem 5 is a comparison problem with an unknown larger amount. Students might write the equation $798 + 298 = \square$ or draw comparison bars and then add.

Comparison Bars

Grove Street | 798 | 298 |

Elm Street | ? |

$798 + 298 = \square$

Problem 6 is a comparison problem with misleading language and an unknown smaller amount. Students might draw comparison bars and then write and solve the subtraction equation 876 − 134 = ☐ or the addition equation 134 + ☐ = 876.

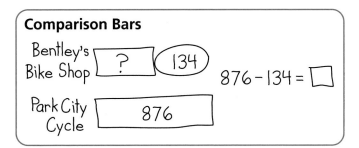

Problem 7 is an unknown difference comparison problem that does not use the word *more* or *fewer.* Students might draw comparison bars and then write and solve 250 + ☐ = 682 or 682 − 250 = ☐.

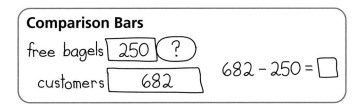

Problem 8 is a Change Plus unknown start problem. Students might use a Math Mountain to write the subtraction equation 610 − 256 = ☐. Or they might write a situation equation, reverse the partners to get 256 + ☐ = 610, and solve by counting on.

Math Mountain	Solution Equation
T 610 /\ ☐ 256 P P	610 − 256 = ☐

If time allows, have groups of students write the following:

● a word problem with an unknown start

● a comparison problem with an unknown difference

● a comparison problem with an unknown amount

Have groups exchange problems, solve, and present their solutions.

 Class Management

Looking Ahead Even if your students have not mastered solving multi-digit word problems, move on to Unit 3. Addition and subtraction word problems appear throughout the Remembering section in Unit 3.

 **Quick Quiz**

See Assessment Guide for Unit 2 Quick Quiz 2.

 **Ongoing Assessment**

As students solve and discuss problems 5 through 8, ask students to explain how they decide what kind of problem each one is.

Extending the Lesson

Going Further: Missing Digits

Goal: Use logical reasoning to identify missing digits in multi-digit additions and subtractions.

Materials: MathBoard materials, Student Activity Book pages 95–96

✔ **NCTM Standards:**
Number and Operations
Problem Solving
Reasoning and Proof

▶ Find the Missing Digits WHOLE CLASS

Have students look at exercise 1 on Student Activity Book page 95. Ask students to describe what they see. Possible answer: It's an addition exercise. You know the sum. You don't know some of the digits of the numbers that you are adding.

● Now look at the ones places of the numbers. How many ones must be in the second number? 7 How do you know? There are 6 ones in the sum. The only way to get 6 ones in the sum is to add 7 to 9, because 9 plus 7 equals 16. Write 7 in the ones place of the first number.

● Now look at the tens places of the numbers. How many tens must be in the first number? 3 How do you know? There are 12 tens in the sum. There is 1 ten from adding 7 plus 9, and there are 8 tens in the second number. That's 9 tens. So you need 3 more tens to get 12 tens. Write 3 in the tens place of the first number.

● What is the completed addition? 39 plus 87 equals 126.

Using a similar set of questions, lead the class through the solution of exercise 2. Begin by pointing out that this exercise is different because it involves a subtraction.

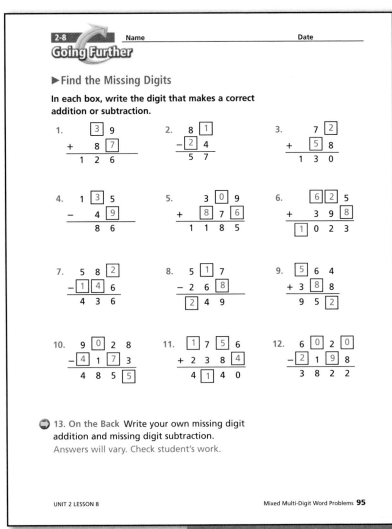

Have students work in pairs to solve exercises 3–12.

On the Back If time permits, each student should write an original missing digit addition exercise and subtraction exercise. Partners should then work individually to solve each other's exercises.

Intervention
for students having difficulty
SMALL GROUPS

Double-Digit Code Breaker

Materials: MathBoard materials, Math Journals

Write this exercise on the board.

```
   A A
 + B B
 ─────
   C C
```

Explain that a letter used more than once stands for the same number, but each different letter is a different number.

Have students work in small groups on their MathBoards to find as many numbers as possible that fit the pattern.

```
  11      77      44
 +22     +11     +33
 ───     ───     ───
  33      88      77
```

On Level
for students having success
SMALL GROUPS

Triple-Digit Code Breaker

Materials: MathBoard materials, Math Journals

Write this exercise on the board.

```
   A A A
 + B B B
 ───────
   C C C
```

Explain that a letter used more than once stands for the same number, but each different letter is a different number.

Have students work in small groups on their MathBoards to find as many numbers as possible that fit the pattern.

```
  111     444     222
 +222    +555    +666
 ────    ────    ────
  333     999     888
```

Challenge
for students seeking a challenge
SMALL GROUPS

Palindrome Total

Materials: MathBoard materials, Math Journals

Write this exercise on the board.

```
     A A A
 +   B B B
 ─────────
   D C C D
```

Explain that a letter used more than once stands for the same number, but each different letter is a different number. The sum is a *palindrome*. A palindrome is a number that reads the same from left to right as from right to left.

Have students work in small groups on their MathBoards to find as many numbers as possible that fit the pattern.

```
  555     444     999
 +666    +777    +222
 ─────   ─────   ─────
 1,221   1,221   1,221
```

Also Use
Challenge Master for 2-8

 Math Writing Prompt

Intervention

Create Your Own
Write a comparison problem using multi-digit numbers. Explain how to solve your problem.

 Math Writing Prompt

On Level

Justify
When you add two 3-digit numbers will the total always be a 3-digit number? Explain.

 Math Writing Prompt

Challenge

Predict
Do you think 152 − 137 and 155 − 140 have the same difference? Explain your thinking.

③ Homework and Spiral Review

Homework **Goal:** Additional Practice

✓ Include students' completed Homework page as part of their portfolios.

Remembering **Goal:** Spiral Review

This Remembering page would be appropriate anytime after today's lesson.

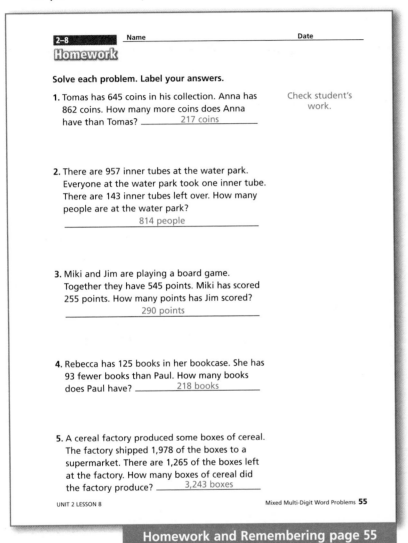

2-8 Name _____ Date _____
Homework

Solve each problem. Label your answers.

1. Tomas has 645 coins in his collection. Anna has 862 coins. How many more coins does Anna have than Tomas? ____217 coins____

Check student's work.

2. There are 957 inner tubes at the water park. Everyone at the water park took one inner tube. There are 143 inner tubes left over. How many people are at the water park?
____814 people____

3. Miki and Jim are playing a board game. Together they have 545 points. Miki has scored 255 points. How many points has Jim scored?
____290 points____

4. Rebecca has 125 books in her bookcase. She has 93 fewer books than Paul. How many books does Paul have? ____218 books____

5. A cereal factory produced some boxes of cereal. The factory shipped 1,978 of the boxes to a supermarket. There are 1,265 of the boxes left at the factory. How many boxes of cereal did the factory produce? ____3,243 boxes____

UNIT 2 LESSON 8   Mixed Multi-Digit Word Problems **55**

Homework and Remembering page 55

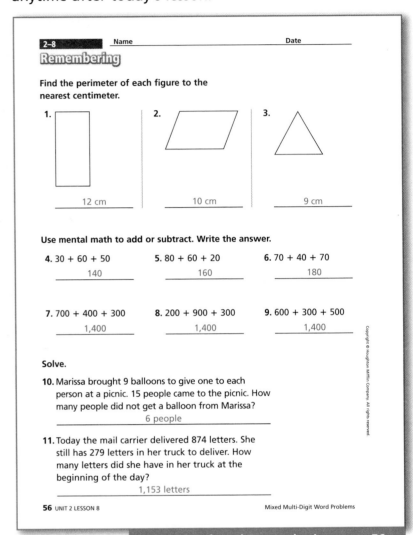

2-8 Name _____ Date _____
Remembering

Find the perimeter of each figure to the nearest centimeter.

1.   2.   3.

12 cm   10 cm   9 cm

Use mental math to add or subtract. Write the answer.

4. 30 + 60 + 50   5. 80 + 60 + 20   6. 70 + 40 + 70
   140   160   180

7. 700 + 400 + 300   8. 200 + 900 + 300   9. 600 + 300 + 500
   1,400   1,400   1,400

Solve.

10. Marissa brought 9 balloons to give one to each person at a picnic. 15 people came to the picnic. How many people did not get a balloon from Marissa?
6 people

11. Today the mail carrier delivered 874 letters. She still has 279 letters in her truck to deliver. How many letters did she have in her truck at the beginning of the day?
1,153 letters

56 UNIT 2 LESSON 8   Mixed Multi-Digit Word Problems

Homework and Remembering page 56

Home or School Activity

Arts Connection

Create an Advertisement Have students create an advertisement for a store that is having a sale on items that cost more than $100. Explain that for each item, the advertisement should show the regular price and the sale price. Have students include at least three items in the ad. When students are finished, have them calculate the difference between the regular price and the sale price for each item.

CAL'S WAREHOUSE
STUPENDOUS STOREWIDE SALE

22-inch Flat TV
Regular Price: $1,850
Cal's Stupendous Sale Price: $999

Megaram 66 Laptop
Regular Price: $1,248
Cal's Stupendous Sale Price: $677

Port-a-Tune Player
Regular Price: $219
Cal's Stupendous Sale Price: $144

Unit Review and Test

Lesson Objective

● **Assess student progress on unit objectives.**

The Day at a Glance

Today's Goals	Materials
Quick Practice Review any skills you choose to meet the needs of your students.	Unit 2 Test, Student Activity Book pages 97–98
1 Assessing the Unit ▶ Assess student progress on unit objectives. ▶ Use activities from unit lessons to reteach content.	Unit 2 Test, Form A or B, Assessment Guide (optional)
2 Extending the Assessment ▶ Use remediation for common errors.	Unit 2 Performance Assessment, Assessment Guide (optional)
There is no homework assignment on a test day.	

Quick Practice

 5 MINUTES   **Goal:** Review any skills you choose to meet the needs of your students

If you are doing a unit review day, use any of the Quick Practice activities that provide support for your students. If this is a test day, omit Quick Practice.

 Class Management

Review and Test Day You may want to choose a quiet game or other activity (reading a book or working on homework for another subject) for students who finish early.

Assessing the Unit

Assess Unit Objectives

45 MINUTES (more if schedule permits)

Goal: Assess student progress on unit objectives

Materials: Student Activity Book pages 97–98; Assessment Guide Unit 2 Test Form A or B (optional), Unit 2 Performance Assessment (optional)

▶ Review and Assessment

If your students are ready for assessment on the unit objectives, you may use either the test on the Student Activity Book pages or one of the forms of the Unit 2 Test in the Assessment Guide to assess student progress.

If you feel that students need some review first, you may use the test on the Student Activity Book pages as a review of unit content, and then use one of the forms of the Unit 2 Test in the Assessment Guide to assess student progress.

To assign a numerical score for all of these test forms, use 10 points for each question.

You may also choose to use the Unit 2 Performance Assessment. Scoring for that assessment can be found in its rubric in the Assessment Guide.

▶ Reteaching Resources

The chart at the right lists the test items, the unit objectives they cover, and the lesson activities in which the objective is covered in this unit. You may revisit these activities with students who do not show mastery of the objectives.

---

2 Unit Test

Name _____ Date _____

Solve each problem. Label your answer. *Show your work.*

1. Helga is a dog walker. Today she walked 8 beagles and some terriers. Altogether she walked 14 dogs. How many terriers did she walk?
   _____6 terriers_____

2. Li Wei had some apples. She gave 9 of the apples to her friends. She has 5 apples left. How many apples did she start with?
   _____14 apples_____

3. Luis received 6 cards. He received 7 fewer cards than Carlos received. How many cards did Carlos receive?
   _____13 cards_____

4. Wanda has 12 crayons. James has 9 crayons. How many more crayons does Wanda have than James?
   _____3 crayons_____

5. On Tuesday, Rashid polished 143 rocks. He polished some more rocks on Wednesday. He polished 228 rocks altogether. How many rocks did Rashid polish on Wednesday?
   _____85 rocks_____

6. Some students were playing in the schoolyard. Then 119 students went into the school. Now there are 286 students in the schoolyard. How many students were in the schoolyard to start with?
   _____405 students_____

UNIT 2   Test **97**

Student Activity Book page 97

Unit Test Items	Unit Objectives Tested	Activities to Use for Reteaching
1–7	**2.1** Solve a variety of word problems involving addition and subtraction.	Lesson 1, Activities 2 and 4 Lesson 2, Activity 2 Lesson 3, Activity 2 Lesson 4, Activity 2 Lesson 6, Activity 1 Lesson 7, Activity 1
8–10	**2.2** Write equations and use comparison bars to represent and solve word problems.	Lesson 2, Activity 2 Lesson 3, Activity 2 Lesson 5, Activity 1

Student Activity Book page 98

2 Unit Test

Name _____ Date _____

Solve. Label your answer.

Show your work.

7. Pat has 425 pennies in his collection. Miguel has 201 fewer pennies. How many pennies does Miguel have?

____224 pennies____

Write an equation and then solve each problem. Label your answer.

8. On Monday and Tuesday, Franco spent 5 hours doing homework altogether. He did homework for 2 hours on Tuesday. How many hours did Franco spend doing homework on Monday?

$5 - 2 = \boxed{}$ or $2 + \boxed{} = 5$; 3 hours

9. Tony had some baseball cards. Jeremy gave him 8 more. Then he had 19 baseball cards. How many did he have to start?

$\boxed{} + 8 = 19$ or $19 - 8 = \boxed{}$; 11 baseball cards

10. **Extended Response** Elsa read 13 books this month. She read 6 fewer books than Cliff read. Draw Comparison Bars to represent the problem.

Cliff | ? books
Elsa | 13 books (6 books)

How many books did Cliff read? ___19 books___

Explain how you know who read more books, Elsa or Cliff.

Possible answer: Cliff read more books because the problem says Elsa read 6 fewer books than Cliff.

98 UNIT 2   Test

▶ Assessment Resources

Free Response Tests
Unit 2 Test, Student Activity Book pages 97–98
Unit 2 Test, Form A, Assessment Guide

Extended Response Item
The last item in the Student Activity Book test and in the Form A test will require an extended response as an answer.

Multiple Choice Test
Unit 2 Test, Form B, Assessment Guide

Performance Assessment
Unit 2 Performance Assessment, Assessment Guide
Unit 2 Performance Assessment Rubric, Assessment Guide

▶ Portfolio Assessment

Teacher-selected Items for Student Portfolios:

- Homework, Lessons 2, 4, 6, and 8

- Class Activity work, Lessons 5 and 7

Student-selected Items for Student Portfolios:

- Favorite Home or School Activity

- Best Writing Prompt

② Extending the Assessment

Unit Objective 2.1

Solve a variety of word problems involving addition and subtraction.

Common Error: Unable to Identify the Relevant Information

Students may have difficulty identifying what they need to find.

Remediation Have students circle the information provided and label it (for example, total, partner, larger amount, smaller amount).

Common Error: Cannot Explain Why an Operation Was Chosen

Students may have difficulty explaining why a word problem involves addition or subtraction

Remediation Have students make up addition and subtraction problems. Ask them to explain how they know the problem is about addition or subtraction. Reinforce the language of operations by posing questions such as "Are you putting groups together?" or "Are you taking groups apart?".

Common Error: Makes Incorrect Computations

Sometimes students have difficulty solving word problems because they do not know basic additions and subtractions.

Remediation Have students make Math Mountain cards of the basic additions and subtractions they don't know. Or, students can practice with flash cards.

Common Error: Doesn't Know How to Begin When Problems Have Larger Numbers

When problems involve larger numbers, student may have difficulty deciding how to begin.

Remediation Have students rewrite the problem using smaller numbers. Then have students draw a diagram using the smaller numbers (Comparison Bars or a Math Mountain) to help organize the information in the problem. When they've organized the information, have them replace the smaller numbers with the original numbers.

Common Error: Has Difficulty Deciding Whether to Add or to Subtract

Students may have difficulty determining if a word problem involves addition or subtraction.

Remediation Have students use blocks to act out a problem. As they take various actions, help students make connections to addition or subtraction by asking questions such as,

- Are you putting groups together? (add)
- Are you separating a group into parts? (subtract)
- Are you taking some away? (subtract)
- Are you comparing numbers? (subtract)

Have students make lists of words that mean to add or to subtract.

Unit Objective 2.2

Write equations and use comparison bars to represent and solve word problems.

Common Error: Draws Comparison Bars Incorrectly

Students may draw and label the Comparison Bars incorrectly.

Remediation Point out to students that the smaller amount and the difference are connected. Have students write "larger", "smaller", and "difference" inside the correct part of the Comparison Bar diagram and have them use this as a reference as they work through problems.

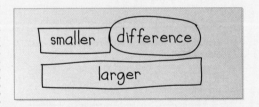

Common Error: Writes an Incorrect Equation

When translating a word problem into a math sentence, students may write the wrong equation.

Remediation Have students work in pairs to solve problems. Partners should read aloud the problems and then work together to identify the unknowns and write the equations. They can draw a picture or model the problems with base-ten blocks to help organize the information and write the equations.

Figures, Angles, and Triangles

UNIT B REVIEWS CLASSIFYING quadrilaterals and identifying parallel sides and perpendicular sides in figures. Lines of symmetry and congruent figures are introduced. In the activities in this unit, students decompose and compose quadrilaterals and classify triangles according to lengths of sides and measures of angles. Students estimate the measures of angles using benchmark angles, discover that the sum of the angles in a triangle is 180°, and find the measure of a third angle in a triangle given the measure of two other angles.

Big Idea Properties of Quadrilaterals
and Triangles

Planning Unit B

See pages xvii and xviii for a list of unit materials and manipulatives
that are available in the *Math Expressions* Kit.

Lesson Title	Lesson Resources	Materials and Manipulatives	
		Math Expressions	**Other**
1 Symmetry and Congruence	Family Letter Student Activity Book pages 99–106 Homework and Remembering pages 57–58	Transparency of Student Activity Book page 100 (optional), rulers, Tangrams or Tangrams (Copymaster M30)	Overhead projector (optional), scissors, plastic mirrors, tracing paper or unlined paper, Math Journals, envelopes
2 Label Figures and Draw Diagonals	Student Activity Book pages 107–110 Homework and Remembering pages 59–60	Rulers, cutouts from Lesson 1, Student Activity Book page 101	Scissors, tracing paper (optional), Math Journals, card stock
3 Angles and Triangles	Student Activity Book pages 111–116 Homework and Remembering pages 61–62	Centimeter Rulers (Copymaster M26), MathBoard materials	Straws, colored flexible rods, (blue, red, and yellow) such as pipe cleaners or chenille sticks, chart paper (optional), scissors, index cards, Math Journals
4 Angle Measures	Student Activity Book pages 117–120 Homework and Remembering pages 63–64	Centimeter Rulers (Copymaster M26), Measure by Filling Angles (Copymaster M38), MathBoard materials	Straws, scissors
✓ Unit Review and Test	Student Activity Book pages 121–122 Assessment Guide		

Unit B Assessment

✓ Unit Objectives Tested	Unit Test Items	Lessons
B.1 Identify figures that are congruent and draw lines of symmetry on figures.	1, 2	1
B.2 Label figures with letters and compose and decompose quadrilaterals.	3, 10	2, 3
B.3 Classify triangles by the lengths of sides or by the measures of their angles.	4–9	3

Formal Assessment

Open or Free Response Tests

- Unit Review and Test (Student Activity Book pages 121–122, Teacher's Guide pages 261–264)
- Unit B Test Form A (Assessment Guide)
- Unit B Open Response Test (Test Generator)
- Test Bank Items for Unit B (Test Generator)

Multiple Choice Tests

- Unit B Test Form B (Assessment Guide)
- Unit B Multiple Choice Test (Test Generator)
- Test Bank Items for Unit B (Test Generator)

Performance Tasks

- Unit B Performance Assessment (Assessment Guide)

Informal Assessment

Ongoing Assessment

- In every Teacher's Guide lesson

Performance Assessment

- Class discussions
- Small-group work
- Individual work on teacher-selected tasks

Portfolios

- See Unit B Review and Test for suggestions for selecting items for portfolios.
- Some Homework pages are noted as suitable for portfolio inclusion.

Review Opportunities

Homework and Remembering

- Homework pages provide review of recently taught topics.
- Remembering pages provide spiral review.

Teacher's Guide

- Unit Review and Test (page 261)

Test Generator CD-ROM

- Test Bank Items can be used to create custom review sheets.

Unit B Teaching Resources

Reaching All Learners

Extra Help
Lesson 1, page 234
Lesson 3, page 246
Lesson 4, page 256

English Learners
Lesson 1, page 232

Advanced Learners
Lesson 3, page 250

Individualizing Instruction

Activities
• Intervention (in every lesson)
• On Level (in every lesson)
• Challenge (in every lesson)

Math Writing Prompts
• Intervention (in every lesson)
• On Level (in every lesson)
• Challenge (in every lesson)

Challenge Masters
• (for every lesson)

Cross-Curricular Links • Home or School Activities

 Science Connection
Find the Center of Gravity
(Lesson 2, page 242)

 Social Studies Connections
Roof Angles (Lesson 3, page 252)
Communication with Symbols
(Lesson 4, page 260)

Teaching Unit B

Putting Research into Practice for Unit B

From Current Research: Mathematical Arguments

In grades 3–5, teachers should emphasize the development of mathematical arguments. As students' ideas about figures evolve, they should formulate conjectures about geometric properties and relationships. Using drawings, concrete materials, and geometry software to develop and test their ideas, they can articulate clear mathematical arguments about why geometric relationships are true. For example: "You can't possibly make a triangle with two right angles because if you start with one side of the triangle across the bottom, the other two sides go straight up. They're parallel, so they can't possibly ever meet, so you can't get it to be a triangle."

National Council of Teachers of Mathematics. *Principles and Standards for School Mathematics.* Reston: NCTM, 2000. p. 165.

Estimating Angles

Students in grades 3–5 should measure the attributes of a variety of physical objects and extend their work to measuring more complex attributes, including area, volume, and angle. They will learn that length measurements in particular contexts are given specific names, such as *perimeter, width, height, circumference,* and *distance.* They can begin to establish some benchmarks by which to estimate or judge the size of objects. For example, they learn that a "square corner" is called a *right angle* and establish this as a benchmark for estimating the size of other angles.

National Council of Teachers of Mathematics. *Principles and Standards for School Mathematics.* Reston: NCTM, 2000. p. 171.

Mathematical Vocabulary

When discussing figures, students in grades 3–5 should be expanding their mathematical vocabulary by hearing terms used repeatedly in context. As they describe shapes, they should hear, understand, and use mathematical terms such as *parallel, perpendicular, face, edge, vertex, angle, trapezoid, prism,* and so forth, to communicate geometric ideas with greater precision. For example, as students develop a more sophisticated understanding of how geometric shapes can be the same or different, the everyday meaning of *same* is no longer sufficient, and they begin to need words such as *congruent* and *similar* to explain their thinking.

National Council of Teachers of Mathematics. *Principles and Standards for School Mathematics.* Reston: NCTM, 2000. p. 166.

Other Useful References: Classifying Quadrilaterals, Classifying Triangles

National Council of Teachers of Mathematics. *Developing Mathematical Reasoning in Grades K–12 (1999 Yearbook).* Ed. Lee V. Stiff. Reston: NCTM, 1999.

Math Background

Symmetry and Congruence In Unit B, students are introduced to lines of symmetry for the first time. They will see that a line of symmetry divides a figure in half so that if you fold the figure along the line, the two halves will match exactly. Each half of the figure formed by a line of symmetry is described as a congruent half. Students will also discover that a figure can be divided into congruent halves by lines other than lines of symmetry. For example, in a rectangle, a diagonal is not part of a line of symmetry, but it does divide the rectangle into two congruent halves. The introduction to congruent halves extends to having students identify congruent figures.

Classifying Triangles In grade 2, students drew unique triangles by varying side lengths and angles. They classified these triangles using their own criteria and language: categories such as "three-sides-equal" triangles and "no-big-angle" triangles were appropriate. In this unit, students classify triangles according to lengths of sides using the terms *equilateral, isosceles, and scalene*, and according to the measure of angles using the terms *obtuse, acute,* and *right*. Although these terms should be heard, seen, and used, it is not expected that all students will master them at this grade level.

Composing and Decomposing Quadrilaterals In this unit, students continue to investigate the relationship between different quadrilaterals and triangles by dividing quadrilaterals with diagonals and composing quadrilaterals with triangles. Through these investigations, students build their ideas about properties of figures and how they are related, laying the conceptual foundation for development of area formulas of complex figures in subsequent years.

Estimating Measures of Angles In grade 2, students experimented with making big angles and small angles and drawing triangles starting with different sizes of angles. In this unit, students use benchmark angles like 90° and 180° to estimate the measures of angles. These skills in estimating angles will provide students with the foundation to use protractors successfully in subsequent years. As with all measurement, estimating is an integral part of the process.

Sum of Measures of Angles in a Triangle In this unit, students physically rearrange the angles of a triangle to form a straight angle and to discover that the sum of the measures of the angles in a triangle is 180°. They then apply this property of triangles to find the measure of a missing angle in a triangle.

Math Expressions Geometry Poster

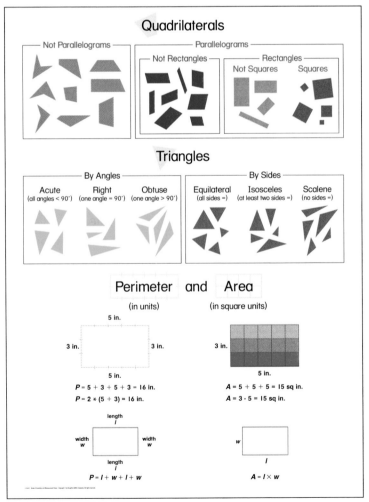

MINI UNIT B

LESSON 1

Symmetry and Congruence

Lesson Objectives

- Draw lines of symmetry.
- Identify congruent halves of figures and congruent figures.

The Day at a Glance

Today's Goals	Materials	**123** Math Talk
1 Teaching the Lesson **A1:** Review types of quadrilaterals and the concepts of parallel and perpendicular. **A2:** Draw the lines of symmetry in figures. **A3:** Identify congruent halves of figures and congruent figures. **2 Extending the Lesson** ▶ Differentiated Instruction **3 Homework and Spiral Review**	Transparency of Student Activity Book page 100 and overhead projector (optional) Scissors Rulers Plastic mirrors Envelopes Tracing paper or unlined paper Tangrams or Tangrams (Copymaster M30) Student Activity Book pages 99–106 Homework and Remembering pages 57–58 Math Journals Family Letter	In today's activities, the students are involved in discussion as they ▶ identify and name quadrilaterals ▶ define and recognize parallel and perpendicular lines ▶ draw lines of symmetry in figures ▶ identify congruent figures

Teaching the Lesson

Review Geometry Concepts

 15 MINUTES

Goal: Review types of quadrilaterals and the concepts of parallel and perpendicular.

Materials: Student Activity Book page 99

✓ **NCTM Standards:**
 Geometry
 Connections

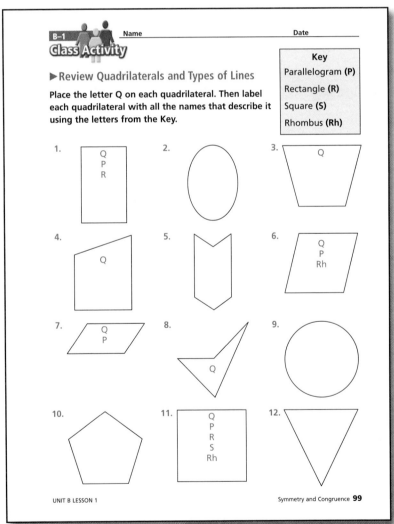

| B-1 | Name _____ | Date _____ |

Class Activity

▶ Review Quadrilaterals and Types of Lines

Place the letter Q on each quadrilateral. Then label each quadrilateral with all the names that describe it using the letters from the Key.

Key
Parallelogram (P)
Rectangle (R)
Square (S)
Rhombus (Rh)

1. Q P R
2.
3. Q
4. Q
5.
6. Q P Rh
7. Q P
8. Q
9.
10.
11. Q P R S Rh
12.

UNIT B LESSON 1   Symmetry and Congruence **99**

Student Activity Book page 99

▶ **Review Quadrilaterals and Types of Lines** WHOLE CLASS

Have students complete Student Activity Book page 99. When they are finished, discuss the answers.

Ask for a volunteer to define parallel lines and parallel line segments. Parallel lines are everywhere the same distance apart. They go on forever and never meet. Parallel line segments are parts of parallel lines.

● Which figures on page 99 have parallel sides? figures 1, 3, 4, 5, 6, 7, and 11

Ask for a volunteer to define perpendicular lines and perpendicular line segments. Perpendicular lines meet at right angles. Perpendicular line segments are parts of perpendicular lines.

● Which figures on page 99 have perpendicular sides? figures 1, 4, and 11

Some students may also note that in certain figures two line segments may be perpendicular if one side is extended to meet another side.

● Which figures have both parallel sides and perpendicular sides? figures 1, 4, and 11

Math Talk in Action

How can you remember what *parallel* means?

Juan: The double *l* in the word parallel looks like a pair of parallel lines.

Tina: The word also sounds a bit like "a pair of Ls."

How can you check if two line segments are perpendicular?

Tina: You can put a piece of paper with a square corner along the edge to check. This figure is not perpendicular because the line segments do not meet at a right angle.

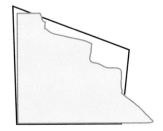

Explore Symmetry

 25 MINUTES

Goal: Draw the lines of symmetry in figures.

Materials: Student Activity Book pages 100–102, transparency of Student Activity Book page 100 and overhead projector (optional), scissors, rulers (1 per student), plastic mirrors, envelopes (one per student)

 NCTM Standards:
Measurement
Geometry
Reasoning and Proof

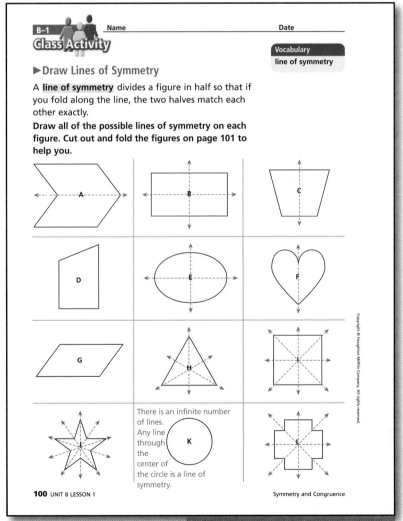

Student Activity Book page 100

▶ Draw Lines of Symmetry WHOLE CLASS

On the board or on an overhead transparency of Student Activity Book page 100, draw the line of symmetry for figure A.

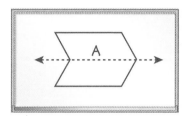

Point out that this line divides figure A into two pieces.

● **How do these two pieces compare?** They are the same size and shape.

● **What will happen if I cut out figure A and fold it along the line?** The two halves will match.

Explain to students that the line you drew is called a line of symmetry. A line of symmetry divides a figure in half so that if you fold the figure along the line, the two halves will match exactly. Point out that a line of symmetry is sometimes called a mirror line because the half on one side of the line looks like the reflection of the other half in a mirror. We say a figure has symmetry if it can be folded along a line so that the two halves match exactly.

✋ Alternate Approach

Plastic Mirrors To verify a line of symmetry, students can place a transparent mirror alongside it. If one half of the figure appears to fall directly on top of the other half, the mirror is on a line of symmetry.

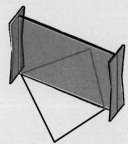

Activity continued ▶

Symmetry and Congruence   **231**

❶ Teaching the Lesson (continued)

Use the overhead transparency of Student Activity Book page 100 or draw an enlarged version of figure B on the board and invite a volunteer to draw a line of symmetry in the figure.

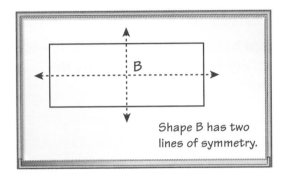

Shape B has two lines of symmetry.

Tell students that a figure may have more than one line of symmetry, or it may have no lines of symmetry. Ask another volunteer to draw a different line of symmetry on figure B.

Some students may suggest a diagonal as a possible line of symmetry for figure B.

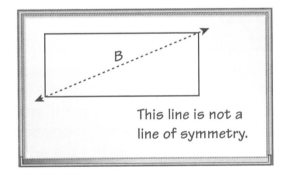

This line is not a line of symmetry.

Demonstrate that this line is not a line of symmetry by cutting out a copy of figure B and folding it along the diagonal. Explain that when two halves do not match when folded, the line is not a line of symmetry.

Have students cut out the copies of the figures on page 101 so they can fold to test their lines of symmetry. Then have students complete Student Activity Book page 100.

 Math Talk

After students have completed the exercise, discuss the results together. If students disagree on their responses, invite them to the overhead or the board to explain their thinking.

- Which figures have no lines of symmetry?
  figures D and G

- Which figures have only one line of symmetry?
  figures A, C, F

- Which figures have exactly two lines of symmetry?
  figures B, E

- Which figures have three or more lines of symmetry? figures H, I, J, K, L

- Which figure has the most lines of symmetry?
  figure K

- How many lines of symmetry does it have?
  an infinite number

 Ongoing Assessment

This activity provides an ideal opportunity to informally assess students' skills at identifying lines of symmetry. Circulate as students work and note those who readily identify lines of symmetry and those who need extra support.

 Class Management

Looking Ahead Have students save the cutouts from Student Activity Book page 101 in an envelope to reuse in Lesson 2.

Activity 3

Congruent Parts and Figures

 20 MINUTES

Goal: Identify congruent halves of figures and congruent figures.

Materials: Student Activity Book pages 100, 103–104, rulers (1 per student), tracing paper or unlined paper

✓ **NCTM Standards:**
Measurement
Geometry
Reasoning and Proof

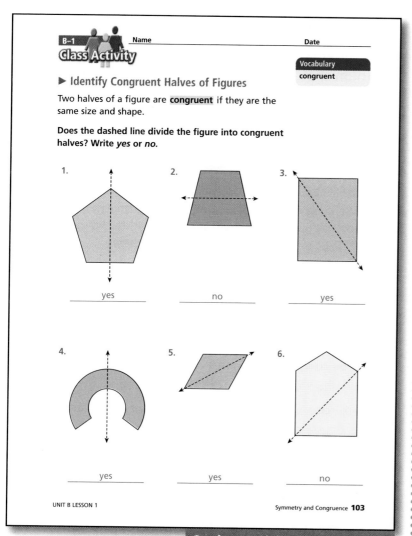

Student Activity Book page 103

▶ Identify Congruent Halves of Figures

WHOLE CLASS

Have students look back at the line of symmetry drawn for figure A on Student Activity Book page 100. Point out that the two halves are exactly the same size and shape. Explain that when two halves are the same size and the same shape we say they are *congruent.* A line of symmetry divides a figure into congruent halves.

Point out that a line does not have to be a line of symmetry to divide a figure into congruent halves. You can show this by drawing a large rectangle on the board and marking one of the diagonals. Show students that although the line is not a line of symmetry, the two halves are congruent. If necessary, demonstrate by cutting out a copy of the figure, cutting it in half along a diagonal, and matching up the halves so they fit exactly on top of one another.

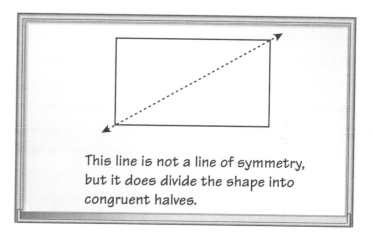

This line is not a line of symmetry, but it does divide the shape into congruent halves.

Direct student's attention to Student Activity Book page 103 and have students complete exercises 1–6 as a class.

Activity continued ▶

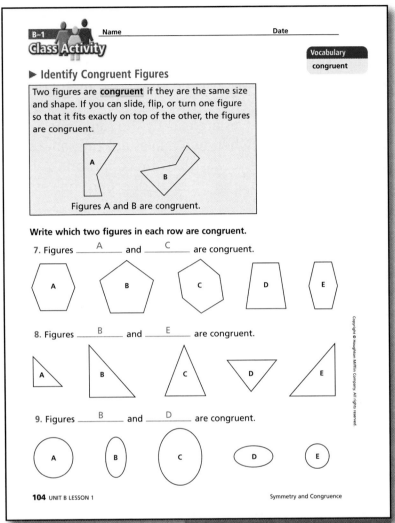

▶ Identify Congruent Figures

WHOLE CLASS

Explain that we can also speak of two figures as being congruent. Two figures are congruent if they are the same size and shape. Emphasize that the figures do not have to be positioned in the exact same way. If you can slide, flip, or turn one figure to fit exactly on top of another, the two figures are congruent. Refer students to Student Activity Book page 104 and have them look at congruent figures A and B. Tell students that they can check whether the figures are congruent by tracing one of them and then fitting the tracing exactly over the other.

Give students a few minutes to complete exercises 7–9. Tell them that if they are not sure whether two figures are congruent, they can trace one and try to fit the tracing exactly over the other. Discuss the results together.

Differentiated Instruction

Extra Help Have students look at Student Activity Book page 104 and ask questions to help students quickly eliminate figures that cannot be congruent to the others.

▶ Without tracing, how do you know that figures B and D in exercise 7 aren't congruent to any other figure? Figure B has five sides and figure D has four sides. All of the other figures have six sides.

▶ In exercise 8, how do you know that figures A, B, and E will not be congruent to figures C or D? Figures A, B, and E have right angles; figures C and D don't.

▶ In exercise 9, why can't figure A be congruent to any others? The only one that is the same shape is figure E and it's much smaller than figure A.

② Extending the Lesson

Activities for Individualizing

Intervention
for students having difficulty
INDIVIDUALS

Identify Congruent Figures

Materials: tangrams or Tangrams (Copymaster M30)

Students show which tangram figures are congruent.

If I place the two small triangles on top of each other, I see that they are the same size and shape. They are congruent.

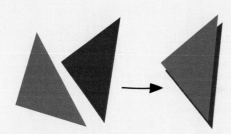

The two large triangles are also congruent.

On Level
for students having success
INDIVIDUALS

Make Congruent Figures

Materials: tangrams or Tangrams (Copymaster M30)

Students join together two tangrams to create figures that are congruent to another tangram.

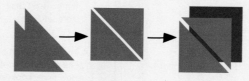  

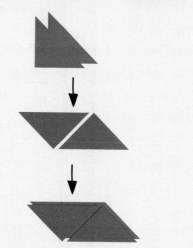

Challenge
for students seeking a challenge
INDIVIDUALS

Build Two Congruent Figures

Materials: tangrams or Tangrams (Copymaster M30)

Students build a figure using the two largest triangle tangrams and then create a congruent figure using all of the remaining tangrams.

Also Use
Challenge Master for B-1

 Math Writing Prompt

Intervention

Explain Your Thinking
Lian has two figures but she is not sure that they are congruent. Explain how she can test whether they are congruent.

 Math Writing Prompt

On Level

You Decide
Benito claims that all triangles are congruent. Do you agree or disagree? Explain your answer.

 Math Writing Prompt

Challenge

Draw a Diagram
Draw two congruent figures. Explain why they are congruent.

③ Homework and Spiral Review

✓ On this Homework page, students draw lines of symmetry and identify congruent pairs of figures.

This Remembering page is appropriate anytime after today's lesson.

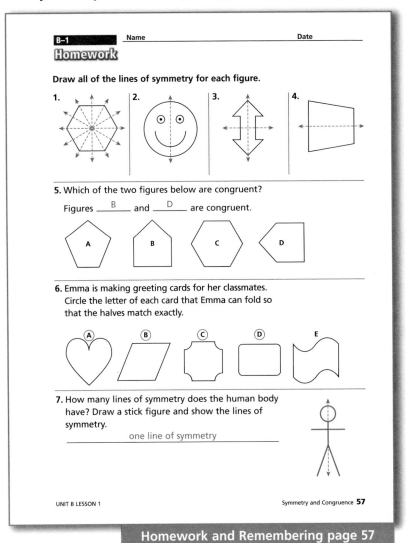

Homework and Remembering page 57

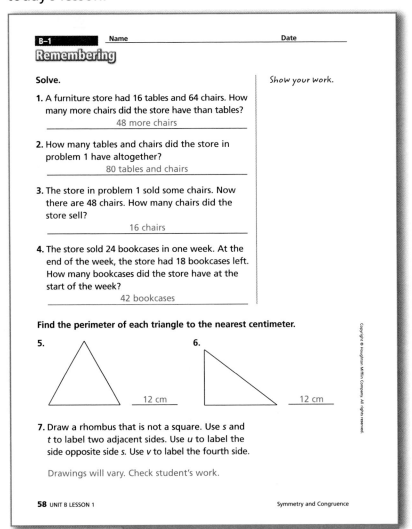

Homework and Remembering page 58

Home and School Connection

Family Letter Have students take home the Family Letter on Student Activity Book page 105. This letter explains how the concepts of symmetry and congruence are developed in *Math Expressions*. It gives parents and guardians a better understanding of the learning that goes on in math class and creates a bridge between school and home. A Spanish translation of this letter is on the following page in the Student Activity Book.

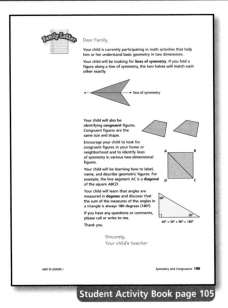

Student Activity Book page 105

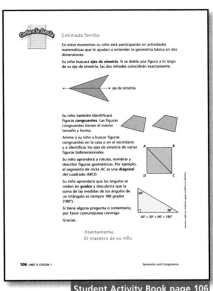

Student Activity Book page 106

Label Figures and Draw Diagonals

Lesson Objectives

- Label and name figures using letters.
- Understand the relationship between the diagonals of quadrilaterals and the triangles they form.

The Day at a Glance

Today's Goals	Materials	123 Math Talk
1 Teaching the Lesson **A1:** Label vertices and name figures using letters. **A2:** Draw diagonals in quadrilaterals to form triangles. **2 Extending the Lesson** ► Differentiated Instruction **3 Homework and Spiral Review**	Rulers Scissors Tracing paper (optional) Cutouts from Lesson 1, Student Activity Book page 101 Student Activity Book pages 107–110 Homework and Remembering pages 59–60 Math Journals	In today's activities, the students are involved in discussion as they ► label the vertices of figures ► name figures using letter labels ► draw diagonals in quadrilaterals ► investigate the properties of diagonals ► explore the triangles formed by diagonals drawn in different quadrilaterals

1 Teaching the Lesson

Label Figures

 15 MINUTES

Goal: Label vertices and name figures using letters.

Materials: Student Activity Book page 107, rulers (1 per student)

 NCTM Standards:
Geometry
Representation

▶ Label Corners with Letters   WHOLE CLASS

Draw a quadrilateral on the board.

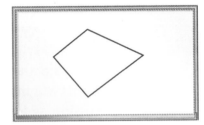

Explain that it is sometimes helpful to give a figure a name with letters. To name this figure with letters, first label its corners with capital letters. Label the vertices *W, X, Y,* and *Z.*

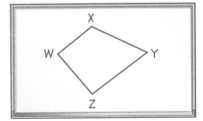

Explain that to name a figure with letters you start at any corner and list the letters in order as you go around the figure clockwise or counterclockwise.

Point out that one name for the figure on the board is *WXYZ.* Point to each vertex as you say its name, and then write *WXYZ* on the board next to the figure.

● What are some other names for this figure? *XYZW, XWZY, YZWX, YXWZ, ZWXY, ZYXW, WZYX*

● Can you name the figure *WYXZ?* no

● Why not? Those letters are not in order around the figure.

Have students complete Student Activity Book page 107. When they are finished, discuss their answers.

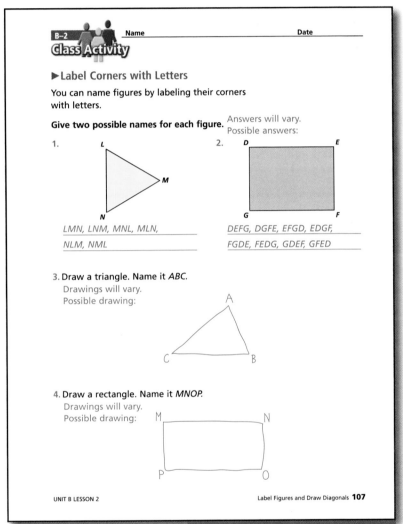

Student Activity Book page 107

 Ongoing Assessment

Ask students to draw a triangle and a rectangle and to label them with letters. Have students provide two possible names for each figure using their letter labels.

Draw Diagonals

 45 MINUTES

Goal: Draw diagonals in quadrilaterals to form triangles.

Materials: rulers (1 per student), scissors (1 pair per student), tracing paper (optional), Student Activity Book pages 108–109

 NCTM Standards:
Measurement
Geometry
Reasoning and Proof

▶ Diagonals WHOLE CLASS

Draw quadrilateral *STUV* on the board.

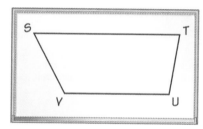

Explain to students that they can name a line segment using the letter labels at each endpoint in either order. Point to side *ST.*

- Give two names for this side. *ST and TS*

- Name all the other sides in two ways. *TU or UT, UV or VU,* and *VS or SV*

Draw a diagonal from *V* to *T.*

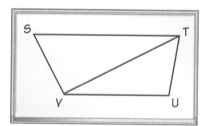

Tell students that a line segment that connects two corners of a quadrilateral and is not a side of the quadrilateral is called a diagonal.

- What is the name of this diagonal? *TV or VT*

- How do you know? *Its endpoints are T and V.*

Add a second diagonal *SU* to the quadrilateral on the board.

- What is the name of this diagonal? *SU or US*

Have students complete exercises 5–14 on Student Activity Book pages 108–109. Some students may want to use tracing paper to trace the triangles formed so that they can check if the triangles are congruent. They can also trace, cut out, and fold the quadrilaterals to check for symmetry.

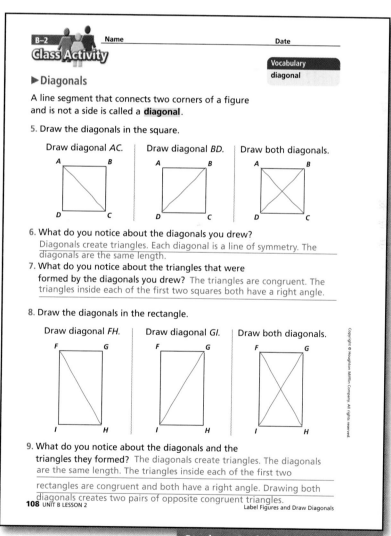

Student Activity Book page 108

Activity continued ▶
Label Figures and Draw Diagonals   **239**

① Teaching the Lesson (continued)

For each exercise, invite students to share their observations. Encourage them to use the geometry words they learned earlier. You may need to review the meanings of such terms as *congruent, line of symmetry,* and *right angle.*

Here are some questions you might ask for each exercise:

- Are the two diagonals the same length?

- Are the two triangles formed by each diagonal congruent?

- When you drew both diagonals, were any pairs of triangles congruent?

- Are the diagonals lines of symmetry?

- Are the triangles formed by the first diagonal congruent to the triangles formed by the second diagonal?

- Look at the angles in the triangles formed when one diagonal is drawn. Do both triangles have right angles?

- Look at the four triangles formed when both diagonals are drawn. Do all four triangles have right angles?

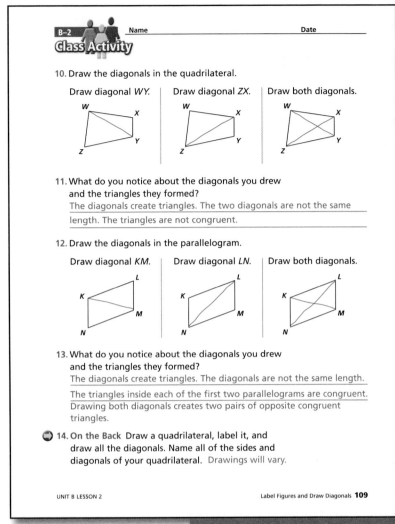

Student Activity Book page 109

 Math Talk in Action

When is a diagonal of a quadrilateral a line of symmetry?

Elia: A diagonal is a line of symmetry when the two triangles it makes are congruent.

Sophie: I'm not sure that is enough. The triangles might be congruent and still not match each other when you fold over the diagonal.

Huy: Yeah. I only think the square matches when you fold along the diagonal.

Why don't you think the other quadrilaterals match when they fold onto themselves?

Huy: The opposite corners aren't in the same place along the diagonal. They have to be opposite each other, exactly halfway along the diagonal for the two triangles to match.

② Extending the Lesson

Intervention
for students having difficulty
`INDIVIDUALS`

Diagonal Halves

Materials: cutouts B, C, G, and I from Lesson 1, scissors

Students investigate which figures form two congruent triangles when cut along their diagonals.

Students can use the quadrilaterals from Lesson 1 and cut each figure along its diagonal.

Encourage students to slide, flip, and turn each half to check if the triangles are congruent.

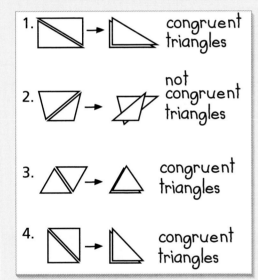

1. congruent triangles
2. not congruent triangles
3. congruent triangles
4. congruent triangles

On Level
for students having success
`PAIRS`

Diagonal Clues

Materials: rulers (1 per student)

In pairs, students take turns secretly drawing a quadrilateral with one or two diagonals and provide clues to their partners to help them name the figure. Specify that clues should mention only the diagonals and the triangles they form.

> The diagonals are equal in length and all four triangles they form are congruent. What is the figure?

> The triangles formed by one diagonal are congruent but they do not have right angles. What is the figure?

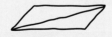

Challenge
for students seeking a challenge
`SMALL GROUPS`

Compare Diagonals

Students create a chart comparing the diagonals of different quadrilaterals and the triangles they form.

Property of diagonals	Square	Rectangle
diagonals are lines of symmetry	yes	no
diagonals are equal in length	yes	yes
one diagonal forms congruent triangles	yes	yes

Also Use
Challenge Master for B-2

 Math Writing Prompt

Intervention

Explain Your Thinking
Luk Sun has drawn a diagonal line in a parallelogram, but he is unsure whether the diagonal is a line of symmetry. Explain what he can do to test whether the diagonal is a line of symmetry.

 Math Writing Prompt

On Level

Draw a Picture
Use a picture to help explain why a triangle does not have any diagonals.

 Math Writing Prompt

Challenge

Make a Comparison
How are the diagonals of squares and rectangles similar? How are they different?

3 Homework and Spiral Review

B-2 Homework Goal: Additional Practice

On this Homework page, students name figures using letters and draw diagonals on quadrilaterals to form triangles.

B-2 Remembering Goal: Spiral Review

This Remembering page is appropriate anytime after today's lesson.

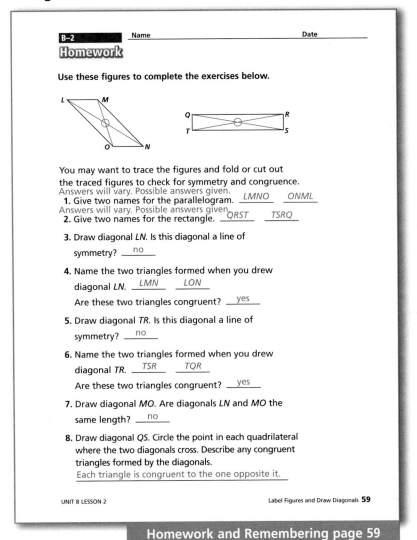

B-2 Homework

Name _____ Date _____

Use these figures to complete the exercises below.

You may want to trace the figures and fold or cut out the traced figures to check for symmetry and congruence.
Answers will vary. Possible answers given.
1. Give two names for the parallelogram. _LMNO_ _ONML_
Answers will vary. Possible answers given.
2. Give two names for the rectangle. _QRST_ _TSRQ_

3. Draw diagonal *LN*. Is this diagonal a line of symmetry? _no_

4. Name the two triangles formed when you drew diagonal *LN*. _LMN_ _LON_
Are these two triangles congruent? _yes_

5. Draw diagonal *TR*. Is this diagonal a line of symmetry? _no_

6. Name the two triangles formed when you drew diagonal *TR*. _TSR_ _TQR_
Are these two triangles congruent? _yes_

7. Draw diagonal *MO*. Are diagonals *LN* and *MO* the same length? _no_

8. Draw diagonal *QS*. Circle the point in each quadrilateral where the two diagonals cross. Describe any congruent triangles formed by the diagonals.
Each triangle is congruent to the one opposite it.

UNIT B LESSON 2   Label Figures and Draw Diagonals **59**

Homework and Remembering page 59

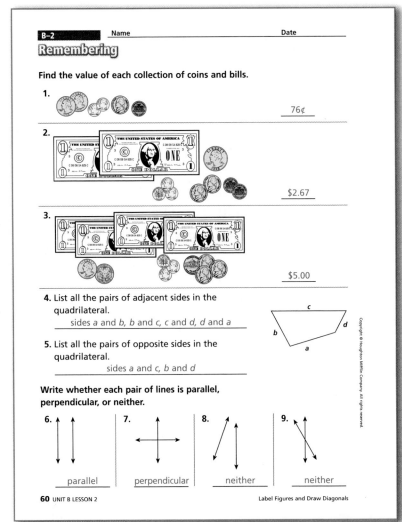

B-2 Remembering

Name _____ Date _____

Find the value of each collection of coins and bills.

1. _76¢_

2. _$2.67_

3. _$5.00_

4. List all the pairs of adjacent sides in the quadrilateral.
sides *a* and *b*, *b* and *c*, *c* and *d*, *d* and *a*

5. List all the pairs of opposite sides in the quadrilateral.
sides *a* and *c*, *b* and *d*

Write whether each pair of lines is parallel, perpendicular, or neither.

6. _parallel_

7. _perpendicular_

8. _neither_

9. _neither_

60 UNIT B LESSON 2   Label Figures and Draw Diagonals

Homework and Remembering page 60

Home or School Activity

 Science Connection

Find the Center of Gravity An object's center of gravity is its balance point.

Invite students to draw quadrilaterals on card stock and to cut out the figures. Next, ask them to draw the two diagonals in all of their figures. Challenge students to try to balance each figure on the eraser end of a pencil at the point where the two diagonals intersect.

Angles and Triangles

Lesson Objectives

- **Understand what an angle is and name angles by size.**

- **Describe and name triangles.**

- **Understand the relationship between quadrilaterals and triangles.**

Vocabulary		
angle	right triangle	equilateral triangle
right angle	acute triangle	isosceles triangle
acute angle	obtuse triangle	scalene triangle
obtuse angle		

The Day at a Glance

Today's Goals	Materials	123 Math Talk
1 Teaching the Lesson **A1:** Compare and name angles. **A2:** Classify triangles by lengths of sides and sizes of angles. **A3:** Build quadrilaterals from two congruent triangles. **2 Extending the Lesson** ▶ Differentiated Instruction **3 Homework and Spiral Review**	Straws Colored flexible rods, such as pipe cleaners or chenille sticks Centimeter rulers Chart paper (optional) Scissors Index cards MathBoard materials Student Activity Book pages 111–116 Homework and Remembering pages 61–62 Math Journals	In today's activities, the students are involved in discussion as they ▶ make angles with straws ▶ compare and name angles ▶ classify and name triangles ▶ build quadrilaterals from triangles

Teaching the Lesson

Introduce Angles

 20 MINUTES

Goal: Compare and name angles.

Materials: Student Activity Book page 111, straws (4 per student), colored flexible rods, such as pipe cleaners or chenille sticks (2 per student)

✔ **NCTM Standards:**
Geometry
Reasoning and Proof

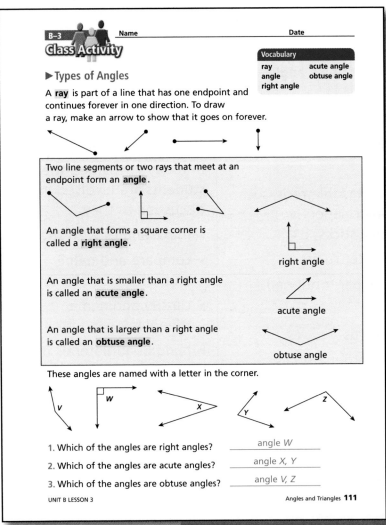

Student Activity Book page 111

Teaching Note

Language and Vocabulary Students should not be expected to master all of the new vocabulary in this lesson. Students will revisit these terms in Remembering problems and in future grades.

▶ **Types of Angles** WHOLE CLASS

Discuss the meanings of the geometry terms introduced on Student Activity Book page 111.

Explain to students that the size of an angle is the amount of rotation, or turn, from one side to the other. Connect two straws with a pipe cleaner or chenille stick. Leave one straw fixed and rotate the other straw to form angles of different sizes. Tell students that rotating the straw more creates larger angles. Show students pairs of angles and ask them which is larger.

Demonstrate how to make an angle smaller by rotating one straw closer to the other. Next, demonstrate how to make an angle larger by rotating one straw away from the other straw.

Then distribute materials to students and invite them to create a right angle using two of their straws.

Ask students to use their remaining two straws to make an angle smaller than a right angle, or an acute angle.

Have students make an angle larger than a right angle, or an obtuse angle.

Then ask students to complete exercises 1–3 on Student Activity Book page 111.

Classify Triangles

 30 MINUTES

Goal: Classify triangles by lengths of sides and sizes of angles.

Materials: Student Activity Book pages 112–114, centimeter rulers (1 per student), chart paper (optional)

 NCTM Standards:
Geometry
Reasoning and Proof
Connections

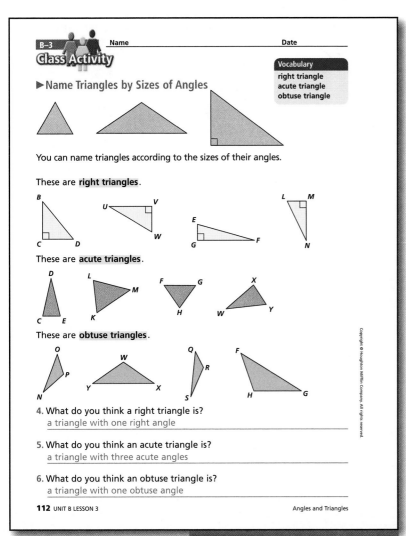

Student Activity Book page 112

▶ Name Triangles by Sizes of Angles

WHOLE CLASS

Have students look at the three triangles at the top of Student Activity Book page 112. Talk about the similarities and differences among the three triangles.

● How many angles does each of the triangles have? three

● Do you see a right angle in any of the triangles? yes

● In which triangle? the third triangle

● Do you see an obtuse angle in any of the triangles? yes

● In which triangle? the middle triangle

● What kind of an angle is each angle in the first triangle? acute

Write *obtuse, acute,* and *right* on the board.

Explain that we use these words to name triangles according to the sizes of their angles. Tell students that they will now try to determine which word goes with each of the three triangles.

Turn students' attention to the examples of each type of triangle. Encourage them to think about what is the same about each group of triangles in order to help figure out which word can be used to describe each type of triangle. Students can work in pairs to classify the angles in each triangle and complete exercises 4–6.

As a class, come up with definitions of *right triangle, acute triangle,* and *obtuse triangle* and write them on the board or chart paper.

Here are some possible definitions:

right triangle: a triangle with one right angle

acute triangle: a triangle with three angles, each smaller than right angles

obtuse triangle: a triangle with one angle larger than a right angle

Activity continued ▶

1 Teaching the Lesson (continued)

Have students look at the three triangles at the top of the Student Activity Book page 112 once again. Ask these questions to help students label each triangle according to the sizes of its angles.

- Check the angles in the first triangle. What kind of triangle is it? acute

- Check the angles in the second triangle. What kind of triangle is it? obtuse

- Check the angles in the third triangle. What kind of triangle is it? right

Encourage students to explore the characteristics of triangles. Have them try to draw a variety of triangles, both possible and impossible, such as triangles with the following characteristics:

- two acute angles

- two right angles

- two obtuse angles

Talk about why some of these "triangles" cannot exist. For example, two right angles would prevent two of the sides from joining.

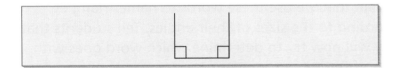

Invite students to share any interesting observations they made while drawing. For example, they might mention that if a triangle has one obtuse angle, the other two angles must be acute.

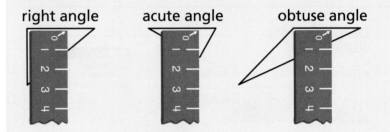
246 UNIT B LESSON 3

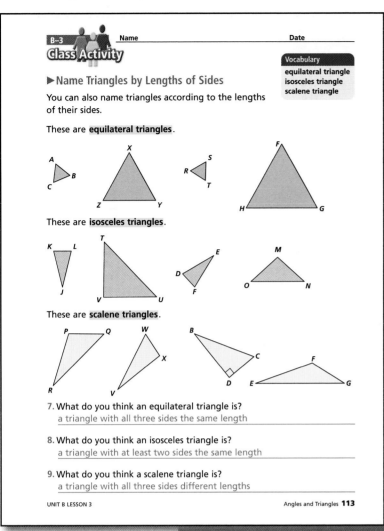

▶ Name Triangles by Lengths of Sides

PAIRS

Direct students' attention once again to the three triangles at the top of Student Activity Book page 112. This time, have them focus on the side lengths of each triangle. Talk about the similarities and differences among the triangles.

● What do you notice about the lengths of sides of the first triangle? All sides are the same length.

● What about the second triangle? Two sides are the same length and one is of a different length.

● What about the third triangle? All of the sides are different lengths.

Write these words on the board and read them aloud.

scalene   isosceles   equilateral

Explain that we use these words to name triangles based on the length of their sides.

Have students look at the examples of each type of triangle on Student Activity Book page 113. Encourage them to think about what is the same about each group of triangles in order to help them figure out the meanings of the words on the board. Students can work in pairs to measure the lengths of the sides of each triangle and complete exercises 7–9.

Together, come up with definitions of *equilateral triangle, isosceles triangle,* and *scalene triangle* and record them on the board or chart paper. Here are some possible definitions:

equilateral triangle: a triangle with all sides the same length

isosceles triangle: a triangle with at least two sides the same length

scalene triangle: a triangle with no sides the same length

Point out that an equilateral triangle can also be classified as isosceles because it has at least two sides the same length.

Teaching Note

Math Background Be aware that definitions may vary slightly among resources. For example, there are two possible definitions of an isosceles triangle:

1. a triangle with at least two sides the same length

2. a triangle with exactly two sides the same length

According to the second definition, an equilateral triangle is not isosceles. *Math Expressions* uses the first definition.

Activity continued ▶

① Teaching the Lesson (continued)

Have students look at the three triangles at the top of the previous page once again. Ask these questions to help students label each triangle according to the lengths of its sides:

- Measure the sides of the first triangle. What kind of triangle is it? equilateral

- How can you name the triangle in two ways? acute, equilateral

- Measure the sides of the second triangle. What kind of triangle is it? isosceles

- How can you name the triangle in two ways? obtuse, isosceles

- Measure the sides of the third triangle. What kind of triangle is it? scalene

- How can you name the triangle in two ways? right, scalene

Challenge students to try to draw these triangles and explain why they cannot exist.

- an equilateral right triangle

- an equilateral obtuse triangle

Encourage students to share their observations. For example, they might mention that all of the angles in an equilateral triangle are acute, so an equilateral triangle cannot be an obtuse or right triangle.

► Name Triangles by Sizes of Angles and Lengths of Sides INDIVIDUALS

Have students turn their attention to exercise 10 on Student Activity Book page 114. Explain that the symbol in the corner of the triangle shows that the angle is a right angle.

- If a triangle has a right angle, what kind of triangle is it? It is a right triangle.

Ask students to measure the lengths of the sides of the triangle in exercise 10.

- How many sides are the same length? 2 sides

- If a triangle has two sides the same length, what kind of triangle is it? It is an isosceles triangle.

Ask students to complete exercises 10–15 independently.

248 UNIT B LESSON 3

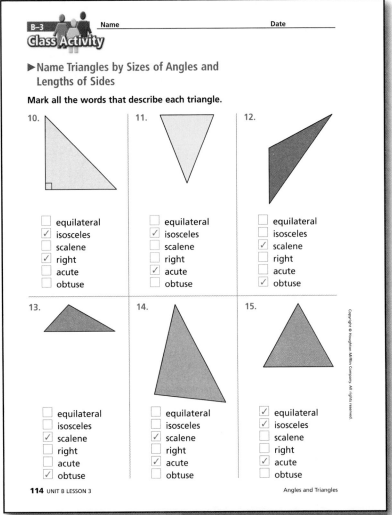

Student Activity Book page 114

✓ Ongoing Assessment

Ask students to draw the following triangles to show their understanding of different types of triangles.

► Draw an equilateral triangle.

► Draw an obtuse isosceles triangle.

► Draw a right scalene triangle.

Build Quadrilaterals from Triangles

 10 MINUTES

Goal: Build quadrilaterals from two congruent triangles.

Materials: Student Activity Book pages 115–116, scissors (1 pair per student), centimeter rulers (1 per student)

 NCTM Standards:
Geometry
Reasoning and Proof
Connections

▶ Build Quadrilaterals from Triangles

INDIVIDUALS

Have students cut out the two obtuse triangles from Student Activity Book page 115.

Borrow a pair of triangles from a student and demonstrate how to make a quadrilateral by matching up two of the sides of equal length.

● There are many ways to form a quadrilateral from these two triangles. I want you to experiment to find as many different ways as you can. Trace each quadrilateral you make.

After a few minutes, invite volunteers to share some of the quadrilaterals they created. There are six possible figures in all.

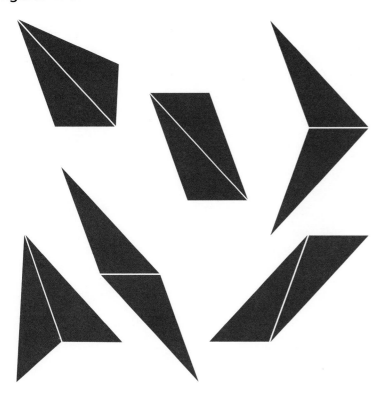

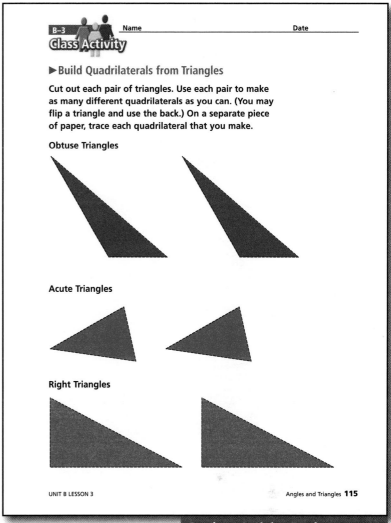

Student Activity Book page 115

● What do you call the line segment where the two triangles are joined? a diagonal

Ask students to repeat the activity using the acute triangles. Here are three possible quadrilaterals:

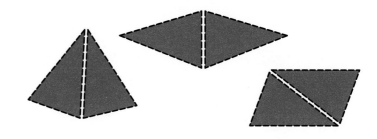

Activity continued ▶

Finally, have students repeat the activity with the right triangles. Here are three possible quadrilaterals:

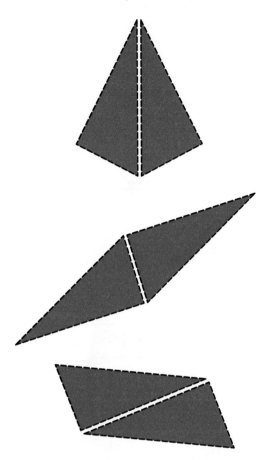

The Learning Classroom

Building Concepts Challenge students to draw and cut out two congruent triangles, that can be used to build a square.

② Extending the Lesson

Differentiated Instruction Activities for Individualizing

Intervention
for students having difficulty

INDIVIDUALS

Colored Side Lengths

Materials: colored flexible rods such as pipe cleaners or chenille sticks (blue rods cut in 10-cm lengths, red rods cut in 8-cm lengths, and yellow rods cut in 6-cm lengths)

Students make an equilateral, isosceles, and scalene triangle using the different colored rods.

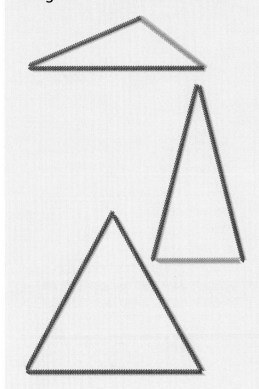

On Level
for students having success

SMALL GROUPS

Match Names and Triangles

Materials: index cards

Create a set of cards, each with a different triangle name or picture. Invite students to help. Students then play a matching game by turning over one picture card and one name card at a time and trying to find matches.

RIGHT SCALENE	◣
RIGHT ISOSCELES	◢
ACUTE ISOSCELES	▷
OBTUSE ISOSCELES	◁
EQUILATERAL	△
OBTUSE SCALENE	◁
ACUTE SCALENE	◹

Challenge
for students seeking a challenge

SMALL GROUPS

Angles of Equal Measure

Materials: MathBoard materials

Students investigate the relationship between the number of congruent angles and the number of sides with equal measures in a triangle. First, students draw an equilateral, isosceles, and scalene triangle. For each triangle, they then trace an angle and place their tracing over the other angles to test for congruence. Students share and record their discoveries.

> An equilateral triangle has three angles of equal measure. An isosceles triangle has two angles of equal measure. All three of the angles in a scalene triangle have different measures.

Also Use
Challenge Master for B-3

 Math Writing Prompt

Intervention

Create Your Own Method
Adra wants to check whether or not an angle is a right angle. Suggest a method she can use.

 Math Writing Prompt

On Level

Draw a Picture
Can a triangle have two right angles? Include a drawing with your explanation.

 Math Writing Prompt

Challenge

Explain Your Thinking
Explain why you cannot draw an obtuse equilateral triangle.

③ Homework and Spiral Review

Homework **Goal:** Additional Practice

✓ Include students' work for page 61 as part of their portfolios.

Remembering **Goal:** Spiral Review

This Remembering page is appropriate anytime after today's lesson.

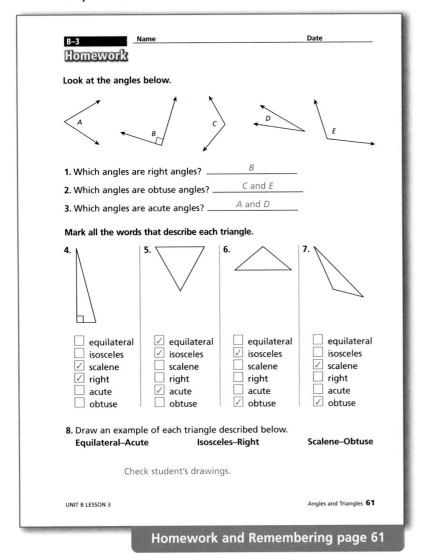

B–3   Name _____ Date _____

Homework

Look at the angles below.

1. Which angles are right angles? _____ *B* _____

2. Which angles are obtuse angles? _____ *C and E* _____

3. Which angles are acute angles? _____ *A and D* _____

Mark all the words that describe each triangle.

4.
- ☐ equilateral
- ☐ isosceles
- ☑ scalene
- ☑ right
- ☐ acute
- ☐ obtuse

5.
- ☑ equilateral
- ☑ isosceles
- ☐ scalene
- ☐ right
- ☑ acute
- ☐ obtuse

6.
- ☐ equilateral
- ☑ isosceles
- ☐ scalene
- ☐ right
- ☐ acute
- ☑ obtuse

7.
- ☐ equilateral
- ☐ isosceles
- ☑ scalene
- ☐ right
- ☐ acute
- ☑ obtuse

8. Draw an example of each triangle described below.

  Equilateral–Acute   **Isosceles–Right**   **Scalene–Obtuse**

Check student's drawings.

UNIT B LESSON 3   Angles and Triangles **61**

Homework and Remembering page 61

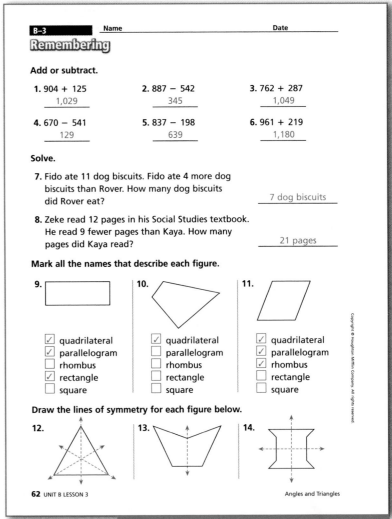

B–3   Name _____ Date _____

Remembering

Add or subtract.

1. $904 + 125$ 1,029

2. $887 - 542$ 345

3. $762 + 287$ 1,049

4. $670 - 541$ 129

5. $837 - 198$ 639

6. $961 + 219$ 1,180

Solve.

7. Fido ate 11 dog biscuits. Fido ate 4 more dog biscuits than Rover. How many dog biscuits did Rover eat?   7 dog biscuits

8. Zeke read 12 pages in his Social Studies textbook. He read 9 fewer pages than Kaya. How many pages did Kaya read?   21 pages

Mark all the names that describe each figure.

9.
- ☑ quadrilateral
- ☑ parallelogram
- ☐ rhombus
- ☑ rectangle
- ☐ square

10.
- ☑ quadrilateral
- ☐ parallelogram
- ☐ rhombus
- ☐ rectangle
- ☐ square

11.
- ☑ quadrilateral
- ☑ parallelogram
- ☑ rhombus
- ☐ rectangle
- ☐ square

Draw the lines of symmetry for each figure below.

12.   **13.**   **14.**

62 UNIT B LESSON 3   Angles and Triangles

Homework and Remembering page 62

Home or School Activity

 Social Studies Connection

Roof Angles The sides of a peaked roof meet to form an angle. In places where there is frequent snow and rain, roof sides typically meet to form acute angles. A steeper roof allows rain and snow to run off easily. In more arid parts of the world, roof slope is less critical, so roof sides can form obtuse angles.

Invite students to explore their neighborhoods and to sketch the angles formed by different roofs.

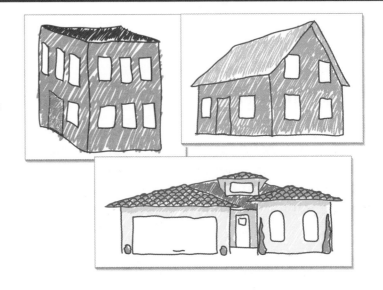

Angle Measures

Lesson Objectives

- Estimate angle measures by comparing them to angles with known measures.
- Discover that the sum of the measures of the angles in any triangle is 180 degrees.
- Given the measures of two angles in a triangle, find the measure of the third angle.

Vocabulary

degree
straight angle
ray

The Day at a Glance

Today's Goals	Materials	123 Math Talk
1 Teaching the Lesson **A1:** Learn about degrees as units of measure and estimate angle measures. **A2:** Discover that the sum of the measures of the angles in any triangle is 180 degrees. **A3:** Calculate the measure of the third angle, given the measure of the other two angles in a triangle. **2 Extending the Lesson** ▶ Differentiated Instruction **3 Homework and Spiral Review**	Straws Centimeter rulers Scissors Measure by Filling Angles (Copymaster M38) MathBoard materials Student Activity Book pages 117–120 Homework and Remembering pages 63–64 Math Journals	In today's activities, the students are involved in discussion as they ▶ learn that angles are measured in units called degrees ▶ recognize several benchmark angles ▶ estimate angle measures by comparing them with known angle measures ▶ discover that the sum of the measures of the three angles in any triangle is 180 degrees ▶ find missing angle measures in triangles

Teaching the Lesson

Estimate Angle Measures

 20 MINUTES

Goal: Learn about degrees as units of measure and estimate angle measures.

Materials: Student Activity Book pages 117–118, straws

✔ **NCTM Standards:**
Geometry
Measurement
Connections

▶ Introduce Degrees WHOLE CLASS

Invite students to suggest different units of measure and to explain their use. Answers will vary. Possible answers: Centimeters and inches measure length. Pounds measure weight.

Draw several different angles on the board. Remind students that the size of an angle is the amount of rotation, or turn, from one side to the other side.

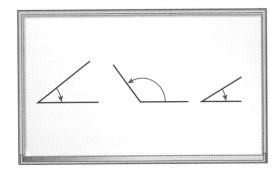

Explain to students that the size of an angle is measured in units called degrees.

Refer students to Student Activity Book page 117. Ask them to examine the 1-degree angle. Point out that 1 degree is a very small rotation.

Refer students to the 5-degree angle and explain that an angle's measure is the total number of 1-degree angles that fit inside it. Then introduce the symbol (°) for degrees.

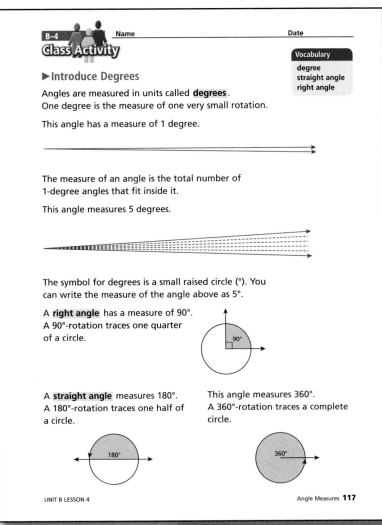

Student Activity Book page 117

Hold up two straws and show students how to rotate one straw to trace a complete circle.

Demonstrate a 90° rotation using the two straws.

● What kind of angle is this? a right angle

Explain to students that the measure of a right angle is 90° and point out that a 90° rotation is one quarter of a circle.

Next, rotate the straw to show a 180° angle and tell students that this angle is twice the size of a 90° angle.

● If this angle is twice the size of a 90° angle, what is its measure? 180°

Emphasize for students that a 180° rotation traces a half-circle. Explain that a 180° angle is called a straight angle; it looks like a straight line because the rays that form the sides of the angle point in opposite directions.

Rotate the straw to show a complete circle and indicate that this angle is twice the size of a 180° angle.

● If this angle is twice the size of a 180° angle, what is its measure? 360°

Tell students that a 360° rotation traces a complete circle. Explain that a 360° angle looks like a single ray because the two rays that form the sides of the angle align and point in the same direction.

▶ **Angle Measures** WHOLE CLASS

Draw an angle that is approximately 80° on the board and include a dashed line at 90° for reference.

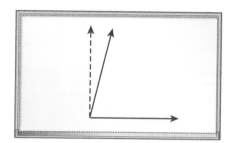

● Is the measure of this angle greater than or less than 90°? It is less than 90°.

Point out that the measure of this angle is slightly less than 90°, so you can estimate that its measure is approximately 80°.

Together, complete exercise 1 on Student Activity Book page 118. Draw a 45° angle on the board and show a dashed line at 90°.

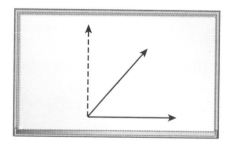

● How many angles like this one will fit inside a 90° angle? two angles

● What number, if you double it, is equal to 90? 45

Tell students that the measure of this angle is approximately 45°.

Activity continued ▶

① Teaching the Lesson (continued)

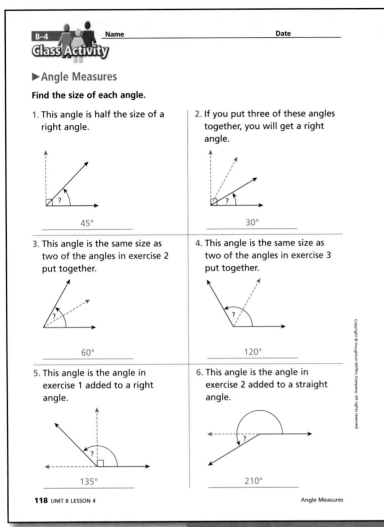

Angle Measures

Find the size of each angle.

1. This angle is half the size of a right angle.

   45°

2. If you put three of these angles together, you will get a right angle.

   30°

3. This angle is the same size as two of the angles in exercise 2 put together.

   60°

4. This angle is the same size as two of the angles in exercise 3 put together.

   120°

5. This angle is the angle in exercise 1 added to a right angle.

   135°

6. This angle is the angle in exercise 2 added to a straight angle.

   210°

118 UNIT B LESSON 4

Angle Measures

Student Activity Book page 118

Emphasize for students that they can estimate the measure of an angle by comparing it to angles with given measures. Have students complete exercises 2–6.

Differentiated Instruction

Extra Help Some students will benefit from using their arms to form 90°, 180°, and 360° angles. In pairs, students can take turns making and identifying these angles. When students are comfortable with these benchmark angles, encourage them to experiment with making other angles and estimating their measures.

✓ Ongoing Assessment

Ask students about angles made by the hands of a clock.

▶ What is the measure of the angle formed on a clock when the minute hand points to 12 and the hour hand points to 6?

▶ What is the measure of the angle formed on a clock when the minute hand points to 12 and the hour hand points to 3?

Find the Sum of the Measures of the Angles of a Triangle

 20 MINUTES

Goal: Discover that the sum of the measures of the angles in any triangle is 180 degrees.

Materials: Student Activity Book page 119, centimeter rulers (1 per student), scissors (1 pair per student)

 NCTM Standards:
Geometry
Measurement
Connections

▶ Join Angles of a Triangle PAIRS

Have students follow the directions on Student Activity Book page 119 to draw a triangle, cut it out, tear off the corners, and rearrange the corners to form a straight angle (180°).

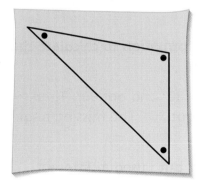

Students can work in pairs to complete exercises 7–10. Circulate while students are working and help those who are having difficulty.

When students are finished, discuss their answers. Ask students to name the types of triangles they drew. right triangle, isosceles triangle, acute triangle, obtuse triangle, scalene triangle, equilateral triangle

● Did everyone make straight angles when they rearranged the angles of their triangles? yes

Summarize by pointing out that the sum of the measures of the three angles in any triangle is 180°.

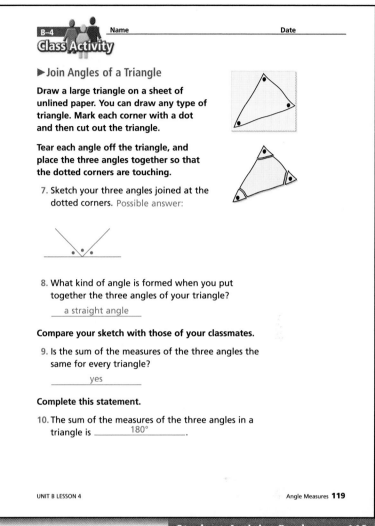

B-4
Class Activity
Name _____ Date _____

▶ Join Angles of a Triangle

Draw a large triangle on a sheet of unlined paper. You can draw any type of triangle. Mark each corner with a dot and then cut out the triangle.

Tear each angle off the triangle, and place the three angles together so that the dotted corners are touching.

7. Sketch your three angles joined at the dotted corners. Possible answer:

8. What kind of angle is formed when you put together the three angles of your triangle?
   a straight angle

Compare your sketch with those of your classmates.

9. Is the sum of the measures of the three angles the same for every triangle?
   yes

Complete this statement.

10. The sum of the measures of the three angles in a triangle is _____ 180° _____.

UNIT B LESSON 4   Angle Measures **119**

Student Activity Book page 119

Teaching the Lesson (continued)

Activity 3

Find the Missing Angle Measure in a Triangle

 20 MINUTES

Goal: Calculate the measure of the third angle, given the measure of the other two angles in a triangle.

Materials: Student Activity Book page 120

 NCTM Standards:
Geometry
Connections
Communication

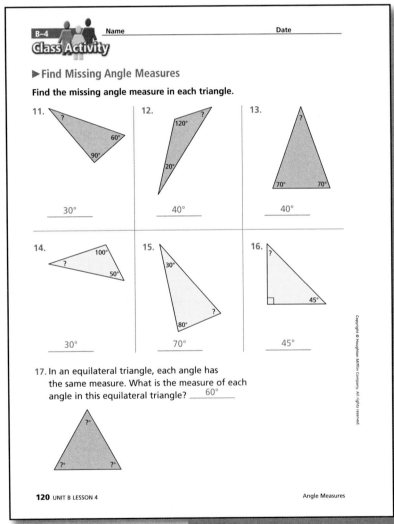

Student Activity Book page 120

▶ **Find Missing Angle Measures** [PAIRS]

Have students work in pairs to find the missing angle measure in exercise 11 on Student Activity Book page 120.

When they are finished, discuss their methods of solving as a class.

Ask students to complete exercises 12–17 in pairs. When they are finished, invite volunteers to record their answers on the board.

Math Talk in Action

What information do we know that can help us calculate the measure of the missing angle measure?

Aida: We know that the sum of the measures of angles in a triangle is 180°.

Explain how you used this information to calculate the measure of the missing angle.

Enrico: I subtracted 90° from 180° and got 90°. Then I subtracted 60° from 90° and got 30°. The missing angle has a measure of 30°.

Seema: I got the same answer but I used a different method.

Enrico: What did you do?

Seema: I added 90° and 60° and got 150°. Then I subtracted 150° from 180° and got 30°.

Both methods are correct. Adding two numbers together before subtracting them from another number is the same as subtracting the two numbers one at a time.

Teaching Note

Watch For! You may need to remind some students that the square in the angle in exercise 16 shows that it is a right angle. Ask them to tell you the measure of a right angle. 90°

② Extending the Lesson

Intervention
for students having difficulty
`PAIRS`

Fill-in Angles

Materials: Measure by Filling Angles (Copymaster M38), scissors (1 pair per student)

Students work in pairs to find the measures of the angles on Copymaster M38. They first cut out the 10° angle. For each angle, they place the 10° angle along the ray and trace it. Then, they rotate the 10° angle to align it with the first tracing, and trace it again. Students repeat this procedure until their tracings fill the entire angle.

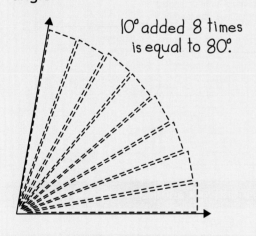

10° added 8 times is equal to 80°.

On Level
for students having success
`INDIVIDUALS`

Rays and Angles

Materials: MathBoard materials

Have students draw on their MathBoards to test whether the following statements are true or false:

The measure of an angle changes when one ray is rotated.

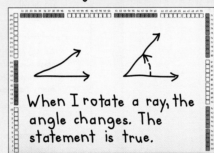

When I rotate a ray, the angle changes. The statement is true.

The measure of an angle does not change when the length of its rays changes.

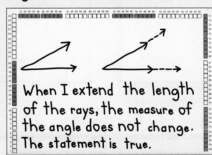

When I extend the length of the rays, the measure of the angle does not change. The statement is true.

Challenge
for students seeking a challenge
`PAIRS`

Classroom Angles

Students work in pairs to identify angles in the classroom and to estimate their measures.

> The corner of my desk is a 90° angle.
>
> The W on the wall has 45° angle's in it.
>
> Two tiles on the floor meet to form a 180° angle.
>
> The collar of Han's shirt looks like an 80° angle.

Also Use
Challenge Master for B-4

Math Writing Prompt
Intervention

Draw a Picture
If Philip draws an angle that is a straight line, what is the measure of this angle? Include a drawing with your answer.

Math Writing Prompt
On Level

Explain Your Thinking
Jocelyn draws a right triangle with one angle measuring 30°. What are the measures of the other two angles? Explain your thinking.

Math Writing Prompt
Challenge

Compare and Contrast
How is the process of measuring an angle like measuring a line segment? How is it different?

③ Homework and Spiral Review

Homework **Goal:** Additional Practice

On this Homework page, students measure angles based on given information.

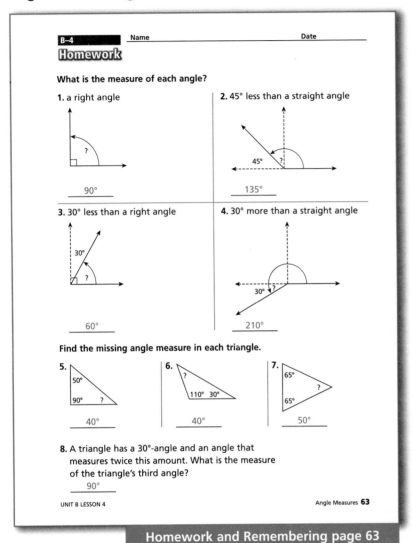

Remembering **Goal:** Spiral Review

This Remembering page is appropriate anytime after today's lesson.

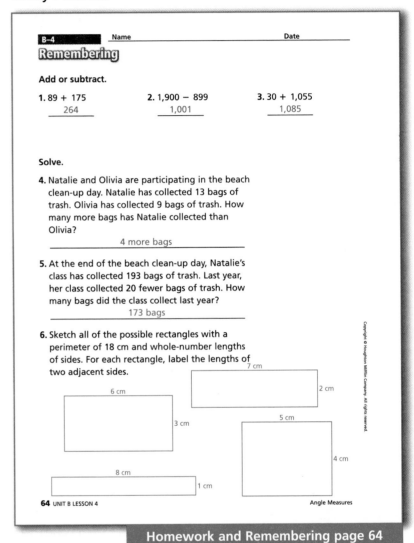

Homework and Remembering page 63

Homework and Remembering page 64

Home or School Activity

Social Studies Connection

Communication with Symbols Before telecommunications, people sent messages moving wooden arms mounted at the tops of towers. They put the arms at different angles to represent letters.

Challenge students to create their own signaling system by holding their arms at different angles. Ask them to draw diagrams for their system and to test it with a classmate.

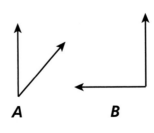

260 UNIT B LESSON 4

Unit Review and Test

Lesson Objective

● Assess student progress on unit objectives.

The Day at a Glance

Today's Goals	Materials
❶ Assessing the Unit ▶ Assess student progress on unit objectives. ▶ Use activities from unit lessons to reteach content. **❷ Extending the Assessment** ▶ Use remediation for common errors. There is no homework assignment on a test day.	Unit B Test, Student Activity Book pages 121–122 Unit B Test, Form A or B, Assessment Guide (optional) Unit B Performance Assessment, Assessment Guide (optional)

 Class Management

Review and Test Day You may want to choose a quiet game or other activity (reading a book or working on homework for another subject) for students who finish early.

Assessing the Unit

Assess Unit Objectives

🕐 **45 MINUTES (more if schedule permits)**

Goal: Assess student progress on unit objectives.

Materials: Student Activity Book pages 121–122; Assessment Guide (optional)

▶ Review and Assessment

If your students are ready for assessment on the unit objectives, you may use either the test on the Student Activity Book pages or one of the forms of the Unit B Test in the Assessment Guide to assess student progress.

If you feel that students need some review first, you may use the test on the Student Activity Book pages as a review of unit content, and then use one of the forms of the Unit B Test in the Assessment Guide to assess student progress.

To assign a numerical score for all of these test forms, use 10 points for each question.

You may also choose to use the Unit B Performance Assessment. Scoring for that assessment can be found in its rubric in the Assessment Guide.

▶ Reteaching Resources

The chart lists the test items, the unit objectives they cover, and the lesson activities in which the objective is covered in this unit. You may revisit these activities with students who do not show mastery of the objectives.

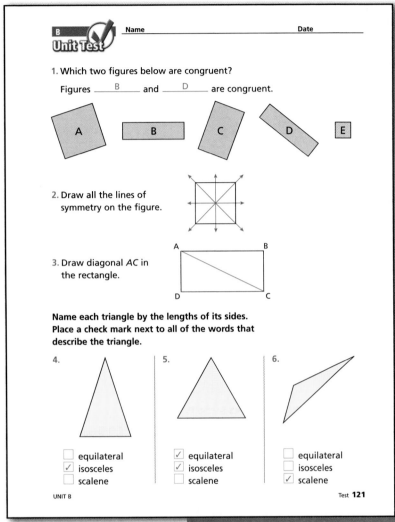

Student Activity Book page 121

Unit Test Items	Unit Objectives Tested	Activities to Use for Reteaching
1, 2	**B.1** Identify figures that are congruent and draw lines of symmetry on figures.	Lesson 1, Activities 2 and 3
3, 10	**B.2** Label figures with letters and compose and decompose quadrilaterals.	Lesson 2, Activities 2 and 3 Lesson 3, Activity 3

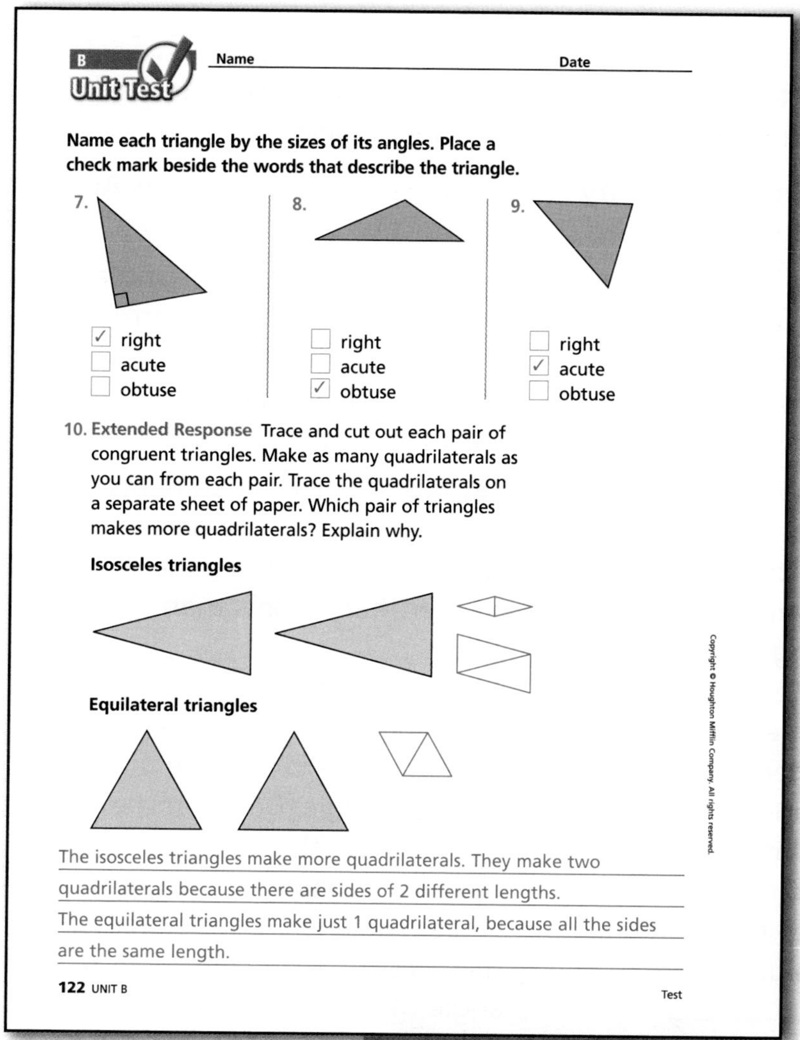

Student Activity Book page 122

Unit Test
Name _____ Date _____

Name each triangle by the sizes of its angles. Place a check mark beside the words that describe the triangle.

7.
☑ right
☐ acute
☐ obtuse

8.
☐ right
☐ acute
☑ obtuse

9.
☐ right
☑ acute
☐ obtuse

10. **Extended Response** Trace and cut out each pair of congruent triangles. Make as many quadrilaterals as you can from each pair. Trace the quadrilaterals on a separate sheet of paper. Which pair of triangles makes more quadrilaterals? Explain why.

Isosceles triangles

Equilateral triangles

The isosceles triangles make more quadrilaterals. They make two quadrilaterals because there are sides of 2 different lengths.
The equilateral triangles make just 1 quadrilateral, because all the sides are the same length.

122 UNIT B   Test

Unit Test Items	Unit Objectives Tested	Activities to Use for Reteaching
4–9	**B.3** Classify triangles by length of sides or measure of angles.	Lesson 3, Activity 2

▶ **Assessment Resources**

Free Response Tests
Unit B Test, Student Activity Book pages 121–122
Unit B Test, Form A, Assessment Guide

Extended Response Item
The last item in the Student Activity Book test and in the Form A test will require an extended response as an answer.

Multiple Choice Test
Unit B Test, Form B, Assessment Guide

Performance Assessment
Unit B Performance Assessment, Assessment Guide
Unit B Performance Assessment Rubric, Assessment Guide

▶ **Portfolio Assessment**

Teacher-selected Items for Student Portfolios:

- Homework, Lesson 1
- Class Activity work, Lessons 1, 4

Student-selected Items for Student Portfolios:

- Favorite Home or School Activity
- Best Writing Prompt

② Extending the Assessment

Unit Objective B.1

Identify figures that are congruent and draw lines of symmetry on figures.

Common Error: Draws Lines of Symmetry Incorrectly

When drawing lines of symmetry on figures, students may include lines that are not lines of symmetry.

Remediation Have students fold a paper circle or square in half four different ways to demonstrate that lines of symmetry divide a figure into two congruent halves.

Common Error: Identifies Too Few Lines of Symmetry

When drawing lines of symmetry on figures, students may identify some, but not all, of the lines of symmetry. For example, they may recognize the vertical and horizontal lines of symmetry of a square but not the lines of symmetry along the diagonals.

Remediation To help students identify all the lines of symmetry of a figure, encourage them to fold the figure in different ways to try to find lines of symmetry.

Unit Objective B.2

Label figures with letters and compose and decompose quadrilaterals.

Common Error: Doesn't Identify All of the Quadrilaterals that Can be Composed

When students are asked to compose quadrilaterals from two congruent triangles, they may not identify all possible quadrilaterals.

Remediation Have students compose quadrilaterals from two congruent scalene triangles. They begin by drawing matching color line segments along each congruent side. In each triangle, they might color the longest side red, the next shorter side blue, and the shortest side green. They then make quadrilaterals by joining corresponding sides of the triangles—green to green, red to red, and blue to blue.

Common Error: Doesn't Recognize Congruent Quadrilaterals

When students are asked to compose quadrilaterals from two congruent triangles, they may not recognize that some of the quadrilaterals they create are congruent.

Remediation Have students compose quadrilaterals from two isosceles triangles. Have them sketch the quadrilaterals, cut them out, and place them on top of each other in different positions to check which ones are congruent.

Unit Objective B.3

Classify triangles by length of sides or measure of angles.

Common Error: Identifies Angles Incorrectly

When trying to name triangles by angles, students may incorrectly identify an angle as having a measure equal to, greater than, or less than a right angle.

Remediation Have students use an index card to help decide if an angle has a measure equal to, greater than, or less than a right angle.
Explain that any square corner is a right angle. So the square corner of an index card or piece of paper is a right angle. Demonstrate how students can align the corner of the card or paper to the given angle. The angle will be greater than, less than, or congruent to the angle of the card or paper.

Common Error: Doesn't Distinguish Between Equilateral and Isosceles Triangles

Some students may have difficulty distinguishing between isosceles and equilateral triangles.

Remediation Draw an equilateral and isosceles triangle on the board. Invite students to use a meter stick or yardstick and colored chalk to highlight the sides of equal length in the triangles.

Use Addition and Subtraction

UNIT 3 PROVIDES EXPERIENCE with various representations and contexts for addition and subtraction, while continuing to develop and practice computation methods that are meaningful and easily used by students. Students are expected to apply their knowledge of place value to compare, order, and round numbers. They will then use rounding to estimate sums and differences. Students will also extend money skills to make change. More complex word problems are also introduced.

UNIT 3 CONTENTS

Unit 3 Assessment

✓ Unit Objectives Tested	Unit Test Items	Lessons
3.1 Compare, order, and round whole numbers and estimate sums and differences.	1–6, 9	1–3
3.2 Find the value of and represent money amounts with coins and bills, count change, compare and round money amounts, and estimate sums and differences.	7, 8, 17–20	4–7
3.3 Interpret data in a table or graph, make bar graphs, and complete tables.	10–13	8–10, 15, 16
3.4 Solve word problems with two steps, multi-steps, extra or hidden information, and identify problems with insufficient information.	14–16	11–14

Formal Assessment

Open or Free Response Tests

- Quick Quizzes (Assessment Guide)
- Unit Review and Test (Student Activity Book pages 175–178, Teacher's Guide pages 391–394.
- Unit 3 Test Form A (Assessment Guide)
- Unit 3 Open Response Test (Test Generator)
- Test Bank Items for Unit 3 (Test Generator)

Multiple Choice Tests

- Unit 3 Test Form B (Assessment Guide)
- Unit 3 Multiple Choice Test (Test Generator)
- Test Bank Items for Unit 3 (Test Generator)

Performance Tasks

- Unit 3 Performance Assessment (Assessment Guide)

Informal Assessment

Ongoing Assessment

- In every Teacher's Guide lesson

Performance Assessment

- Class discussions
- Small-group work
- Quick Practice (in every lesson)
- Individual work on teacher-selected tasks

Portfolios

- See Unit 3 Review and Test for suggestions for selecting items for portfolios.
- Some Homework pages are noted as suitable for portfolio inclusion.

Review Opportunities

Homework and Remembering

- Homework pages provide review of recently taught topics.
- Remembering pages provide spiral review.

Teacher's Guide

- Unit Review and Test (page 391)

Test Generator CD-ROM

- Test Bank Items can be used to create custom review sheets.

Planning Unit 3

See pages xvii and xviii for a list of unit materials and manipulatives that are available in the *Math Expressions* Kit.

Lesson Title	Lesson Resources	Materials and Manipulatives Math Expressions	Other
1 Round to the Nearest Hundred	Family Letter Student Activity Book pages 123–126 Homework and Remembering pages 65–66	MathBoard materials, Demonstration Secret Code Cards (Copymasters M3-M18)	Calculators, Math Journals
2 Round to the Nearest Ten	Student Activity Book pages 127–130 Homework and Remembering pages 67–68	MathBoard materials, Demonstration Secret Code Cards (Copymasters M3-M18), Secret Code Cards (Copymasters M19–M22), Number Path (Copymaster M39)	Index cards, calculators, "Geometry Park" CD (Illumisware 2002), Math Journals
3 Compare Whole Numbers	Student Activity Book pages 131–132 Homework and Remembering pages 69–70 **Quick Quiz 1**	MathBoard materials, Number Path (Copymaster M39), Secret Code Cards (Copymasters M19–M22)	Number cubes, *The Greatest Gymnast of All* by Stuart J. Murphy (HarperTrophy, 1998), Math Journals, base ten blocks
4 Money Values	Student Activity Book pages 133–136 Homework and Remembering pages 71–72	MathBoard materials, Play Money (Copymaster M40)	Overhead coins, number cubes, overhead projector, index cards, Math Journals, snack bags or envelopes
5 Represent Money Amounts in Different Ways	Student Activity Book pages 137–138 Homework and Remembering pages 73–74	MathBoard materials, Play Money (Copymaster M40), Coin Strips (Copymaster M41)	Price tags, number cubes (1–6), index cards, Math Journals, real or play money
6 Make Change	Student Activity Book pages 139–140 Homework and Remembering pages 75–76	MathBoard materials, Play Money (Copymaster M40)	Store flyers, Math Journals, *Ox-Cart Man* by Donald Hall (Puffin Books, 1983), overhead projector and coins (optional)
7 Round Money Amounts	Student Activity Book pages 141–144 Homework and Remembering pages 77–78 **Quick Quiz 2**	MathBoard materials	Index cards, Math Journals

Planning Unit 3

Lesson Title	Lesson Resources	Materials and Manipulatives	
		Math Expressions	**Other**
8 Ask Addition and Subtraction Questions from Tables	Student Activity Book pages 145–148 Homework and Remembering pages 79–80	MathBoard materials, transparency of Student Activity Book page 145 (optional)	Sheet protectors, overhead projector (optional), sticky notes, Math Journals
9 Complete Tables	Student Activity Book pages 149–152 Homework and Remembering pages 81–82	MathBoard materials, Inch Grid Paper (Copymaster M42)	Math Journals
10 More Practice with Tables	Student Activity Book pages 153–154 Homework and Remembering pages 83–84	MathBoard materials, Play Money (Copymaster M40)	Calculators (optional), counters, blocks (red and blue), paper bag, Math Journals
11 Word Problems with Extra or Hidden Information	Teacher's Resource Book Problem Bank 13 Student Activity Book pages 155–156 Homework and Remembering pages 85–86		Math Journals, highlighters
12 Word Problems with Not Enough Information	Teacher's Resource Book Problem Bank 14 Student Activity Book pages 157–160 Homework and Remembering pages 87–88	MathBoard materials	Scissors, tape, Math Journals
13 Solve Two-Step Word Problems	Teacher's Resource Book Problem Bank 15 Student Activity Book pages 161–162 Homework and Remembering pages 89–90		Index cards, Math Journals, highlighters (2 different colors)
14 Solve Multi-Step Word Problems	Teacher's Resource Book Problem Banks 16 and 17 Student Activity Book pages 163–166 Homework and Remembering pages 91–92	Math Board materials	Index cards, Math Journals, *Math Mysteries* by Jack Silbert (Scholastic, 1995)
15 Read and Create Bar Graphs	Student Activity Book pages 167–170 Homework and Remembering pages 93–94	10 × 10 grid (Copymaster M43)	Index cards, rulers, class list, connecting cubes, Math Journals, overhead projector and transparencies (optional)
16 Read and Create Bar Graphs with Multi-Digit Numbers	Student Activity Book pages 171–174 Homework and Remembering pages 95–96 **Quick Quiz 3**	MathBoard materials, Data Tables (Copymaster M44), Centimeter Grid Paper (Copymaster M31)	Crayons, Math Journals, Index cards
17 Data Day		Inch Grid Paper (Copymaster M42)	Sentence strips, paper bag, gym mat, masking tape, index cards, rulers, calendar, Hula Hoops, construction paper, poster board, markers, crayons, connecting cubes, sticky notes, student graphs
✓ Unit Review and Test	Student Activity Book pages 175–178 Assessment Guide		

Unit 3 Teaching Resources

Differentiated Instruction

Reaching All Learners

Extra Help

Lesson 2, page 275   Lesson 3, page 282
Lesson 5, page 298   Lesson 6, page 305
Lesson 7, page 311   Lesson 8, page 319
Lesson 8, page 320   Lesson 9, page 326
Lesson 12, page 346   Lesson 15, page 371
Lesson 16, page 379   Lesson 16, page 381

English Learners

Lesson 1, page 267
Lesson 4, page 291
Lesson 5, page 299
Lesson 8, page 321
Lesson 12, page 347
Lesson 14, page 363

Advanced Learners

Lesson 5, page 300
Lesson 10, page 335

Individualizing Instruction

Activities
- Intervention (in every lesson)
- On Level (in every lesson)
- Challenge (in every lesson)

Math Writing Prompts
- Intervention (in every lesson)
- On Level (in every lesson)
- Challenge (in every lesson)

Challenge Masters
- (for every lesson)

Cross-Curricular Links • Home or School Activities

 Social Studies Connections

Coin Design (Lesson 4, page 296)
Name That Face (Lesson 5, page 302)
Bartering (Lesson 6, page 308)
Mathematicians in History (Lesson 13, page 360)

 Real-World Connections

Shopping Spree (Lesson 7, page 316)
Surveying and Reporting (Lesson 16, page 384)

 Language Arts Connections

Homonyms (Lesson 8, page 324)
Editing Word Problems (Lesson 11, page 344)
Step-by-Step Directions (Lesson 14, page 368)

 Math-to-Math Connection

Pattern Puzzles (Lesson 12, page 352)

 Technology Connection

Computer Art (Lesson 9, page 332)

 Music Connection

Rap a Round (Lesson 2, page 280)

 Science Connections

Your Town's Weather (Lesson 10, page 338)
How Many Legs? (Lesson 15, page 376)

 Literature Connection

The Greatest Gymnast of All (Lesson 3, page 288)

Teaching Unit 3

Putting Research into Practice for Unit 3

From Current Research: Statistics and Learning to Use Data

Processes like organizing data and conventions like labeling and scaling are crucial to data representation and are strongly connected to the concepts and processes of measurement. Given the difficulties students experience, instruction might need to differentiate these processes and conventions more sharply. Fundamental concepts...such as the conventions of scaling in graphs...need more careful attention in initial instruction.

National Research Council. "Developing Proficiency with Whole Numbers." *Adding It Up: Helping Students Learn Mathematics.* Washington, D.C.: National Academy Press, 2001. pp. 288–294

Estimation

[Computation estimation] requires recognizing that the appropriateness of an estimate is related to the problem and its context . . . Estimating the results of a computation is a complex activity that should integrate all strands of mathematical proficiency. Its potential benefit is lost, however, if it is treated as a separate skill and taught as a set of isolated rules and techniques. Its benefit is realized when students are allowed to draw on other strands to find ways to simplify calculations and compensate for that simplification. For example, the representation students make of the mathematical situation enables them to make simple, appropriate estimates . . . [E]stimation is a good indicator of students' productive disposition—in this case, their propensity to make sense of mathematical situations so that they understand that estimates are not wild guesses but informed, approximate solutions.

National Research Council. "Developing Proficiency with Whole Numbers."

Adding It Up: Helping Children Learn Mathematics. Washington, D.C.: National Academy Press, 2001. p. 216

Other Useful References: Addition, Subtraction, and Estimating

Rubenstein, R.N. Computational estimation and related mathematical skills. *Journal for Research in Mathematics Education, 16,* 1985. pp. 106–119.

Sowder, J.T., & Wheeler, M.M. The development of concepts and procedures used in computational estimation. *Journal for Research in Mathematics Education, 20,* 1989. pp. 130–146.

Math Background

Use Rounding to Estimate Sums and Differences

Rounding

Students learn how to round numbers to the nearest ten or nearest hundred. They first establish the tens or hundreds above and the tens or hundreds below the number they are rounding. Then they determine, using place value, place-value drawings, or Secret Code Cards, which ten or hundred is closer to the number they are rounding.

Round to the Nearest Hundred

3̲64   Underline the place to which you are rounding.

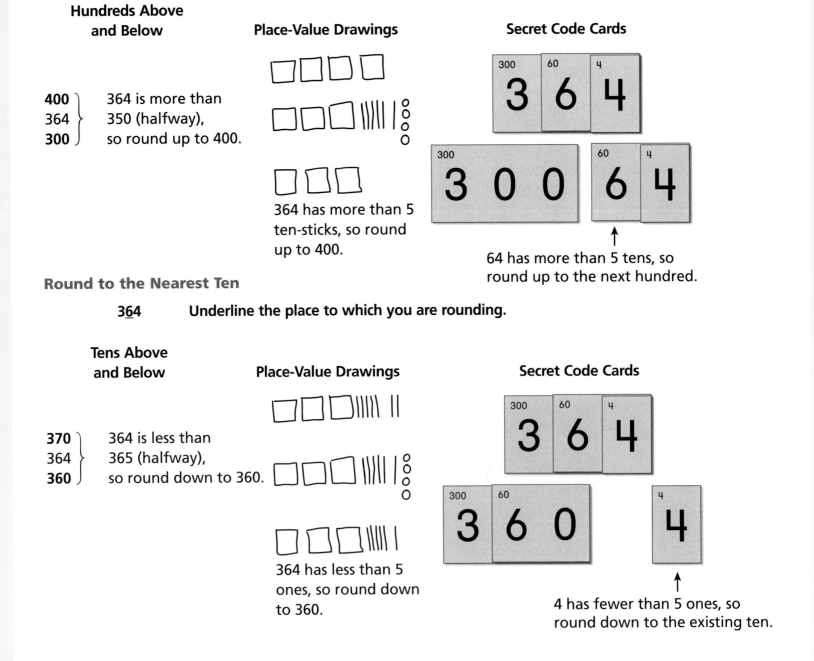

Hundreds Above and Below

400 ⎫
364 ⎬ 364 is more than 350 (halfway), so round up to 400.
300 ⎭

Place-Value Drawings

364 has more than 5 ten-sticks, so round up to 400.

Secret Code Cards

64 has more than 5 tens, so round up to the next hundred.

Round to the Nearest Ten

36̲4   Underline the place to which you are rounding.

Tens Above and Below

370 ⎫
364 ⎬ 364 is less than 365 (halfway), so round down to 360.
360 ⎭

Place-Value Drawings

364 has less than 5 ones, so round down to 360.

Secret Code Cards

4 has fewer than 5 ones, so round down to the existing ten.

Estimating Sums and Differences

For rounding to estimate sums or differences, students round each number to the nearest ten or nearest hundred, and then add or subtract.

There are 48 children on one bus and 33 on another bus. About how many children are there altogether?

48 rounds to 50
33 rounds to 30.

Add 50 and 30 to get an estimate of 80.

Rounding Money Amounts

Students round money amounts to the nearest dime or nearest dollar, using the rules for rounding. If the amount is equal to or more than half of the next whole dime (or dollar) amount, round up. If it is less than half of the next whole dime (or dollar) amount, round down.

Round $3.62 to the Nearest Dime

Underline the place to which you are rounding. Find the digit to the right of the dimes place. Since 2¢ is less than half of a dime, round down to the lesser dime: $3.60.

$3.70 ⎫
$3.62 ⎬ $3.62 is less than $3.65 (halfway),
$3.60 ⎭ so round down to $3.60.

Round $3.62 to the Nearest Dollar

Underline the place to which you are rounding. Find the digits to the right of the dollars place. Since 62¢ is more than half of a dollar, round up to the greater dollar: $4.00.

$4.00 ⎫
$3.62 ⎬ $3.62 is more than $3.50 (halfway),
$3.00 ⎭ so round up to $4.00.

Data in Tables and in Bar Graphs

A major focus of this unit is learning to understand tables and bar graphs. As students interact with these data formats, they continually write and solve problem situations and pose questions for their classmates from the data they can read in these formats.

Working with bar graph scales builds on students' earlier work with understanding the scale in rulers and how it is built from small lengths. This helps students see the lengths involved in bar graphs, and the bars in bar graphs help students think of the bar graph scale, rulers, and number lines as a length model (for example, the 6 does not mean that point, it means 6 of the length units used in the scale). Work with both horizontal and vertical bar graph scales helps to prepare students for work with such scales on coordinate grids in Unit G.

Working with tables helps students learn to look across rows and down columns. This helps to prepare them for the array and area situations they will encounter in Unit 4 in multiplication and division situations. Students will continue to interact with tables in Units 4 and 5 where they will use the multiplication table and solve small scrambled mini-multiplication tables called Missing Number Puzzles. Students return to a focused use of tables in Unit 7, where tables summarize measurement information.

Problem Solving

Complex Word Problems

Students continue the study of word problems in this unit using real-world situations. Students will solve problems with extra information, determining which of the given information is required for the solution and which information can be ignored. They will also solve word problems with implied (hidden) information. Students are also presented with problems that cannot be solved because they do not include all the necessary information. Students will need to recognize that this type of problem is unsolvable and tell what additional information is needed. Students will also encounter problems that require two or more steps to solve.

This program's strong and continuous focus on solving a wide range of word problems helps with language development. The Math Talk approach to discussing word problems and their solutions facilitates language growth and reasoning.

This systematic and research-based focus on word problems has changed the word problem solving modes of many students. They no longer just look at the numbers and do something with them (for example, add or subtract all numbers they see); they think about the situation, try to understand it, and make a drawing if it will help.

Round to the Nearest Hundred

Lesson Objectives

- Round numbers to the nearest hundred.
- Round to estimate sums and differences and check calculations.

Vocabulary
estimate
round

The Day at a Glance

Today's Goals	Materials	Math Talk
Quick Practice Count by tens and hundreds. **1 Teaching the Lesson** A1: Round numbers to the nearest hundred. A2: Estimate sums and differences and estimate to decide if answers are reasonable. **2 Extending the Lesson** ▶ Differentiated Instruction **3 Homework and Spiral Review**	MathBoard materials Demonstration Secret Code Cards Secret Code Cards Calculators Student Activity Book pages 123–126 Homework and Remembering pages 65–66 Math Journals Family Letter	In today's activities, the students are involved in discussion as they ▶ describe situations in which estimates might be useful ▶ share strategies for rounding numbers to the nearest hundred ▶ determine whether their answers are reasonable

Quick Practice

 5 MINUTES **Goal:** Count by tens and hundreds.

Tens and Hundreds Count Have a Student Leader direct the class in a counting by tens or hundreds activity. The leader writes a number on the board, points to it, says the number aloud, instructs the class whether to add or subtract 10 or 100, and gives the class a signal. The rest of the class responds by counting and continues the pattern until the leader instructs them to stop.

Leader: (Writes 50 on the board and points to it.) 50. Add 10. Begin.

Class: 60, 70, 80, 90, 100, 110

Leader: Stop. (Writes 800 on the board and points to it.) 800. Subtract 100. Begin.

Class: 700, 600, 500, 400, 300

Leader: Stop.

1 Teaching the Lesson

Activity 1

Round Up or Down

 30 MINUTES

Goal: Round numbers to the nearest hundred.

Materials: MathBoard materials, Demonstration Secret Code Cards (Copymasters M3–M18), Student Activity Book page 123

✔ **NCTM Standard:**
Number and Operations

The Learning Classroom

Building Concepts Point out that estimation is a useful skill in the real world when you don't have pencil and paper or a calculator to use. Estimation is also useful when you use a calculator. If you should press a wrong key or forget to press a key, a quick estimate will tell you that the answer on the calculator is not correct.

Possible strategies students may use to estimate 494 + 128 + 368:

▶ Round to the hundreds place and add: 500 + 100 + 400 = 1,000.

▶ Round the numbers to other numbers that are easy to add. For example, 500 + 125 + 375 = 1,000.

▶ Leave the first digit of each number and change the rest of the digits to 0, and add: 400 + 100 + 300 = 800. (This method is sometimes called *front-end estimation.*)

▶ Round to the tens place and add: 490 + 130 + 370 = 990.

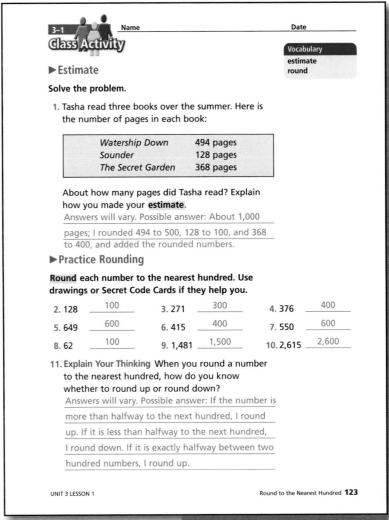

Student Activity Book page 123

▶ Estimate WHOLE CLASS

Math Talk Ask students to share what they know about estimation. Mention these ideas if they do not bring them up.

● An estimate tells *about* how many or *about* how much.

● Estimation is used when an exact number or measurement is not needed, or when there is not an exact number.

Then ask students to describe real-life situations in which someone might make an estimate. Offer some suggestions: shoppers in grocery stores, someone planning a party, or a person going to a movie. Read aloud problem 1 and have students make their estimates. Ask a few students to share their strategies for estimating the answer. Some possible strategies students might suggest are shown in the column to the left.

Round Using Place-Value Drawings Discuss rounding numbers in real-world situations and in mathematics.

- Many of you made your estimates by rounding the number to another number that was easier to add. Every day, you can use many strategies for rounding numbers. For example, if you want to be sure you have enough money to pay for items at a store, you might round all the prices up and then add them. In math, there are rules that tell you when to round up and when to round down. In this lesson, we'll look at the rules for rounding to the hundreds place.

Write 368 on the left side of the board, leaving enough room above and below the number. Ask students to do the same on their MathBoards.

- We are going to round 368 to the hundreds place. What digit is in the hundreds place? 3 Let's underline the 3 so we remember the place we are rounding to.

- We want to round to the nearest hundred. First, let's find the two hundred numbers that 368 is between. Which hundred number is right below 368? 300 Which hundred number is right above 368? 400

Write 300 below 368 and 400 above it, having students do the same. Then ask students to make place-value drawings for the three numbers. Choose one student to draw them on the board.

- Which hundred number is nearest to 368? 400 How can you tell from your drawings? There are more than five ten-sticks.

Have students explain why 400 is the nearest hundred. For a sample of classroom dialogue, see **Math Talk in Action** in the side column.

Have students draw an arrow from 368 to 400 to show that we round up.

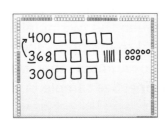

 Math Talk in Action

Why do you think 400 is the nearest hundred to 368?

Gwen: 368 is about 370. That's closer to 400 than 300.

Did anyone use a different strategy?

Saeed: I did. Halfway between 300 and 400 is 350, so 368 is more than halfway between 300 and 400.

Did anyone use the place-value drawings to help them?

Peter: I did. 300 has 3 hundred-boxes and 400 has 4 hundred-boxes. The number halfway would have 3 hundred-boxes and 5 ten-sticks. 368 has more than 5 ten-sticks, so it must be closer to 400 than 300.

Activity continued ▶

Teaching the Lesson (continued)

Alternate Approach

Use a Number Line Students can draw a number line marked by hundreds from 0 to 900 with tick marks for 50s. When they place the number to be rounded on the number line they can see which hundred it is closer to and round to that hundred.

The Learning Classroom

Building Concepts You may want to extend the activity by asking students to give examples of numbers that round to 400 (350–399; 401–449). This allows students to explore that some numbers round up to 400 and others round down 400.

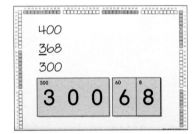

Round Using Secret Code Cards Demonstrate another way to round with Demonstration Secret Code Cards. Erase the place-value drawings and the arrow, and ask students which Secret Code Cards are needed to build 368. Have a volunteer build the number.

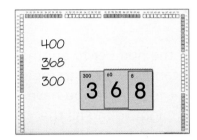

Tell students that to figure out how to round to the hundreds place, they should "open up" the Secret Code Cards, separating 3 hundreds from the rest of the number.

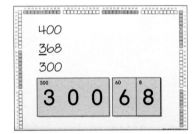

Explain that to determine whether to round up or down, they should look at the 68.

● Does 68 have more than 5 tens or fewer than 5 tens? more than 5 tens

● So, the 68 is closer to 100 than to 0 and is rounded up to the next hundred. *Draw an arrow from 368 to 400.*

Now discuss rounding down.

● When rounding 368 to the nearest hundred, it is rounded *up* to 400. Can anyone think of a number that would be rounded *down* to 300? Possible answer: 349

Erase 368 and replace it with the number suggested. Choose a volunteer to use place-value drawings to explain why we round down. Have a second volunteer explain the rounding, using the Demonstration Secret Code Cards.

Next, erase everything except 300 and 400. Draw a line across the board between the two numbers. Ask students to suggest several numbers that would round up to 400, and write those numbers above the line. Then ask for numbers that would round down to 300, and write them below the line. See sample in the left side column.

▶ Practice Rounding   INDIVIDUALS

Have students look back at the Practice Rounding section on Student Activity Book page 123 and make sure each student knows what to do. Give students a few minutes to round the numbers to the nearest hundred in exercises 2–10.

Make sure to discuss exercises 9–10 which show 4-digit numbers. Remind students to underline the number in the hundreds place to help them remember which place to round to. The hundreds above and below 1,481 are 1,400 and 1,500. When using Secret Code Cards, students separate 81 from 1,400 and determine whether 81 has more or fewer than 5 tens. If students need additional practice rounding to the nearest hundred, give them more 4-digit numbers to round.

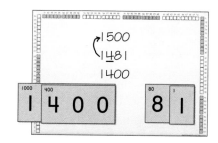

Rounding Rules Write 450 on the board, and ask how students would round it to the nearest hundred. Some may already know the rounding rule. Explain that because 450 is exactly halfway between 400 and 500, it is impossible to figure out how to round it. For this reason, people have agreed to round up whenever a number is exactly halfway between 2 hundred numbers. So we round 450 up to 500.

Problem 11 on Student Activity Book page 123 asks students to explain the rule for rounding to the nearest hundred. Ask for suggestions. Ask a volunteer to explain the rule. The class should listen to the explanations and ask questions to help the presenter clarify their thinking. Here is one way to state the rule:

- If the number is more than halfway to the next hundred, round up.

- If the number is less than halfway to the next hundred, round down.

- If the number is exactly halfway between two hundreds, round up.

Ongoing Assessment

To check that students understand the concept of rounding to the nearest hundred, ask questions such as:

▶ What is 54 rounded to the nearest hundred? 100 What about 32? 0

▶ What is 983 rounded to the nearest hundred? 1,000 What about 1,012? 1,000

▶ What is 750 rounded to the nearest hundred? 800

Activity 2

Estimate Sums and Differences

 25 MINUTES

Goal: Estimate sums and differences and estimate to decide if answers are reasonable.

Materials: MathBoard materials, Demonstration Secret Code Cards (Copymasters M3–M18), Student Activity Book page 124

 NCTM Standards:
Number and Operations
Reasoning and Proof

 Class Management

Looking Ahead At the end of this unit, students will have the opportunity to work on Data Projects as part of the activities in Data Day (see pages 385–390). The individual project has students working with nutrition labels, so you may want to ask students to start collecting nutrition labels from home. The class project has students working with can tabs, so you may want to ask students to start collecting can tabs at home. These tabs will also be used in Estimation Day (see Unit 7).

 Math Talk in Action

Do you think the answer for exercise 18 is reasonable?

Trevor: I think the answer is reasonable.

Can you explain why?

Trevor: First, I rounded 1,041 to 1,000 and 395 to 400. Next, I subtracted the two rounded numbers and got 600. 600 is pretty close to 646, so it's reasonable.

Did anyone find another answer?

Madeleine: I did. I don't think it's a reasonable answer because you have to add, not subtract. When you add the two rounded numbers, you get 1,400, which is not close to 646. So the answer of 646 is not reasonable.

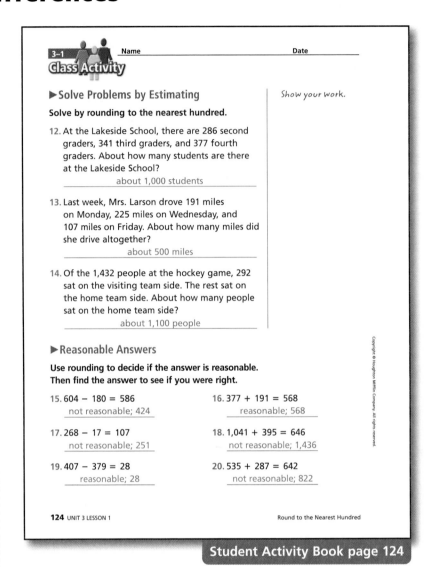

Student Activity Book page 124

▶ Solve Problems by Estimating WHOLE CLASS

Explain that one way to estimate a sum or difference is to round each number and then add or subtract. Have a volunteer read aloud problem 12. Point out that the word *about* indicates that the problem is asking for an estimate, not an exact answer. Give students a minute to estimate, and then discuss the answer with the class. Have students complete problems 13 and 14 on their own.

▶ Reasonable Answers INDIVIDUALS

Read aloud the directions for exercises 15–20. Explain that rounding and then adding or subtracting is a good way to check if your answer is reasonable. Have a volunteer show how to do exercise 15. Have students complete the rest of the exercises independently, and discuss the answers as a class.

② Extending the Lesson

Intervention
for students having difficulty

PAIRS

Round Using Drawings

Materials: MathBoard materials

One student writes a 3-digit number on the MathBoard. The other student makes a place-value drawing for that number and writes the 2 hundred numbers that the 3-digit number is in between.

The first student looks at the place-value drawing and the 2 hundred numbers and rounds the number to the nearest hundred. Then students switch roles and repeat the activity.

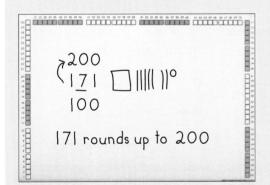

On Level
for students having success

PAIRS

Estimate and Check

Materials: MathBoard materials, calculators (1 per pair)

One student writes a 3-digit addition or subtraction exercise on the MathBoard. The other student uses rounding to make an estimate for each sum or difference. Pairs find the actual sum or difference using a calculator and discuss if the estimate is close to the actual answer. Then students switch roles and repeat the activity.

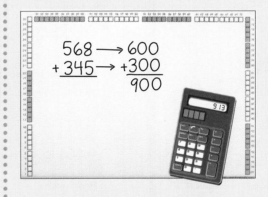

Challenge
for students seeking a challenge

PAIRS

Find Other Strategies

Materials: MathBoard materials calculators (1 per pair)

Challenge students to find strategies other than rounding to the nearest hundred to estimate the sums for the expressions below. Have them show their strategies on their Mathboards and discuss them with other pairs.

$105 + 875$	$352 + 148$
$219 + 178$	$215 + 759$
$347 + 706$	$1{,}255 + 2{,}812$

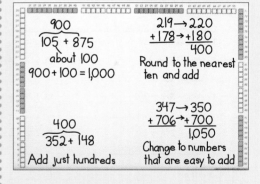

Also Use
Challenge Master for 3-17

 Math Writing Prompt

Intervention

Explain the Steps
Describe how you would round 274 to the nearest hundred.

 Math Writing Prompt

On Level

Real-World Application
Describe a situation when you or someone you know used estimation to solve a problem.

 Math Writing Prompt

Challenge

Explain Your Thinking
The Mississippi River is about 2,340 miles long. The Nile River is about 4,160 miles long. Is the difference more or less than 2,000 miles? Explain.

③ Homework and Spiral Review

3-1
Homework **Goal:** Additional Practice

✓ This Homework page provides practice in rounding numbers to the nearest hundred.

3-1
Remembering **Goal:** Spiral Review

This Remembering page would be appropriate anytime after today's lesson.

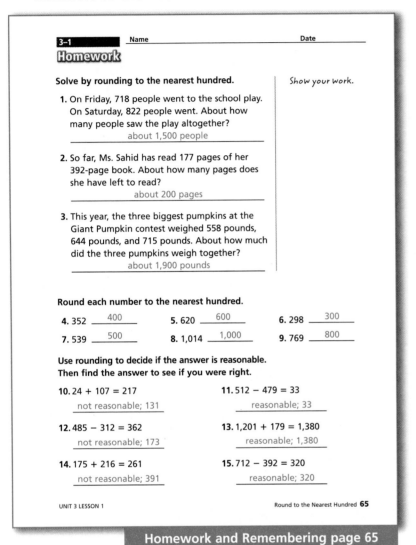

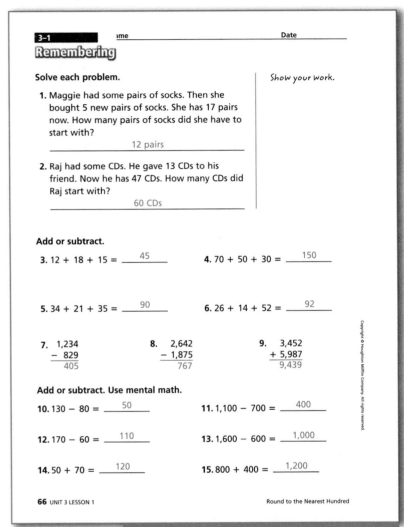

3-1 Name _____ Date _____
Homework

Solve by rounding to the nearest hundred.   Show your work.

1. On Friday, 718 people went to the school play. On Saturday, 822 people went. About how many people saw the play altogether?
   about 1,500 people

2. So far, Ms. Sahid has read 177 pages of her 392-page book. About how many pages does she have left to read?
   about 200 pages

3. This year, the three biggest pumpkins at the Giant Pumpkin contest weighed 558 pounds, 644 pounds, and 715 pounds. About how much did the three pumpkins weigh together?
   about 1,900 pounds

Round each number to the nearest hundred.

4. 352 _400_   5. 620 _600_   6. 298 _300_
7. 539 _500_   8. 1,014 _1,000_   9. 769 _800_

Use rounding to decide if the answer is reasonable. Then find the answer to see if you were right.

10. 24 + 107 = 217
    not reasonable; 131

11. 512 − 479 = 33
    reasonable; 33

12. 485 − 312 = 362
    not reasonable; 173

13. 1,201 + 179 = 1,380
    reasonable; 1,380

14. 175 + 216 = 261
    not reasonable; 391

15. 712 − 392 = 320
    reasonable; 320

UNIT 3 LESSON 1   Round to the Nearest Hundred **65**

Homework and Remembering page 65

3-1 Name _____ Date _____
Remembering

Solve each problem.   Show your work.

1. Maggie had some pairs of socks. Then she bought 5 new pairs of socks. She has 17 pairs now. How many pairs of socks did she have to start with?
   12 pairs

2. Raj had some CDs. He gave 13 CDs to his friend. Now he has 47 CDs. How many CDs did Raj start with?
   60 CDs

Add or subtract.

3. 12 + 18 + 15 = _45_

4. 70 + 50 + 30 = _150_

5. 34 + 21 + 35 = _90_

6. 26 + 14 + 52 = _92_

7. 1,234
    − 829
    ‾‾‾‾‾
      405

8. 2,642
    − 1,875
    ‾‾‾‾‾
      767

9. 3,452
    + 5,987
    ‾‾‾‾‾
    9,439

Add or subtract. Use mental math.

10. 130 − 80 = _50_

11. 1,100 − 700 = _400_

12. 170 − 60 = _110_

13. 1,600 − 600 = _1,000_

14. 50 + 70 = _120_

15. 800 + 400 = _1,200_

66 UNIT 3 LESSON 1   Round to the Nearest Hundred

Homework and Remembering page 66

Home and School Connection

Family Letter Have children take home the Family Letter on Student Activity Book page 125. This letter explains how the concepts of rounding, ordering, estimating, interpreting data, and solving a variety of words problems are developed in *Math Expressions.* It gives parents and guardians a better understanding of the learning that goes on in math class and creates a bridge between school and home. A Spanish translation of this letter is on the following page in the Student Activity Book.

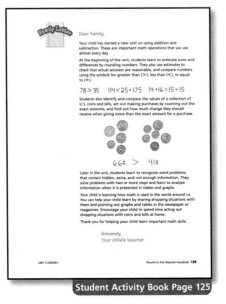

Student Activity Book Page 125

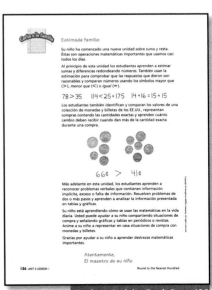

Student Activity Book Page 126

Round to the Nearest Ten

Lesson Objectives

● **Round numbers to the nearest ten.**

● **Use rounding to estimate sums and differences.**

Vocabulary
round

The Day at a Glance

Today's Goals	Materials	Math Talk
Quick Practice Round whole numbers to the nearest hundred.	MathBoard materials Demonstration Secret Code Cards Secret Code Cards Number Path (Copymaster M39) Index cards Calculators Student Activity Book pages 127–130 Homework and Remembering pages 67–68 Math Journals "Geometry Park" CD (Illumisware, 2002)	In today's activities, the students are involved in discussion as they ▶ share strategies for rounding numbers to the nearest ten ▶ determine whether their answers are reasonable
1 **Teaching the Lesson** **A1:** Round numbers to the nearest ten. **A2:** Round to estimate sums and differences, and estimate to decide if answers are reasonable.		
2 **Extending the Lesson** ▶ Going Further: Estimation Methods ▶ Differentiated Instruction		
3 **Homework and Spiral Review**		

Quick Practice

🕐 **5 MINUTES** **Goal:** Round whole numbers to the nearest hundred.

Rounding Practice Have a Student Leader write these six numbers on the board.

241   870   350   562   109   1,729

The Student Leader points to each number and says, "Round to the nearest hundred." When the leader gives a signal, students respond in unison with the rounded number.

Leader (pointing to 241): Round to the nearest hundred.

Class: 200

Teaching the Lesson

Round Up or Down

 30 MINUTES

Goal: Round numbers to the nearest ten.

Materials: MathBoard materials, Demonstration Secret Code Cards (Copymasters M3–M18), Secret Code Cards (Copymasters M19–M22), Student Activity Book pages 127–128

✔ **NCTM Standard:**
Number and Operations

Teaching Note

Math Background Remind students that rounding is only one way to estimate. Have students discuss why estimates are useful. They can also generate a list of situations in which estimation is used.

▶ **Round to the Nearest Ten** WHOLE CLASS

Tell students that today they will focus on rounding numbers to the nearest ten.

Round with Place-Value Drawings Write 43 on the board, leaving room above and below the number.

● Which digit is in the tens place? 4 *Underline the 4.*

Ask a volunteer to come to the board and demonstrate how to use a place-value drawing to round 43 to the nearest ten. Provide help as needed. Encourage other students to ask questions if they don't understand. Here are the steps that should be demonstrated.

● Find the tens numbers just below and just above 43. Then make place-value drawings for all three numbers. Since 40 has 4 ten-sticks, and 50 has 5 ten-sticks, the number halfway between 40 and 50 would have 4 ten-sticks and 5 circles. 43 has 4 ten-sticks and 3 circles so it is less than halfway to 50. So 43 rounds down to 40. Draw an arrow from 43 to 40 to indicate that we round down.

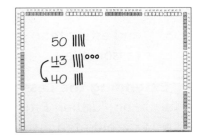

Round with Secret Code Cards Erase the place-value drawings and the arrow on the board, and have a volunteer show how to round the number 43 using the Demonstration Secret Code Cards. Encourage other students to ask questions if they don't understand and offer help as needed. Following are the steps the student should follow.

● Build 43 with Secret Code Cards. Open up the cards, separating the 4 tens from the rest of the number (the 3 ones). The ones card has fewer than 5 ones, so we round down to 40. Draw an arrow from 43 to 40 to show that we round down.

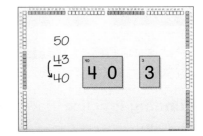

Erase the board and write 276 on the left side, asking students to do the same on their MathBoards. Have them round the number to the nearest ten. Make sure students underline the digit in the tens place. Emphasize that they only look at the digits to the right of the place they are rounding to. In this case, look at the ones. Because there are more than 5 ones, round up.

3–2
Class Activity

Name _____ Date _____

▶ Round 2-Digit Numbers to the Nearest Ten

Round each number to the nearest ten.

1. 63 ___60___   2. 34 ___30___

3. 78 ___80___   4. 25 ___30___

5. 57 ___60___   6. 89 ___90___

7. 42 ___40___   8. 92 ___90___

▶ Round 3-Digit Numbers to the Nearest Ten

Round each number to the nearest ten.

9. 162 ___160___   10. 741 ___740___

11. 309 ___310___   12. 255 ___260___

13. 118 ___120___   14. 197 ___200___

15. 503 ___500___   16. 246 ___250___

17. **Explain Your Thinking** When you round a number
to the nearest ten, how do you know whether to
round up or round down?
Answers will vary. Possible answer: If the number
is less than halfway to the next ten, round down.
If the number is exactly halfway between or more
than halfway to next ten, round up.

UNIT 3 LESSON 2   Round to the Nearest Ten **127**

▶ Round 2-Digit Numbers to the Nearest Ten

INDIVIDUALS

Have students complete exercises 1–8. Have students discuss how they
rounded in exercise 4. Point out that 25 is halfway between 20 and 30.
When a number is exactly halfway between two tens, we round up to
the next ten.

▶ Round 3-Digit Numbers to the Nearest Ten

INDIVIDUALS

Have students complete exercises 9–16 independently. They can use
drawings or cards as needed. Then discuss exercise 17, which asks
students to explain the rule for rounding to the nearest ten.

Differentiated Instruction

Extra Help Some students may not
see that when rounding to the tens
place, the digit in the ones place
determines the direction of rounding.
It is important that students look at
the digit to the right of the place to
which they are rounding to
determine whether to round a
number up or down. Remind
students that this is also true when
rounding to the nearest hundred.
The digit in the tens place tells which
direction to round. It is helpful to
underline the place to which you are
rounding and then look to the next
smaller place to decide whether to
go up or stay with that number. If
students are ready, you may want to
demonstrate that when rounding to
the nearest thousand, the digit in the
hundreds place tells the direction in
which any 4-digit number is rounded.

Students who are still struggling
should use place-value drawings and
Secret Code Cards.

The Learning Classroom

Building Concepts As students discuss
the rule for rounding in exercise 17
on Student Activity Book page 127,
have them think of a number of
different examples before writing
their explanation.

Make sure that students understand
that most of the time when you
round a number to the nearest ten,
the number will end in 0. For
example, 527 rounds to 530 when
you round it to the nearest ten.
However, numbers such as 203 and
399 rounded to the nearest ten are
200 and 400, which have two zeros.

Activity continued ▶

Teaching the Lesson (continued)

Teaching Note

Watch For! Students may round 3-digit numbers to the nearest hundred instead of to the nearest ten. Remind them to underline the digit in the place they are rounding to avoid rounding to the wrong place.

 Ongoing Assessment

To check that students understand the concept of rounding to the nearest ten, ask questions such as:

▶ What is 37 rounded to the nearest ten? What is 4 rounded to the nearest ten?

▶ What is 346 rounded to the nearest ten? What is 1,438 rounded to the nearest ten?

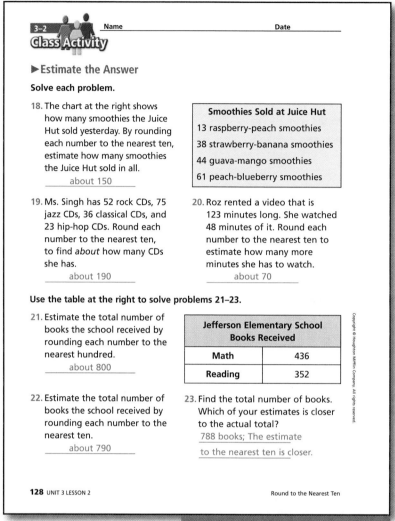

3–2
Class Activity
Name _____ Date _____

▶**Estimate the Answer**

Solve each problem.

18. The chart at the right shows how many smoothies the Juice Hut sold yesterday. By rounding each number to the nearest ten, estimate how many smoothies the Juice Hut sold in all.
    _____about 150_____

Smoothies Sold at Juice Hut
13 raspberry-peach smoothies
38 strawberry-banana smoothies
44 guava-mango smoothies
61 peach-blueberry smoothies

19. Ms. Singh has 52 rock CDs, 75 jazz CDs, 36 classical CDs, and 23 hip-hop CDs. Round each number to the nearest ten, to find *about* how many CDs she has.
    _____about 190_____

20. Roz rented a video that is 123 minutes long. She watched 48 minutes of it. Round each number to the nearest ten to estimate how many more minutes she has to watch.
    _____about 70_____

Use the table at the right to solve problems 21–23.

21. Estimate the total number of books the school received by rounding each number to the nearest hundred.
    _____about 800_____

Jefferson Elementary School Books Received	
Math	436
Reading	352

22. Estimate the total number of books the school received by rounding each number to the nearest ten.
    _____about 790_____

23. Find the total number of books. Which of your estimates is closer to the actual total?
    788 books; The estimate to the nearest ten is closer.

128 UNIT 3 LESSON 2   Round to the Nearest Ten

Student Activity Book page 128

▶ **Estimate the Answer** INDIVIDUALS

Math Talk Remind students that one of the ways to estimate the answer to a word problem involving addition or subtraction is to round each number to the nearest ten or hundred and then add or subtract.

Have students independently work on problems 18–23 and then use the **Solve and Discuss** structure to have volunteers share their solutions.

Estimate Sums and Differences

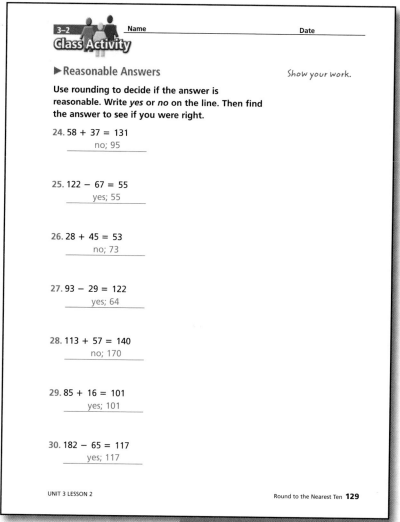

3-2
Class Activity

Name _____ Date _____

▶ **Reasonable Answers**   *Show your work.*

Use rounding to decide if the answer is
reasonable. Write *yes* or *no* on the line. Then find
the answer to see if you were right.

24. 58 + 37 = 131
    _____ no; 95 _____

25. 122 − 67 = 55
    _____ yes; 55 _____

26. 28 + 45 = 53
    _____ no; 73 _____

27. 93 − 29 = 122
    _____ yes; 64 _____

28. 113 + 57 = 140
    _____ no; 170 _____

29. 85 + 16 = 101
    _____ yes; 101 _____

30. 182 − 65 = 117
    _____ yes; 117 _____

UNIT 3 LESSON 2   Round to the Nearest Ten **129**

Student Activity Book page 129

25 MINUTES

Goal: Round to estimate sums and
differences, and estimate to decide if
answers are reasonable.

Materials: MathBoard materials,
Secret Code Cards (1 set per student)
(Copymasters M19–M22), Student
Activity Book pages 129–130

✔ **NCTM Standards:**
Number and Operations
Reasoning and Proof

The Learning Classroom

Helping Community You may want to
have students work in Helping Pairs
to complete problems 25–30 on
Student Activity Book page 129.
Students can work together to round
sets of numbers and then add and
subtract independently. Have them
compare their estimates to check
that they added or subtracted the
rounded numbers correctly before
comparing the estimate with the
actual answer.

▶ Reasonable Answers   INDIVIDUALS

Explain to students that rounding and then estimating are a good way
to check if an answer is reasonable. Read aloud the directions on
Student Activity Book page 129 and have a volunteer show how to do
exercise 24. The student should round 58 to 60 and 37 to 40 and then
add to get an estimate of 100. The answer given, 131, is too big.

Have students complete the exercises 25–30 independently, and discuss
the answers as a class.

② Extending the Lesson

Going Further: Estimation Methods

▶ Different Ways to Estimate

WHOLE CLASS

Explain that there are a number of other ways to estimate besides rounding the numbers to the nearest ten or hundred and finding the sum or difference as we did in this lesson.

Clustering Point out that when numbers cluster around the same ten or hundred you can use clustering to estimate the sum. Direct students' attention to exercise 1.

● What ten do these numbers cluster around? 60

So we can add 60 three times to get an estimate of 180. Have students complete exercises 1–4.

Front-End Estimation Explain that front-end estimation is another strategy that can be used when you need a quick estimate. In this method, add just the digits farthest to the left. For example, in order to make an estimate of the total weight of 675, 430, 43, and 110 pounds, add 600, 400, and 100 for an estimate of 1,100 pounds.

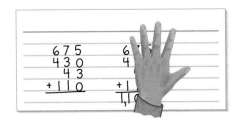

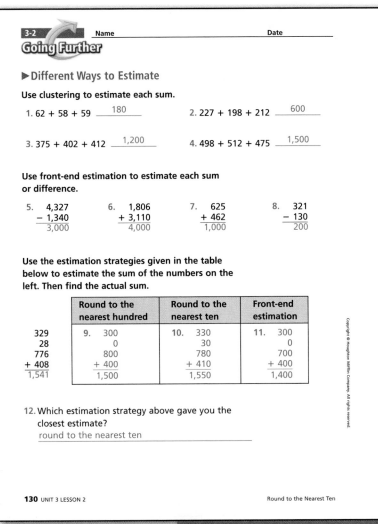

Student Activity Book page 130

Point out to students that you do not add 43 when estimating in this example. In this case, 43 does not have a number in the hundreds place like the other three numbers.

Have students complete exercises 5–12 independently and discuss their answers.

Intervention
for students having difficulty

INDIVIDUALS

Around the Path

Materials: Secret Code Cards, MathBoard materials or Number Path (Copymaster M39).

Have students separate their Secret Code Cards into two piles (tens and ones), shuffle each pile, and place them face down. Each student should form a 2-digit number with the top cards from each pile and write it on their MathBoards.

Then they should shade in their 2-digit number on the Number Path and circle the tens numbers that come before and after their number.

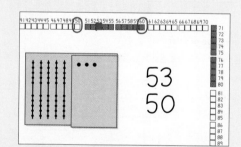

Students should see which ten number their 2-digit number is closer to and know whether to round up or round down.

On Level
for students having success

PAIRS

Round and Round

Materials: index cards (20 per pair)

Have each student write 2- or 3-digit numbers that do not end in a 0 on five of the index cards. Then have them make matching cards with the numbers rounded to the nearest ten.

Have students shuffle all 20 cards, pass out 5 cards to each player, and place the rest of the cards face down in a pile. Players take turns asking each other for a card that matches one of their cards. If they make a match, they ask for another matching card. If they can't make a match, they draw a card from the pile and it is the other player's turn. The player with the most matches wins.

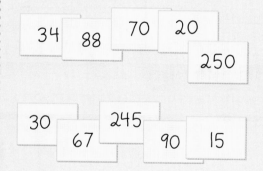

Challenge
for students seeking a challenge

PAIRS

Select a Strategy

Materials: calculators (1 per pair)

One student writes an addition expression with three 3-digit numbers. The other student uses any estimation strategy to make an estimate of the sum and writes it on the paper. The first student uses a calculator to find the actual sum. The difference between the actual sum and the estimate is awarded to the player who made the estimate. Students switch roles so that each has three opportunities to make the estimate. The student with the lowest number of points wins the game.

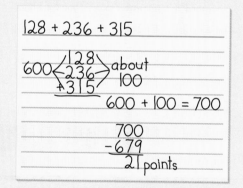

Also Use
Challenge Master for 3-2

 Math Writing Prompt

Intervention

Explain Your Thinking
Describe how you would round the number 867 to the nearest ten.

 Math Writing Prompt

On Level

Are They the Same?
Round 145 and 153 to the nearest ten. Are the rounded numbers the same? Explain why or why not.

Math Writing Prompt

Challenge

Greater Than or Less Than?
When you round both numbers up to estimate a sum, will your estimate always be greater than or less than the actual sum? Explain your thinking.

Round to the Nearest Ten   **279**

③ Homework and Spiral Review

✓ Include children's completed Homework page as part of their portfolios.

This Remembering page would be appropriate anytime after today's lesson.

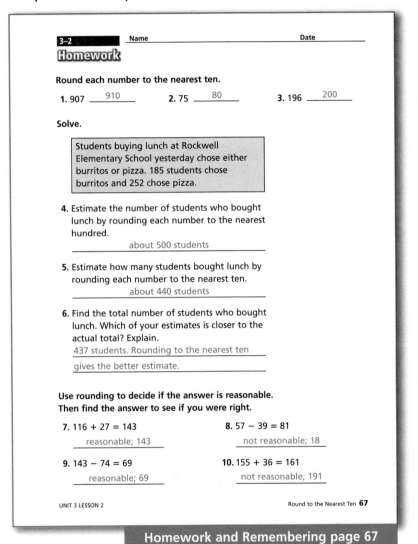

3-2   Name _____ Date _____
Homework

Round each number to the nearest ten.

1. 907 ___910___   2. 75 ___80___   3. 196 ___200___

Solve.

> Students buying lunch at Rockwell Elementary School yesterday chose either burritos or pizza. 185 students chose burritos and 252 chose pizza.

4. Estimate the number of students who bought lunch by rounding each number to the nearest hundred.
___about 500 students___

5. Estimate how many students bought lunch by rounding each number to the nearest ten.
___about 440 students___

6. Find the total number of students who bought lunch. Which of your estimates is closer to the actual total? Explain.
___437 students. Rounding to the nearest ten___
___gives the better estimate.___

Use rounding to decide if the answer is reasonable. Then find the answer to see if you were right.

7. 116 + 27 = 143
   reasonable; 143

8. 57 − 39 = 81
   not reasonable; 18

9. 143 − 74 = 69
   reasonable; 69

10. 155 + 36 = 161
   not reasonable; 191

UNIT 3 LESSON 2   Round to the Nearest Ten **67**

Homework and Remembering page 67

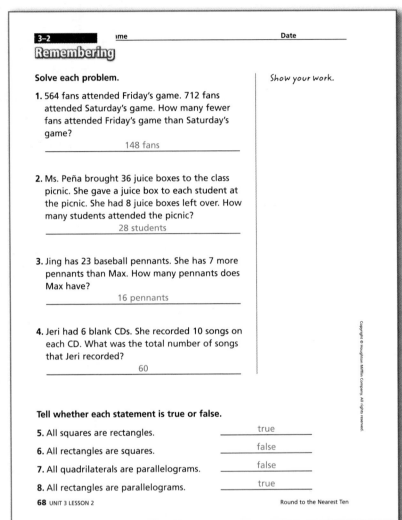

3-2   Name _____ Date _____
Remembering

Solve each problem.   *Show your work.*

1. 564 fans attended Friday's game. 712 fans attended Saturday's game. How many fewer fans attended Friday's game than Saturday's game?
___148 fans___

2. Ms. Peña brought 36 juice boxes to the class picnic. She gave a juice box to each student at the picnic. She had 8 juice boxes left over. How many students attended the picnic?
___28 students___

3. Jing has 23 baseball pennants. She has 7 more pennants than Max. How many pennants does Max have?
___16 pennants___

4. Jeri had 6 blank CDs. She recorded 10 songs on each CD. What was the total number of songs that Jeri recorded?
___60___

Tell whether each statement is true or false.

5. All squares are rectangles. ___true___

6. All rectangles are squares. ___false___

7. All quadrilaterals are parallelograms. ___false___

8. All rectangles are parallelograms. ___true___

68 UNIT 3 LESSON 2   Round to the Nearest Ten

Homework and Remembering page 68

Home or School Activity

 Music Connection

Rap a Round Use the "Geometry Park" CD (Illumisware 2002) to help students with their rounding skills. Students can rap to "Slip to the Side" which reinforces the importance of the number 5 in rounding. After students have learned the lyrics to this, challenge them to make up their own songs, raps, or rhymes. They can share these with classmates to help others with the rules of rounding.

Compare Whole Numbers

Lesson Objectives

- Compare and order whole numbers.
- Compare the values of expressions.

Vocabulary

compare
equal to (=)
greater than (>)
less than (<)

The Day at a Glance

Today's Goals	Materials	Math Talk
Quick Practice Round whole numbers to the nearest ten or hundred. **1 Teaching the Lesson** **A1:** Compare and order whole numbers. **A2:** Compare values of expressions by calculating and by estimating or by using number sense. **2 Extending the Lesson** ▶ Differentiated Instruction **3 Homework and Spiral Review**	MathBoard materials Base ten blocks Secret Code Cards Number Path (Copymaster M39) Number cubes Student Activity Book pages 131–132 Homework and Remembering pages 69–70 Math Journals Quick Quiz 1 (Assessment Guide) *The Greatest Gymnast of All* by Stuart J. Murphy (Harper Trophy, 1998)	In today's activities, the students are involved in discussion as they ▶ describe how to compare whole numbers ▶ share strategies for comparing values of expressions

Quick Practice

 5 MINUTES   **Goal:** Round whole numbers to the nearest ten or hundred.

Rounding Practice Have the Student Leader write the six numbers at the right on the board.

The Student Leader points to each number and says either "Round to the nearest hundred," or "Round to the nearest ten." When the leader gives a signal, students respond in unison with the rounded number.

Leader (pointing to 349): Round to the nearest hundred.
Class: 300
Leader (pointing to 349): Round to the nearest ten.
Class: 350

271
983
349
628
115
1,257

1 Teaching the Lesson

Compare and Order Whole Numbers

25 MINUTES

Goal: Compare and order whole numbers.

Materials: MathBoard materials, base ten blocks, Student Activity Book page 131

 NCTM Standards:
Number and Operations
Communication

Differentiated Instruction

Extra Help If students have a hard time remembering which way the greater than, less than symbol should point, use the simple drawings below to help them.

First, draw the greater than symbol.

Then, turn the symbol into a fish's mouth.

Explain that the fish's open mouth always faces the larger number.

Show students that the fish's open mouth can go in either direction as long as it still opens to the larger number.

▶ **Compare Numbers** WHOLE CLASS

Explain to the class that they will be comparing numbers to decide if one number is greater than or less than another or if the numbers are equal. Point out that we use the symbols for greater than, less than, and equal to show the comparison. Write and label the symbols on the MathBoard and write the two numbers to be compared as shown below.

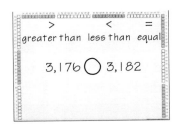

Encourage students to use different methods to compare the numbers.

Use place-value drawings.

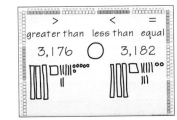

● Do the numbers have the same number of thousands? yes

● Do the numbers have the same number of hundreds? yes

● Do the numbers have the same number of tens? no Which number has the greater number of tens? 3,182

● Which is the greater number? 3,182

● Which symbol should be placed in the circle? <

Point out that the point of the symbol always points to the smaller number and the wide, open part always points to the larger number.

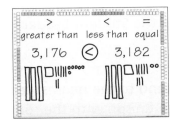

Ask a volunteer to read the comparison statement. Three thousand, one hundred seventy-six is less than three thousand, one hundred eighty-two.

Another way to compare numbers is to line up the numbers as if you were going to add them. Then begin comparing from left to right until the digits are not the same.

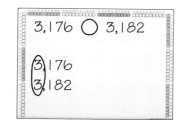

Use place value.

Draw a loop around the digits in the thousands place of both numbers.

● Do the numbers have the same number of thousands? yes

Draw a loop around the digits in the hundreds place of both numbers.

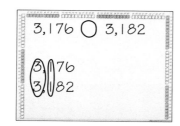

● Do the numbers have the same number of hundreds? yes

Draw a loop around the digits in the tens place of both numbers.

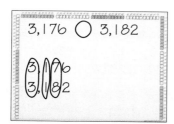

● Do the numbers have the same number of tens? no
● Which number has the greater number of tens? 3,182
● Which symbol should we put in the circle? less than

Have a volunteer write the greater than symbol in the circle.

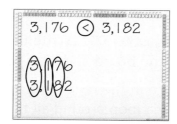

Have students work independently to complete exercises 1–10 on Student Activity Book page 131. Discuss any difficulties student may have had.

Activity continued ▶

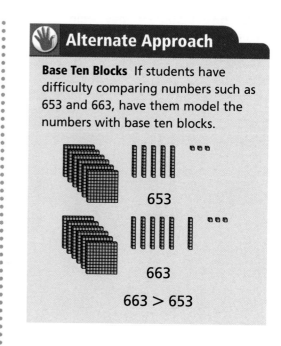

✋ **Alternate Approach**

Base Ten Blocks If students have difficulty comparing numbers such as 653 and 663, have them model the numbers with base ten blocks.

653

663

663 > 653

Teaching Note

Watch For! Students may begin comparing numbers from the right, missing the fact that the place farthest left has the greatest value.

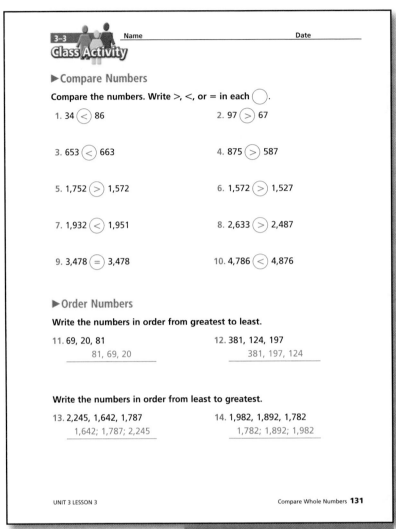

Student Activity Book page 131

The activity sheet contains:

3-3
Name
Date

Class Activity

▶ Compare Numbers

Compare the numbers. Write >, <, or = in each ◯.

1. 34 ⓐ< 86
2. 97 ⓐ> 67
3. 653 ⓐ< 663
4. 875 ⓐ> 587
5. 1,752 ⓐ> 1,572
6. 1,572 ⓐ> 1,527
7. 1,932 ⓐ< 1,951
8. 2,633 ⓐ> 2,487
9. 3,478 ⓐ= 3,478
10. 4,786 ⓐ< 4,876

▶ Order Numbers

Write the numbers in order from greatest to least.

11. 69, 20, 81
   81, 69, 20
12. 381, 124, 197
   381, 197, 124

Write the numbers in order from least to greatest.

13. 2,245, 1,642, 1,787
   1,642; 1,787; 2,245
14. 1,982, 1,892, 1,782
   1,782; 1,892; 1,982

UNIT 3 LESSON 3   Compare Whole Numbers **131**

▶ Order Numbers [WHOLE CLASS]

Write the example shown on the right, on the board. Elicit methods from the students on ordering these numbers from least to greatest. One method is shown.

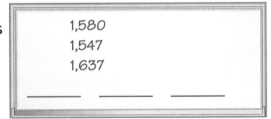

1,580
1,547
1,637
___ ___ ___

- What is the greatest place in the numbers in which the digits differ? hundreds (Draw a loop around all the hundreds digits.)

- Which number is the largest? 1,637 (Write this number on the blank farthest to the right on the board and cross out 1,637 above.)

- What is the greatest place in the remaining two numbers in which the digits differ? tens (Draw a loop around all the tens digits.)

- Which number is smaller? 1,547 (Write 1,547 in the first blank and 1,580 in the middle blank.)

Have students complete exercises 11–14 independently.

Compare Values of Expressions

▶ Multi-Step Comparisons [WHOLE CLASS]

Explain to the class that sometimes numbers have to be added or subtracted before they are compared.

Write this problem on the board and read it aloud to students.

Tim has 36 baseball cards and 29 football cards. Pilar has 24 baseball cards and 38 football cards. Who has more cards?

Write this comparison statement on the board. Explain that we can write this open comparison statement to start to solve the problem.

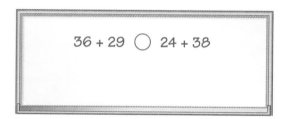

$$36 + 29 \bigcirc 24 + 38$$

- How much is 36 + 29? 65
- How much is 24 + 38? 62

Write these numbers under the expressions on the board.

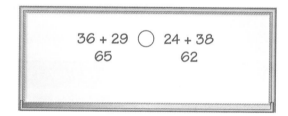

$$36 + 29 \bigcirc 24 + 38$$
$$65 62$$

- Which is greater, 65 or 62? 65
- What symbol belongs in the circle? greater than

Have a volunteer write the correct symbol in the circle and read the comparison sentence 36 plus 29 is greater than 24 plus 38.

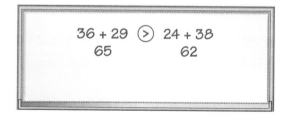

$$36 + 29 \;\gtrdot\; 24 + 38$$
$$65 62$$

- Who has more cards? Tim

Have students complete exercises 15–22 on Student Activity Book page 132 independently. Have students record the value for each expression under the expression so they can compare the values easily, and write the symbol.

Activity continued ▶

 20 MINUTES

Goal: Compare values of expressions by calculating and by estimating or using number sense.

Materials: Student Activity Book page 132

 NCTM Standards:
Number and Operations
Communication

 **Ongoing Assessment**

To check that students understand the concept of comparing and ordering whole numbers, ask questions such as:

▶ In Chicago, Illinois, the three tallest buildings are the Aon Center, which is 1,136 ft tall, the John Hancock Center, which is 1,127 ft tall, and the Sears Tower, which is 1,450 ft tall. Write the heights of these three buildings in order from shortest to tallest.

The Learning Classroom

Helping Community You may want to have students work in Helping Pairs to complete exercises 15–22 on Student Activity page 132. Students can work independently to find the sums or differences. Then have them compare their sums or differences to be sure they are correct before they write the symbol in the circle.

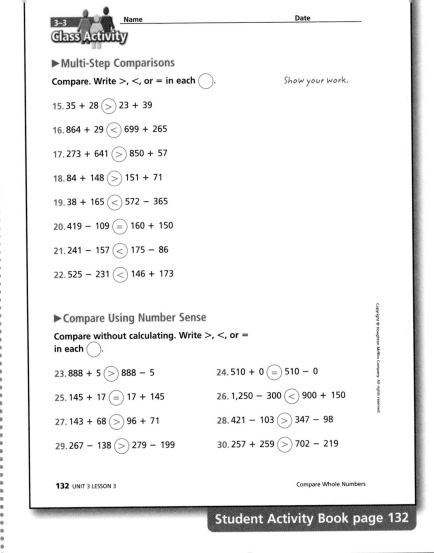

▶ **Multi-Step Comparisons**

Compare. Write >, <, or = in each ◯.   *Show your work.*

15. 35 + 28 ⊙(>) 23 + 39

16. 864 + 29 (<) 699 + 265

17. 273 + 641 (>) 850 + 57

18. 84 + 148 (>) 151 + 71

19. 38 + 165 (<) 572 − 365

20. 419 − 109 (=) 160 + 150

21. 241 − 157 (<) 175 − 86

22. 525 − 231 (<) 146 + 173

▶ **Compare Using Number Sense**

Compare without calculating. Write >, <, or = in each ◯.

23. 888 + 5 (>) 888 − 5

24. 510 + 0 (=) 510 − 0

25. 145 + 17 (=) 17 + 145

26. 1,250 − 300 (<) 900 + 150

27. 143 + 68 (>) 96 + 71

28. 421 − 103 (>) 347 − 98

29. 267 − 138 (>) 279 − 199

30. 257 + 259 (>) 702 − 219

132 UNIT 3 LESSON 3   Compare Whole Numbers

Student Activity Book page 132

▶ Compare Using Number Sense [WHOLE CLASS]

Read students this problem: Tim and Gail each have 10 apples. Tim gives 4 apples away. Gail picks 4 more apples. Who has more apples? Gail

● Ask students to explain why you do not need to add or subtract to answer the question. Since they both started with 10 apples, the person who got 4 more apples would have more apples than the person who gave 4 away.

Give students a few minutes to complete exercises 23–26 on Student Activity Book page 132 and discuss the answers.

Then have students look at exercise 27.

● Is 143 + 68 more or less than 200? more than 200

● Is 96 + 71 more or less than 200? less than 200

Using **Solve and Discuss,** complete exercises 28–30.

Ongoing Assessment

See Assessment Guide for Unit 3 Quick Quiz 1.

286   UNIT 3 LESSON 3

② Extending the Lesson

Intervention
for students having difficulty

PAIRS

Number Path Comparisons

Materials: Secret Code Cards (1 set per student), MathBoard materials or Number Path (Copymaster M39)

Have students shuffle their Secret Code Cards and divide them into two piles of tens and ones (number side face down). Each student uses the top cards from each pile to make a 2-digit number. (They can see if their numbers are correct by looking at the back of their Secret Code Cards.)

Both students should indicate their numbers on the Number Path as shown below. Then each student should write 2 comparisons for the numbers.

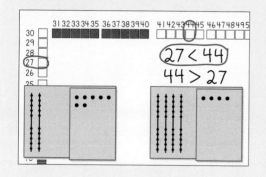

On Level
for students having success

INDIVIDUALS

Comparison Toss

Materials: number cube (labeled 1–6), MathBoard materials

One student writes any 2-digit number on the MathBoard and then rolls the number cube. If the student rolls a 1, 2, or 3, the other student writes a 2-digit number that is less than the original number; otherwise, the other student writes a 2-digit number that is greater than the original number.

The 2 on the cube means I need a number that is less than 53, so I'll choose 50.

Students should then write a comparison sentence using the correct symbol.

53 > 50

Then, have students switch roles and repeat the activity.

Challenge
for students seeking a challenge

INDIVIDUALS

Ordered Populations

The populations of the six largest cities and towns in New Mexico are shown alphabetically in the table below.

City	Population
Albuquerque	463,874
Farmington	40,563
Las Cruces	75,015
Rio Rancho	56,614
Roswell	44,058
Santa Fe	65,127

Have students reorder the cities and their populations from least populated to most populated.

Also Use
Challenge Master for 3-3

 Math Writing Prompt

Intervention

Connected Math
How do you think a Number Path can help you compare numbers? Explain.

 Math Writing Prompt

On Level

Write Your Own Real-World Application
A museum has 2,016 gems and 2,061 minerals on display. Does the museum have more gems or more minerals on display? Explain how you decided.

 Math Writing Prompt

Challenge

Is Ten Dollars Enough?
You want to buy three model trucks that cost $2.99 each plus the glue you need to put the models together. The glue costs $1.25. Is $10 enough? Decide without calculating. Explain your thinking.

③ Homework and Spiral Review

3–3
Homework Goal: Additional Practice

Use this Homework page to provide students with more practice comparing and ordering numbers.

3–3
Remembering Goal: Spiral Review

This Remembering page would be appropriate anytime after today's lesson.

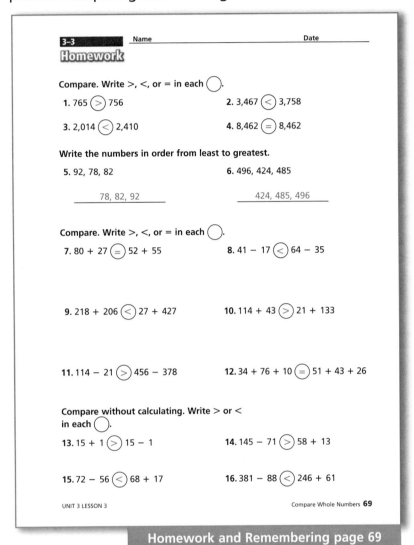

3–3 Name _____ Date _____
Homework

Compare. Write >, <, or = in each ◯.

1. 765 ⊙ 756   **2.** 3,467 ⊙ 3,758

3. 2,014 ⊙ 2,410   **4.** 8,462 ⊙ 8,462

Write the numbers in order from least to greatest.

5. 92, 78, 82   **6.** 496, 424, 485

78, 82, 92   424, 485, 496

Compare. Write >, <, or = in each ◯.

7. 80 + 27 ⊙ 52 + 55   **8.** 41 − 17 ⊙ 64 − 35

9. 218 + 206 ⊙ 27 + 427   **10.** 114 + 43 ⊙ 21 + 133

11. 114 − 21 ⊙ 456 − 378 **12.** 34 + 76 + 10 ⊙ 51 + 43 + 26

Compare without calculating. Write > or < in each ◯.

13. 15 + 1 ⊙ 15 − 1   **14.** 145 − 71 ⊙ 58 + 13

15. 72 − 56 ⊙ 68 + 17   **16.** 381 − 88 ⊙ 246 + 61

UNIT 3 LESSON 3   Compare Whole Numbers **69**

Homework and Remembering page 69

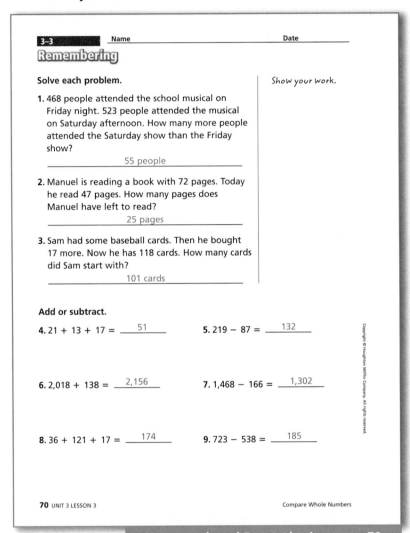

3–3 Name _____ Date _____
Remembering

Solve each problem.   *Show your work.*

1. 468 people attended the school musical on Friday night. 523 people attended the musical on Saturday afternoon. How many more people attended the Saturday show than the Friday show?

_____ 55 people _____

2. Manuel is reading a book with 72 pages. Today he read 47 pages. How many pages does Manuel have left to read?

_____ 25 pages _____

3. Sam had some baseball cards. Then he bought 17 more. Now he has 118 cards. How many cards did Sam start with?

_____ 101 cards _____

Add or subtract.

4. 21 + 13 + 17 = ___51___   **5.** 219 − 87 = ___132___

6. 2,018 + 138 = ___2,156___   **7.** 1,468 − 166 = ___1,302___

8. 36 + 121 + 17 = ___174___   **9.** 723 − 538 = ___185___

70 UNIT 3 LESSON 3   Compare Whole Numbers

Homework and Remembering page 70

Home or School Activity

 Literature Connection

The Greatest Gymnast of All When students are using comparison language in math, such as *greater, less, more,* and *fewer,* it's the perfect time to introduce antonyms. To emphasize the similarity between math and language comparisons, have students read *The Greatest Gymnast of All* by Stuart J. Murphy. After students have read the story, have them write pairs of antonyms and put them in comparison sentences. For example, Joey is *taller* than Ann. Ann is *shorter* than Joey.

Money Values

Vocabulary

penny
nickel
dime
quarter
coin equivalents

Lesson Objectives

- Review the values of a penny, nickel, dime, and quarter.
- Determine and compare the values of collections of coins and bills.

The Day at a Glance

Today's Goals	Materials	Math Talk
Quick Practice Round to the nearest ten or hundred.	Play money or Play Money (Copymaster M40)	In today's activities, the students are involved in discussion as they
① Teaching the Lesson **A1:** Review the names and values of U.S. coins. **A2:** Use various strategies to find the values of collections of coins and bills. **A3:** Compare the values of collections of coins and bills.	Snack bags or envelopes Overhead projector and coins (optional) Number cubes Student Activity Book pages 133–136	▶ identify similarities and differences among coins ▶ determine coin equivalencies ▶ identify the values of groups of coins and bills
② Extending the Lesson ▶ Differentiated Instruction	Homework and Remembering pages 71–72 Math Journals	▶ explain how they determine the value of a collection of coins and bills
③ Homework and Spiral Review		

Quick Practice

🕐 **5 MINUTES**   **Goal:** Round to the nearest ten or hundred.

Rounding Practice Have a Student Leader write the following six numbers on the board.

> 168   129   172   354   1,409   240

The Student Leader points to each number and says "Round to the nearest ten," or "Round to the nearest hundred." When the leader gives a signal, students respond in unison with the rounded number.

Leader (pointing to 168): Round to the nearest ten.

Class: 170

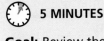 **Teaching the Lesson**

Reviewing Quarters, Dimes, Nickels, and Pennies

 5 MINUTES

Goal: Review the names and values of U.S. coins.

Materials: sets of play money (1 quarter, 1 dime, 1 nickel, and 1 penny per student) or Play Money (Copymaster M40); Student Activity Book page 133, snack bags or envelopes

 NCTM Standards:
Number and Operations
Communication
Representation

Class Management

Looking Ahead Have students keep their money cut-outs in a snack bag or envelope for future use.

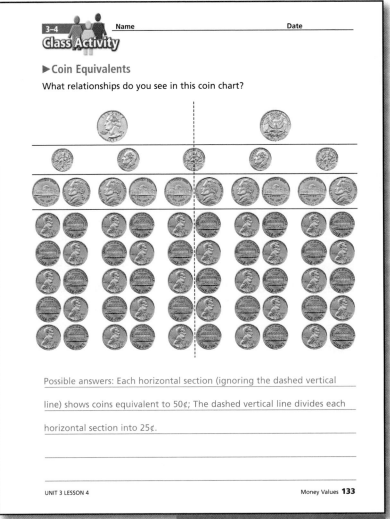

Student Activity Book page 133

▶ Coin Equivalents WHOLE CLASS

Distribute a set of play money to each student or have students cut out the coins on Play Money (Copymaster M40). Discuss the similarities and differences.

Have students look at the chart on Student Activity Book page 133. Ask them about the relationships they see in the coin chart. They should mention the following points:

● Each horizontal section (ignoring the dashed line) shows coins equivalent to 50¢.

● The dashed vertical line divides each horizontal section in half. The coins in each half are equivalent to 25¢.

Ask a few simple questions about coin equivalents that can be answered using the chart on Student Activiy Book page 133.

- What are some combinations of coins that are equivalent to a dime? 2 nickels, 10 pennies, 1 nickel and 5 pennies

- What are some combinations of coins that are equivalent to a quarter? 5 nickels; 25 pennies; 2 dimes and 1 nickel; 4 nickels and 5 pennies, and so on

▶ Coin Values WHOLE CLASS

Hold up each coin, and say its value aloud. Have students respond with the name of the coin.

- A 25¢ coin is a … quarter! A 10¢ coin is a … dime! A 5¢ coin is a … nickel! A 1¢ coin is a … penny!

Repeat this activity. Scramble the order of the coins.

Now hold up the coins one at a time, and have students name each coin.

 Dime!   Quarter!

Finally, hold up the coins one at a time, and have students show fingers to indicate the value. (They can flash 2 tens and a 5 to show a quarter's value.)

 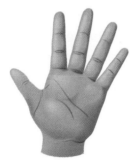

If you think students could benefit from additional practice with naming coins and their values, you might use the above activities as Quick Practice activities at the beginning of the next several lessons.

Differentiated Instruction

English Learners The activity will be especially powerful for Spanish and other nonnative English speakers. In Spanish, a quarter is often referred to as a "25¢ coin." The other U.S. coins are referred to in a similar way. The activity will also be helpful for native English speakers who need more practice associating each coin with its name and value.

Teaching the Lesson (continued)

Activity 2

Find the Value of Collections of Coins

 20 MINUTES

Goal: Use various strategies to find the values of collections of coins and bills.

Materials: sets of money (two $1 bills, 8 quarters, 10 dimes, 10 nickels, and 10 pennies per student), set of overhead money (optional), overhead projector (optional), Student Activity Book page 134

✔ **NCTM Standards:**
Number and Operations
Reasoning and Proof
Communication

Teaching Note

Watch For! Some students might have difficulty counting on. Review how to skip count by 2s, 5s, 10s and 25s. Then as the class is counting on using the coins, ask the students what kind of coin they are counting and what type of skip counting is necessary.

▶ **Ways to Count the Value of Coins** WHOLE CLASS

Ask students to take 1 quarter, 1 dime, and 3 nickels from their sets of coins. Give them a few minutes to find the total value of the coins. Then choose a student to explain the counting method he or she used, using overhead coins to demonstrate if necessary. Ask anyone who used a different counting method to present it. Here are some ways students might count:

● Arrange the coins into groups whose values are easy to add.

30¢   +   10¢   +   10¢   = 50¢

● Count up, starting with the coin with the largest value.

25¢   35¢   40¢   45¢   50¢

Next, have students select one $1 bill, 3 quarters, 4 dimes, and 3 pennies and find the value of this collection. Select students who used different counting strategies to explain them.

Be sure that students understand what the cent sign, dollar sign, and the decimal point stand for. Remind them that cent signs are never shown with decimal points or dollar signs. Dollar signs can be shown with decimal points. Review with them that the dollar value is to the left of the decimal point, and the cents value (the amount under a dollar) is to the right of the decimal point.

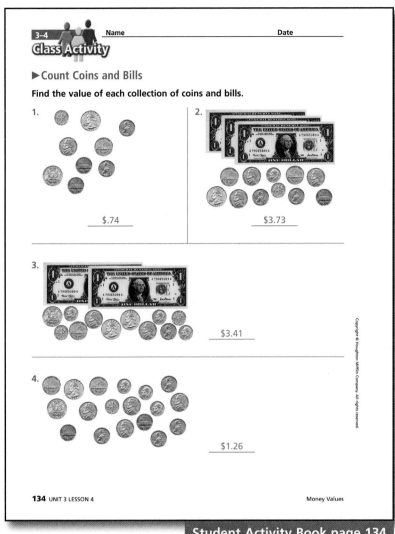

Student Activity Book page 134

▶ Count Coins and Bills WHOLE CLASS

Introduce (or review) the idea of counting up from the coin with the greatest value to the coin with the least value. Have students select 1 quarter, 5 dimes, 3 nickels, and 2 pennies and arrange the coins in order of value on their desks. Arrange the corresponding overhead coins on the projector. Have students count up with you to find the value, pointing to each coin as they count it.

25¢   35¢   45¢   55¢   65¢   75¢   80¢   85¢   90¢   91¢   92¢

Repeat this for two $1 bills, 3 quarters, 2 dimes, 5 nickels, and 1 penny.

Have students complete exercises 1–4 on Student Activity Book page 134. Discuss their results and counting strategies. Some may group coins by circling them. Others may count up, writing the cumulative totals as they count.

Watch For! Students must count over $2 in this activity. If some students find counting from $1.95 to $2.05 difficult, suggest they pretend they have 2 nickels instead of 1 dime so they can count "$1.95, $2.00, $2.05."

Activity 3

Compare Money Amounts

 15 MINUTES

Goal: Compare the values of collections of coins and bills.

Materials: Student Activity Book page 135

 NCTM Standards:
Number and Operations
Problem Solving
Reasoning and Proof
Communication
Connections
Representation

 Ongoing Assessment

To be sure that students understand how to determine the value of a set of coins and bills, ask questions such as:

▶ If you had a pocketful of coins, how would you find the total value of the coins?

▶ Leo has 1 quarter, 2 nickels and 3 dimes. He said he has 65¢. How do you know he is correct?

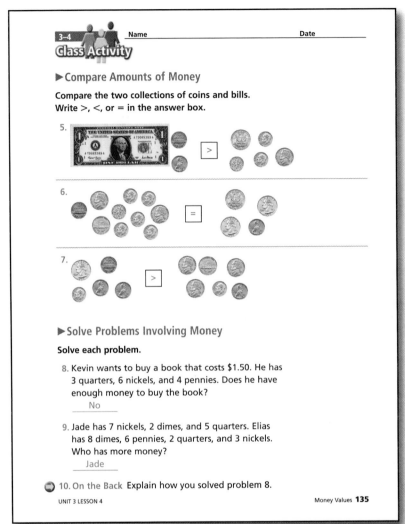

Student Activity Book page 135

▶ Compare Amounts of Money WHOLE CLASS

Read aloud the directions to exercises 5–7 on Student Activity Book page 135. Make sure everyone knows what to do. You may need to review the meaning of the symbols >, < and =. (You might remind students that the bigger part of the < or > symbol opens to the greater amount.)

Give students a few minutes to complete exercises 5–7. Then review the answers.

▶ Solve Problems Involving Money WHOLE CLASS

Using **Solve and Discuss**, have students solve problems 8–9. Allow them to use money or to draw coins if they need to.

On the Back Have students explain how they solved question 8 if there is time.

② Extending the Lesson

Activities for Individualizing

Intervention
for students having difficulty

PAIRS

Counting Patterns

Materials: quarters, dimes, nickels, and pennies (10 of each coin per pair)

Give each pair of students a set of coins. Partner A counts the pennies by 2s and slides the coins across the table to Partner B. Partner A counts the nickels by 5s, the dimes by 10s, and the quarters by 25s, sliding the coins with each new number. When Partner B has all the coins, he or she follows the same procedure, sliding the coins back to the first student. On the next round, have students begin with the quarters and count the coins in order of descending value. As students become comfortable with these counting patterns, they can create collections of coins for each other and practice counting on to find the value of the coins.

10 20 30 40 50
60 70 80 90 100

On Level
for students having success

SMALL GROUPS

The Banking Game

Materials: several sets of coins per group

Students in each group select one student to be the banker, who begins the game with all the coins. The game is played in rounds. In each round, the banker hands out coins randomly to each student. The students count their coins. The student with the most money keeps the coins while the other students give their coins back to the banker. The game continues until the banker has no more coins to distribute. Students count the coins that they have kept. The student with the greatest amount of money wins the game.

I have $1.22, but I have to give it back to the banker because Hannah has $2.24.

Challenge
for students seeking a challenge

PAIRS

Coin Combinations . . .

Materials: number cubes (labeled 1–6, 2 per pair)

Partner A tosses the cubes and uses the digits to name an amount of money. (If both cubes show the same digit, students toss them again until the digits are different.) Partner A writes a combination of coins for the amount using the fewest coins possible.

Hazel has 53¢. That's 2 quarters plus 3 pennies, or 5 coins.

Hazel has 35¢. That's 1 quarter plus 1 dime, or 2 coins. I can add 35¢ to my score.

Partner B uses the same digits to name a different amount of money, and then writes a combination of coins for that amount using the fewest coins possible. The student who used the fewest coins adds the amount to his or her score and tosses the cubes again. The first player whose score is more than $2.00 wins the game.

Also Use
Challenge Master for 3-4

 Math Writing Prompt

Intervention

Money Patterns

What skip counting patterns do you use when counting quarters, nickels, and dimes? Use drawings to explain the patterns.

 Math Writing Prompt

On Level

Counting Strategy

What strategy do you use when you need to find the value of a number of coins and bills? Explain your thinking.

 Math Writing Prompt

Challenge

Other Ways

Danny has 51¢ in his pocket. If he has 5 coins in his pocket, what are the coins? Explain.

③ Homework and Spiral Review

3-4

Homework **Goal:** Additional Practice

Use this Homework page to provide students with more practice comparing money amounts.

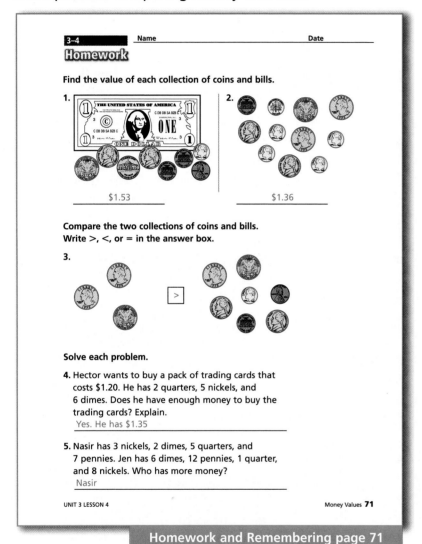

3-4

Remembering **Goal:** Spiral Review

This Remembering page would be appropriate anytime after today's lesson.

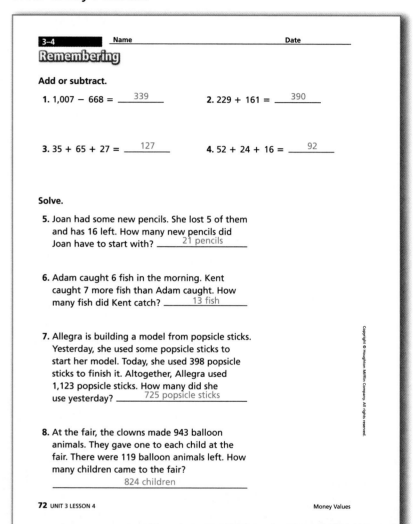

Homework and Remembering page 71

Homework and Remembering page 72

Home or School Activity

Social Studies Connection

Coin Design Have students look at the designs on a penny, a nickel, a dime, a quarter, a half dollar, a Susan B. Anthony dollar, and a Golden dollar. Have students make a poster showing who is on the front and what is on the back of each coin.

Coin	Who's on Front?	What's on Back?
Penny	Abraham Lincoln	The Lincoln Memorial
Nickel	Thomas Jefferson	Jefferson's Home, Monticello
Dime	Franklin Delano Roosevelt	A torch, an oak branch, and an olive branch

296 UNIT 3 LESSON 4

Represent Money Amounts in Different Ways

Lesson Objectives

● Represent amounts of money in various ways.

● Practice counting out the exact amount of money to make a purchase.

Vocabulary
dollar
exact

The Day at a Glance

Today's Goals	Materials	Math Talk
Quick Practice Round numbers to the nearest ten and hundred. **1 Teaching the Lesson** A1: Determine different coin combinations for given amounts. A2: Identify how to pay for items with exact change. **2 Extending the Lesson** ▶ Differentiated Instruction **3 Homework and Spiral Review**	MathBoard materials Real or play money Play Money (Copymaster M40) Coin Strips (Copymaster M41) Price tags Number cubes Index cards Student Activity Book pages 137–138 Homework and Remembering pages 73–74 Math Journals	In today's activities, the students are involved in discussion as they ▶ identify different coin combinations to make a dollar ▶ recall ways to find the value of a collection of coins ▶ explain strategies to make a dollar amount ▶ act out a sales transaction

Quick Practice

 5 MINUTES **Goal:** Round numbers to the nearest ten and hundred.

Rounding Practice: Have the Student Leader write the following six numbers on the board.

238   721   364   1,298   1,550   981

The Student Leader points to each number and says either, "Round to the nearest hundred," or, "Round to the nearest ten." When the leader gives a signal, students respond in unison with the rounded number.

Leader (pointing to 238): Round to the nearest ten.
Class: 240

Class Management

The students have seen this activity several times. You might want to change it slightly by dividing the students into two teams. One student from each team competes with a student from the other team.

Teaching the Lesson

Finding Equivalent Coin Combinations

 15 MINUTES

Goal: Determine different coin combinations for given amounts.

Materials: MathBoard materials, real or play money (8 quarters, 10 dimes, 10 nickels, 10 pennies per student) or Play Money (Copymaster M40), Coin Strips (Copymaster M41), Student Activity Book page 137

✔ **NCTM Standards:**
Number and Operations
Problem Solving
Communication
Connections

Differentiated Instruction

Extra Help Have students who struggled with the coin activities in Lesson 4 use Coin Strips (Copymaster M41) that show the coin values by size. Since the pennies are small, students may find it easier to fold a strip of pennies or tear off groups of them than to cut out individual pennies.

 Math Talk in Action

Why do you think it's important to know how to make a certain amount of money in different ways?

Latasha: It's important because you might want to buy something and you need to know that there is more than just one way to get to that amount.

Can you give me an example?

Latasha: If a soda costs 75¢, you might not have 3 quarters, but you might have 1 quarter and 5 dimes. You can still buy the soda because you have the 75¢.

Very good.

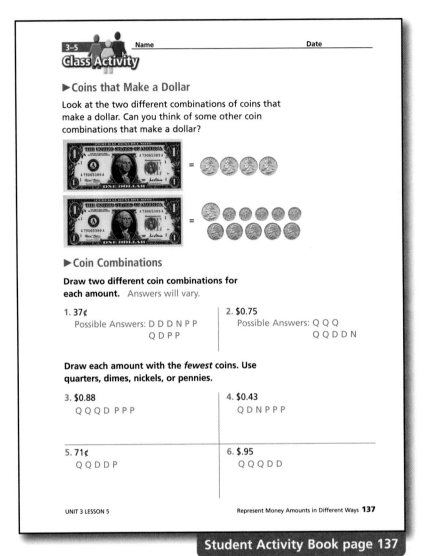

Student Activity Book page 137

▶ Coins that Make a Dollar WHOLE CLASS

Have students look at Student Activity Book page 137 and discuss the different ways to make a dollar. For each set of coins, have the class count the coins (from greatest to least value) in unison to check that the total is a dollar.

Have students suggest other ways to make a dollar while the rest of the class works on their MathBoards. Allow students to use real or play sets of money if they need to, or just represent the coins with circles labeled with letters or their values, or just write letters.

  D

▶ Coin Combinations INDIVIDUALS

Have students complete exercises 1–6 and then use **Solve and Discuss** to have students compare their answers and strategies.

Shopping with Exact Change

▶ Model Making a Purchase WHOLE CLASS

Math Talk Have students share what they know about buying things with money.

- the cashier determines the total cost of the items
- the customer pays for the items
- the cashier gives the customer change back if there is any

Put the 37¢ price tag on a pencil and the 56¢ price tag on a ruler. Choose two volunteers to act out purchasing the pencil and the ruler. Have the customer get some play money. Explain that the shopkeeper does not have a cash register or any coins, so the customer will have to pay with the exact amount.

Customer: (Brings pencil and ruler to cashier) I would like to buy these two items.

Shopkeeper: I'll make out a sales slip and find your total cost.

```
pencil $0.37
ruler  $0.56
       _____
       $0.93
```

Shopkeeper: Your total cost is 93¢. I do not have any coins, so you will need to give me the exact change.

Customer: Twenty-five, fifty, seventy-five, eighty-five, ninety, ninety-one, ninety-two, ninety-three.

Shopkeeper: I'll draw 3 quarters, 1 dime, 1 nickel, and 3 pennies to record the sale.

```
pencil $0.37
ruler  $0.56
       _____
       $0.93

QQQDNPPP
```

Ask the class to give other coin combinations the customer could have used to make the purchase with the exact amount.

Activity continued ▶

 30 MINUTES

Goal: Identify how to pay for items with exact change.

Materials: Price tags: (37¢ and 56¢), play money, Student Activity Book page 138

✓ **NCTM Standards:**
Number and Operations
Problem Solving
Communication
Connections

Differentiated Instruction

English Learners Some students may not follow the procedures for purchasing items when the steps are presented in English. Tell these students that in this first activity students will set up a scenario with props to model the activity they will do on the Student Activity Book page.

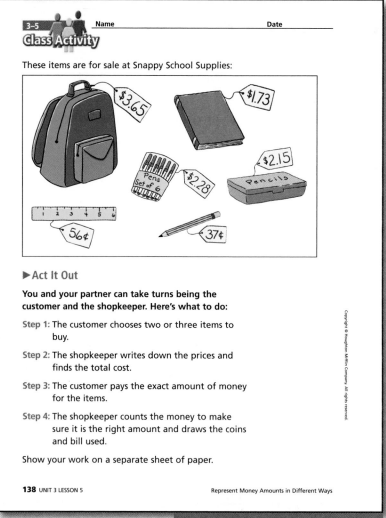

Student Activity Book page 138

▶ Act It Out PAIRS

Divide the class into pairs and explain that they are going to act out a sales purchase like the two volunteers just did. Remind them that the shopkeeper will not have any coins or a cash register so the shopkeeper will have to make out a sales slip and the customer will have to pay with the exact amount.

Read aloud the steps on Student Activity Book page 138. Then, have a student give out play money to each pair. Allow students to shop for 20 minutes and then choose a few pairs to describe the items the customer bought, how the shopkeeper found the total, and which coins and bills the customer used.

Make sure students understand that a customer does not always have to pay with an exact amount of money. Sometimes they may not have an exact amount and pay too much. In that case, they need to get change back.

Extending the Lesson

Intervention
for students having difficulty

PAIRS

How Many Ways?

Materials: MathBoard materials

Have one student write an amount less than one dollar on his or her MathBoard. Then have the other student use coin drawings to represent the amount in as many ways as possible. Have students switch roles and repeat the activity.

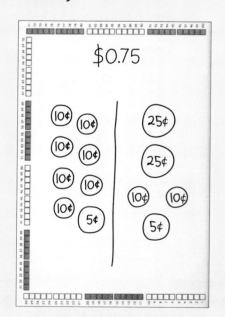

$0.75

On Level
for students having success

PAIRS

Count It Up!

Materials: 1 number cube per pair (labeled 1–6), play money (8 quarters, 10 dimes, 10 nickels, 10 pennies per student)

Have each player arrange the money in front of them. Then have players agree on a target amount of money between $3.00 and $5.00 and write it down.

Partner A rolls the number cube, takes that number of coins from the pile of money and writes the value of the coins. Partner B repeats the same process.

After each turn, players add the new amount to the old total.

The first player to *exactly* reach the target amount wins.

TARGET $4.00

3 quarters is 75¢
5 quarters is $1.25
My total so far is
$2.00

Challenge
for students seeking a challenge

PAIRS

Drawing for Dollars

Materials: Index cards (20 per pair)

Have pairs of students cut index cards in half to make ten 1¢ cards, ten 5¢ cards, eight 10¢ cards, eight 25¢ cards, and four 50¢ cards.

Have them place all the cards face down. Each student draws five cards from the pile.

Students take turns asking each other for a specific coin card needed to make a $1.00. If Partner B does not have it, Partner A must draw a card from the pile of coin cards. Players place groups of cards for $1.00 off to the side. When the pile of coin cards is gone, players add their dollar amounts and the player with the most money wins.

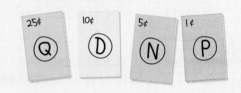

Also Use
Challenge Master for 3-5

 Math Writing Prompt

Intervention

Represent Coins
Edith counted her coins like this: "10 cents, 15 cents, 20 cents, 21 cents, 22 cents." What coins does Edith have? Use a picture to help you explain your answer.

 Math Writing Prompt

On Level

Draw a Picture
Draw three ways a customer can *exactly* pay for something that costs $2.35. Explain how you know you have the correct amount.

 Math Writing Prompt

Challenge

Make a List
Draw all six ways you can make $1.50 using dimes, quarters, and dollar bills. Explain how you organized your list so that you didn't miss any ways.

③ Homework and Spiral Review

This Homework page gives students practice adding money and counting out exact change.

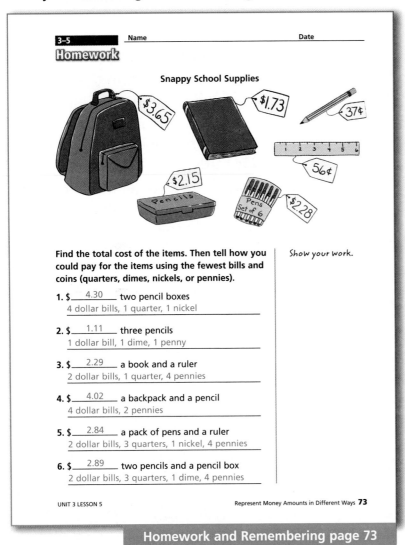

Snappy School Supplies

$3.65

$1.73

37¢

56¢

$2.15

Pencils

Pens Set of 6

$2.28

Find the total cost of the items. Then tell how you could pay for the items using the fewest bills and coins (quarters, dimes, nickels, or pennies).   *Show your work.*

1. $ __4.30__ two pencil boxes
   4 dollar bills, 1 quarter, 1 nickel

2. $ __1.11__ three pencils
   1 dollar bill, 1 dime, 1 penny

3. $ __2.29__ a book and a ruler
   2 dollar bills, 1 quarter, 4 pennies

4. $ __4.02__ a backpack and a pencil
   4 dollar bills, 2 pennies

5. $ __2.84__ a pack of pens and a ruler
   2 dollar bills, 3 quarters, 1 nickel, 4 pennies

6. $ __2.89__ two pencils and a pencil box
   2 dollar bills, 3 quarters, 1 dime, 4 pennies

UNIT 3 LESSON 5   Represent Money Amounts in Different Ways **73**

Homework and Remembering page 73

This Remembering page would be appropriate anytime after today's lesson.

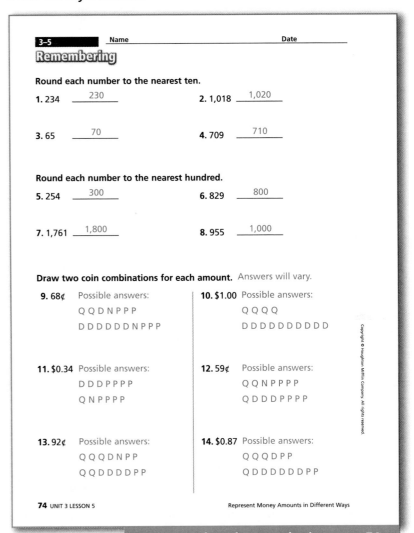

Round each number to the nearest ten.

1. 234 __230__   2. 1,018 __1,020__

3. 65 __70__   4. 709 __710__

Round each number to the nearest hundred.

5. 254 __300__   6. 829 __800__

7. 1,761 __1,800__   8. 955 __1,000__

Draw two coin combinations for each amount. Answers will vary.

9. 68¢ Possible answers: 10. $1.00 Possible answers:
   Q Q D N P P P   Q Q Q Q
   D D D D D D N P P P   D D D D D D D D D D

11. $0.34 Possible answers: 12. 59¢ Possible answers:
    D D D P P P P   Q Q N P P P P
    Q N P P P P   Q D D D P P P P

13. 92¢ Possible answers: 14. $0.87 Possible answers:
    Q Q Q D N P P   Q Q Q D P P
    Q Q D D D D P P   Q D D D D D D P P

74 UNIT 3 LESSON 5   Represent Money Amounts in Different Ways

Homework and Remembering page 74

Home or School Activity

Social Studies Connection

Name That Face Have students find out whose face appears on $1, $5, $10, and $20 bills. Challenge them to also find any other historical information on money.

Make Change

Lesson Objective
● **Use the Counting On strategy to make change from purchases.**

Vocabulary
change

The Day at a Glance

Today's Goals	Materials	Math Talk
Quick Practice Count coin values.	Overhead projector and coins (optional)	In today's activities, the students are involved in discussion as they
1 Teaching the Lesson A1: Count on to make change. A2: Act out real-life shopping situations.	Play money Store flyers Student Activity Book pages 139–140	► describe shopping experiences they have had
2 Extending the Lesson ► Differentiated Instruction	Homework and Remembering pages 75–76	► identify two meanings for the word *change*
3 Homework and Spiral Review	Math Journals *Ox-Cart Man* by Donald Hall (Puffin Books, 1983)	► share their solution strategies for making change

Quick Practice

 5 MINUTES **Goal:** Count coin values.

Counting Coins: Write a sequence of quarters (Qs), dimes (Ds), nickels (Ns), and pennies (Ps) on the board, in that order. Point to the coins in order as the class counts on to find the total.

Q Q Q Q Q D D N N N P

Teacher: Count on to find the total amount.
Class: 25¢, 50¢, 75¢, $1.00, $1.25, $1.35, $1.45, $1.50, $1.55, $1.60, $1.65, $1.66.

Then, add coins to or erase coins from the sequence, and the class counts again. Repeat this several times.

Class Management

This is the first time this activity is used. Lead the activity yourself today so students understand how it works. Tomorrow a Student Leader can take over.

① Teaching the Lesson

Use the Counting On Strategy

 15 MINUTES

Goal: Count on to make change.

Materials: Student Activity Book page 139, play money (two $5 bills, five $1 bills, 8 quarters, 10 dimes, 10 nickels, and 10 pennies per student) or, overhead projector and coins, Play Money (Copymaster M40)

 NCTM Standards:
Number and Operations
Problem Solving
Communication
Connections

Teaching Note

Language and Vocabulary The word *purchase* is used frequently in this lesson. Some students, especially English learners, might not understand its meaning as both a verb and a noun. Tell students that this word means *to buy* as well as *the item or items bought.*

▶ Share Shopping Experiences | WHOLE CLASS |

Math Talk Have students talk about getting change back.

● When does someone get money back from a cashier? When they have paid more money than the items cost.

● What word do we use for the money we get back when we buy something? change

Discuss the two ways people use the word *change* when talking about money.

● People sometimes think of *change* as small amounts of money. For example, a person might say that a few coins are "loose change."

● The money a person gets back when they pay more than the total cost is also called *change.*

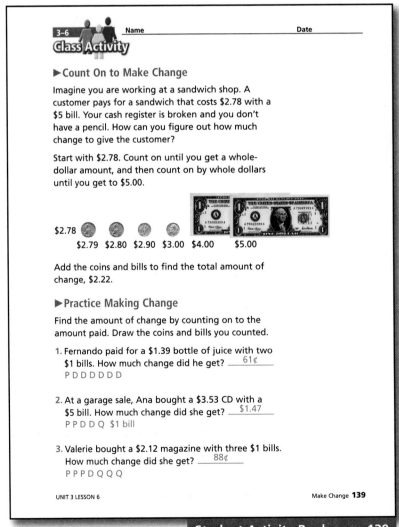

Student Activity Book page 139

▶ Count On to Make Change WHOLE CLASS

Have a student volunteer read aloud the shopping situation in the box on Student Activity Book page 139. Allow several students to share their ideas on how to figure out how much change the customer should get back.

Have students pass out sets of play money or Copymaster M40 to the class and then read through the Counting On strategy with students. As you read aloud the steps for counting on, students should count on with their money.

● Many cashiers make change by counting on from the total amount the customer pays. Let's try this strategy for this example. Use your coins to count out the change with me.

● What was the total cost for the sandwich? $2.78 How did the customer pay? with a $5.00 bill

● First, let's start by counting on 2 pennies to get to a nice even amount with no extra cents. $2.79, $2.80

● Now we want to count on to get to the next whole dollar. We can add 2 dimes. $2.90, $3.00

● Finally, we'll add on whole dollars until we reach $5.00. $4.00, $5.00

● Now, look at the money we counted. What is the total amount of change we gave back to the customer? 2 dollars and 22 cents. That's $2.22

Explain to students they don't have to use exactly this order. For example, they could have counted on 2 dimes, then 2 pennies, and then 2 dollars. The important thing is to start with the purchase price and count on to the total amount the customer paid.

▶ Practice Making Change INDIVIDUALS

You may want to solve the first word problem as a class, and then use the **Solve and Discuss** structure for problems 2 and 3.

Alternate Approach

Visual Learners While you demonstrate the Counting On strategy for making change, you may wish to use a transparent set of money on the overhead projector so students can check that they are counting on correctly. If you have large coins, you could also have student volunteers count on to find the change.

Differentiated Instruction

Extra Help Making change can be a tough skill for many students. You might want to begin by having students make change by counting on to $1.00. Give students several examples until you feel they are ready to make change for greater amounts.

Activity 2

Run a Shop

 30 MINUTES

Goal: Act out real-life shopping situations.

Materials: Student Activity Book page 140

✔ **NCTM Standards:**
Number and Operations
Problem Solving
Connections
Communication

The Learning Classroom

Building Concepts When students practice math concepts in real-life situations, they will conceptualize and take ownership of their learning. To create this environment, have students make and use their own lists of items and prices. The price of each item should be less than $3.00. Students can also set up shopping learning centers. They can put price tags on small items they find around the classroom and practice buying items and making change with other classmates.

✔ Ongoing Assessment

Observe students as they complete Student Activity Book page 140. Check to make sure students are adding their items correctly. Be sure students are starting from the total amount of their purchases and counting on to the amount paid. Check to see if they are beginning by adding pennies to get to the 5¢ mark, then adding nickels if necessary, then dimes, and so on. Remind student customers that they should always count their change to be sure it is correct.

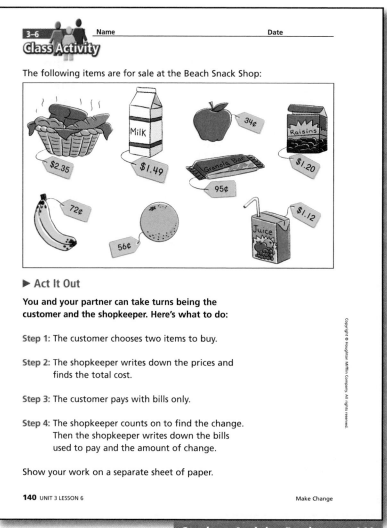

3–6
Class Activity
Name _____ Date _____

The following items are for sale at the Beach Snack Shop:

Milk $1.49 · $2.35 · 34¢ · Raisins $1.20 · Granola Bar 95¢ · 72¢ · 56¢ · Juice $1.12

▶ **Act It Out**

You and your partner can take turns being the customer and the shopkeeper. Here's what to do:

Step 1: The customer chooses two items to buy.

Step 2: The shopkeeper writes down the prices and finds the total cost.

Step 3: The customer pays with bills only.

Step 4: The shopkeeper counts on to find the change. Then the shopkeeper writes down the bills used to pay and the amount of change.

Show your work on a separate sheet of paper.

140 UNIT 3 LESSON 6   Make Change

Student Activity Book page 140

▶ Act It Out PAIRS

Divide the class into pairs. You may wish to pair students who are skilled at working with coins with those who aren't.

Read aloud the instructions for Student Activity Book page 140 and make sure students know what to do. You may want to demonstrate a sales purchase, with a student playing the roles of the shopkeeper and customer. Allow students 25 minutes or so to shop, and then choose a few pairs to demonstrate one of their purchases. They should tell what items were purchased, how they found the total, and how they determined how much change to give.

② Extending the Lesson

Intervention
for students having difficulty

PAIRS

The Yard Sale

Materials: play money (8 quarters, 10 dimes, 10 nickels, 8 pennies per student pair)

Have students make a list of items for sale at a flea market or garage sale. No price should be more than 50¢. Have students draw five of the items mentioned that cost 50¢ or less on their MathBoards with a price tag for each one.

Tell students that they are going to be buying and selling these items. Students take turns being the customer, who pays for items with 50¢, and the shopkeeper, who gives correct change for the purchase by using the counting-on strategy. When you feel students have mastered this activity, change it so the customer pays with $1.00.

On Level
for students having success

SMALL GROUPS

Shopping

Materials: store flyers, play money (two $5 bills, five $1 bills, 8 quarters, 10 dimes, 10 nickels, and 10 pennies per student)

Have each group take one store flyer. Each group needs to decide which student is the cashier for the group and which students are the customers. Explain that each customer selects three items from the flyer and the cashier adds the prices for these items. The customers give the cashier a whole-dollar amount and then the cashier gives the change. All customers should check that the correct amount of change is given back. Students switch roles and start the shopping again.

Challenge
for students seeking a challenge

PAIRS

Larger Purchases

Materials: store flyers, play money (two $20 bills, two $10 bills, two $5 bills, five $1 bills, 8 quarters, 10 dimes, 10 nickels, and 10 pennies per student pair)

Give a flyer to each pair of students. You may wish to use flyers that have larger item prices. One student in each pair is a customer and the other student is the cashier. The customer picks three items from the flyer and the cashier adds the prices of these items. The customer gives the cashier only bills to pay for the items. The cashier gives back change and the customer checks to see if it is correct. Students switch roles and repeat.

Also Use
Challenge Master for 3-6

 Math Writing Prompt

Intervention

Why Change?
As a customer, why is important to know how to make change?

 Math Writing Prompt

On Level

From Least to Greatest
When people count change, they often start with the coin of least value. Why is this so?

 Math Writing Prompt

Challenge

Fewest Number of Bills and Coins
Jon buys a toy for $3.12. He pays for it with $5. He estimates and says he should get $2 and some coins back. Is he correct? Explain.

Make Change **307**

③ Homework and Spiral Review

3-6
Homework **Goal:** Additional Practice

This Homework page provides more practice with making change.

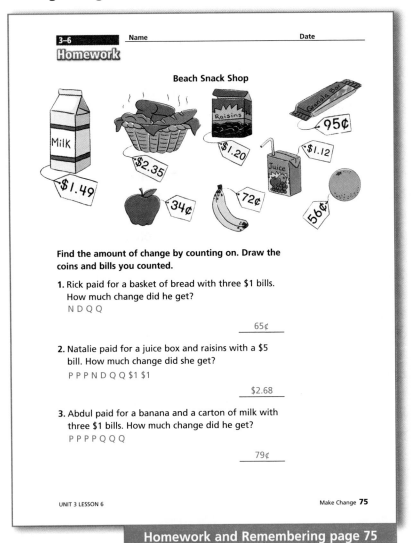

3-6 Name _____ Date _____
Homework

Beach Snack Shop

Milk $1.49 $2.35   Raisins   95¢
34¢ $1.20   Juice $1.12   72¢   56¢

Find the amount of change by counting on. Draw the coins and bills you counted.

1. Rick paid for a basket of bread with three $1 bills. How much change did he get?
   N D Q Q
   _____ 65¢

2. Natalie paid for a juice box and raisins with a $5 bill. How much change did she get?
   P P P N D Q Q $1 $1
   _____ $2.68

3. Abdul paid for a banana and a carton of milk with three $1 bills. How much change did he get?
   P P P P Q Q Q
   _____ 79¢

UNIT 3 LESSON 6   Make Change **75**

Homework and Remembering page 75

3-6
Remembering **Goal:** Spiral Review

This Remembering page would be appropriate anytime after today's lesson.

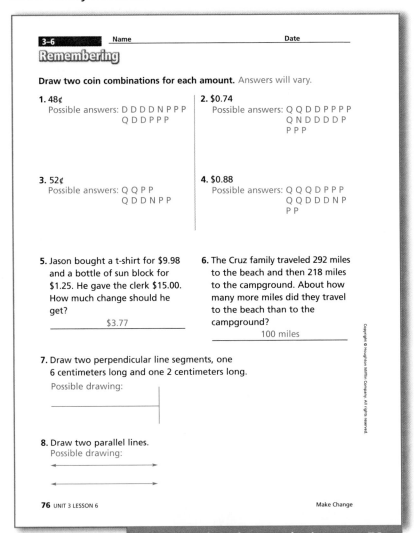

3-6 Name _____ Date _____
Remembering

Draw two coin combinations for each amount. Answers will vary.

1. 48¢
   Possible answers: D D D D N P P P
   Q D D P P P

2. $0.74
   Possible answers: Q Q D D P P P P
   Q N D D D D P
   P P P

3. 52¢
   Possible answers: Q Q P P
   Q D D N P P

4. $0.88
   Possible answers: Q Q Q D P P P
   Q Q D D D N P
   P P

5. Jason bought a t-shirt for $9.98 and a bottle of sun block for $1.25. He gave the clerk $15.00. How much change should he get?
   _____ $3.77

6. The Cruz family traveled 292 miles to the beach and then 218 miles to the campground. About how many more miles did they travel to the beach than to the campground?
   _____ 100 miles

7. Draw two perpendicular line segments, one 6 centimeters long and one 2 centimeters long.
   Possible drawing:

8. Draw two parallel lines.
   Possible drawing:

76 UNIT 3 LESSON 6   Make Change

Homework and Remembering page 76

Home and School Connection

 Social Studies Connection

Bartering Ask students if they have ever bought something without paying money for it. Tell them that before there was money, people traded things instead of buying them. A farmer might trade chickens for fabric to make clothes. This is called *bartering* or *trading*.

Have students read the *Ox Cart Man* by Donald Hall to learn about bartering and shopping practices in earlier times.

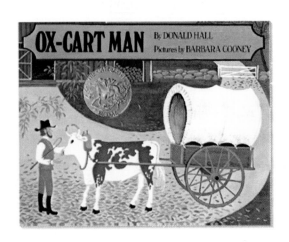

Round Money Amounts

Lesson Objectives

● Round money amounts to the nearest dime or dollar.

● Make estimates in real-world situations involving money.

Vocabulary
round
estimate
rounding rules

The Day at a Glance

Today's Goals	Materials	Math Talk
Quick Practice Add the values of different coins to find a total.	MathBoard materials	In today's activities, the students are involved in discussion as they
1 Teaching the Lesson **A1:** Round money amounts to the nearest dollar or dime. **A2:** Estimate sums involving money.	Index cards Student Activity Book pages 141–144 Homework and Remembering pages 77–78	► create place-value drawings to explain when to round up or down ► decide whether to round up or down to make an estimate
2 Extending the Lesson ► Going Further: More Estimation Strategies ► Differentiated Instruction	Math Journals Quick Quiz 2 (Assessment Guide)	► consider how to make estimates involving money to be sure they have enough money to cover the actual cost
3 Homework and Spiral Review		

Quick Practice

 5 MINUTES   **Goal:** Add the values of different coins to find a total.

Counting Coins The Student Leader writes a sequence of quarters (Qs), dimes (Ds), nickels (Ns), and pennies (Ps) on the board, in that order. The leader points to the letters in order as the class counts on to find the total. (See Unit 3 Lesson 6.)

Q Q Q Q D D D N N P P P

The leader should repeat this several times, adding coins to or erasing coins from the sequence.

Class Management

The Student Leader should remind the class to pause after saying each subtotal. This allows enough time for all students to calculate the total. If necessary, have the leader use a signal that tells the class when it is time to answer.

① Teaching the Lesson

Round to the Nearest Dime or Dollar

 20 MINUTES

Goal: Round money amounts to the nearest dollar or dime.

Materials: MathBoard materials, Student Activity Book page 141

 NCTM Standards:
Number and Operations
Problem Solving
Representation

Teaching Note

Language and Vocabulary
Students may not initially grasp how the *dimes place* and the *tens place* are used interchangeably in this activity. Explain that it is acceptable to use the term *dimes place* when talking about how to round money amounts. If students are confused, reinforce the connection between a dime and ten.

3-7
Class Activity

Name _____ Date _____

▶ **Round Amounts of Money**

Round each amount first to the nearest dime and then to the nearest dollar.

		Rounded to the nearest dime	Rounded to the nearest dollar
1.	$3.62	$3.60	$4.00
2.	$5.09	$5.10	$5.00
3.	$1.25	$1.30	$1.00
4.	$2.99	$3.00	$3.00
5.	$7.50	$7.50	$8.00

Solve each problem.   *Show your work.*

6. Carl spent $3.35 on a sandwich and $1.85 on a drink. Estimate the total amount he spent by rounding the prices to the nearest dollar and adding.
   about $5.00

7. Rose spent 85¢ on a pen, 32¢ on an eraser, and 78¢ on a pencil sharpener. Estimate the total amount she spent by rounding the prices to the nearest dime and adding.
   about $2.00

8. Aisha spent $4.12 on a book, $3.65 on a magazine, and $1.75 on a greeting card. Estimate the total amount she spent by rounding the prices to the nearest dollar and adding.
   about $10.00

UNIT 3 LESSON 7   Round Money Amounts **141**

Student Activity Book page 141

▶ Round Amounts of Money [WHOLE CLASS]

Have students look at exercise 1 on Student Activity Book page 141. Ask students how they would round $3.62 to the nearest dime. Possible response: First I looked at the digit to the right of the dimes place. It is a 2, which means 2¢. Since 2¢ is less than half of a dime, we round down to $3.60.

If necessary, write $3.62 on the left side of the board and underline the 6. Ask students what the dime amounts above and below this amount are and write them on the board. $3.60 and $3.70 Have a student create place value drawings for the three numbers and explain how the drawings show that we should round down.

$3.70
$3.62
$3.60

Now ask students how to round $3.62 to the nearest dollar. See the possible explanation below.

- First I looked at the digits to the right of the dollars place. They are 6 and 2, which means 6 dimes and 2 pennies, or 62¢. Since 62¢ is more than half of a dollar, we round up to $4.00.

If necessary, write $3.62 on the board. Then, ask the students what the dollar amounts above and below $3.62 are. $3.00 and $4.00 Write them on the board, above and below the $3.62. Again, have a student create place-value drawings and explain how the drawings show that we should round up to $4.00.

Have students work independently to complete exercises 2–5.

Review Rules of Rounding Remind students of these rules when rounding to the nearest dime:

- If the amount is equal to or more than half of the next ten (or whole dime amount), round up.

- If the amount is less than half of the next ten (or whole dime amount), round down.

Remind students of these rules when rounding to the nearest dollar:

- If the amount is equal to or more than half of the next whole dollar amount, round up.

- If the amount is less than half of the next whole dollar amount, round down.

Have students work independently on problems 6–8, which ask them to estimate sums of money by rounding to the nearest dime or dollar.

Differentiated Instruction

Extra Help Students may need a brief review of the halfway points used when rounding. Explain that when rounding to the nearest ten, if the digit to the right of the tens place is 5 (the halfway point) or higher, you should round up to the next ten. Similarly, when rounding to the nearest dime, if the digit to the right of the dimes place is 5 cents (the halfway point) or higher, you should round up to the next dime. When rounding to the nearest dollar, students should remember that 50 cents is the halfway point.

✓ Ongoing Assessment

Make sure students understand the concept of rounding to the nearest dime or dollar.

▶ What are the dime amounts above and below $4.53?

▶ Which of the two amounts will you round to? Why?

▶ What are the dollar amounts above and below $4.53?

▶ Which of the two amounts will you round to? Why?

Activity 2

Make Estimates Involving Money

 35 MINUTES

Goal: Estimate sums involving money.

Materials: MathBoard materials, Student Activity Book pages 142–143

 NCTM Standards:
Numbers and Operations
Problem Solving

The Learning Classroom

Building Concepts When students solve real-world problems or act out shopping situations, they learn when to round prices up or down. When students make these connections between math and their everyday lives, they see a purpose for their learning.

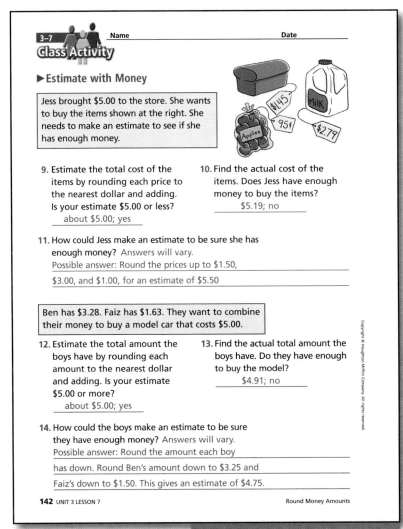

3-7 Name _____ Date _____

Class Activity

▶ **Estimate with Money**

Jess brought $5.00 to the store. She wants to buy the items shown at the right. She needs to make an estimate to see if she has enough money.

$1.45   95¢ $2.79

9. Estimate the total cost of the items by rounding each price to the nearest dollar and adding. Is your estimate $5.00 or less?
   about $5.00; yes

10. Find the actual cost of the items. Does Jess have enough money to buy the items?
    $5.19; no

11. How could Jess make an estimate to be sure she has enough money? Answers will vary.
    Possible answer: Round the prices up to $1.50,
    $3.00, and $1.00, for an estimate of $5.50

Ben has $3.28. Faiz has $1.63. They want to combine their money to buy a model car that costs $5.00.

12. Estimate the total amount the boys have by rounding each amount to the nearest dollar and adding. Is your estimate $5.00 or more?
    about $5.00; yes

13. Find the actual total amount the boys have. Do they have enough to buy the model?
    $4.91; no

14. How could the boys make an estimate to be sure they have enough money? Answers will vary.
    Possible answer: Round the amount each boy
    has down. Round Ben's amount down to $3.25 and
    Faiz's down to $1.50. This gives an estimate of $4.75.

142 UNIT 3 LESSON 7   Round Money Amounts

Student Activity Book page 142

▶ Estimate with Money [WHOLE CLASS]

Using the **Solve and Discuss** structure, have students solve problems 9–11. Discuss the fact that if Jess estimates by rounding to the nearest dollar, she may think she has enough money, when she actually does not.

Help students see that if Jess rounds all the prices up, she can be sure her estimate is more than the actual total. Students may suggest rounding up to the next dollar or rounding up to other numbers that are easy to add (for example, $1.50 for $1.45).

Math Talk Discuss with the class the benefits of rounding the cost of items up in problems involving money. Students may suggest that:

● overestimating the cost guarantees that you'll know quickly and accurately whether or not you have enough money to make purchases.

● rounding can make it easier to add a series of prices or money amounts.

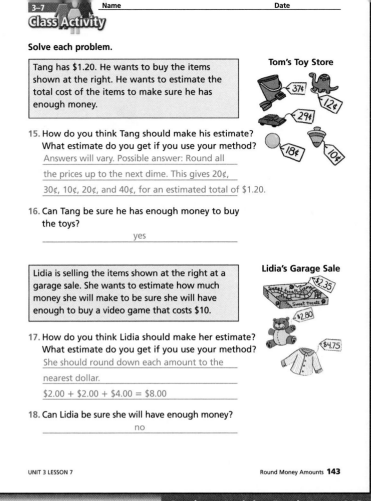

3-7 Name _____ Date _____

Class Activity

Solve each problem.

Tang has $1.20. He wants to buy the items shown at the right. He wants to estimate the total cost of the items to make sure he has enough money.

Tom's Toy Store

37¢   12¢
29¢
18¢   10¢

15. How do you think Tang should make his estimate? What estimate do you get if you use your method?

Answers will vary. Possible answer: Round all
the prices up to the next dime. This gives 20¢,
30¢, 10¢, 20¢, and 40¢, for an estimated total of $1.20.

16. Can Tang be sure he has enough money to buy the toys?

yes

Lidia is selling the items shown at the right at a garage sale. She wants to estimate how much money she will make to be sure she will have enough to buy a video game that costs $10.

Lidia's Garage Sale

$2.35
$2.80
$4.75

17. How do you think Lidia should make her estimate? What estimate do you get if you use your method?

She should round down each amount to the
nearest dollar.
$2.00 + $2.00 + $4.00 = $8.00

18. Can Lidia be sure she will have enough money?

no

Round Money Amounts **143**

Student Activity Book page 143

Next have students solve problems 12–14. In this situation, the two boys need to round down to be sure they have enough money. Again, students may suggest rounding down to the next dollar or rounding down to other numbers that are easy to add (for example, $3.25 for $3.28, or $1.50 for $1.63).

Have students solve problems 15–18 on Student Activity Book page 143. In these problems, students will again need to determine when it is beneficial to round up and when it is better to round down.

Watch For! If students do not fully understand the benefits of estimating by rounding all amounts down or all amounts up, they may simply add the money amounts to find a total, and forgo rounding altogether. Explain that it is best to round prices up when you already know how much money there is to spend (as in problems 11 and 15). On the other hand, it is best to round money amounts down when you don't know if you have enough money (as in problems 14 and 17).

Class Management

Looking Ahead At the end of this unit, students will have the opportunity to work on Data Projects as part of the activities in Data Day (see pages 385–390). The individual and class projects have students working with nutrition labels and can tabs, so you may want to remind students to continue collecting these things at home. Remember, these tabs will also be used in Estimation Day (see Unit 7).

Quick Quiz

See Assessment Guide for Unit 3 Quick Quiz 2.

Round Money Amounts **313**

Goal: Estimate by using compatible numbers and using mental math.

Materials: Student Activity Book page 144

✓ **NCTM Standards:**
Numbers and Operations
Problem Solving

▶ Use Mental Math to Estimate

WHOLE CLASS

Write these money amounts on the board:

$2.89

$1.69

$4.29

Explain that you can use mental math to make a quick estimate by looking for amounts of cents that when added will be close to $1 or for amounts of cents that are close to $1.

● Are there any amounts of cents close to $1? Yes, 89¢

● Are there any amounts of cents that when added are close to $1? Yes, 69¢ and 29¢.

Summarize their thinking by writing this on the board.

$2.89 — about $1

$1.69
        ⟩ about $1
+ $4.29

$7 + $2 = $9

▶ Different Ways to Estimate with Money

$3.31   69¢ $5.89

Estimate the total cost of the notebook, marker, and baseball cap using the strategies given below.

Round to the nearest dollar	Use Mental Math

1. $3.00
      $1.00
 + $6.00
      $10.00
	2. $3.31 ⟍ about $1
	     $0.69 ⟋
	 + $5.89 — about $1
	 $8 + $2 = $10

Complete.

3. What is the actual cost of the notebook, marker, and baseball cap? Use your estimates above to check that your answer is reasonable.
$9.89

4. What estimation strategy would you use to estimate the cost of several items when shopping? Explain. Answers will vary. Possible answer: Round up to the nearest dollar even if price is under halfway to be sure I'll have enough money.

144 UNIT 3 LESSON 7   Round Money Amounts

Student Activity Book page 144

▶ Different Ways to Estimate with Money INDIVIDUALS

Have students look at the items at the top of Student Activity Book page 144. Explain that they will use rounding and mental math to estimate the total cost of the items.

Give students a few minutes to complete the page. Use **Solve and Discuss,** and have students demonstrate how they estimated, checked the reasonableness of an answer, and decided what strategy they would use to be sure they have enough money when shopping.

Intervention
for students having difficulty

INDIVIDUALS

Money Maker

Materials: MathBoard materials

Have students write 4 different 3-digit numbers on their MathBoards. To help them round each number to the nearest ten and hundred, they should write the tens and hundreds numbers that come before and after the number as shown below. Then students should decide how to round the number to the nearest ten and hundred and circle the two rounded numbers.

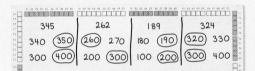

Once students have circled the rounded numbers, they can insert the decimal points to see that rounding money amounts is done the same way as rounding 3-digit numbers.

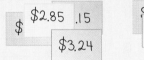

On Level
for students having success

PAIRS

Money Match Up

Materials: index cards (16)

Have each student take 8 index cards. On 4 of the index cards, they should write any money amount that doesn't end in a 0 and is less than $4.99. On the other 4 index cards, they write the amount of money rounded to the nearest dime and nearest dollar.

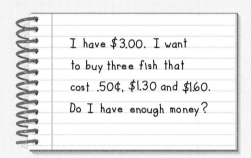

Once the 16 cards are created, students should shuffle them and place them face down in a 4 × 4 array. Players take turns randomly selecting two cards to try to make a money match. If the cards do not match, students should flip them back over and the next player tries to make a match. Once all the matches have been made, the player with the most money matches wins!

Challenge
for students seeking a challenge

PAIRS

Round Up or Down?

Have one student write a word problem that involves rounding two money amounts to estimate how much money someone has to buy something. The other student writes a problem involving finding the estimated cost of some items. Ask partners to switch problems and determine whether it is better to round up or down to make the estimate for that situation.

> I have $3.00. I want to buy three fish that cost .50¢, $1.30 and $1.60. Do I have enough money?

Also Use
Challenge Master for 3-7

 Math Writing Prompt

Intervention

Explain Your Thinking
Explain how you would round $5.55 to the nearest dollar?

 Math Writing Prompt

On Level

Explain a Rule
Round $1.77 to the nearest dime. Write a rule that could be used to round to the nearest dime.

Math Writing Prompt

Challenge

Generalize
Give an example of when you would round both addends down when estimating a sum of money.

③ Homework and Spiral Review

Homework **Goal:** Additional Practice

This Homework page gives students practice in rounding money amounts.

Remembering **Goal:** Spiral Review

This Remembering page would be appropriate anytime after today's lesson.

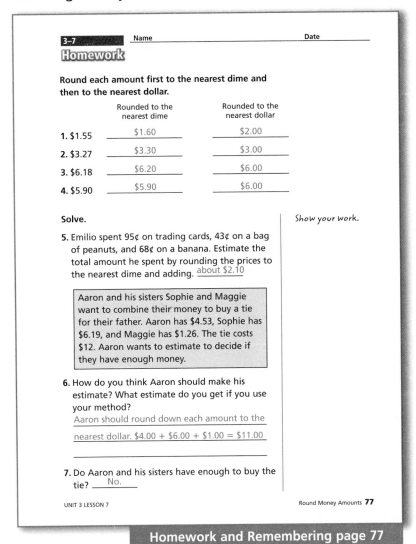

3-7 Name _____ Date _____
Homework

Round each amount first to the nearest dime and then to the nearest dollar.

	Rounded to the nearest dime	Rounded to the nearest dollar
1. $1.55	$1.60	$2.00
2. $3.27	$3.30	$3.00
3. $6.18	$6.20	$6.00
4. $5.90	$5.90	$6.00

Solve.

Show your work.

5. Emilio spent 95¢ on trading cards, 43¢ on a bag of peanuts, and 68¢ on a banana. Estimate the total amount he spent by rounding the prices to the nearest dime and adding. about $2.10

> Aaron and his sisters Sophie and Maggie want to combine their money to buy a tie for their father. Aaron has $4.53, Sophie has $6.19, and Maggie has $1.26. The tie costs $12. Aaron wants to estimate to decide if they have enough money.

6. How do you think Aaron should make his estimate? What estimate do you get if you use your method?
   Aaron should round down each amount to the
   nearest dollar. $4.00 + $6.00 + $1.00 = $11.00

7. Do Aaron and his sisters have enough to buy the tie? _____ No. _____

UNIT 3 LESSON 7   Round Money Amounts **77**

Homework and Remembering page 77

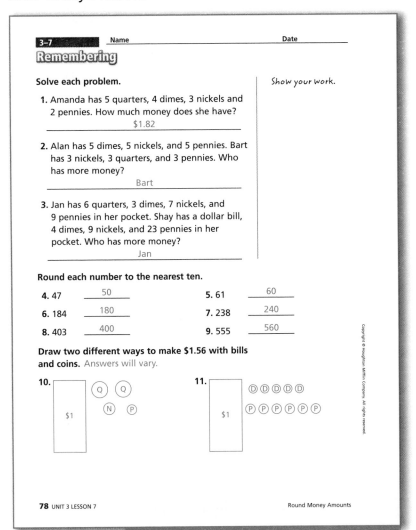

3-7 Name _____ Date _____
Remembering

Solve each problem.

Show your work.

1. Amanda has 5 quarters, 4 dimes, 3 nickels and 2 pennies. How much money does she have?
   $1.82

2. Alan has 5 dimes, 5 nickels, and 5 pennies. Bart has 3 nickels, 3 quarters, and 3 pennies. Who has more money?
   Bart

3. Jan has 6 quarters, 3 dimes, 7 nickels, and 9 pennies in her pocket. Shay has a dollar bill, 4 dimes, 9 nickels, and 23 pennies in her pocket. Who has more money?
   Jan

Round each number to the nearest ten.

4. 47	50	5. 61	60
6. 184	180	7. 238	240
8. 403	400	9. 555	560

Draw two different ways to make $1.56 with bills and coins. Answers will vary.

10.   11.

78 UNIT 3 LESSON 7   Round Money Amounts

Homework and Remembering page 78

Home or School Activity

Real-World Connection

Shopping Spree First, have the students decide how much play money under $50 they would like to spend on a shopping spree. Have them record the amount and the prices of several items they would like to buy from a local store flyer. Next, they should estimate the cost of the items to decide if they have enough money. Then they check to see if they are correct by finding the actual cost.

Ask Addition and Subtraction Questions from Tables

Lesson Objectives

- Interpret information in tables.
- Write and solve problems based on tables with data.

Vocabulary
table
row
column
cell

The Day at a Glance

Today's Goals	Materials	Math Talk
Quick Practice Count coin values.	MathBoard materials	In today's activities, the students are involved in discussion as they
① Teaching the Lesson A1: Understand how information is organized in a table. A2: Use information to ask and answer questions in tables.	Transparency of Student Activity Book page 145 and overhead projector (optional) Sticky notes Sheet protectors	▶ talk about their experiences with charts and tables ▶ use data in tables to ask addition and subtraction questions
② Extending the Lesson ▶ Going Further: Patterns in Tables ▶ Differentiated Instruction	Student Activity Book pages 145–148	
③ Homework and Spiral Review	Homework and Remembering pages 79–80 Math Journals	

Quick Practice

🕐 **5 MINUTES** **Goal:** Count coin values.

Counting Coins The Student Leader writes a sequence of quarters (Qs), dimes (Ds), nickels (Ns), and pennies (Ps) on the board, in that order. The leader points to the coins in order as the class counts on to find the total.

    Q Q Q Q Q Q D N N N P P

Leader: (Pointing to the coins) Count on to find the total amount.

Class: 25¢, 50¢, 75¢, $1.00, $1.25, $1.50, $1.60, $165, $1.70, $1.75, $1.76, $1.77

The Student Leader should repeat this several times, adding coins to or erasing coins from the sequence.

Teaching the Lesson

Introduce Tables

 15 MINUTES

Goal: Understand how information is organized in a table.

Materials: Student Activity Book page 145, transparency of Student Activity Book page 145 (optional), overhead projector (optional)

✔ **NCTM Standards:**
Number and Operations
Data Analysis and Probability

Teaching Note

Language and Vocabulary
Students often have trouble remembering the distinction between *row* and *column.* To help them remember, gesture from left to right when you talk about rows, and up and down when you talk about columns. To further reinforce that columns are vertical, you may also want to have students connect columns in a table with columns in architecture.

 Class Management

You may want to make a transparency of Student Activity Book page 145 and display it during this discussion.

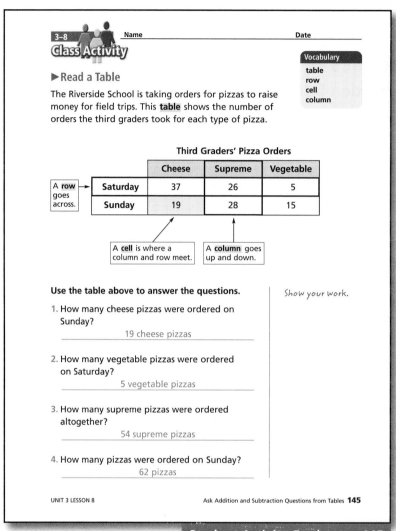

Student Activity Book page 145

Transcription of Student Activity Book page 145:

3–8 **Class Activity** Name _____ Date _____

▶Read a Table

Vocabulary
table
row
cell
column

The Riverside School is taking orders for pizzas to raise money for field trips. This **table** shows the number of orders the third graders took for each type of pizza.

Third Graders' Pizza Orders

	Cheese	Supreme	Vegetable
Saturday	37	26	5
Sunday	19	28	15

A **row** goes across.
A **cell** is where a column and row meet.
A **column** goes up and down.

Use the table above to answer the questions.

Show your work.

1. How many cheese pizzas were ordered on Sunday?
   19 cheese pizzas

2. How many vegetable pizzas were ordered on Saturday?
   5 vegetable pizzas

3. How many supreme pizzas were ordered altogether?
   54 supreme pizzas

4. How many pizzas were ordered on Sunday?
   62 pizzas

UNIT 3 LESSON 8   Ask Addition and Subtraction Questions from Tables **145**

▶ Read a Table WHOLE CLASS

123 Math Talk Ask students where they have seen tables and charts. Possible responses: newspapers, magazines, nutrition labels, textbooks

Turn students' attention to the *Pizza Orders* table on Student Activity Book page 145. Ask students to explain what the table shows.

Explain that tables are arranged in *rows* and *columns,* and ask students to run their fingers across the row for Saturday.

● **What do the numbers in the Saturday row tell us?** how many of each pizza type was sold on Saturday

Next, have students run their fingers down the column for Supreme pizza.

● **What do the numbers in the column labeled *Supreme* tell us?** the number of Supreme pizzas sold each day

Explain that the rectangles where a column and row meet are called *cells*. Have students put one finger on *Sunday* and another on *Cheese*. Ask them to slide their fingers across and down until they meet. If you are using a transparency, demonstrate as students follow along.

- What number is in this cell? 19

- What does this number tell us? The number of cheese pizzas that sold on Sunday.

Have students practice finding particular cells.

- Can someone explain how to find how many Supreme pizzas were sold on Saturday? Move one finger from Supreme and the other from Saturday.

- Find the cell that contains the number 5. What does this number tell us? The number of vegetable pizzas sold on Saturday.

Give students a few minutes to answer questions 1–4, then discuss the answers.

▶ Create Your Own WHOLE CLASS

Have a volunteer choose two cells in the table and identify each cell for the class by saying both the day and the pizza type. Ask students to mark the two cells lightly in pencil in their books. Mark the cells on the transparency if you are using one.

Ask if anyone can suggest an addition question based on these two cells. For example, if the student chose the number of cheese pizzas sold on Saturday and the number of cheese pizzas sold on Sunday, the following is a possible question:

- How many cheese pizzas did the third graders sell over the weekend?

Have another volunteer explain how he or she would find the answer to the question. (Do not require the student to actually find the answer.)

Now ask if anyone can think of a subtraction question based on the same two cells. The following is a possible question:

- How many more cheese pizzas did the third graders sell on Saturday than on Sunday?

Again, have a student explain how he or she would find the answer. Repeat this process a few times, with different volunteers choosing the cells and suggesting the questions.

① Teaching the Lesson (continued)

Activity 2

Write and Answer Addition and Subtraction Questions

 35 MINUTES

Goal: Use information to ask and answer questions in tables.

Materials: Student Activity Book page 146, sticky notes

 NCTM Standards:
Number and Operations
Algebra
Data Analysis and Probability
Communication

Differentiated Instruction

Extra Help When answering addition or subtraction questions some students may have trouble remembering which cell to refer to. To help them remember, have them mark the cells with small sticky notes that remove easily. When they have answered the questions, they can remove the sticky note and use them to mark other cells.

3–8
Class Activity

Name _____ Date _____

▶Use a Table

This table shows the number of animals a veterinarian treated over three months.

Animals Treated

	Dogs	Cats	Birds	Reptiles	All Animals
January	68	118	25	11	222
February	94	106	8	19	227
March	122	77	19	26	244
3-Month Total	284	301	52	56	693

5. Fill in the total for each column and row.

6. Write two addition questions about this table.
   Answers will vary.
   _____
   _____
   _____

7. Write two subtraction questions about this table.
   Answers will vary.
   _____
   _____
   _____
   _____

146 UNIT 3 LESSON 8   Ask Addition and Subtraction Questions from Tables

Student Activity Book page 146

▶ Use a Table [WHOLE CLASS]

Have students read the table on Student Activity Book page 146 and encourage a volunteer to explain the table. Ask questions like the ones below to make sure students understand how the table is organized.

● How many reptiles did the vet treat in March? 26

● How many cats did the vet treat in February? 106

Point out that the bottom row, *3-Month Total,* and the last column, *All Animals,* are not filled in and prompt students to explain the purpose of the blank cells in the table.

● What information belongs in the bottom row? the total number of each type of animal treated over the 3-month period

● How can you find the number that goes at the bottom of the *Dogs* column? Add 68, 94, and 122.

- What information belongs in the last column? the total number of animals treated each month

- How can you find the number that goes at the end of the *January* row? Add 68, 118, 25, and 11.

Direct students' attention to the blank cell in the lower right corner.

- What information goes in this cell? the total number of animals (all types) treated over the 3-month period

Give students a few minutes to complete exercise 5, finding the totals and filling in the blank row and column. Discuss the results with the class and have students explain the two ways to find the overall total.

Have students write addition and subtraction questions about this table in exercises 6 and 7. To demonstrate, ask a volunteer to suggest an addition question, or suggest one yourself. Here is one example:

- In January, how many dogs and cats did the vet treat altogether?

Have a student explain how he or she would find the answer.

Have students trade papers to answer each other's questions for exercises 6 and 7. Then have them return the papers and check each other's work using Student Activity Book page 146. For a sample classroom dialogue, see **Math Talk in Action.** If time allows, choose students to share the questions they wrote.

 Math Talk in Action

Amit: How many of the animals treated in February were not dogs?

Rebecca: I know that the vet treated 227 animals in February, and 94 of the animals were dogs. So 227 − 94 is 133. 133 of the animals treated in February were not dogs.

Amit: How did you know that only 94 of the 227 animals treated were dogs?

Rebecca: I looked in the *February* row and the *Dog* column. That cell told me that 94 dogs were treated in February.

The Learning Classroom

Helping Community Having students work in pairs is a simple way to promote cooperation between advanced and struggling learners. Before partner work begins, the activity should be clearly outlined in a linear, step-by-step fashion. The more advanced learner in each pair may then mimic your actions and suggestions to better help his or her partner.

Differentiated Instruction

English Learners Trading papers to answer each other's questions for Exercises 6 and 7 is particularly helpful for **English Learners**. Whenever possible, have them share the word problems they create and explain their actions or ideas aloud to you or to a partner when solving problems.

②Extending the Lesson

Going Further: Patterns in Tables

▶Find a Pattern in a Table   WHOLE CLASS

Have students look at the tables on Student Activity page 147. Ask the following questions:

● **How are the first two tables different from the last table?** The first two tables have labels for columns, but not for rows.

● **What information does the first table show?** the number of blocks in a tower, starting at Row 1 through Row 7

● **How can you tell how many blocks should be in Row 6 of the block tower?** Subtract 1 block from the number of blocks in Row 5.

● **What pattern do you see in the number of blocks as a row is added to the block tower?** The number of blocks decreases by 1 block.

Have students use the pattern to complete the table and answer question 1. Discuss students' answers as a class.

Have students look at the second table.

● **What information does the second table show?** the amount of money in a savings account

● **How does the amount of money in the savings account change from one week to the next week?** It decreases.

● **What pattern do you see?** The amount of money in the account decreased $15 from Week 1 to Week 2 and Week 4 to Week 5.

Have students complete the second table and answer question 2. Discuss their answers as a class.

▶Find a Pattern in a Table

Complete the tables and answer the questions.

Blocks in a Tower

Row 1	Row 2	Row 3	Row 4	Row 5	Row 6	Row 7
8 Blocks	7 Blocks	6 Blocks	5 Blocks	4 Blocks	3 Blocks	2 Blocks

1. What pattern did you use to complete the table?
   I subtracted 1 block for each row.

Money in Savings Account

Week 1	Week 2	Week 3	Week 4	Week 5	Week 6	Week 7
$300	$285	$270	$255	$240	$225	$210

2. If the pattern continues, how much money do you predict will be in the savings account in week 8? Explain.
   $195; I subtracted $15.00 each week.

Water Level in Tank

	Hour 1	Hour 2	Hour 3	Hour 4	Hour 5	Hour 6
Tank A	4 in.	5 in.	6 in.	7 in.	8 in.	9 in.
Tank B	6 in.	8 in.	10 in.	12 in.	14 in.	16 in.

3. How would you describe the pattern for each tank?
   Tank A increases 1 in. per hour; Tank B increases
   2 in. per hour.

4. On the Back Create your own table with a pattern. Describe the pattern.

UNIT 3 LESSON 8   Ask Addition and Subtraction Questions from Tables **147**

Student Activity Book page 147

Using **Solve and Discuss**, complete the third table and answer question 3.

On the Back As time allows, have students share their own tables in exercise 4.

The Learning Classroom

Building Concepts Working with tables gives students the opportunity to experience addition and subtraction in an alternate context. Identifying patterns in the tables in this activity gives students practice in identifying and describing quantitative changes involving addition and subtraction.

Intervention
for students having difficulty

PAIRS

Topsy-Turvy Tables

Materials: sheet protectors, Student Activity Book page 147

Have students trace part of the outline of the third table on Student Activity page 147 using a sheet protector or transparency and name it *Garden Tool Sales.* Have them label the columns Thursday, Friday, and Saturday and label the rows *shovel* and *rake.* Have students make up numbers sold for each day and tool, and then fill in the cells. Next, have them draw a 2-column table with 3 rows. Ask students to complete the second table so that it contains exactly the same information as the first table.

Garden Tool Sales	Thursday	Friday	Saturday
shovel	13	12	16
rake	15	20	17

Garden Tool Sales	shovel	rake
Thursday	13	15
Friday	12	20
Saturday	16	17

Ask students to explain how the second table expresses the same information as the first table, even though it looks different.

Math Writing Prompt

Intervention

In Your Own Words
Explain the difference between rows and columns. Use a drawing to help you explain.

On Level
for students having success

PAIRS

What's Missing?

Have partners draw a 2-row, 3-column table, using information they make up about the number of students in Grades 3 and 4 whose favorite sport is baseball, basketball, or soccer. After they have completed the table, one partner should ask an addition or subtraction question about the data in the table. Have partners switch roles and repeat asking questions several times.

Favorite Sports	Baseball	Basketball	Soccer
Grade 3	29	24	14
Grade 4	22	23	25

Math Writing Prompt

On Level

Critical Thinking
Why do you think people use tables to organize data? Explain your thinking.

Challenge
for students seeking a challenge

INDIVIDUALS

This Table Shows . . .

Have students make up and write sentences about the numbers of tickets sold to a concert on Thursday and Friday by Mr. Simon's Class, Ms. Tran's class, and Mrs. Jackson's class. Have students make a table for this data and give it a title.

On Thursday, Mr. Simon's class sold 54 tickets to the concert, Ms. Tran's class sold 68, and Mrs. Jackson's class sold 57. On Friday, Mr. Simon's class sold 48 tickets, Ms. Tran's class sold 50, and Mrs Jackson's class sold 62.

Ticket Sales for Classes	Mr. Simon	Ms. Tran	Mrs. Jackson
Thursday	54	68	57
Friday	48	50	62

Then have partners ask each other questions about the data in the table that involve addition and subtraction.

Also Use
Challenge Master for 3-8

Math Writing Prompt

Challenge

Real-World Application
Think of a situation when you might use a table to display data. Is a table the best way to organize this information? Explain.

③ Homework and Spiral Review

3–8
Homework **Goal:** Additional Practice

This Homework page helps students use information in tables.

3–8
Remembering **Goal:** Spiral Review

This Remembering page would be appropriate anytime after today's lesson.

3–8 Name _____ Date _____
Homework

This table shows the number of tickets sold for the early and late showings of each movie at the Palace Theater last Saturday.

Saturday Ticket Sales

	Jungle Adventure	Hannah the Hero	Space Race
Early Show	72	109	143
Late Show	126	251	167

1. How many fewer tickets were sold for the early showing of *Jungle Adventure* than for the late showing?
54 tickets

2. How many more tickets were sold for the late showing of *Hannah the Hero* than for the late showing of *Space Race*?
84 tickets

This table shows the number of pizza, pasta, and salad orders at Luigi's Pizzeria last Tuesday and Wednesday.

Orders at Luigi's Pizzeria

	Pizza	Pasta	Salads
Tuesday	45	27	18
Wednesday	51	65	29

3. Write one addition question and one subtraction question based on the table above, and then find the answers.
Answers will vary. Possible questions: How many orders of pasta were taken on Tuesday and Wednesday together?; 92; How many more pizzas were sold on Wednesday than on Tuesday?; 6

UNIT 3 LESSON 8   Ask Addition and Subtraction Questions from Tables **79**

Homework and Remembering page 79

3–8 Name _____ Date _____
Remembering

1. Draw a square with a perimeter of 12 centimeters. Label the sides with their lengths.

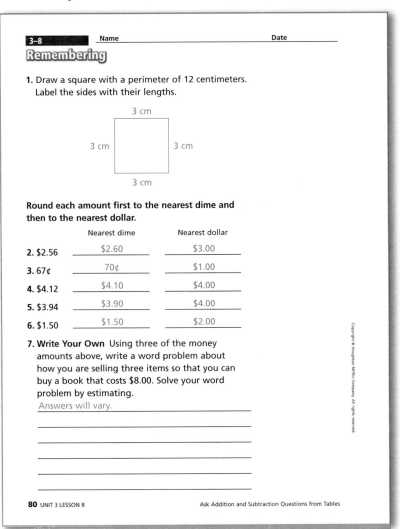

```
        3 cm
     ┌────────┐
3 cm │        │ 3 cm
     │        │
     └────────┘
        3 cm
```

Round each amount first to the nearest dime and then to the nearest dollar.

	Nearest dime	Nearest dollar
2. $2.56	$2.60	$3.00
3. 67¢	70¢	$1.00
4. $4.12	$4.10	$4.00
5. $3.94	$3.90	$4.00
6. $1.50	$1.50	$2.00

7. Write Your Own Using three of the money amounts above, write a word problem about how you are selling three items so that you can buy a book that costs $8.00. Solve your word problem by estimating.
Answers will vary.

_____
_____
_____
_____
_____

80 UNIT 3 LESSON 8   Ask Addition and Subtraction Questions from Tables

Homework and Remembering page 80

Home or School Activity

Language Arts Connection

Homonyms Homonyms are words that are spelled or pronounced the same, but have different meanings. Introduce homonyms to students with the examples *row, table,* and *cell.* Have students think about the meaning of those three words and encourage students to set up a chart to organize their thinking. Students should be thinking of the meaning of the words in mathematics and their meaning outside of math class.

Challenge students to think of other homonyms.

Math	Homonym	Non-math
It goes across in a table.	row	Something you do to move a boat.
Displays data	table	Something you eat on.
A rectangle in a table.	cell	Something in your body.

324 UNIT 3 LESSON 8

Complete Tables

Lesson Objectives

- Use information in tables to create and solve word problems.
- Complete tables.

Vocabulary
table
row
column
cell

The Day at a Glance

Today's Goals	Materials	Math Talk
Quick Practice Round whole numbers to the nearest ten or hundred.	MathBoard materials	In today's activities, the students are involved in discussion as they
1 Teaching the Lesson **A1:** Review tables and create word problems based on information in tables. **A2:** Complete tables and ask questions about the data.	Inch Grid Paper (Copymaster M42) Student Activity Book pages 149–152 Homework and Remembering pages 81–82	▶ review and explain how to use tables ▶ suggest word problems
2 Extending the Lesson ▶ Going Further: Logical Reasoning ▶ Differentiated Instruction	Math Journals	
3 Homework and Spiral Review		

Quick Practice

 5 MINUTES   **Goal:** Round whole numbers to the nearest ten or hundred.

Class Management

The Student Leader should allow enough time between their signals so all students can calculate and prepare their response. Rounding a number in the thousands to the nearest ten or hundred might require a longer pause.

Rounding Practice The Student Leader writes the six numbers below on the board. The leader points to the numbers one at a time and says either "Round to the nearest ten," or, "Round to the nearest hundred." When the leader gives a signal, students respond in unison with the rounded number.

698   236   459   1,980   2,333   7,777

Leader (pointing to 698): Round to the nearest ten.

Class: 700

1 Teaching the Lesson

Activity 1

Review Tables

 20 MINUTES

Goal: Review tables and create word problems based on information in tables.

Materials: Student Activity Book page 149

✓ **NCTM Standards:**
Number and Operations
Data Analysis and Probability
Problem Solving
Communication

Differentiated Instruction

Extra Help Some students may still be struggling to understand what the numbers in a table represent. Have students move one finger from the number to the row and another finger to the column and then tell what the number represents.

3–9
Class Activity

Name _____ Date _____

▶ Analyze Tables

This table shows the number of people who went on different rides at an amusement park.

Number of People Who Went on Rides

	Roller Coaster	Ferris Wheel	Bumper Cars
Monday	383	237	185
Tuesday	459	84	348
Wednesday	106	671	215

Use the table above to answer the questions.

1. What do the numbers in the row for Tuesday stand for?
   The number of people who rode on the Roller Coaster, Ferris Wheel, and Bumper Cars on Tuesday.

2. What do the numbers in the column for bumper cars stand for?
   The number of people who rode on bumper cars on Monday, Tuesday, and Wednesday.

3. Find the cell with 106 in it. What does this number stand for?
   The number of people who rode on the Roller Coaster on Wednesday.

UNIT 3 LESSON 9   Complete Tables **149**

Student Activity Book page 149

▶ Analyze Tables WHOLE CLASS

Ask a volunteer to explain what the table shows on Student Activity Book page 149. Review the terms *row, column,* and *cell* with the following questions.

- Run your finger across the row for Wednesday. What do the numbers in this row tell us? the number of people who rode rides on Wednesday

- Run your finger down the column for roller coaster. What do the numbers in this column tell us? the number of people who rode the roller coaster each day

- Find the cell that contains the number 84. What does this number tell us? the number of people who rode the Ferris Wheel on Tuesday

- How many people rode bumper cars on Monday? 185

Solve and Discuss Have students look at questions 1–3 at the bottom of the page and discuss the answers as a class.

Comparison Questions Challenge students to think of comparison word problems and questions using data from the table on Student Activity Book page 149. Remind students that comparison questions use the words *more, fewer, less,* and so on. Volunteers should give the complete problem, not just the question. You may need to offer an example.

● On Tuesday, 459 people rode the roller coaster and 106 people rode the roller coaster on Wednesday. How many *more* people rode the roller coaster on Tuesday than on Wednesday?

Choose several students to suggest different word problems. Discuss whether each suggestion is indeed a comparison problem. Then have each student who suggested a word problem discuss how they would solve it. It is not necessary to have students find the solution.

Now ask students to think of some Put Together word problems. Again, allow several students to share their word problems and explain how they would solve them. Here are two examples:

● On Monday, 237 people rode the Ferris Wheel and 185 people rode bumper cars. How many people rode the Ferris Wheel and the bumper cars in all on Monday?

● On Tuesday, 459 people rode the roller coaster and 106 people rode the roller coaster on Wednesday. How many people rode the roller coaster on Tuesday and Wednesday combined?

Teaching the Lesson (continued)

Complete Tables

 30 MINUTES

Goal: Complete tables and ask questions about the data.

Materials: Student Activity Book page 150

 NCTM Standards:
Numbers and Operations
Data Analysis and Probability
Problem Solving
Communication

Teaching Note

Watch For! Since the last column in many tables is a *Total* column, students may begin to automatically add to find values for *every* last column. Remind students to pay close attention to every row and column label. Emphasize that these labels are often hints for how to fill in empty cells. For example, in the first table in Student Activity Book page 150, the word *Left* in the last column's label *Loaves Left* points to the need for subtraction, not addition.

The Learning Classroom

Building Concepts Whole-class practice allows less advanced students to benefit from the knowledge of more advanced students without having to ask for help directly. It also provides the teacher with a quick and easy means of assessing the progress of the class as a whole.

Fill in the Tables

4. This table shows the number of loaves of bread baked and sold last week at the Lotsa Dough Bakery. Fill in the empty cells.

Bread Sales at Lotsa Dough Bakery

	Loaves Baked	Loaves Sold	Loaves Left
Monday	122	38	84
Tuesday	113	47	66
Wednesday	145	56	89
Thursday	134	96	38
Friday	91	47	44

5. This table shows the number of CDs and videotapes sold at the Sound Out Music Store last week. Fill in the empty cells.

Sound Out Music Sales

	CDs	Videotapes	Total
Monday	62	19	81
Tuesday	73	32	105
Wednesday	88	45	133
Thursday	94	26	120
Friday	155	68	223
Saturday	228	66	294

150 UNIT 3 LESSON 9   Complete Tables

Student Activity Book page 150

▶ Fill in the Tables [WHOLE CLASS]

Have a student explain what the *Lotsa Dough Bakery* table on Student Activity Book page 150 shows. Make sure students understand how the columns are related: for each day, the number in the first column shows how many loaves were baked, the number in the second column shows how many of those loaves were sold, and the number in the third column shows how many of those loaves were left (that is, how many were *not* sold).

Explain to students that this table has some empty cells. Have students suggest ways to figure out how to fill them in.

● Let's start with the empty cell in the top row. What information should this cell show? the number of loaves left over on Monday

- Can anyone make up a word problem we could use to find the missing number? The bakery made 122 loaves of bread on Monday. They sold 38 of the loaves. How many loaves were left?

Give students time to find the answer, 84, and then have a volunteer show the solution on the board.

Have students work independently to fill in the rest of the table. Students do not need to write the word problems, but they should think carefully about the information they know and the unknown numbers they need to find. After most of the class has finished, choose students to share their answers and explain how they found them. (Students should just describe their solution methods; they do not need to explain every step of their computations.)

Next, have a student explain what the *Sound Out Music Sales* data table shows. Make sure students understand that the Total column shows the total number of CDs and videotapes sold each day. Have students work independently to fill in the empty cells, and then select students to share and explain their answers.

▶ Compare Data INDIVIDUALS

Have students use the completed tables on Student Activity Book page 150 to write two comparison questions using the words *more* or *less*. Here are a few examples of students' questions:

- How many more loaves were baked on Wednesday than on Monday?

- On Tuesday, how many more loaves were baked than were sold?

- How many fewer loaves were left on Thursday than on Friday?

- How many fewer loaves were sold on Tuesday than on Thursday?

- How many more CDs were sold on Saturday than on Monday?

- How many fewer CDs and videotapes were sold on Thursday than on Friday?

- How many fewer videotapes than CDs were sold on Friday?

Select students to read aloud their questions and explain how to find the answers. They do not need to find the solution, unless you feel they need the practice.

Ongoing Assessment

Check students' understanding of how to locate specific information in tables.

▶ How can you find how much more there is of one thing than another using a table?

▶ How can you find the total of all the items listed in one row?

② Extending the Lesson

Going Further: Logical Reasoning

Goal: Solve logic problems with tables.

Materials: Student Activity Book pages 151–152

✔ **NCTM Standards:**
Number and Operations
Data Analysis and Probability
Problem Solving

Teaching Note

Math Background On this page, students organize the given facts and use logical reasoning to find unknown facts to solve the problem.

▶ Use Logical Reasoning | WHOLE CLASS

Explain that a table can also be used to organize what you know and that you can then use logical reasoning to complete it. Read aloud problem 1 on Student Activity Book page 151. Then draw this table on the board.

	Red	Blue	Green	Yellow
Jan				
Bev				
Luis				
Alex				

Fill in the chart with either *yes* or *no* using the information in the problem.

	Red	Blue	Green	Yellow
Jan	no		no	
Bev	no		no	no
Luis	no			no
Alex	yes	no	no	no

When a *yes* is entered, fill in the rest of that row and the column with *no.* When there is just one empty cell left in a row or a column with all *no,* fill in *yes.*

▶ **Use Logical Reasoning**

Solve each problem.

1. Jan, Bev, Luis, and Alex are wearing different color caps. The colors are red, blue, green, and yellow. Jan's cap is not red or green. Alex's cap is red. Bev's cap is not green or yellow. What color cap is each wearing?

   Jan: yellow; Bev: blue
   Luis: green; Alex: red

	Red	Blue	Green	Yellow
Jan	no	no	no	yes
Bev	no	yes	no	no
Luis	no	no	yes	no
Alex	yes	no	no	no

2. Ty, Sal, Amy, and Lea were in a race. Amy did not finish either first or second. Lea finished last. Sal finished before Ty. In what order did they finish the race?

   Sal, Ty, Amy, Lea

	First	Second	Third	Fourth
Ty	no	yes	no	no
Sal	yes	no	no	no
Amy	no	no	yes	no
Lea	no	no	no	yes

3. Mai, Abdul, Bill, and Rita each play different instruments. The instruments are violin, flute, harp, and guitar. Mai's instrument does not have strings. Bill plays the violin. Abdul does not play the harp. What does each person play?

   Mai: flute; Abdul: guitar
   Bill: violin; Rita: harp

	violin	flute	harp	guitar
Mai	no	yes	no	no
Abdul	no	no	no	yes
Bill	yes	no	no	no
Rita	no	no	yes	no

📝 4. **On the Back** Create your own problem like the ones above. Check student's work.

UNIT 3 LESSON 9   Complete Tables **151**

> **Student Activity Book page 151**

Where do you see one empty cell in a row or column?
column for green and yellow

Write *yes* in those cells. Then continue in this manner until all cells are filled and the problem is solved.

	Red	Blue	Green	Yellow
Jan	no	no	no	yes
Bev	no	yes	no	no
Luis	no	no	yes	no
Alex	yes	no	no	no

Alex has a red cap, Bev has a blue cap, Luis has a green cap, and Jan has a yellow cap.

Have students complete problems 2–4. Have volunteers demonstrate how they solved the problems and present the ones they wrote in exercise 4.

Intervention
for students having difficulty

PAIRS

Compare or Put Together?

Materials: Inch Grid Paper (Copymaster M42)

Have each pair of students draw a 4-column, 4-row table on inch grid paper. Have students label the columns to represent days of the week and the rows to represent some of the items they would sell as a store owner. Then they make up the information that goes in each cell. The table should also have a title. One partner should circle two cells in the table and the other partner should decide whether a comparison word problem, a Put Together word problem, or both would be appropriate. (They do not have to solve the problems.) Have pairs repeat this several times.

Dave's DVD Store Sales — Comparison and Put Together

	Tuesday	Wednesday	Thursday	Friday
Action	56	38	43	54
Drama	49	58	62	66
Comedy	60	38	27	31
Children's	78	61	67	75

Put Together — Comparison

On Level
for students having success

SMALL GROUPS

What's Missing?

Materials: Inch Grid Paper (Copymaster M42)

Ask students to draw a 3-column, 5-row table on grid paper, labeling the rows *Sue, Jack, Leon, Maria,* and *Kim* and the columns *Red Pencils, Blue Pencils,* and *Total Pencils.* To start, one student should present a word problem. The rest of the group should use the problem to fill in empty table cells. As an example, show each group how to complete the "Sue" row of the table by solving the word problem: "Sue has 10 pencils. Three of them are red pencils. How many blue pencils does she have?"

Red and Blue Pencils Owned by Some Students

	Red Pencils	Blue Pencils	Total Pencils
Sue	3	7	10
Jack			
Leon			
Maria			
Kim			

Challenge
for students seeking a challenge

PAIRS

Take a Survey

Have partners create a table to record the hair colors of boys and girls in the class. Then have them decide how they will keep track of the number of boys and girls with each hair color as they count. Have them look around the room, count how many have each hair color, and complete the table.

Have partners record the total for each row and column, check the total by adding both ways and check that the total matches the number of students in their class.

Red	Black	Blonde	Brown
boys I	boys III	boys III	boys IIII
girls II	girls IIIII	girls IIII	girls III

Hair Color of Students

	Red	Black	Blonde	Brown	Total
Girls	2	5	4	3	14
Boys	1	3	3	4	11
Total	3	8	7	7	25

Have them write one word problem that involves addition and one word problem that involves subtraction using the data in the table.

Also Use
Challenge Master for 3-9

 Math Writing Prompt

Intervention

Clue Words

What words are clues that tell you to use addition to solve a word problem using data in a table? What words are clues that tell you to use subtraction?

 Math Writing Prompt

On Level

Justify

If you created a data table, would you use exact numbers or rounded numbers for your data? Explain your thinking with an example.

 Math Writing Prompt

Challenge

Investigate Math

Is it easier to create word problems using a list of data or data organized in a table? Explain your reasoning.

③ Homework and Spiral Review

3-9
Homework **Goal:** Additional Practice

✔ Include students' completed Homework page as part of their portfolios.

3-9 Name _____ Date _____
Homework

1. This table shows how many calendars of each type the third graders ordered from the calendar publisher, the number they sold, and the number they have left. Fill in the empty cells.

Third Grade Calendar Sales

	Number Ordered	Number Sold	Number Left
Playful Puppies	475	387	88
Adorable Kittens	300	123	177
Lovable Lambs	550	471	79

2. Make up a Comparison question about the table that uses the word *more*, and find the answer.
Answers will vary.

3. This table shows the number of students at Lakeside Elementary who participate in various activities. Fill in the empty cells.

Participation in Activities

	Boys	Girls	Total
Band or Chorus	36	43	79
Sports	93	78	171
After-School Clubs	47	39	86

4. Make up a Comparison question about the table that uses the word *fewer*, and write the answer.
Answers will vary.

UNIT 3 LESSON 9   Complete Tables **81**

Homework and Remembering page 81

3-9
Remembering **Goal:** Spiral Review

This Remembering page would be appropriate anytime after today's lesson.

3-9 Name _____ Date _____
Remembering

Solve.   *Show your work.*

1. Alicia had 419 coins in her collection. She gave 78 to her little brother. How many coins does she have now?
341 coins

2. Write an addition word problem that undoes problem 1. Solve your word problem without doing any calculations.
Answers will vary. Possible problem: Alicia had 341 coins. Her brother gave her 78 more coins. How many coins does she have now? ; 419 coins

3. On Saturday, a shoe store sold 278 pairs of women's shoes and 155 pairs of men's shoes. How many pairs of shoes did they sell in all?
433 pairs of shoes

4. Write a subtraction word problem that undoes problem 3. Solve your word problem without doing any calculations.
Answers will vary. Possible answer: On Saturday, a shoe store sold 433 pairs of shoes. 155 of the pairs were men's shoes. How many pairs were women's shoes?; 278 pairs

82 UNIT 3 LESSON 9   Complete Tables

Homework and Remembering page 82

Home or School Activity

 Technology Connection

Computer Art Have students use a computer software program to create tables with graphics. Students can use data from a completed table on a Student Activity Book page or they can create a table with their own data.

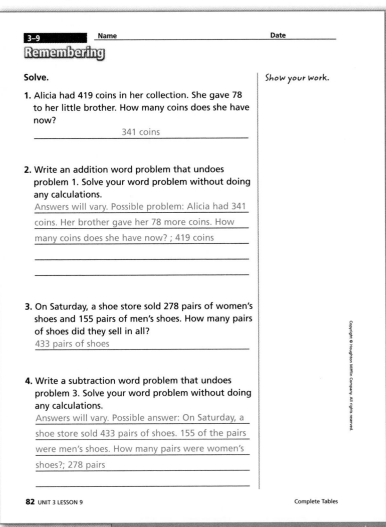

	CDs	Videotapes	Total
Monday	62	19	81
Tuesday	73	32	105
Wednesday	88	45	133

332 UNIT 3 LESSON 9

UNIT 3
LESSON 10

More Practice with Tables

Lesson Objectives

- Create a simple table.
- Practice completing tables in which there is a mathematical relationship between the columns.

The Day at a Glance

Today's Goals	Materials	Math Talk
Quick Practice Round whole numbers to the nearest ten or hundred.	Play money	In today's activities, the students are involved in discussion as they
① Teaching the Lesson A1: Gather data and summarize it in a table. A2: Create word problems based on tables and practice completing tables.	Calculators (optional) Counters Blocks (red and blue) Paper bag Student Activity Book pages 153–154	▶ identify labels for rows and columns in tables ▶ write addition and subtraction questions based on a data table
② Extending the Lesson ▶ Differentiated Instruction	Homework and Remembering pages 83–84	▶ create word problems ▶ explain their completed table
③ Homework and Spiral Review	MathBoard materials Math Journals	

Quick Practice

 5 MINUTES **Goal:** Round whole numbers to the nearest ten or hundred.

Rounding Practice: The Student Leader writes the six numbers below on the board. The leader points to the numbers one at a time and says either, "Round to the nearest ten," or, "Round to the nearest hundred." When the leader gives a signal, students respond in unison with the rounded number.

2,232   111   428   1,220   278   360

Leader (pointing to 2,232): Round to the nearest ten.

Class: 2,230

Class Management

This practice has been done several times already. To make it fresh again, consider making a game of it. Have the Student Leader go around the room to find the time it takes to go through each group of 6 numbers. The class tries to improve on its time each time they go through the numbers.

Teaching the Lesson

Collect Data and Make a Table

 20 MINUTES

Goal: Gather data and summarize it in a table.

Materials: Real or play money (1 penny), Student Activity Book page 153

✔ **NCTM Standards:**
Algebra
Data Analysis and Probability
Communication
Connections
Representation

Teaching Note

Language and Vocabulary Use the words *data, survey,* and *tally* in this activity. Explain that one way to collect data, or information, is to take a survey. When you take a survey, you ask people questions and record their answers using tally marks.

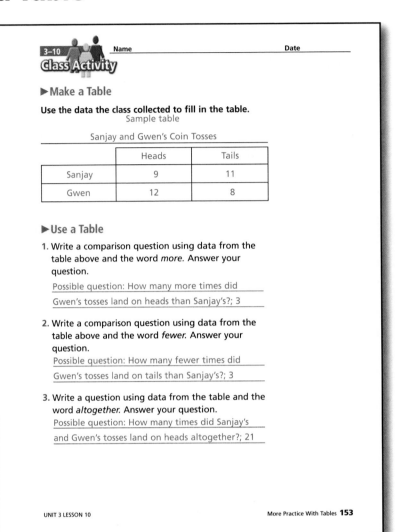

Student Activity Book page 153

▶ Coin Toss WHOLE CLASS

Have a volunteer come to the front of the room and write his or her name on the board. Have the student toss a coin 20 times. Record the result of each toss, H or T, after the student's name. Repeat with another volunteer. Your results should look something like this:

Sanjay: T T H T H T T H H T H H T H H T T
          H T T

Gwen: T H T H H H H T T T H H T T H T H
         H H H

► Make a Table WHOLE CLASS

Now have students look at the blank table on Student Activity Book page 153. Explain that they will fill in the table with the number of heads and tails each student tossed.

Remind students that when they make a table, they should always give it a title. Have students suggest titles for the table. Possible responses: Sanjay and Gwen's Coin Tosses. Have them write the title above the table and label the columns *Heads* and *Tails.*

Have students fill in the table as you provide help to those who need it. Once students are finished with the table, review the results and answer any questions they may have. A sample table is provided.

Sanjay and Gwen's Coin Tosses

	Heads	Tails
Sanjay	9	11
Gwen	12	8

► Use a Table WHOLE CLASS

In order to get students to look closely at their completed tables, ask a few questions such as:

● Who tossed the greatest number of heads? Gwen

● Who tossed the least number of tails? Gwen

Challenge them to suggest addition and subtraction questions based on the table. Have student volunteers share their questions. Some possible questions they might ask are:

● How many fewer times did Sanjay's tosses land on heads than Gwen's tosses? 3

● How many more times did Sanjay's tosses land on tails? 3

● What are the total number of heads tossed by Sanjay and Gwen together? 21

● What are the total number of tails tossed by Sanjay and Gwen? 19

● How do the totals for heads and the total for tails compare? There are more heads than tails.

Activity 2

More Practice Completing Tables

 25 MINUTES

Goal: Create word problems based on tables and practice completing tables.

Materials: Student Activity Book page 154, calculators (optional)

NCTM Standards:
Number and Operations
Algebra
Data Analysis and Probability
Problem Solving
Reasoning and Proof
Communication
Connections
Representation

 Alternate Approach

Calculators Some students might want to check their answers with a calculator.

3–10
Class Activity

Name _____ Date _____

▶ **Analyze Data**

Fill in the missing information in the tables and answer the questions.

This table shows the number of souvenirs the Wildcats baseball team sold last weekend.

Souvenir Sales for Wildcats Baseball Team

	White	Red	Total
Caps	134	77	211
T-shirts	64	109	173
Pennants	59	92	151

4. Which item above had the most total sales? ___caps___

5. Which color T-shirt had the most sales? ___red___

This table shows the number of items the Green Thumb Garden Shop sold at their Spring sale.

Spring Sale at Green Thumb Garden Shop

	Number Before the Sale	Number Sold	Number Left
Spades	232	185	47
Straw Hats	144	68	76
Small Pots	412	342	70
Big Pots	325	227	98

6. Which item had the most sales? ___small pots___

7. Which item has the least number left? ___spades___

154 UNIT 3 LESSON 10   More Practice With Tables

Student Activity Book page 154

▶ **Analyze Data** [WHOLE CLASS]

Have a volunteer explain what the first table on Student Activity Book page 154 shows. Ask what word problem students could solve to find the number that belongs in the empty cell in the first row. Possible response: The team sold 134 white caps and some red caps. They sold 211 caps altogether. How many red caps did they sell?

Give students a minute to solve the problem, and then choose someone to present the solution.

Have students work independently to complete exercises 4–7. Remind them they do not have to write word problems, but they should think carefully about what information they know. Help students who are struggling, or pair struggling students with Helping Partners.

Discuss the results. For each row, have a student state a related word problem and give the answer.

Ongoing Assessment

To check that students understand how to use information in tables, ask questions such as:

▶ How do the column labels help you to fill in missing information in a table?

▶ If there is an empty cell in a row, how can you find the number that goes there?

② Extending the Lesson

Intervention
for students having difficulty

SMALL GROUPS

Picking Blue or Red

Materials: 2 blue blocks, 3 red blocks and a paper bag (each per group), MathBoard materials

Have students place the 5 blocks in the bag. Have one student choose a block from the bag without looking. The student writes B (for blue) or R (for red) on a MathBoard next to his or her name. Then the block is returned to the bag. Students take turns and repeat 20 times. Once the data is collected, have students create a table like the one below to show the information collected.

	Blue	Red

Have them answer these questions:

Did you pick a red more times than you picked a blue?

Why do you think this happened?

Math Writing Prompt
Intervention
Explain Your Thinking
Harry tossed a coin fifty times. He made a table to record his results. He wrote 25 under *heads*. What should he write under *tails?* Explain.

On Level
for students having success

PAIRS

Cover It!

Materials: counters (2 per pair)

Each student should make a table containing information that might be collected in a survey at their school. The column at the right of the table should show a total.

After the tables are complete, students should cover any two numbers in the table with two counters and challenge their partners to figure out what the covered numbers are. Then they can remove both counters to see if their answers are correct.

Favorite Sandwiches of 3rd Graders at Peabody Elementary

	Girls	Boys	Total
Peanut Butter	●	57	65
Ham and Cheese	48	18	●
Tuna	10	3	13

Math Writing Prompt
On Level
Critical Thinking
Sanjay and Gwen each toss a penny 40 times. Then they create a data table showing their results. Is it likely that the same number will appear in every cell? Explain.

Challenge
for students seeking a challenge

PAIRS

Find the Missing Numbers

Copy the table below onto the board. Each set of pairs should copy it on paper and find the missing numbers.

Favorite Subjects at Pine Avenue Elementary School

	3rd Graders	4th Graders	Total
Gym	53		97
Music			84
Art	25		
Total Students in Each Grade	123		250

Have students redraw the table on the board with the empty cells. They show the order in which they were able to fill in the cells by labeling the empty cells from A (1st step) to F (6th step).

Also Use
Challenge Master for 3-10

Math Writing Prompt
Challenge
Predict
If you put 2 red blocks and 1 blue block in a bag, and pick a block without looking 30 times, predict what your data table will look like. Explain your answer.

③ Homework and Spiral Review

This Homework page provides students with extra practice in completing tables.

This Remembering page would be appropriate anytime after today's lesson.

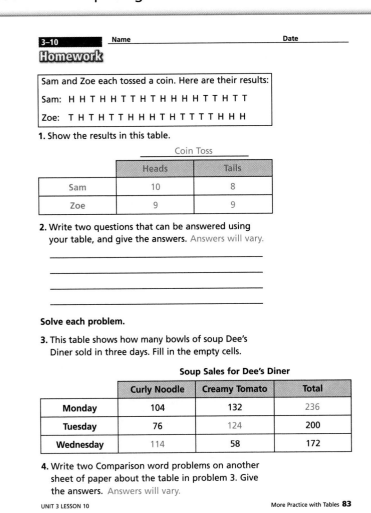

3–10   Name _____ Date _____
Homework

Sam and Zoe each tossed a coin. Here are their results:

Sam: H H T H H H T T H T H H H H T T H T T

Zoe: T H T H T T H H H T H T T T T H H H

1. Show the results in this table.

Coin Toss

	Heads	Tails
Sam	10	8
Zoe	9	9

2. Write two questions that can be answered using your table, and give the answers. Answers will vary.

_____

_____

_____

_____

Solve each problem.

3. This table shows how many bowls of soup Dee's Diner sold in three days. Fill in the empty cells.

Soup Sales for Dee's Diner

	Curly Noodle	Creamy Tomato	Total
Monday	104	132	236
Tuesday	76	124	200
Wednesday	114	58	172

4. Write two Comparison word problems on another sheet of paper about the table in problem 3. Give the answers. Answers will vary.

UNIT 3 LESSON 10   More Practice with Tables **83**

Homework and Remembering page 83

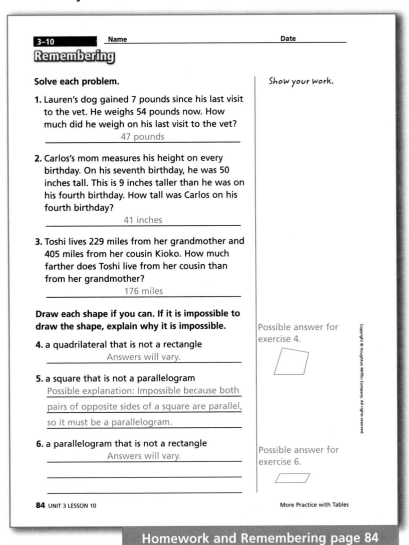

3–10   Name _____ Date _____
Remembering

Solve each problem.   *Show your work.*

1. Lauren's dog gained 7 pounds since his last visit to the vet. He weighs 54 pounds now. How much did he weigh on his last visit to the vet?

47 pounds

2. Carlos's mom measures his height on every birthday. On his seventh birthday, he was 50 inches tall. This is 9 inches taller than he was on his fourth birthday. How tall was Carlos on his fourth birthday?

41 inches

3. Toshi lives 229 miles from her grandmother and 405 miles from her cousin Kioko. How much farther does Toshi live from her cousin than from her grandmother?

176 miles

Draw each shape if you can. If it is impossible to draw the shape, explain why it is impossible.

4. a quadrilateral that is not a rectangle

Answers will vary.

5. a square that is not a parallelogram

Possible explanation: Impossible because both pairs of opposite sides of a square are parallel, so it must be a parallelogram.

6. a parallelogram that is not a rectangle

Answers will vary.

_____

_____

Possible answer for exercise 4.

Possible answer for exercise 6.

84 UNIT 3 LESSON 10   More Practice with Tables

Homework and Remembering page 84

Home or School Activity

 Science Connection

Your Town's Weather Remind students that tables provide us with useful information without using a lot of words. Tell students that tables are often used to summarize weather data. Have students use a newspaper or the Internet to find weather data they can display in a table.

Temperatures at Noon

	Reedvale	Jefferson Park
Monday	67°F	68°F
Tuesday	63°F	59°F

Word Problems with Extra or Hidden Information

Lesson Objective
● Represent and solve word problems with extra or hidden information.

The Day at a Glance

Today's Goals	Materials	Math Talk

Quick Practice Round whole numbers to the nearest ten or hundred.
 	
1 Teaching the Lesson
A1: Solve word problems with extra information.
A2: Recognize and solve word problems with hidden information.
 	
2 Extending the Lesson
▶ Differentiated Instruction
 	
3 Homework and Spiral Review
	Highlighters
	Student Activity Book
	   pages 155–156
	Homework and
	   Remembering pages 85–86
	Math Journals
		In today's activities, the students are involved in discussion as they
		
		▶ explain how they solve word problems
		
		▶ learn how to take notes to help them solve word problems
		
		▶ identify hidden information in a word problem

Quick Practice

🕐 **5 MINUTES**   **Goal:** Round whole numbers to the nearest ten or hundred.

Rounding Practice The Student Leader writes the six numbers below on the board. The leader points to the numbers one at a time and says either, "Round to the nearest ten," or, "Round to the nearest hundred." When the leader gives a signal, students respond in unison with the rounded number.

209   853   1,325   487   662   744

Leader (pointing to 209): Round to the nearest ten.

Class: 210

Teaching the Lesson

Recognize Extra Information in Word Problems

 25 MINUTES

Goal: Solve word problems with extra information.

Materials: Student Activity Book page 155, highlighters

✓ **NCTM Standards:**
Number and Operations
Problem Solving
Communication
Representation

Teaching Note

What to Expect from Students
Many students will prefer to use the cross-out method when dealing with word problems. Be sure to monitor this closely so that students do not become confused and start crossing out information they need to solve the problem.

3–11
Class Activity   Name _____   Date _____

▶ **Solve Problems with Extra Information**

Read each problem. Cross out any extra information. Then solve.

1. Emma solved 9 math problems ~~and answered 7 reading questions~~. Her sister solved 8 math problems. How many math problems did they solve in all?
   _____ 17 math problems _____

2. Mark had 6 shirts ~~and 5 pairs of pants~~. Today his aunt gave him 4 more shirts ~~and another pair of pants~~. How many shirts does he have now?
   _____ 10 shirts _____

3. A parking lot had 179 cars ~~and 95 trucks~~. Then 85 cars left the lot. How many cars are in the parking lot now?
   _____ 94 cars _____

4. Laura had some roses in a vase. From her garden, she picked 7 more roses ~~and 6 daisies~~. Now she has 12 roses in all. How many roses did she have at first?
   _____ 5 roses _____

5. Nikko had 245 pennies ~~and 123 nickels~~. His brother gave him 89 more pennies ~~and 25 more nickels~~. How many pennies does Nikko have now?
   _____ 334 pennies _____

UNIT 3 LESSON 11   Word Problems with Extra or Hidden Information **155**

Student Activity Book page 155

▶ Solve Problems with Extra Information [WHOLE CLASS]

Using **Solve and Discuss,** have students solve problem 1 on Student Activity Book page 155. Remember to select students who used different strategies to present their solutions.

● **What is difficult about this word problem?** Some of the numbers given are not needed to solve the problem.

● **How can we figure out which numbers we need and which we don't?** Possible response: We can look at what the question is asking and then cross out the information we don't need.

Note Taking If students do not suggest taking notes as a problem-solving strategy, introduce it now. Demonstrate note taking as a quick way to keep track of information in a word problem.

 Math Talk Explain that using abbreviations when taking notes is a way to save time.

- What information is given first in the problem? Emma solved 9 math problems. I'll write Emma's name, and then I'll write 9M. I wrote *M* instead of *math problems* to save time.

Emma   9M

- What information is given next? She answered 7 reading questions. What should we add to our notes? We could add 7R next to Emma's name.

Emma   9M   7R

- What other information is given? Her sister solved 8 math problems. What should we add to our notes now? We could write down *sister* with 8M next to it.

Emma   9M   7R
Sister   8M

- What is the question asking us about? math problems Do we need the information about reading questions? no We can cross that information out.

Emma   9M   ~~7R~~
Sister   8M

- What else does the question ask? How many math problems did they solve in all. Have a student write the equation on the board.

$9 + 8 = \boxed{}$

- What is the total? 17 math problems

Allow students to share their thoughts on taking notes as a problem-solving strategy. Some may find taking notes helpful; others may not need to take any notes.

Have students solve problems 2–5 independently and then discuss the results as a class.

Alternate Approach

Highlight It Have students read the problem and highlight the information that they need to solve the problem with a highlighter. Then have them read the problem again reading only the highlighted information. Ask them if the problem still makes sense and can be solved without the other information.

 Ongoing Assessment

To be sure that students understand extra information problems, ask questions such as:

▶ Why is it important to read a word problem carefully?

▶ How do you decide what information is important?

▶ How do you know when information is extra?

Teaching the Lesson (continued)

Activity 2

Recognize Hidden Information in Word Problems

🕐 **25 MINUTES**

Goal: Recognize and solve word problems with hidden information.

Materials: Student Activity Book page 156

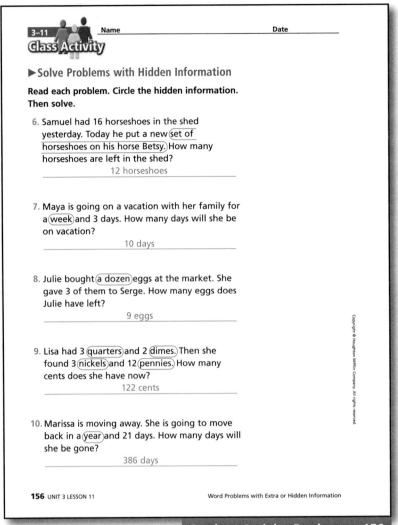

3-11
Class Activity   Name _____ Date _____

▶ Solve Problems with Hidden Information

Read each problem. Circle the hidden information. Then solve.

6. Samuel had 16 horseshoes in the shed yesterday. Today he put a new (set of horseshoes on his horse Betsy.) How many horseshoes are left in the shed?
_____ 12 horseshoes _____

7. Maya is going on a vacation with her family for a (week) and 3 days. How many days will she be on vacation?
_____ 10 days _____

8. Julie bought (a dozen) eggs at the market. She gave 3 of them to Serge. How many eggs does Julie have left?
_____ 9 eggs _____

9. Lisa had 3 (quarters) and 2 (dimes.) Then she found 3 (nickels) and 12 (pennies.) How many cents does she have now?
_____ 122 cents _____

10. Marissa is moving away. She is going to move back in a (year) and 21 days. How many days will she be gone?
_____ 386 days _____

156 UNIT 3 LESSON 11   Word Problems with Extra or Hidden Information

Student Activity Book page 156

Information That Is Hidden in Problems 7–10

Problem 7: There are 7 days in a week.

Problem 8: There are 12 eggs in a dozen.

Problem 9: There are 25 cents in a quarter, 10 cents in a dime, 5 cents in a nickel, and 1 cent in a penny.

Problem 10: A year (usually) has 365 days.

▶ **Solve Problems with Hidden Information** WHOLE CLASS

Have students read problem 6 on Student Activity Book page 156 and ask the following questions.

● **What is different about this word problem?** The problem does not give all the numbers we need in order to solve it.

● **Can we still solve this problem?** Yes. **How do you know?** Even though the number is not given, we still know it.

● **How can we figure out the number that is not given in this problem?** We know that horses have 4 feet.

● **How can we solve this problem?** Subtract the number of feet a horse has (4) from the number of horseshoes Samuel has (16) to get the number of horseshoes left (12).

Have students solve problems 7–10. See the side column for hidden information in problems 7–10.

② Extending the Lesson

Activities for Individualizing

Intervention
for students having difficulty

PAIRS

What Is Extra?

Have students write a word problem that has extra information. Tell them to write the necessary parts of the word problem, and then add one piece of extra information. When partners have completed their word problems, have them exchange their word problems and solve each other's word problem. Pairs should discuss their answers and strategies.

Billy has 4 packs of gum and 2 bags of candy. Jennette has 10 packs of gum. How many packs of gum do they have altogether?

On Level
for students having success

SMALL GROUPS

What Is Extra or Hidden?

Have students write two word problems: one with one piece of extra information and another with one piece of hidden information. Tell students to be sure to include all information necessary to solve both problems. When students have written their word problems, exchange problems with the student to the right, and solve their new word problems. When students have completed the problems, they should give them back to the writer to be corrected. Then have pairs discuss any answers that are not correct.

1. Marcel has one cat and seven fish. Javier has two cats and a hamster. How many cats do they have altogether?

2. Milly's cat can jump four feet in the air. How many inches can the cat jump?

Challenge
for students seeking a challenge

SMALL GROUPS

Double Hidden and Extra Information

Have students write two word problems: one with two pieces of extra information and another with two pieces of hidden information. When students have completed their word problems, have them exchange problems with the student to their right and solve. Students should discuss their answers and strategies.

1. Anita has 3 skirts, 6 pairs of pants, and 5 pairs of shorts. Marina has 4 skirts, 8 pairs of pants, and 2 pairs of shorts. How many skirts do the girls have altogether?

2. Arthur has 7 quarters and 2 nickels. How many cents does he have altogether?

Also Use
Challenge Master for 3-11

 Math Writing Prompt
Intervention
Problem-Solving Strategy
When you have extra information in a word problem, what is a strategy that you can use to help you solve the word problem? Explain your thinking.

 Math Writing Prompt
On Level
You Decide
Which kind of word problem is easier for you to solve: one with extra information or one with hidden information? Explain.

 Math Writing Prompt
Challenge
Real-World Application
Give an example of where you might need to solve a problem with hidden information in real life. How might you find the hidden information if you do not know it?

 # Homework and Spiral Review

3-11
Homework Goal: Additional Practice

This Homework page provides students with more practice in solving these types of word problems.

3-11
Remembering Goal: Spiral Review

This Remembering page would be appropriate anytime after today's lesson.

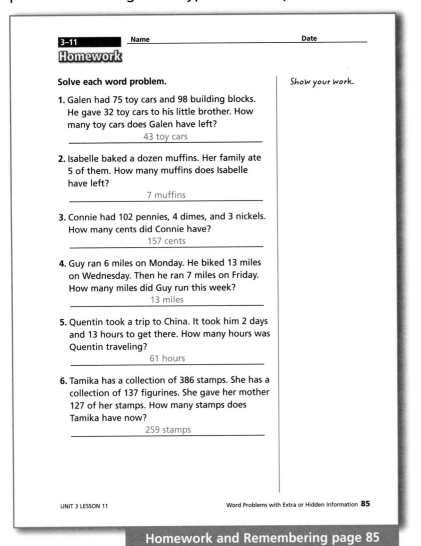

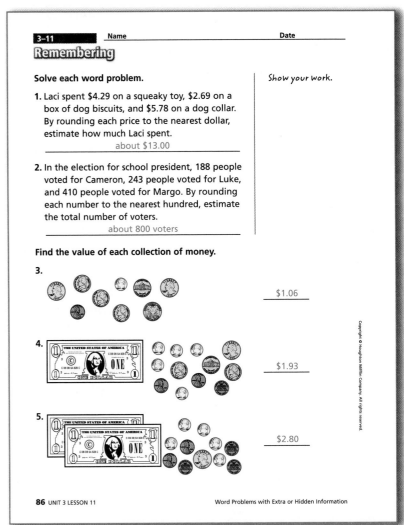

Homework and Remembering page 85

Homework and Remembering page 86

Home or School Activity

 ### Language Arts Connection

Editing Word Problems Give students a copy of the word problem to the right. It has mistakes in punctuation, capitalization, and spelling. Altogether, there are six errors.

Have students work in pairs to make a list identifying the errors in the word problem. If time allows have students write a problem containing hidden information and a total of six errors in spelling, punctuation, or capitalization.

> Ryan walked 2 blocks; to the library. He borrowed 2 books. Each book weighed 1 Pound. Then he walk 3 blocks two the grocery store. He bought a galon of milk that weighed 3 pounds. Then he walked 5 blocks home? How much weight did he carry from the grocery store to home?

344 UNIT 3 LESSON 11

UNIT 3

LESSON

12

Word Problems with Not Enough Information

Lesson Objectives

- Identify word problems with not enough information to solve and identify the information needed.
- Rewrite word problems with not enough information.

The Day at a Glance

Today's Goals	Materials	Math Talk
Quick Practice Count coin values.	Scissors	In today's activities, the students are involved in discussion as they
1 Teaching the Lesson **A1:** Identify information needed to solve word problems. **A2:** Rewrite word problems including the needed information.	Tape MathBoard materials Student Activity Book pages 157–160 Homework and Remembering pages 87–88 Math Journals	▶ identify word problems with not enough information ▶ determine what a word problem is asking
2 Extending the Lesson ▶ Differentiated Instruction		▶ explain how to solve a word problem
3 Homework and Spiral Review		

Quick Practice

 5 MINUTES   **Goal:** Count coin values.

Counting Coins The Student Leader writes a sequence of quarter (Qs), dimes (Ds), nickels (Ns), and pennies (Ps) on the board, in that order. The leader points to the coins in order as the class counts on to find the total amount.

Q Q Q D D D D D D N N P

Leader: Count on to find the total amount.

Class: 25¢, 50¢, 75¢, 85¢, 95¢, $1.05, $1.15, $1.25, $1.35, $1.40, $1.45, $1.46

The leader adds coins to or erases coins from the sequence, and the class counts again. Repeat this several times.

Class Management

To be sure that everyone is counting coin values correctly and easily, divide the class into smaller groups. Once the Student Leader has gone through the first sequence of coins with the entire class, have the leader make other sequences and direct these toward each group, one group at a time.

① Teaching the Lesson

Recognize Word Problems with Not Enough Information

 35 MINUTES

Goal: Identify information needed to solve word problems.

Materials: Student Activity Book pages 157–158

✓ **NCTM Standards:**
Number and Operations
Problem Solving
Communication
Connections

Differentiated Instruction

Extra Help Remind students about note taking from the previous lesson. Have them suggest ways this problem-solving strategy could help them with problems 1, 2, or 3.

3-12
Class Activity
Name _____ Date _____

▶ **Solve Word Problems with Not Enough Information**

Read each problem. Is there a way to solve it? Explain.

1. Sara bought 8 bananas at the fruit market. She put them in a bowl with some oranges. How many pieces of fruit are in the bowl?
   No; You need to know how many oranges
   are in the bowl.

2. Josh had some money in his pocket. He spent $1.25 on a bottle of juice. How much money does he have left?
   No; You need to know how much money he
   has in his pocket.

Tell what information is needed to solve each problem.

3. Meg bought 3 mystery books and put them on the shelf with her other mystery books. How many mystery books are now on the shelf?
   the number of mystery books on the shelf
   before the new ones were added

4. Our school has 5 soccer balls, 6 basketballs, and 4 footballs. Today, some of the footballs were lost. How many balls does the school have now?
   the number of footballs that were lost

UNIT 3 LESSON 12   Word Problems with Not Enough Information **157**

Student Activity Book page 157

▶ Solve Word Problems with Not Enough Information WHOLE CLASS

Allow students a few minutes to try to solve problem 1.

- **What information does this problem give us?** Sara bought 8 bananas and put them in a bowl with oranges.

- **What does the question ask us to find?** the number of pieces of fruit in the bowl

- **What would we need to do to find the answer?** Add the number of bananas and the number of oranges.

- **Do we have enough information to solve the problem?** no **What else do we need to know?** the number of oranges in the bowl

Then have students try to solve problem 2. Discuss the problem together.

- What information does this problem give us? Josh had some money, and he spent $1.25.

- What does the question ask us to find? the amount of money Josh has left

- What would we need to do to find the answer? Subtract the amount he spent from the amount he started with.

- Do we have enough information to solve the problem? no What else do we need to know? the amount Josh started with

Now read problem 3 aloud and have students tell what other information is needed to solve the problem.

 **Math Talk in Action**

Is there a way to solve problem 3?

Jonelle: I don't think so. I think we need to know how many mystery books Meg had on her shelf to start.

What information could we add to the problem to solve it?

Christopher: We could say that Meg brought 3 mystery books and put them on the shelf with her 11 other mystery books. Then we can find out how many mystery books are on the shelf now.

Very good!

Have students read problem 4 on their own and identify what information is needed to solve it. Then discuss as a class how problem 3 could be rewritten so it can be solved.

Activity continued ▶

① Teaching the Lesson (continued)

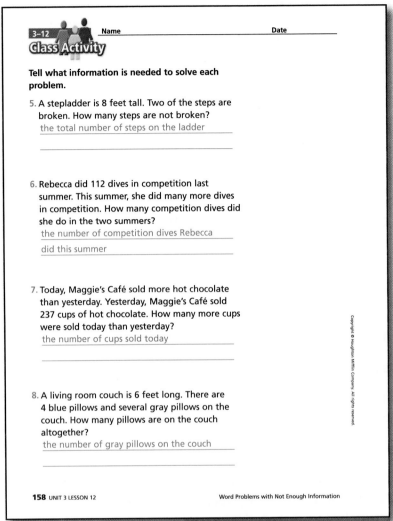

| 3-12 | Name _____ | Date _____ |

Class Activity

Tell what information is needed to solve each problem.

5. A stepladder is 8 feet tall. Two of the steps are broken. How many steps are not broken?

   the total number of steps on the ladder

   _____

6. Rebecca did 112 dives in competition last summer. This summer, she did many more dives in competition. How many competition dives did she do in the two summers?

   the number of competition dives Rebecca

   did this summer

7. Today, Maggie's Café sold more hot chocolate than yesterday. Yesterday, Maggie's Café sold 237 cups of hot chocolate. How many more cups were sold today than yesterday?

   the number of cups sold today

   _____

8. A living room couch is 6 feet long. There are 4 blue pillows and several gray pillows on the couch. How many pillows are on the couch altogether?

   the number of gray pillows on the couch

   _____

158 UNIT 3 LESSON 12   Word Problems with Not Enough Information

Student Activity Book page 158

Follow the same procedure for problems 5–8 on Student Activity Book page 158. Ask students if there is enough information to solve each problem. Ask what additional information is needed, and then ask for a way to rewrite the problem so it can be solved. Note that problems 5 and 8 contain extra information: the height of the ladder and the length of the couch are not relevant.

Practice Identifying Problems with Not Enough Information

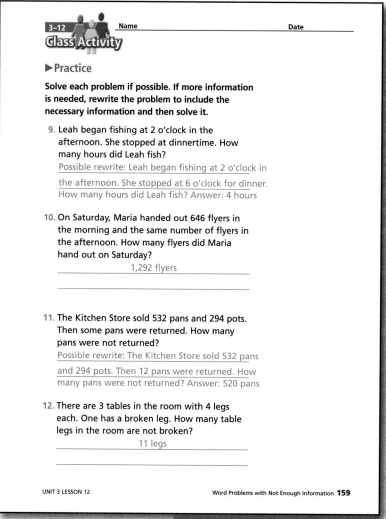

Student Activity Book page 159

 20 MINUTES

Goal: Rewrite word problems including the needed information.

Materials: Student Activity Book pages 159–160

 NCTM Standards:
Numbers and Operations
Problem Solving
Communication
Connections

▶ Practice WHOLE CLASS

Using **Solve and Discuss**, have students solve problems 9–12 if possible. For the problems with not enough information (problems 9 and 11), have students share their rewritten problem and its solution. Possible problems that students may write including the information needed are given below:

Problem 9: Possible rewrite: Leah began fishing at 2 o'clock in the afternoon. She stopped at 6 o'clock for dinner. How many hours did Leah fish? 4 hours

Problem 11: Possible rewrite: The kitchen store sold 532 pans and 294 pots. 12 pans were returned. How many pans were not returned? 520

Activity continued ▶

① Teaching the Lesson (continued)

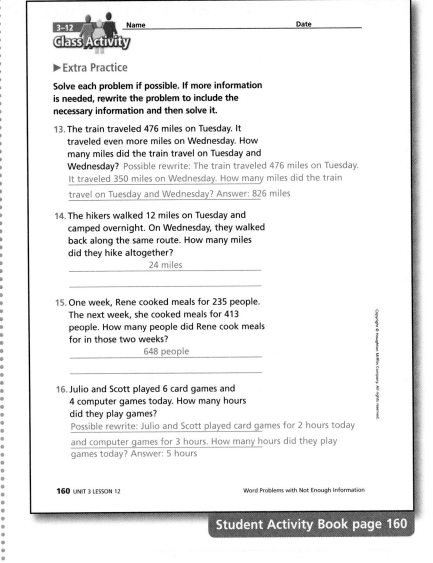

Student Activity Book page 160

The worksheet shows:

3–12 Class Activity Name _____ Date _____

▶ **Extra Practice**

Solve each problem if possible. If more information is needed, rewrite the problem to include the necessary information and then solve it.

13. The train traveled 476 miles on Tuesday. It traveled even more miles on Wednesday. How many miles did the train travel on Tuesday and Wednesday? Possible rewrite: The train traveled 476 miles on Tuesday. It traveled 350 miles on Wednesday. How many miles did the train travel on Tuesday and Wednesday? Answer: 826 miles

14. The hikers walked 12 miles on Tuesday and camped overnight. On Wednesday, they walked back along the same route. How many miles did they hike altogether?
    24 miles

15. One week, Rene cooked meals for 235 people. The next week, she cooked meals for 413 people. How many people did Rene cook meals for in those two weeks?
    648 people

16. Julio and Scott played 6 card games and 4 computer games today. How many hours did they play games? Possible rewrite: Julio and Scott played card games for 2 hours today and computer games for 3 hours. How many hours did they play games today? Answer: 5 hours

160 UNIT 3 LESSON 12   Word Problems with Not Enough Information

Ongoing Assessment

As students work individually on Student Activity Book page 160, circulate around the room and have students explain the steps they go through to solve a word problem. Students should explain the following:

▶ First, I find out what information the problem gives me. I can ask myself, "What do I know?"

▶ Then, I reread the question the word problem asks. I can say to myself, "What do I want to know?"

▶ Finally, I check to be sure if I have enough information to solve the problem.

▶ Extra Practice INDIVIDUALS

Have students independently solve problems 13–16. For the problems with missing information (problems 13 and 16), students should write their rewritten problem and its solution. Possible problems that students may write including the information needed are given below:

Problem 13: Possible rewrite: The train traveled 476 miles on Tuesday. It traveled 350 miles on Wednesday. How many miles did the train travel on Tuesday and Wednesday? 826 miles

Problem 16: Possible rewrite: Julio and Scott played card games for 2 hours today and computer games for 3 hours. How many hours did they play games today? 5 hours

② Extending the Lesson

Activities for Individualizing

Intervention
for students having difficulty

PAIRS

What's Missing?

Materials: Homework and Remembering page 87, MathBoard materials

Have students read the first word problem on the Homework page together. Each student should individually decide if there is enough information to solve the problem. If there is enough information, they should solve the problem and compare answers. If not, they should write what else they need to know on their MathBoards and then rewrite the problem together.

Problem 2:

> How many ducks flew away?

> What number of ducks is some?

Then continue in the same manner with as many problems as time allows.

On Level
for students having success

SMALL GROUPS

Missing Information Detective

Materials: Student Activity Book page 157, scissors, tape, MathBoard

Have students cut out two word problems from Student Activity Book page 157 that do not have enough information. Students should tape the word problems on their MathBoards, decide on a reasonable answer for the problem, and solve the problem. Once they've finished both problems, they should have other students tell what the missing information was by using the answers.

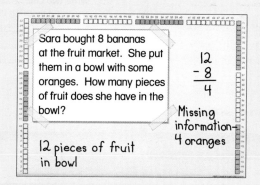

> Sara bought 8 bananas at the fruit market. She put them in a bowl with some oranges. How many pieces of fruit does she have in the bowl?
>
> $\begin{array}{r} 12 \\ -\ 8 \\ \hline 4 \end{array}$
>
> Missing information— 4 oranges
>
> 12 pieces of fruit in bowl

Challenge
for students seeking a challenge

PAIRS

Find the Unknown

Materials: MathBoard materials

Have each student write a word problem with missing information on their MathBoards with a reasonable answer given. Students exchange MathBoards and write an equation using an empty box to represent the missing number. Then they solve the equation and write what the missing number represents. Students return the MathBoards to check each other's equations.

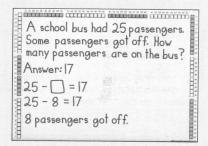

> A school bus had 25 passengers. Some passengers got off. How many passengers are on the bus?
>
> Answer: 17
>
> $25 - \square = 17$
>
> $25 - 8 = 17$
>
> 8 passengers got off.

Also Use
Challenge Master for 3-12

 Math Writing Prompt

Intervention

Write About It
Explain how you know when a problem is missing information.

 Math Writing Prompt

On Level

Explain Your Thinking
How can you use the note taking strategy to help you solve problems with missing information?

 Math Writing Prompt

Challenge

Investigate Math
What are two ways you could find the missing number in this equation: $12 - \square = 5$?

③ Homework and Spiral Review

Homework **Goal:** Additional Practice

This Homework page gives students practice identifying problems with not enough information.

Remembering **Goal:** Spiral Review

This Remembering page would be appropriate anytime after today's lesson.

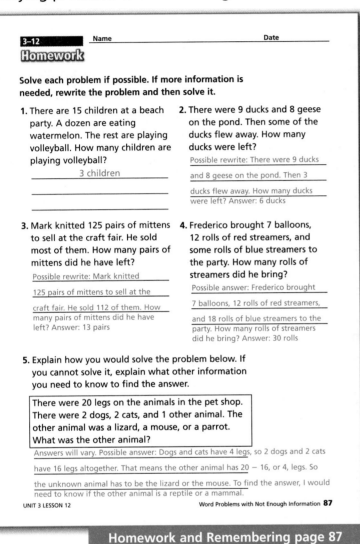

3–12 Name _____ Date _____
Homework

Solve each problem if possible. If more information is needed, rewrite the problem and then solve it.

1. There are 15 children at a beach party. A dozen are eating watermelon. The rest are playing volleyball. How many children are playing volleyball?

   _____ 3 children _____

   _____

   _____

2. There were 9 ducks and 8 geese on the pond. Then some of the ducks flew away. How many ducks were left?

   Possible rewrite: There were 9 ducks

   and 8 geese on the pond. Then 3

   ducks flew away. How many ducks
   were left? Answer: 6 ducks

3. Mark knitted 125 pairs of mittens to sell at the craft fair. He sold most of them. How many pairs of mittens did he have left?

   Possible rewrite: Mark knitted

   125 pairs of mittens to sell at the

   craft fair. He sold 112 of them. How
   many pairs of mittens did he have
   left? Answer: 13 pairs

4. Frederico brought 7 balloons, 12 rolls of red streamers, and some rolls of blue streamers to the party. How many rolls of streamers did he bring?

   Possible answer: Frederico brought

   7 balloons, 12 rolls of red streamers,

   and 18 rolls of blue streamers to the
   party. How many rolls of streamers
   did he bring? Answer: 30 rolls

5. Explain how you would solve the problem below. If you cannot solve it, explain what other information you need to know to find the answer.

   > There were 20 legs on the animals in the pet shop. There were 2 dogs, 2 cats, and 1 other animal. The other animal was a lizard, a mouse, or a parrot. What was the other animal?

   Answers will vary. Possible answer: Dogs and cats have 4 legs, so 2 dogs and 2 cats

   have 16 legs altogether. That means the other animal has 20 − 16, or 4, legs. So

   the unknown animal has to be the lizard or the mouse. To find the answer, I would
   need to know if the other animal is a reptile or a mammal.

UNIT 3 LESSON 12   Word Problems with Not Enough Information **87**

Homework and Remembering page 87

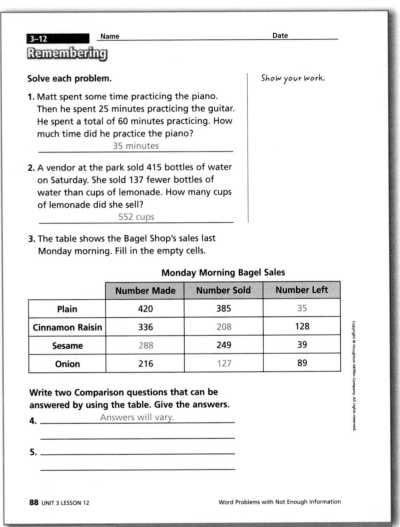

3–12 Name _____ Date _____
Remembering

Solve each problem.   *Show your work.*

1. Matt spent some time practicing the piano. Then he spent 25 minutes practicing the guitar. He spent a total of 60 minutes practicing. How much time did he practice the piano?

   _____ 35 minutes _____

2. A vendor at the park sold 415 bottles of water on Saturday. She sold 137 fewer bottles of water than cups of lemonade. How many cups of lemonade did she sell?

   _____ 552 cups _____

3. The table shows the Bagel Shop's sales last Monday morning. Fill in the empty cells.

   Monday Morning Bagel Sales

	Number Made	Number Sold	Number Left
Plain	420	385	35
Cinnamon Raisin	336	208	128
Sesame	288	249	39
Onion	216	127	89

Write two Comparison questions that can be answered by using the table. Give the answers.

4. _____ Answers will vary. _____

   _____

5. _____

   _____

88 UNIT 3 LESSON 12   Word Problems with Not Enough Information

Homework and Remembering page 88

Home or School Activity

 Math-to-Math Connection

Pattern Puzzle Write these pattern puzzles on the board and have students copy them. Then have students try to determine a rule so that each sequence follows a pattern. Once students are done, have them compare their completed patterns, and encourage them to discuss the similarities and differences between each of the solutions. Make sure students see that some of the puzzles do not have enough information, and in these cases, students will find that many solutions may be correct for one pattern puzzle.

2, 4, ___, ___, 10, ___

___, 3, ___, ___, ___, ___

AA, ZZ, ___, YY, CC, ___, DD, WW, ___

Ab, ___, Cd, De, ___, ____

Aa, ___, ___, ___, ___

UNIT 3
LESSON

13

Solve Two-Step Word Problems

Lesson Objective
● Solve word problems requiring two steps.

Vocabulary
net gain

The Day at a Glance

Today's Goals	Materials	Math Talk
Quick Practice Count coin values. **1 Teaching the Lesson** A: Represent and solve two-step word problems. **2 Extending the Lesson** ▶ Differentiated Instruction **3 Homework and Spiral Review**	Index cards Highlighters (2 different colors) Student Activity Book pages 161–162 Homework and Remembering pages 89–90 Math Journals	In today's activities, the students are involved in discussion as they ▶ share their strategies for solving two-step word problems

Quick Practice

   5 MINUTES   **Goal:** Count coin values.

Counting Coins The Student Leader writes a sequence of quarters (Qs), dimes (Ds), nickels (Ns), and pennies (Ps) on the board, in that order. The leader points to the coins in order as the class counts on to find the total amount.

Q Q Q Q D D D D N N P P

Leader: Count on to find the total amount.

Class: 25¢, 50¢, 75¢, $1.00, $1.10, $1.20, $1.30, $1.40, $1.45, $1.50, $1.51, $1.52

The leader adds coins to or erases coins from the sequence, and the class counts again. Repeat this several times.

① Teaching the Lesson

Solve Two-Step Word Problems

 55 MINUTES

Goal: Represent and solve two-step word problems.

Materials: Student Activity Book pages 161–162

 NCTM Standards:
Number and Operations
Problem Solving
Reasoning and Proof

 Class Management

To keep students interested and to check they understand how to solve problems with two steps, you may want to divide the problems in this activity into two or three sections. Have students solve problem 1 and have the class review it. Proceed in this manner by solving problems 2 and 3 and then work on problems 4–6 and finally problems 7–10.

3–13 Class Activity

Name _____ Date _____

▶ **Solve Two-Step Word Problems**

Show your work.

Solve each problem. Label your answers.

1. The Hillside bus had 14 passengers. When it stopped, 5 people got off and 8 people got on. How many people are riding the Hillside bus now?

   _____ 17 people _____

2. There are 15 fish in a tank. 12 are goldfish, and the others are angelfish. How many more goldfish are there than angelfish?

   _____ 9 goldfish _____

3. Luther had 11 sheets of colored paper. 6 were orange, and the rest were blue. Today he used 2 sheets of blue paper. How many sheets of blue paper does Luther have now?

   _____ 3 sheets _____

4. Sun Mi picked 14 apricots. Celia picked 5 fewer apricots than Sun Mi. How many apricots did Sun Mi and Celia pick altogether?

   _____ 23 apricots _____

5. Annie took 8 photographs at home and 7 photographs at school. Her sister Amanda took 6 fewer photographs than Annie. How many photographs did Amanda take?

   _____ 9 photographs _____

UNIT 3 LESSON 13   Solve Two-Step Word Problems **161**

Student Activity Book page 161

▶ **Solve Two-Step Word Problems** WHOLE CLASS

Using **Solve and Discuss**, have students solve problems 1–5 on Student Activity Book page 161. Make sure a variety of methods are presented. There are different ways to approach the problems on the next page. Equations and diagrams are shown in the descriptions, but many students will use representations that differ from those shown, and will be able to do some or all of the steps mentally.

Problem 1: Add and subtract according to how the problem is presented.

$$14 - 5 + 8 = \boxed{17}$$

start got got now
       off   on

Another way to solve the problem is to subtract the number of people who got off from the number who got on, and add the result to the original number of passengers.

$$8 - 5 = 3 \rightarrow 14 + 3 = \boxed{17}$$

got got   start   now
on   off

Problem 2: Find the number of angelfish, and then find the difference between this number and the number of goldfish.

total
15
12    $\boxed{3}$
goldfish   angelfish

$$12 + \boxed{3} = 15 \rightarrow$$
   g   a   t

angelfish $\boxed{3}$ $\boxed{?}$
goldfish $\boxed{12}$ $? = 9$

Problem 3: Find the number of blue sheets Luther started with, and subtract 2 to find the number he has now.

total
11
6    $\boxed{5}$
orange   blue

$$6 + \boxed{5} = 11 \rightarrow 5 - \boxed{2} = 3$$
  o   b   t   had used now

Another way to figure it out is to subtract the 2 sheets Luther used from the original 11, and then figure out how many of the remaining sheets must be blue if 6 are orange.

$$11 - 2 = \boxed{9} \rightarrow$$
had used now

9
6    $\boxed{3}$
orange   blue

$$6 + \boxed{3} = 9$$
  o   b   t

Activity continued ▶

Solve Two-Step Word Problems **355**

Problem 4: Find the number of apricots Celia picked, and add the result to the 14 Sun Mi picked.

Celia $\boxed{?}\;\boxed{5}$ Sun Mi $\boxed{14}$ $? = 9 \;\rightarrow\; 9 + 14 = \boxed{23}$

                                   c   s   total

Problem 5: Add 8 and 7 to find the total number of photographs Annie took, and subtract 6 to find the number Amanda took.

$8 + 7 = \boxed{15}$ $\rightarrow$ Amanda $\boxed{?}\;\boxed{6}$ $? = 9$
home school total   Annie $\boxed{15}$

▶ Solve and Discuss   WHOLE CLASS

Student Activity Book page 162

Continue working through problems 6–10 on Student Activity Book page 162 with the class. Possible approaches students may use are described on the next page. For a sample classroom dialogue, see **Math Talk in Action** in the side column.

⟨123⟩ Math Talk in Action

Will someone share how they solved Problem 8?

Carlo: Well, I started by figuring out that eight dimes is the same as 80¢. But that's not what the problem is about.

That's right. What did you do next?

Carlo: I added 4 to 8 to find out how many nickels Katie had. She had 12 nickels.

Good. Then what?

Carlo: I subtracted 5 from 12. Now Katie has 7 nickels.

That's right. One important thing to do every time you solve a word problem is to read it all the way through before you try to solve it. Why do you think that's a good idea?

Lewis: That way you know what the problem is about.

Problem 6: Add to find the number of mice and gerbils, and subtract the result from 16 or use a Math Mountain to find the number of hamsters.

$$5 + 3 = \boxed{8}$$
mice gerbils total

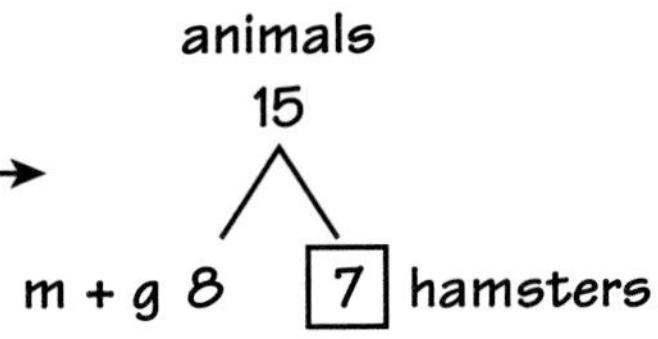

→

animals
15

m + g 8 $\boxed{7}$ hamsters

$$15 - 8 = \boxed{7}$$
a   m + g   h

or

$$8 + \boxed{7} = 15$$
m + g   h   a

You could also start with 15, subtract the number of mice, and then subtract the number of gerbils.

$$15 - 5 - 3 = \boxed{7}$$
animals   mice   gerbils   hamsters

Problem 7: Add 234 and 138 to find the total number of books lent out, and then subtract the 78 books that were returned.

$$234 + 138 = \boxed{372}$$
Saturday   Sunday   total
lent out

→

$$372 - 78 = \boxed{294}$$
lent out   returned   not
returned

Another way is to subtract 78 from 138 to get the "net lent out" for Sunday, and add this to the number lent out on Saturday.

$$138 - 78 = \boxed{60}$$
lent out   returned
Sunday   Sunday

→

$$234 + 60 = \boxed{294}$$
lent out   not
Saturday   returned

Activity continued ▶

Problem 8: Find the number of nickels Katie had to start with, and then subtract 5 nickels.

Dimes $\boxed{8}$ $\boxed{4}$? = 12 → 12 − 5 = $\boxed{7}$
Nickels $\boxed{\quad ? \quad}$ had took left
                                           out

Or you might reason that if Katie started with 4 more nickels than dimes, and then takes out 5 nickels, she will have 1 fewer nickel than dimes, or 7 nickels.

Problem 9: First find the number of sharp colored pencils Tony had to start with, and subtract the result from 12, or use a Math Mountain to figure out how many colored pencils his uncle gave him.

total
14
 /\
9 $\boxed{5}$
dull sharp

9 + $\boxed{5}$ = 14 →
dull sharp total

sharp
now
12
 /\
5 $\boxed{7}$
sharp not
then sharp

5 + $\boxed{7}$ = 12
sharp not sharp
then sharp now

You could also add 9 to 12 to find the number of colored pencils Tony has now, and subtract the 14 colored pencils he had to start with.

9 + 12 = $\boxed{21}$ →   21 − 14 = $\boxed{7}$
dull sharp total   total before now
         now   now   sharp

Problem 10: Find the total number of strawberries José ate, and then find the difference between that total and the 9 strawberries Lori ate.

6 + 7 = 13 →   Lori $\boxed{9}$ $\boxed{?}$? = 4
start more total   José $\boxed{\quad 13 \quad}$
        José

☑ **Ongoing Assessment**

To check that students understand the process of solving two-step word problems, ask them to read one of the problems in this lesson and identify what their first step would be when solving it. Ask if it is possible to solve the problem by using a different first step.

② Extending the Lesson

Activities for Individualizing

Intervention
for students having difficulty

PAIRS

Color the Steps

Materials: Highlighters (2 different colors per student), Homework and Remembering page 89

On Homework page 89, have students highlight each step of problem 1 with different colored highlighters. Seeing the two colors will remind students that there are two steps to be done to solve the word problem. Students may also find it helpful to write Step 1 and Step 2 in the work space provided and highlight them also.

Show your work.

Todd's Dad cut 12 slices of mango. Todd ate 4 of them. Then Todd's mom cut 6 more slices. How many slices of mango were left?

Step 1
$12 - 4 = 8$

Step 2
$8 + 6 = 14$ slices

Students should compare their two steps and answers. Some students may find they have the same answer, but highlighted different steps. Have them discuss these similarities and differences.

On Level
for students having success

PAIRS

Match It

Materials: Index cards (2 per pair)

Each student should write a two-step word problem on an index card. On a strip of paper they should write the equation they would use to solve the problem and fold the paper so the other student cannot see it. Next, students should trade index cards and solve the word problems. Students should write the equation they used on a strip of paper. Finally, both students should compare the equations they wrote. Students should discuss any similarities and differences between the ways they solved the word problems and correct any errors.

Eliza took 13 photos from inside her car and 5 photos from outside her car. If she has a roll of 24 pictures, how many photos can she still take?

$24 - 13 - 5 = 6$ photos

Challenge
for students seeking a challenge

SMALL GROUPS

The Ultimate Word Problem

Materials: Index cards (1 per student)

Have students write a two-step word problem that includes extra information and hidden information on an index card. Then have them exchange their problem with the student to their right. Students solve each other's problems and discuss their solutions.

Nick has 180 pennies and 12 nickels. His sister has 9 quarters. Nick spent 50¢. How much money does he have left?

$\$1.80 + \$.60 - \$.50 = \$1.90$

Also Use
Challenge Master for 3-13

 Math Writing Prompt

Intervention

In Your Own Words
How can you check that your answer to a two-step word problem is correct?

 Math Writing Prompt

On Level

Write Your Own
Brynne wrote this equation $8 - 4 + 2 = 6$ to solve a word problem. Write a word problem that Brynne may have solved.

 Math Writing Prompt

Challenge

Investigate Math
Write a two-step word problem and explain how to solve it in two different ways.

3 Homework and Spiral Review

3-13
Homework **Goal:** Additional Practice

This Homework page allows students to practice solving two-step word problems.

3-13
Remembering **Goal:** Spiral Review

This Remembering page would be appropriate anytime after today's lesson.

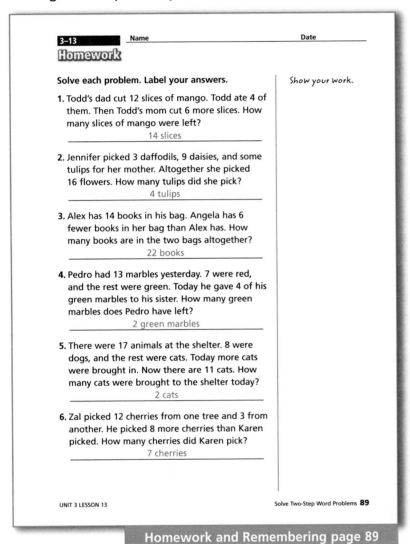

3-13 Name_____ Date_____
Homework

Solve each problem. Label your answers.   Show your work.

1. Todd's dad cut 12 slices of mango. Todd ate 4 of them. Then Todd's mom cut 6 more slices. How many slices of mango were left?
   _____14 slices_____

2. Jennifer picked 3 daffodils, 9 daisies, and some tulips for her mother. Altogether she picked 16 flowers. How many tulips did she pick?
   _____4 tulips_____

3. Alex has 14 books in his bag. Angela has 6 fewer books in her bag than Alex has. How many books are in the two bags altogether?
   _____22 books_____

4. Pedro had 13 marbles yesterday. 7 were red, and the rest were green. Today he gave 4 of his green marbles to his sister. How many green marbles does Pedro have left?
   _____2 green marbles_____

5. There were 17 animals at the shelter. 8 were dogs, and the rest were cats. Today more cats were brought in. Now there are 11 cats. How many cats were brought to the shelter today?
   _____2 cats_____

6. Zal picked 12 cherries from one tree and 3 from another. He picked 8 more cherries than Karen picked. How many cherries did Karen pick?
   _____7 cherries_____

UNIT 3 LESSON 13   Solve Two-Step Word Problems **89**

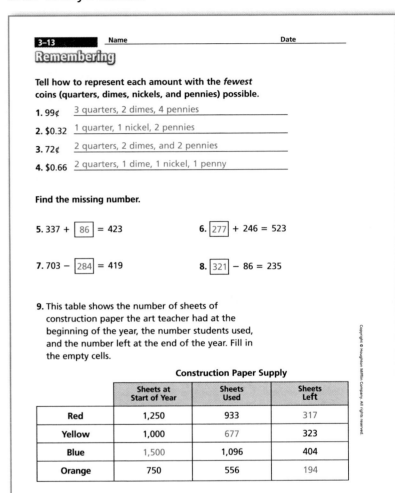

3-13 Name_____ Date_____
Remembering

Tell how to represent each amount with the *fewest* coins (quarters, dimes, nickels, and pennies) possible.

1. 99¢ _3 quarters, 2 dimes, 4 pennies_

2. $0.32 _1 quarter, 1 nickel, 2 pennies_

3. 72¢ _2 quarters, 2 dimes, and 2 pennies_

4. $0.66 _2 quarters, 1 dime, 1 nickel, 1 penny_

Find the missing number.

5. 337 + 86 = 423

6. 277 + 246 = 523

7. 703 − 284 = 419

8. 321 − 86 = 235

9. This table shows the number of sheets of construction paper the art teacher had at the beginning of the year, the number students used, and the number left at the end of the year. Fill in the empty cells.

Construction Paper Supply

	Sheets at Start of Year	Sheets Used	Sheets Left
Red	1,250	933	317
Yellow	1,000	677	323
Blue	1,500	1,096	404
Orange	750	556	194

90 UNIT 3 LESSON 13   Solve Two-Step Word Problems

Home or School Activity

 Social Studies Connection

Mathematicians in History Throughout history there have been many successful mathematicians whose ideas and discoveries are still used today. For example, Ada Byron Lovelace (1815–1852) used mathematics to help design and explain the Analytical Engine (the first computer). Divide students into small groups and have them research assigned mathematicians. A sample list is provided at the right. Have students determine when and where their mathematician lived, and find one contribution they made to mathematics.

Famous Mathematicians

Ada Byron Lovelace (1815–1852)
Leonardo Fibonacci (1170–1250)
Herman Hollerith (1860–1929)
Evelyn Boyd Granville (1924–)
J. Napier (1550–1617)
Sophie Germain (1776–1831)

360 UNIT 3 LESSON 13

UNIT 3
LESSON
14

Solve Multi-Step Word Problems

Lesson Objective
- Solve multi-step word problems requiring two or more steps.

The Day at a Glance

Today's Goals	Materials	Math Talk
Quick Practice Count coin values.	MathBoard materials	In today's activities, the students are involved in discussion as they
1 Teaching the Lesson A1: Solve multi-step word problems. A2: Work in small groups to solve a challenging problem.	Index cards Sentence strips Student Activity Book pages 163–166	▸ explain their strategies for solving multi-step word problems
2 Extending the Lesson ▸ Going Further: Work Backward ▸ Differentiated Instruction	Homework and Remembering pages 91–92 Math Journals	
3 Homework and Spiral Review	*Math Mysteries* by Jack Silbert (Scholastic, 1995)	

Quick Practice

 5 MINUTES   **Goal:** Count coin values.

Counting Coins: The Student Leader writes a sequence of quarters (Qs), dimes (Ds), nickels (Ns), and pennies (Ps) on the board, in that order. The leader points to the coins in order as the class counts on to find the total amount.

Q Q Q Q Q Q D D D N P

Leader: Count on to find the total amount.

Class: 25¢, 50¢, 75¢, $1.00, $1.25, $1.50, $1.60, $1.70, $1.80, $1.85, $1.86

The leader adds coins to or erases coins from the sequence, and the class counts again. Repeat this several times.

Teaching the Lesson

Solve Multi-Step Word Problems

 25 MINUTES

Goal: Solve multi-step word problems.

Materials: Student Activity Book page 163

 NCTM Standards:
Number and Operations
Problem Solving
Reasoning and Proof
Communication

Class Management

Because of the number and complexity of the word problems in this lesson, be sure to allow enough time for this activity. Have students solve problem 1 and then have the class review it. Continue with problems 2–6 and have the class ask questions and review the steps they took to solve the word problems.

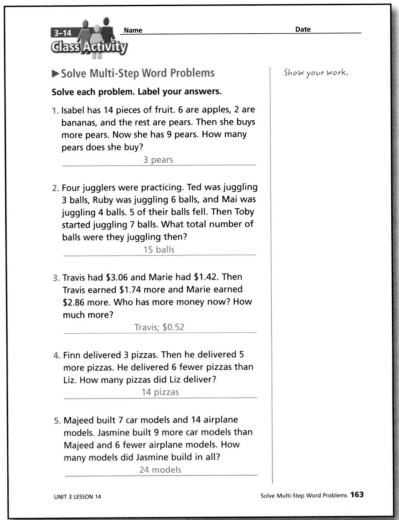

Student Activity Book page 163

▶ Solve Multi-Step Word Problems [WHOLE CLASS]

The multi-step word problems in this lesson are more complex than those in Lesson 13.

Encourage students to organize and keep track of their work by taking notes and labeling their drawings and equations.

Using **Solve and Discuss,** have students solve problems 1–5 on Student Activity Book page 163. There are some ways to approach the problems on the next page. Equations and diagrams are described, but many students will use representations that differ from those shown, and some will be able to do some or all of the steps mentally.

Problem 1: First, find the total number of apples and bananas. Then figure out how many pears Isabel started with. Finally, figure out how many pears she bought.

$$6 + 2 = \boxed{8} \quad \rightarrow \quad \overset{\text{total}}{14}$$

apples bananas a + b

$$8 \quad \boxed{6}$$
a + b   pears

$$8 + 6 = \boxed{14} \quad \rightarrow \quad \overset{\text{total pears}}{9}$$
a + b   pears   total

$$6 \quad \boxed{3}$$
pears   pears
at start bought

$$6 + \boxed{3} = 9$$
start bought total

Problem 2: Add and subtract in the order the information is given.

$$3 \quad + \quad 6 \quad + \quad 4 \quad - \quad 5 \quad + \quad 7$$
Ted   Ruby   Mai   Fell   Toby

Another way to solve this problem is to first find the total number of balls in the air, and then subtract the number that fell.

$$3 \quad + \quad 6 \quad + \quad 4 \quad + \quad 7 \quad - \quad 5$$
Ted   Ruby   Mai   Toby   Fell

In either case, the numbers can be grouped to simplify the calculations. Here we group to get two 10s.

$$\overset{10}{\underbrace{③ \quad + \quad ⑥ \quad + \quad ④}_{} \quad + \quad ⑦ \quad - \quad 5 \quad = \quad 10 + 10 - 5}$$
Ted   Ruby   Mai   Toby   Fell
              10

Problem 3: First find the amount each person has.

Travis: $3.06 + $1.74 = $4.80

Marie: $1.42 + $2.86 = $4.28

Travis has more money. Find how much more by subtracting, or by adding on from $4.28 to $4.80.

Activity continued ▶

Teaching Note

Math Background Grouping the numbers as described in this activity involves applying the Commutative and Associative Properties of Addition.

The Commutative Property says that for any real numbers *a* and *b*,

$$a + b = b + a$$

This means we can switch the order in which two numbers are added and the sum will remain the same. For example, 3 + 5 = 5 + 3.

The Associative Property says that for any real numbers *a*, *b*, and *c*,

$$a + (b + c) = (a + b) + c$$

This means we can group the numbers in an addition expression in any way we want and the sum will remain the same. For example, 3 + (5 + 2) = (3 + 5) + 2.

You don't need to teach students these properties at this time, as most students use them naturally when they add. These properties are formally introduced in Unit 4.

Differentiated Instruction

English Learners Although this activity is not labeled as an English Learner activity, this activity (like many others in this book) is ideal for English Learners. Explaining their strategies aloud and showing their thinking visually is not only important for solving a problem but also for checking their understanding.

Problem 4: First, find the total number of pizzas Finn delivered. Then use the fact that Liz delivered 6 more to figure out how many she delivered.

$$3 \quad + \quad 5 \quad = \quad \boxed{8}$$
pizza   more   total
Finn

→

Finn $\boxed{8}$ ⑥

Liz $\boxed{?}$

? = 14

 Math Talk in Action

Can you change the order of the steps to figure out problem 4?

Matilda: No.

Why not?

Matilda: Because finding the number of pizzas Liz delivered depends on knowing the number of pizzas Finn delivered.

Problem 5: Find the number of car models and airplane models Jasmine built, and then add the results.

J's cars $\boxed{7}$ ⑨   J's planes $\boxed{?}$ ⑥

M's cars $\boxed{?}$ M's planes $\boxed{14}$

? = 16   ? = 8

→

$$16 \quad + \quad 8 \quad = \quad \boxed{24}$$
J's cars   J's planes   total

Activity 2

Solve Challenging Word Problems

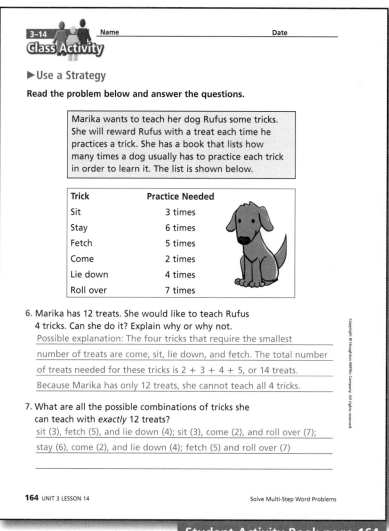

Student Activity Book page 164

 20 MINUTES

Goal: Work in small groups to solve a challenging problem.

Materials: Student Activity Book page 164

 NCTM Standards:
Number and Operations
Problem Solving
Reasoning and Proof
Connections
Representations

▶ Use a Strategy PAIRS

Have students work in pairs to solve the multi-step word problems on Student Activity Book page 164. Select several pairs to share their strategies and solutions.

One strategy for finding all the possible combinations in problem 6 is to start with the first item on the list (sit), which requires 3 treats. Then, figure out how many treats Marika would have left after teaching this trick; in this case, 9. Finally, look for combinations of two tricks (or one additional trick) with this number as the "treat total." Repeat this process for the other items on the list.

 Ongoing Assessment

To check understanding of solving multi-step word problems, have students solve these problems or others like them.

- Jamil had 7 dimes in his pocket. Then he put one dollar's worth of quarters in the same pocket. How many coins does he have now?

- Yvette has 17 books. Eight are mysteries and the rest are science fiction books. Then her grandmother gave her 3 more science fiction books. How many science fiction books does she have now?

Extending the Lesson

Going Further: Work Backward

Goal: Use the Work Backward strategy to solve word problems.

Materials: Student Activity Book pages 165–166, *Math Mysteries* by Jack Silbert

✔ **NCTM Standards:**
Number and Operations
Problem Solving
Reasoning and Proof

▶ Introduce the Work Backward Strategy WHOLE CLASS

Explain to students that the word problems they have solved so far involved following steps in the order they happen to find an answer. In the problems in this activity, an end result is given and they will need to work backward to find what number there was to start with.

Write the following word problem on the board and work though the problem with students.

There were 4 pies left over from a feast. 12 pies were eaten at the feast. Princess May took 2 pies back to her castle before the feast was over. How many pies were at the feast at the beginning?

- How many pies were left over at the feast? 4 pies

- How many pies were eaten or taken by someone?
  14: 12 pies were eaten and Princess May took 2.

- How can I find out how many pies there were in the beginning? You can add 4 and 14 which is 18 pies.

▶ Use the Work Backward Strategy

SMALL GROUPS

Have students solve problem 1 on Student Activity Book page 165 in small groups. Select several groups to share their solutions. Students may use different representations than those shown below, and some will be able to do some or all of the steps mentally.

Problem 1: Start with the final length of fishing line. Work backward by adding 8 then keep working backward by adding the lengths of the 2 pieces of fishing line.

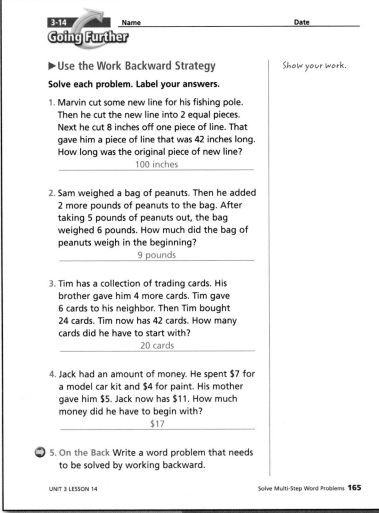

Student Activity Book page 165

Final length	put length back on		1st piece of fishing line		2nd piece of fishing line		original piece of fishing line
42	+ 8	= 50	50	+	50	=	100

Have students complete the remaining problems on the page in small groups. Ask students how they can check their answers to word problems by working backward. Possible response: Put the answer back into the original problem and check that it works.

 **Alternate Approach**

Literature Connection Read aloud or give students a copy of "The Backward Burglar," a short story from Jack Silbert's *Math Mysteries*. Have students work in small groups to solve the problem by using the Work Backward strategy.

Intervention
for students having difficulty

SMALL GROUPS

Cut It Out!

Materials: MathBoard materials, sentence strips

Prepare sentence strips for each group as seen below. Then, have students work as a group to move around or cut the strips in a way that helps them organize the information in order to solve the problem.

> 8 are novels.
>
> 3 are science fiction and the rest are mysteries.
>
> There are 18 books on Ravati's book shelf.
>
> Ravati put 5 more mysteries on the shelf.
>
> How many mysteries are on her shelf now?
>
> 8N + 3SF = 11
>
> 18 − 11 = 7 mysteries
>
> 7M + 5M = 12 mysteries

On Level
for students having success

SMALL GROUPS

Build a Problem

Materials: MathBoard materials (1 per student)

This activity works best with four or more students per group. Have students write the first sentence of a multi-step word problem on their MathBoards. Then, students pass their MathBoards to the student sitting to the left. That student writes the next sentence that would make sense in the word problem. Students continue passing and writing more sentences, letting the sentences grow into a complete multi-step word problem. Once all word problems are complete, MathBoards are returned to their original writers and students should try to solve the problems.

> Alice delivered 8 pizzas. Then she delivered 6 more to another party. Each pizza cost $5. Liz delivered 5 more pizzas than Alice. How much money did Liz make?
>
> 8 + 6 = 14 Alice
>
> 14 + 5 = 19 Liz
>
> 5,5,5,5,5   5,5,5,5,5
> 5,5,5,5,5   5,5,5,5
> $95

Challenge
for students seeking a challenge

PAIRS

Error Detector

Have pairs write a multi-step problem, list each step of the solution process and answer the problem. Have the pairs trade problems and check that the steps of the solution process are correct and that all steps have been correctly computed. They should also make sure the question is answered. If everything has been done correctly, they should write *correct* on the paper. If there are errors, students should circle them and identify what went wrong. Pairs should then return each problem to the pair that wrote it.

> Salma sold some of her old postcards. Saul bought 12 of the postcards. Then Salma sold postcards to Sam, who bought 9 more than Saul. How many postcards did Salma sell?
>   Solution steps:
>   1. Start with the 12 postcards Saul bought.
>   2. Add the 9 postcards Sam bought.
>   3. That's how many postcards Salma sold.
>   12 + 9 = 21 ANSWER
>
> The answer is not correct. They may have read the problem wrong and did not see that Sam has "9 more than Saul". It should be 12 + 12 + 9 = 33 postcards.

Also Use
Challenge Master for 3-14

 Math Writing Prompt

Intervention

Explain Your Thinking
How can you check your answer to a multi-step word problem?

 Math Writing Prompt

On Level

Reasonable Answers
Is there more than one way to solve a multi-step problem? Give an example.

 Math Writing Prompt

Challenge

Describe Your Method
In a multi-step problem, why is it important to check that the question the problem asks is answered?

③ Homework and Spiral Review

3–14
Homework **Goal:** Additional Practice

✓ Include students' completed Homework page as part of their portfolios.

3–14
Remembering **Goal:** Spiral Review

This Remembering page would be appropriate anytime after today's lesson.

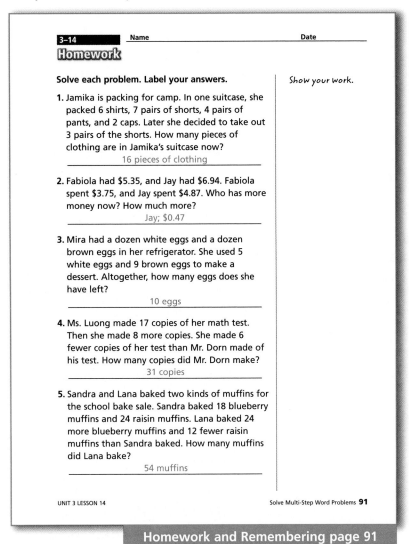

3–14 Name _____ Date _____
Homework

Solve each problem. Label your answers.

Show your work.

1. Jamika is packing for camp. In one suitcase, she packed 6 shirts, 7 pairs of shorts, 4 pairs of pants, and 2 caps. Later she decided to take out 3 pairs of the shorts. How many pieces of clothing are in Jamika's suitcase now?

   16 pieces of clothing

2. Fabiola had $5.35, and Jay had $6.94. Fabiola spent $3.75, and Jay spent $4.87. Who has more money now? How much more?

   Jay; $0.47

3. Mira had a dozen white eggs and a dozen brown eggs in her refrigerator. She used 5 white eggs and 9 brown eggs to make a dessert. Altogether, how many eggs does she have left?

   10 eggs

4. Ms. Luong made 17 copies of her math test. Then she made 8 more copies. She made 6 fewer copies of her test than Mr. Dorn made of his test. How many copies did Mr. Dorn make?

   31 copies

5. Sandra and Lana baked two kinds of muffins for the school bake sale. Sandra baked 18 blueberry muffins and 24 raisin muffins. Lana baked 24 more blueberry muffins and 12 fewer raisin muffins than Sandra baked. How many muffins did Lana bake?

   54 muffins

UNIT 3 LESSON 14   Solve Multi-Step Word Problems **91**

Homework and Remembering page 91

3–14 Name _____ Date _____
Remembering

Round each value to the nearest dollar.

1. $3.50
   $4.00

2. $2.15
   $2.00

3. $7.87
   $8.00

4. $9.79
   $10.00

5. $4.09
   $4.00

6. $5.33
   $5.00

7. The table shows the number of pairs of glasses and contact lenses an optician sold over three months. Fill in the empty cells.

Sales at Optical World

	Glasses	Contacts	Total
May	74	132	206
June	109	105	214
July	68	83	151

8. Write a comparison question using the data in the table above and the word *fewer*. Answer your question.

   Answers will vary.

9. Write an addition question about this table.

   Answers will vary.

92 UNIT 3 LESSON 14   Solve Multi-Step Word Problems

Homework and Remembering page 92

Home or School Activity

Language Arts Connection

Step-by-Step Directions Have students brainstorm a list of activities that need to be done in a special order (brushing their teeth, making a sandwich, and so on). Then have them list as many "time-order" words they can think of that help them explain these activities in sequential order (*first, then, next, finally, lastly,* and so on). Finally, have students write a "How-To" paragraph explaining how to do something in order. Their paragraphs should include a topic sentence, the steps in sequential order, and a closing sentence.

How to Brush Your Teeth

You need to brush your teeth to keep your mouth healthy. First, you open the toothpaste. Then, you squirt the toothpaste on your brush. Next, you move the brush all over your teeth. Finally, you wash your toothbrush off and put it away. Brushing your teeth every day will keep the cavities away.

Read and Create Bar Graphs

Vocabulary

axes
vertical axis
horizontal axis
vertical bar graph
horizontal bar graph
scale

Lesson Objectives

● Write and answer questions using horizontal and vertical bar graphs.

● Create bar graphs to represent data from tables.

The Day at a Glance

Today's Goals	Materials	Math Talk
Quick Practice Round whole numbers to the nearest ten or hundred.	Overhead projector and transparencies (optional)	In today's activities, the students are involved in discussion as they
1 Teaching the Lesson A1: Read and interpret bar graphs. A2: Create bar graphs.	Index cards Rulers Connecting cubes	► read bar graphs ► write and answer questions about bar graphs
2 Extending the Lesson ► Going Further: Surveys ► Differentiated Instruction	Class list 10 × 10 Grid (Copymaster M43)	► make bar graphs
3 Homework and Spiral Review	Student Activity Book pages 167–170 Homework and Remembering pages 93–94 Math Journals	

Quick Practice

🕐 **5 MINUTES** **Goal:** Round whole numbers to the nearest ten or hundred.

Rounding Practice The Student Leader writes the six numbers below on the board.

617   382   455   621   1,792   748

The leader points to each number and says either "Round to the nearest ten" or "Round to the nearest hundred." When the leader gives a signal, students respond in unison with the rounded number.

Leader (pointing to 617): Round to the nearest hundred.

Class: 600

① Teaching the Lesson

Read Bar Graphs

 25 MINUTES

Goal: Read and interpret bar graphs.

Materials: Student Activity Book page 167, index cards, overhead projector (optional), transparency of Student Activity Book page 167 (optional)

✔ **NCTM Standards:**
Number and Operations
Data Analysis and Probability
Problem Solving
Communication

Teaching Note

Language and Vocabulary Review the words *vertical* and *horizontal* with students. Draw the letter T on the chalkboard. Explain that when we say that a line is vertical, it means that the line goes straight up and down.

▶ Which part of the letter T is vertical? the bottom part of the T

Explain that when we say that a line is horizontal, it means that the line goes straight across.

▶ Which part of the letter T is horizontal? the top part of the T

Explain to students that an *axis* is at the side or bottom of a graph, and that an axis has labels. Have them look at the graph *Flowers in Mary's Garden.*

▶ Find the axis called *Number of Flowers.* Is this the horizontal axis or the vertical axis? horizontal How do you know? It goes straight across.

▶ Find the axis called *Kind of Flower.* Is this the horizontal axis or the vertical axis? vertical How do you know? It goes straight up and down.

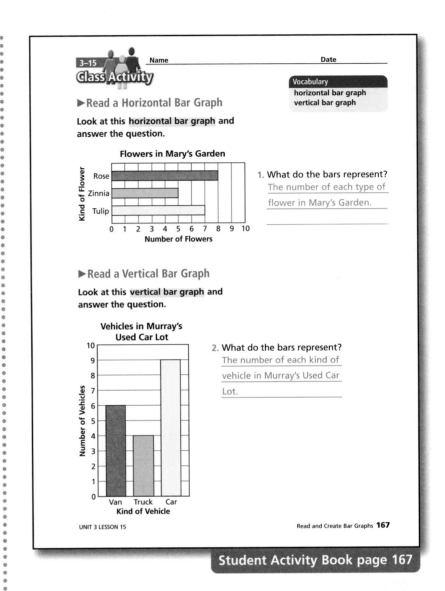

Student Activity Book page 167

▶ Read a Horizontal Bar Graph [WHOLE CLASS]

Have students look at the horizontal bar graph at the top of Student Activity Book page 167 or display a transparency of this page. Explain to students that *bar graphs* use bars to show information. Explain that a horizontal bar graph has bars that go across. Discuss what the bar graph shows and how to read it.

● What is the title of this graph? *Flowers in Mary's Garden*

Point to the vertical axis (*Kind of Flower*) and tell students the axis on the left is called the *vertical axis.*

● What is the label on the vertical axis? *Kind of Flower*

● What kinds of flowers are there? roses, zinnias, and tulips

● What does each bar represent? a different kind of flower

Point to the horizontal axis and explain that the axis on the bottom is called the *horizontal axis.*

● What is the label on the horizontal axis? *Number of Flowers*

● What do the numbers along the horizontal axis represent? number of flowers

Point out that the arrangement of numbers on the horizontal axis is called the *scale,* and that is used to measure the lengths of the bars.

● How is the scale like a ruler? Possible response: It starts at 0, and the numbers are evenly spaced.

● How many tulips are in Mary's garden? 7 tulips How can you tell? The bar for Tulip goes to the line for the number 7 on the scale.

Then ask questions that require students to interpret the graph.

● Which type of flower are there the most of? roses How do you know? The bar for Rose is the longest.

● How many more roses are there than zinnias? 3 more roses How do you know? The bar for Rose is 3 units longer than the bar for Zinnia; The graph shows there are 8 roses and 5 zinnias, and 8 − 5 = 3.

● How many tulips and zinnias are there altogether? 12 tulips and zinnias How do you know? The bar for Tulip shows there are 7 tulips and the bar for Zinnia shows there are 5 zinnias, and 7 + 5 = 12.

▶ Read a Vertical Bar Graph WHOLE CLASS

Now have students look at the vertical bar graph on the bottom of Student Activity Book page 167. Explain that a vertical bar graph has bars that go up and down. Ask questions that require students to interpret the graph.

● What is the title of this bar graph? *Vehicles in Murray's Used Car Lot*

● How many trucks are in the lot? 4 trucks How do you know? The bar for Truck goes up to the line for 4; The bar for Truck is 4 units long.

● Are there more vans or more cars in the lot? more cars How can you tell? The bar for Car is longer than the bar for Van.

● How many vehicles are there in the lot altogether? 19 vehicles How did you know? There are 6 vans, 4 trucks, and 9 cars, and 6 + 4 + 9 = 19.

Math Talk Have student pairs create and answer more questions based on either graph on Student Activity Book page 167. See **Math Talk in Action** in the side column.

Differentiated Instruction

Extra Help Some students may have difficulty focusing on relevant parts of the bar graph. Show students how to use index cards to cover the parts of the graph that they do not need. For example, if students need to find how many roses are in Mary's garden, they can use an index card to cover the bars for zinnia and tulip. They can use another index card to follow the vertical line from the top of the bar to the number on the horizontal axis.

 Math Talk in Action

Juan: How many more cars than trucks are in Murray's used car lot?

Tina: There are 5 more cars than trucks.

Juan: How did you get 5?

Tina: The bar for car goes up to the line for 9. The bar for truck goes up to the line for 4. 9 minus 4 equals 5.

Read and Create Bar Graphs **371**

Teaching the Lesson (continued)

Create Bar Graphs

 25 MINUTES

Goal: Create bar graphs.

Materials: Student Activity Book page 168, overhead projector (optional), transparency of Student Activity Book page 168 (optional), ruler, connecting cubes, index cards

✓ **NCTM Standards:**
Number and Operations
Data Analysis and Probability
Problem Solving
Communication

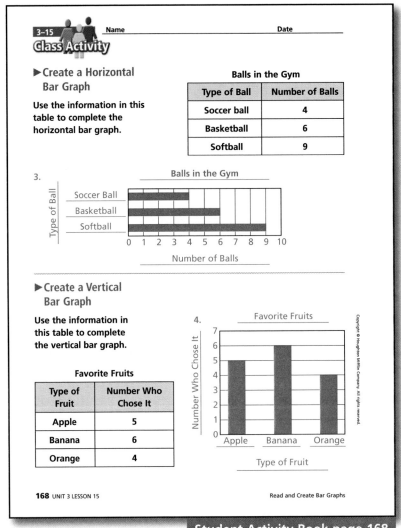

Student Activity Book page 168

▶ Create a Horizontal Bar Graph WHOLE CLASS

Have students look at the table at the top of Student Activity Book page 168 or display a transparency of the page. Then ask:

● **What does this table show?** the number of different kinds of balls in the gym

Tell students that they will make a horizontal bar graph showing the information in the table.

Guide students with their graphs by asking the following questions.

● **What should the title of our graph be?** Balls in the Gym

● **What should the label for the vertical axis be?** Type of Ball

● **What should we write for the three types of balls?** Soccer ball, Basketball, and Softball

Teaching Note

Watch For! Watch for students who begin their graph scales by writing 1 instead of 0 as the first number.

- What should we label the horizontal axis? Number of Balls

- Next let's make the scale. What do we need to do? Start at 0 and go to 10.

The graph should now look like this:

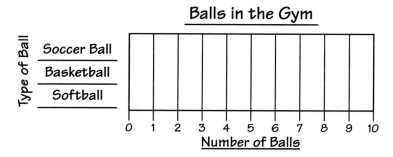

- Now we are ready to make the bars. How many soccer balls are there? 4 soccer balls

- How do we show this on our graph? After "Soccer Ball," draw a bar from 0 to the line for 4 and shade it in. Draw this bar on your graph. Use your ruler to help you draw straight segments.

- What should the bar for "Basketball" look like? It should go from 0 to the line for 6.

- What about the bar for "Softball"? It should go from 0 to 9.

▶ Create a Vertical Bar Graph   INDIVIDUALS

Have students look at the table at the bottom of Student Activity Book page 168.

- What does this table show? favorite fruits

Have students work independently to make a vertical bar graph that shows the information in the table. Suggest they look at the vertical bar graph on Student Activity Book page 167 to help them figure out where the labels go.

- When you make a vertical bar graph, should the bars go up and down or across? up and down

- Where will the scale be? on the left axis

Assist students who are struggling, and allow students to help one another.

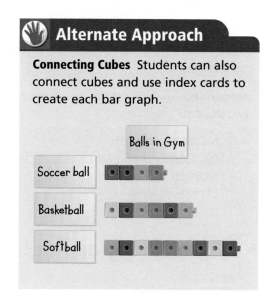

② Extending the Lesson

Going Further: Surveys

Goal: Take a survey and graph the results. Make and check predictions.

Materials: Student Activity Book page 169, class list (1 copy per student)

 NCTM Standards:
Data Analysis and Probability
Problem Solving
Communication

▶ Take a Survey and Record Results

PAIRS

Choose a Topic Have students work in pairs to choose a survey topic and write four answer choices in the tally chart on Student Activity page 169.

Predict Ask students to predict which of the choices will be chosen most often and to write their predictions on a separate piece of paper. After students finish collecting the data, they can check their predictions.

Conduct the Survey Pairs can meet with other students to conduct their survey and record the results. Provide students with a class list to help them keep track of the students they have surveyed.

Remind students how to make tally marks. They should group tally marks and represent 5 votes like this: ⦀⦀.

Graph the Results Once the surveys are complete, have students graph the data from their tally charts and describe their results.

 Class Management

Walk around the room and observe as pairs use their tally charts to create their horizontal bar graphs. Watch for students who omit labels or use incorrect labels on their graphs. Ask questions about their favorites or if their predictions were close.

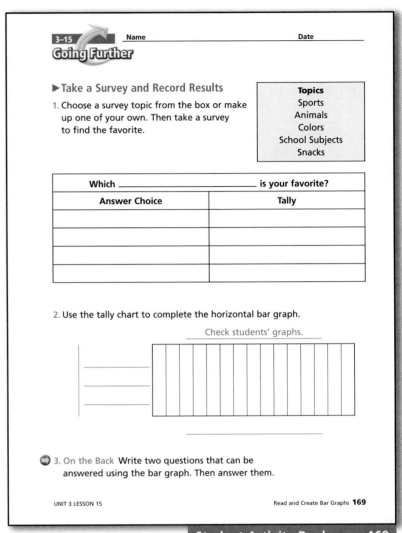

Student Activity Book page 169

▶ Compare Data in Two Forms

WHOLE CLASS

Have students present their data and discuss the two ways they displayed the data.

● Why might you make a tally chart instead of just writing down each answer to the survey question? It is easier to count tallies than to sort and count answers.

● How does a bar graph make it easy to compare data? You can compare different amounts just by comparing the lengths of the bars.

Intervention
for students having difficulty

PAIRS

Cube Count

Materials: red, blue, and green connecting cubes, 10 × 10 Grid (Copymaster M43)

One student uses a handful of cubes and connects the cubes of the same color into cube trains. The other student graphs the results on the 10 × 10 Grid. Students should color one square for each cube of that color.

Students should compare the bar graph to the cube trains. Students then switch roles and repeat the activity.

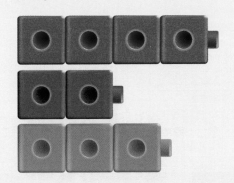

On Level
for students having success

SMALL GROUPS

Team Totals

Have students choose three or four team sports such as softball, football, basketball, and soccer. For each sport, have students find the greatest number of players that a single team can have playing at one time. Then have them work together to create a graph that shows their findings.

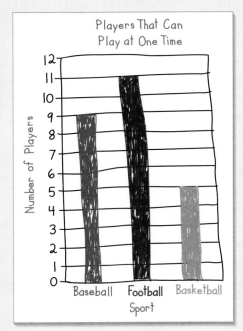

Challenge
for students seeking a challenge

SMALL GROUPS

Explore Scales

Provide students with the bar graph below. Have students discuss how to find the value of the bars. Then have them create and answer questions based on the graph.

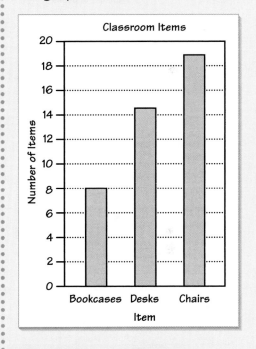

Also Use
Challenge Master for 3-15

 Math Writing Prompt

Intervention
Interpret Data
Look at Student Activity Book page 167. Tell two things the graph shows.

 Math Writing Prompt

On Level
Explain Your Thinking
Think of a few situations in which you might use a bar graph to show data. Explain why a bar graph might be a good way to show the data.

 Math Writing Prompt

Challenge
Draw a Picture
Draw a bar graph that has three bars. The first bar shows 10 students. The second bar is twice as long as the first bar. The third bar is the same length as the second bar. How many students do the three bars show?

③ Homework and Spiral Review

Homework   **Goal:** Additional Practice

This Homework page provides students with more practice reading and making bar graphs.

Remembering   **Goal:** Spiral Review

This Remembering page would be appropriate anytime after today's lesson.

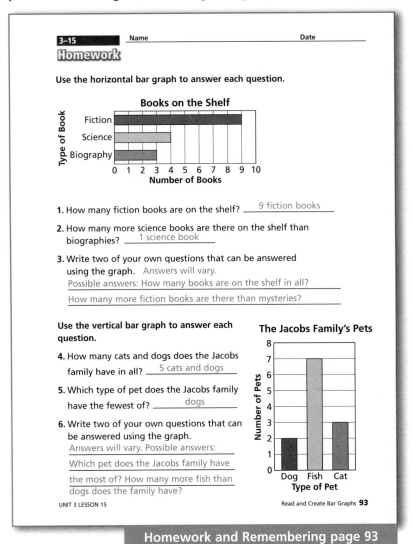

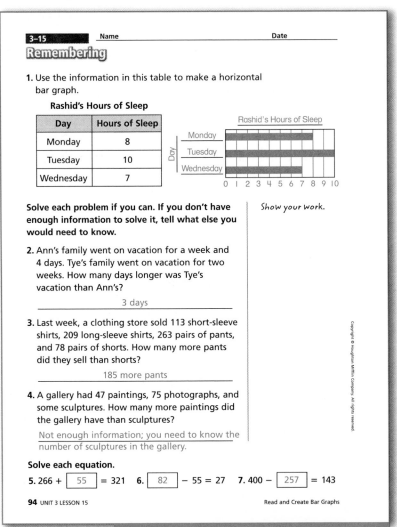

Homework and Remembering page 93

Homework and Remembering page 94

Home or School Activity

Science Connection

How Many Legs? Have students make a bar graph that shows the number of legs on each of the following animals: a chicken, a horse, an ant, and a spider.

Read and Create Bar Graphs with Multi-Digit Numbers

Vocabulary
bar graph
axes
horizontal axis
vertical axis
scale

Lesson Objectives

- Analyze data in horizontal and vertical bar graphs.
- Use information in a table to create horizontal and vertical bar graphs.

The Day at a Glance

Today's Goals	Materials	Math Talk
Quick Practice Round whole numbers to the nearest ten or hundred. **1 Teaching the Lesson** **A1:** Interpret bar graphs with scales that include multi-digit numbers. **A2:** Represent multi-digit data tables with bar graphs. **2 Extending the Lesson** ▶ Differentiated Instruction **3 Homework and Spiral Review**	MathBoard materials Index cards 10 × 10 Grid (Copymaster M43) Centimeter Grid Paper Crayons Data tables (Copymaster M44) Student Activity Book pages 171–174 Homework and Remembering pages 95–96 Math Journals Quick Quiz 3 (Assessment Guide)	In today's activities, the students are involved in discussion as they ▶ interpret bar graphs with multi-digit numbers ▶ write and evaluate questions based on bar graphs ▶ create bar graphs representing multi-digit values

Quick Practice

 5 MINUTES **Goal:** Round whole numbers to the nearest ten or hundred.

Rounding Practice The Student Leader writes the six numbers below on the board. The leader points to the numbers one at a time and says either, "Round to the nearest ten," or, "Round to the nearest hundred." When the leader gives a signal, students respond in unison with the rounded number.

Class Management

Have the Student Leader repeat the series of numbers to make sure that the class has rounded each number to both the nearest ten and the nearest hundred. Monitor the quickness and volume of responses to identify any problems with rounding.

574   105   650   488   1,642   527

Leader (pointing to 574): Round to the nearest hundred.

Class: 600

Teaching the Lesson

Read Bar Graphs with Multi-Digit Numbers

 25 MINUTES

Goal: Interpret bar graphs with scales that include multi-digit numbers.

Materials: Student Activity Book pages 171–172, index cards

✔ **NCTM Standards:**
Number and Operations
Algebra
Data Analysis and Probability
Representation

Teaching Note

Language and Vocabulary Review the words *horizontal, vertical,* and *axis.* Ask students to find a horizontal bar and vertical bar graph in this lesson. Also ask students to tell what information is on the horizontal axis and vertical axis of a graph in this lesson.

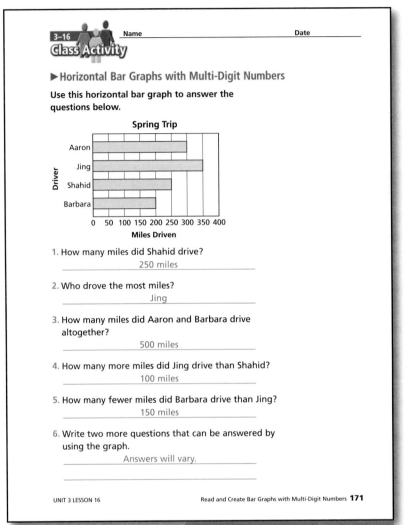

Student Activity Book page 171

► Horizontal Bar Graphs with Multi-Digit Numbers

WHOLE CLASS

Direct students' attention to the horizontal bar graph at the top of Students Activity Book page 171. As a class, examine the graph and its scale.

● What type of bar graph is this? horizontal bar graph

● What does this graph show? the number of miles different people drove on a trip in the spring

● How is the scale of this graph different from the scale of other graphs you have worked on? How is it the same? The scale still starts at 0, but the numbers go much higher than 10.

Explain that although the numbers on the scale might be larger than 10, you read the bar graph the same way as you would if it had a scale of only 0 to 10. Check students' understanding of the multi-digit numbers on the scale.

Ask these questions to check that students understand how to read the graph:

- How many miles did Aaron drive? 300 How do you know? The bar next to Aaron's name stops at the 300 line on the graph.

- Who drove the least number of miles? Barbara How do you know? She has the shortest bar in the graph

Have students work independently to answer the questions following the graph on Student Activity Book page 171. Discuss the answers as a class. Have a few students share the questions they wrote.

 Math Talk in Action

Who wants to share one of the questions you wrote and then answered for this graph?

Mia: Who drove the second greatest number of miles?

Can we answer this question by reading the graph?

Sam: Yes.

Okay. Who can answer Mia's question?

Tom: After Jing, Aaron drove the most miles. His bar on the graph is the second longest.

Correct! Now who else wants to share a question?

Sudir: How long did it take Barbara to drive 200 miles?

Can we answer this question by reading the graph?

Liz: No.

Liz, why don't you think we can answer Sudir's question using the bar graph?

Liz: There is no information on time, so we don't know how long Barbara was driving.

Liz is correct. We don't know the length of each driver's trip. What information would we need to know in order to answer Sudir's question?

Mia: What if we knew how many miles each person was driving per hour?

Great idea, Mia. That information would definitely help us answer the question.

Activity continued ▶

① Teaching the Lesson (continued)

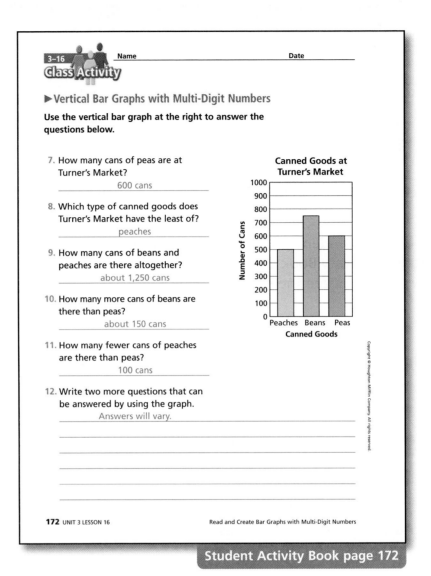

Student Activity Book page 172

Contents of Student Activity Book page 172:

3–16 Class Activity

Name _____ Date _____

▶Vertical Bar Graphs with Multi-Digit Numbers

Use the vertical bar graph at the right to answer the questions below.

7. How many cans of peas are at Turner's Market?
   _____ 600 cans _____

8. Which type of canned goods does Turner's Market have the least of?
   _____ peaches _____

9. How many cans of beans and peaches are there altogether?
   _____ about 1,250 cans _____

10. How many more cans of beans are there than peas?
    _____ about 150 cans _____

11. How many fewer cans of peaches are there than peas?
    _____ 100 cans _____

12. Write two more questions that can be answered by using the graph.
    _____ Answers will vary. _____

Canned Goods at Turner's Market

Number of Cans (y-axis, 0 to 1000)

Canned Goods (x-axis): Peaches, Beans, Peas

172 UNIT 3 LESSON 16   Read and Create Bar Graphs with Multi-Digit Numbers

▶ Vertical Bar Graphs with Multi-Digit Numbers

WHOLE CLASS

As a class, discuss what the bar graph on Student Activity Book page 172 shows and how to read it. Ask about the title and axis labels. Draw students' attention to the bar labeled *Beans*.

● **How is the bar for the cans of beans different from the other bars?** It ends between two lines. There is not a number on the scale to go with it.

● **Can you still figure out how many cans of beans are at the market?** yes **How?** The top of the bar looks like it is halfway between 700 and 800, so there are about 750 cans of beans.

Have students work independently to answer the questions following the graph. Discuss the answers, and have a few students share the questions they wrote.

✓ Ongoing Assessment

To check that students understand interpreting information found in graphs, show them the graph below. Ask them to write three questions that could be answered from the information in the graph. Then have them write the answers.

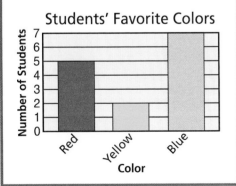

Students' Favorite Colors

Number of Students (y-axis, 0 to 7)

Color (x-axis): Red, Yellow, Blue

Create Bar Graphs with Multi-Digit Numbers

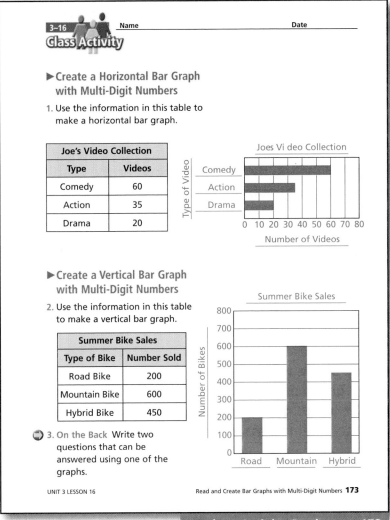

Student Activity Book page 173

 25 MINUTES

Goal: Represent multi-digit data tables with bar graphs.

Materials: MathBoard materials, Student Activity Book pages 173–174, 10 × 10 Grid (Copymaster M43)

 NCTM Standards:
Number and Operations
Algebra
Data Analysis and Probability
Representation
Communication

Differentiated Instruction

Extra Help Have students use 10 × 10 Grid (Copymaster M43) to plan what the scales for their bar graphs should be. Have students label each block at the bottom row of the grid in intervals of 5, 10, 100, or any number that makes sense for the table. Students may want to test different scales before deciding which one to use. They can draw and erase bars of varied lengths to help them decide which scale works best.

▶ Create a Horizontal Bar Graph with Multi-Digit Numbers WHOLE CLASS

Ask the class to look at the table at the top of Student Activity Book page 173. Tell students that they will make a horizontal bar graph to represent the data in the table. Ask these questions to help students begin their graphs.

● What does the table show? the number of videos of various types in Joe's collection

● Judging from the data in the table, how many bars will your graph have? 3 bars What will the bars represent? comedy, action, and drama

● You will be making a horizontal bar graph. Should the bars go up and down or across? across Where will the scale go? on the horizontal axis

Activity continued ▶

Class Management

Observe as students create their horizontal and vertical bar graphs. If some students are having trouble understanding how the intervals between numbers on a scale can affect the dimensions of a graph, draw a blank bar graph on the board.

▶ Use different intervals (for example, 100, 50, and even 25 and 10) to show a bar representing 550 units.

▶ Explain to students that although using smaller intervals sometimes makes it easier to estimate the value of a bar that does not match a number on the scale (such as a bar worth 42 on a graph with a scale labeled in intervals of 5), it can also make a graph clumsy to work with.

Class Management

Looking Ahead At the end of this unit, students will have the opportunity to work on Data Projects as part of the activities in Data Day (see pages 385–390). The individual and class projects have students working with nutrition labels and can tabs, so you may want to remind students to continue collecting these things at home. Remember, these tabs will also be used in Estimation Day (see Unit 7).

Quick Quiz

See the Assessment Guide for Unit 3 Quick Quiz 3.

Ask students to look at the numbers in the table and carefully consider what numbers they think they should put on the scale. For students who suggest labeling the scale by tens, discuss how to draw the bar for the action videos.

● If you label the scale with intervals of 10—0, 10, 20, 30, and so on— how will you draw the bar for the 35 action videos? The end of the bar will be halfway between 30 and 40. **Why?** 35 is not a 10, but it is exactly halfway between two tens, 30 and 40.

For students who suggest labeling by 5s, discuss how far the graph will have to extend to show the total number of comedy videos.

● If you label the scale with intervals of 5—0, 5, 10, 15, 20, and so on— how far will you have to draw the graph in order to show that Joe has 60 comedy videos? The scale will have to show intervals of 5 until at least 60.

▶ Create a Vertical Bar Graph with Multi-Digit Numbers [WHOLE CLASS]

Now have students look at the table *Summer Bike Sales.* Tell them they will make a vertical bar graph of this information. As before, you may want to ask a few questions to get them started. Students may need help determining how to label the scale and how to show that 450 hybrid bikes were sold.

● Using this table, what will the bars on your graph represent? road bikes sold, mountain bikes sold, and hybrid bikes sold

● Will the scale be located on the vertical or horizontal axis? vertical axis

● If you label the scale with intervals of 100—0, 100, 200, 300, 400, and so on—how will you draw the bar for 450 hybrid bikes? The end of the bar will be halfway between 400 and 500.

● If you label the scale with intervals of 50—0, 50, 100, 150, 200, and so on—how will you draw the bar for the hybrid bikes? The bar will end at the 450 line on the graph.

② Extending the Lesson

Intervention
for students having difficulty
PAIRS

Scales for Graphs

Materials: Data Tables (Copymaster M44), Centimeter Grid Paper (Copymaster M31)

Provide pairs with a copy of Data Tables that displays data in the tens and hundreds. Have students choose a data table. On the Centimeter Grid Paper, have each student start to make a bar graph for the table by drawing **only** the scale they would use. Have partners compare their scales and fix any errors.

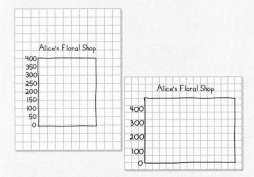

Then have students make the bar graphs on grid paper and compare them.

On Level
for students having success
PAIRS

Graph Data

Materials: Centimeter Grid Paper (Copymaster M31), crayons

Write the following information on the board or chart paper.

In one month, Miranda's Dogwalking Service walks 40 Siberian huskies, 25 German shepherds, and 60 golden retrievers.

Have both students draw a bar graph showing the data using different scales. Then have them compare their graphs and discuss which scale makes the difference in the length of the bars longer.

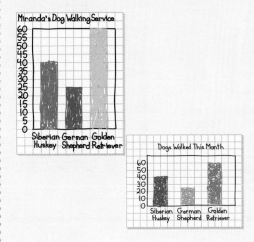

Challenge
for students seeking a challenge
SMALL GROUPS

Double Bar Graphs

Materials: Student Activity Book page 173, crayons

Tell students to add a column to the table about Joe's Video Collection on Student Activity Book page 173 to show the number of videos Joe wishes to own in six months. Then have them think about how to show the new data on the horizontal bar graph they already created without changing the scale or axis labels. If no one suggests a double bar graph, explain that they can draw different colored bars for the new data next to the bars they already drew and make a key to show what each color bar represents.

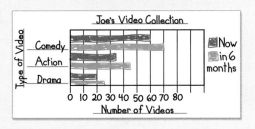

Also Use
Challenge Master for 3-16

Math Writing Prompt
Intervention
Suggest Ideas
List three different things a person could show using a bar graph with multi-digit numbers.

Math Writing Prompt
On Level
Explain Your Reasoning
Explain what you need to do to draw a bar to 25 when you are using a scale 0, 10, 20, 30, and so on.

Math Writing Prompt
Challenge
Difficult Numbers?
Think of three numbers that might be difficult to represent accurately on a bar graph with a scale showing intervals of 50. Then explain how you would change the scale to better represent the numbers.

③ Homework and Spiral Review

3–16
Homework **Goal:** Additional Practice

✔ Include students' completed Homework page as part of their portfolios.

3–16
Remembering **Goal:** Spiral Review

This Remembering page would be appropriate anytime after today's lesson.

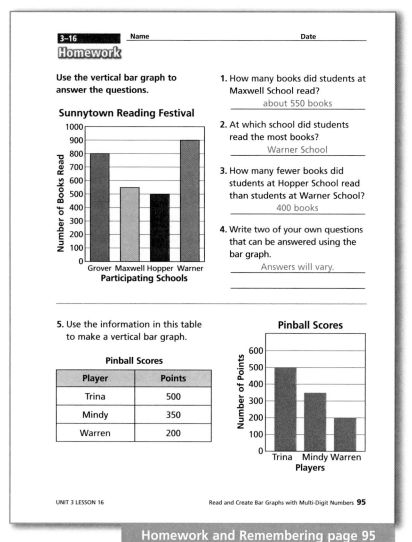

3–16 Name _____ Date _____
Homework

Use the vertical bar graph to answer the questions.

Sunnytown Reading Festival

(Number of Books Read vs Participating Schools: Grover, Maxwell, Hopper, Warner)

1. How many books did students at Maxwell School read?
   about 550 books

2. At which school did students read the most books?
   Warner School

3. How many fewer books did students at Hopper School read than students at Warner School?
   400 books

4. Write two of your own questions that can be answered using the bar graph.
   Answers will vary.

5. Use the information in this table to make a vertical bar graph.

Pinball Scores

Player	Points
Trina	500
Mindy	350
Warren	200

Pinball Scores (bar graph: Number of Points vs Players — Trina, Mindy, Warren)

UNIT 3 LESSON 16   Read and Create Bar Graphs with Multi-Digit Numbers **95**

Homework and Remembering page 95

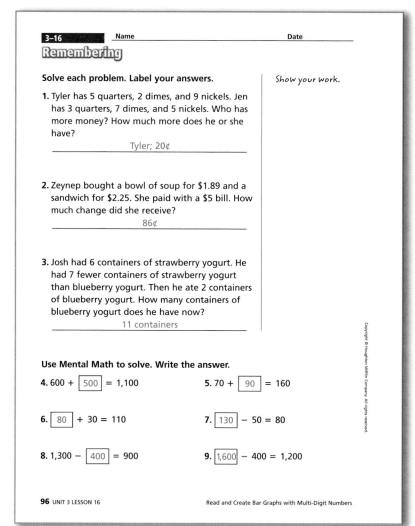

3–16 Name _____ Date _____
Remembering

Solve each problem. Label your answers.   *Show your work.*

1. Tyler has 5 quarters, 2 dimes, and 9 nickels. Jen has 3 quarters, 7 dimes, and 5 nickels. Who has more money? How much more does he or she have?
   Tyler; 20¢

2. Zeynep bought a bowl of soup for $1.89 and a sandwich for $2.25. She paid with a $5 bill. How much change did she receive?
   86¢

3. Josh had 6 containers of strawberry yogurt. He had 7 fewer containers of strawberry yogurt than blueberry yogurt. Then he ate 2 containers of blueberry yogurt. How many containers of blueberry yogurt does he have now?
   11 containers

Use Mental Math to solve. Write the answer.

4. $600 + \boxed{500} = 1{,}100$ 5. $70 + \boxed{90} = 160$

6. $\boxed{80} + 30 = 110$ 7. $\boxed{130} - 50 = 80$

8. $1{,}300 - \boxed{400} = 900$ 9. $\boxed{1{,}600} - 400 = 1{,}200$

96 UNIT 3 LESSON 16   Read and Create Bar Graphs with Multi-Digit Numbers

Homework and Remembering page 96

Home or School Activity

Real-World Connection

Surveying and Reporting Have students survey at least 10 classmates, friends, or family members to find out which of three things they like best. For example, the topic of the survey could be favorite sports (soccer, baseball, or basketball) or favorite desserts (cookies, ice cream, or cake). Students should report the results of their survey in a simple table, then use the table to create a bar graph.

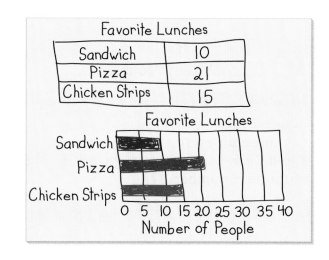

UNIT 3

LESSON

17

Data Day

Objectives

- Collect, organize, represent, interpret, and identify data.
- Use data to make predictions, solve problems, and draw conclusions.

Using Data Day Activities

Data Day is designed to give you maximum flexibility and choice. You can

- choose the activities that are most appropriate for your students
- have all students work on the same activity at the same time, or set up activity centers and allow students to rotate through them after the first two whole class activities are completed
- do many of the activities using only everyday classroom materials
- reuse Data Day at any time, using different sets and sources of data
- use the projects to maintain data interpretation skills

Activity	Goal	Materials
Questions???	Write survey questions.	Sentence strips, paper bag
Tally Up	Create a tally chart and make a table.	*Questions???* bag
Jump It	Find the mode of a data set.	Gym mat, masking tape, index cards, ruler
Where Does It Belong?	Use a Venn diagram to display and interpret data.	Calendar, index cards, Hula Hoops or masking tape
Be a Graph	Represent data with a real graph.	Construction paper
Line It Up	Use a data table to create a line plot.	Poster board, construction paper, markers
Graph It	Represent data in a different format.	Poster board, construction paper, markers
Picture It	Construct a pictograph using data from a tally chart.	Poster board, construction paper, markers
Key Information	Use a symbol to represent data that equals more than 1.	Poster board, crayons
Year at a Glance	Find the range of a data set.	Calendar, Inch Grid Paper (Copymaster M42)
Name That Axis	Interpret data sets and identify appropriate labels.	*Questions???* bag
How Many Inches in a Foot?	Use a line graph to predict data.	Inch Grid Paper, ruler
Match Up	Match data sets to data representations.	Sentence strips
Draw Conclusions	Interpret, analyze, and graph data.	*Questions???* bag, Inch Grid Paper, (Copymaster M42), poster board
Go Horizontal or Vertical	Conduct a simple probability experiment and graph the data.	Paper bag, connecting cubes, index cards
And the Winner Is...	Analyze graphs and write comparison questions.	Student graphs, sticky notes

Collect and Organize Data

Questions???

Materials: Sentence strips, paper bag

Have students brainstorm questions that can be used to conduct a survey. The questions should have a number of possible answers. For example, "What is your favorite TV show?" Students write the questions on sentence strips and place them in a paper bag labeled *Questions???* to be used in a later activity.

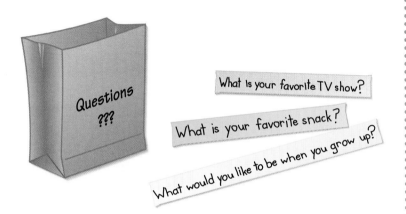

Tally Up

Materials: *Questions???* bag

Students choose a question from the *Questions???* bag. They decide on the choices for the answer to the question and make a tally chart to record the choices. Then they survey their classmates. When the survey is completed they use the tally chart to make a table of the data.

Jump It

Materials: Gym mat, masking tape, index cards, ruler

Students stand behind a masking tape line on a gym mat and jump as far as they can two times. Another student measures and records the length of each jump to the nearest foot on an index card. If students are more comfortable measuring in centimeters, have them use a centimeter ruler. Pairs then arrange the lengths recorded for all students in order from least to greatest and identify the *mode*—the number that appears most often. Students then make a conclusion about how far a typical third grader can jump.
Example: 1, 2, 2, 3, 3, 3, 3, 4. The mode: 3

Where Does It Belong?

Materials: Calendar, 12 index cards, 2 Hula Hoops or masking tape

Make two large overlapping circles on the floor with Hula Hoops or use masking tape. Label one circle with *Months with an "A"* and the other circle with *Months with an "R."* Students use the calendar to write the names of the months on index cards. Then students place the index cards in the proper place in the circles of the Venn diagram outlined on the floor with Hula Hoops or masking tape.

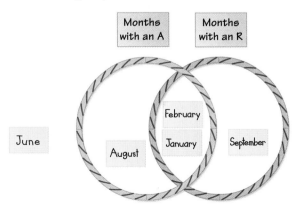

Represent Data in Different Ways

Be a Graph

WHOLE CLASS

Materials: Construction paper

Have students line up by the number of children in their family to form a line plot. Write the numbers 1 through the largest number of children in a family in the class on construction paper and place the paper in front of each row. Explain that each student in the row represents 1 family. Record the data in a large table and display it in the classroom.

Line It Up

PAIRS

Materials: Poster board, construction paper, markers

Students use the table with data about number of children in their families displayed in the classroom to make a line plot on poster board using the letter X to represent the number of students who have that number of children in their family. Students display completed line plots around the classroom.

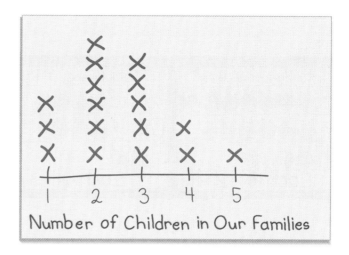

Graph It

PAIRS

Materials: Poster board, construction paper, markers

Students use the table with data about the number of children in their families displayed in the classroom to make a bar graph on poster board, cutting out and gluing bars from construction paper. Students display completed graphs around the classroom.

Picture It

SMALL GROUPS

Materials: Poster board, construction paper, markers

Students use the table with data about the number of children in their families displayed in the classroom to make a pictograph on poster board, cutting out and gluing symbols from construction paper. Students display completed graphs around the classroom.

Represent Data

Key Information

PAIRS

Materials: Poster board, crayons

Students use the tally chart they made in *Tally Up* or make a new tally chart to record the results of a survey to find out how many dogs, cats, and fish are owned by their classmates altogether. Students make a colorful pictograph using the data. Then each pair makes another pictograph of the same information changing the key. Students display both pictographs in the classroom.

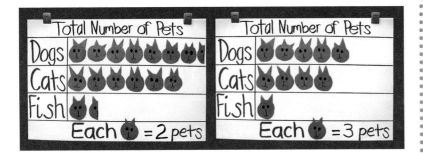

Year at a Glance

PAIRS

Materials: Calendar (one per pair), Inch Grid Paper (Copymaster M42)

Students use a calendar to count the number of letters in each month's name. Each pair makes a bar graph showing the total number of letters in each month's name and gives the graph a title. Next, students find the *range* of the data by calculating the difference between the greatest and least values shown on the bar graph. Students display their bar graphs in the classroom.

Name That Axis

SMALL GROUPS

Materials: *Questions???* bag

Students sit in a circle. The first student draws a question from the *Questions???* bag and suggests a title that could be used for a bar graph of the survey data and turns to the person on his or her right, and says, "Name the axis labels." The second student suggests axes names. When everyone in the group agrees that these labels fit, the second student draws another question and repeats the process.

How Many Inches in a Foot?

PAIRS

Materials: Inch Grid Paper (Copymaster M42), ruler

Each student labels the vertical axis of a graph from 0 to 12 inches and the horizontal axis with last year age and continuing 4 years. Students measure each other's foot to the nearest inch and record it on the graph with a point. Students then add points to the graph to predict the lengths of their foot for the other ages listed. Students connect the four points to make a line graph.

Match Up

SMALL GROUPS

Materials: Sentence strips

Students make line graphs without axis labels to match these descriptions. Students can exchange graphs with another group and match the graphs to the situations.

> The temperature rising and falling throughout the day.

> The depth of a swimming pool measured along the length from the shallow end to the deep end.

> The amount of money George has in his bank account if he doesn't put any money in and spends $20 each week.

Go Horizontal or Vertical

INDIVIDUALS

Materials: Paper bag, connecting cubes (red, blue, yellow), 3 index cards

Have students place connecting cubes (5 red, 3 blue, 1 yellow) in a paper bag, pick one without looking, record the color, and return it to the bag. Repeat this at least 25 times. Students organize their data and make a vertical and a horizontal bar graph with connecting cubes.

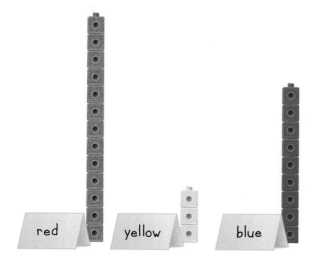

Draw Conclusions

PAIRS

Materials: Inch Grid Paper (Copymaster M41), *Questions???* bag, strips of poster board

Students choose a question from the *Questions???* bag and make a table of three choices that answer the question. Then they fill in the table pretending they surveyed 100 people. Students make a bar graph and write a conclusion based on the data in the graph on a strip of poster board and display it in the classroom.

And the Winner Is...

WHOLE CLASS

Materials: Graphs displayed in room, sticky notes

Student pairs choose their favorite graph from the graphs displayed around the classroom. Pairs vote for that graph by writing two comparison questions that can be answered using the graph on sticky notes and sticking them to the bottom of the graph.

Note: Do this activity after all graphs have been displayed.

Projects

Individual Project: Nutrition Facts Finder

Materials: Nutrition Facts Finder (Copymaster M45), nutrition labels (4 per student), Inch Grid Paper (Copymaster M42), markers or crayons, rulers

Goal: Collect, compare, and graph data using nutrition labels.

Have students bring in nutrition labels from four different types of food. For example, students may collect labels or containers for peanut butter, cheese, cereal, butter and so on. Students should carefully examine the labels to identify the common nutrients they find on each nutrition label, such as calories, fat content, dietary fiber, potassium, calcium, and so on.

Have students choose one of the common nutrients and complete the table on the Nutrition Facts Finder. After students have completed the table, have them make a bar graph of the data on a separate piece of Inch Grid Paper. When students have completed the table, ask them to look at their graphs and draw a conclusion to complete question 4. Then have students present their graphs and share their conclusions. For example, students might conclude that a serving of one of the foods has many more grams of fat than another.

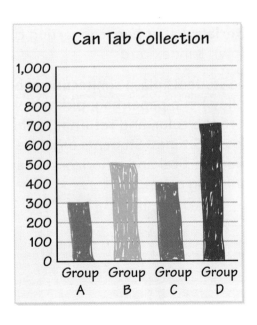

Class Project: Track Data Trends

Materials: Collect and Graph (Copymaster M46), calculator, ruler, poster board, markers or crayons

Goal: Collect, organize, display, and summarize data.

Explain to students that the class is going to work in teams to collect can tabs. Encourage students to bring in as many can tabs as they can (Approximately 10,000 of these tabs will be used in Unit 7 for Estimation Day). Each week, have each team of students combine their can tabs, tabulate their totals with a calculator, and fill in the table for their team on the top of Collect and Graph (Copymaster M46).

Also make a large class bar graph so each team can record its total for each week on the graph by increasing the length of the bar they made for the first week. This graph will show how many tabs each group has collected to date and allow groups to compare their total with that of other groups.

After groups have recorded their team's data for six weeks in the table on Collect and Graph, students should decide on an appropriate scale for their graph, graph their data, and answer the questions. Then, have each group present their graphs to the class so all students can analyze and discuss the data on each team's graph. Have students also discuss and analyze the data on the class graph.

Unit Review and Test

Lesson Objective
● **Assess student progress on unit objectives.**

The Day at a Glance

Today's Goals	Materials
Quick Practice Review any skills you choose to meet the needs of your students.	Unit 3 Test, Student Activity Book pages 175–178
❶ Assessing the Unit ▶ Assess student progress on unit objectives. ▶ Use activities from unit lessons to reteach content.	Unit 3 Test, Form A or B, Assessment Guide (optional)
❷ Extending the Assessment ▶ Use remediation for common errors.	Unit 3 Performance Assessment, Assessment Guide (optional)
There is no homework assignment on a test day.	

Quick Practice

 5 MINUTES   **Goal:** Review any skills you choose to meet the needs of your students.

If you are doing a unit review day, use any of the Quick Practice activities that provide support for your students. If this is a test day, omit Quick Practice.

 Class Management

Review and Test Day You may want to choose a quiet game or other activity (reading a book or working on homework for another subject) for students who finish early.

Assess Unit Objectives

Unit Test Name _____ Date _____

Compare the numbers. Write >, <, or = in each ◯.

1. 742 ⟨>⟩ 724   2. 2,329 ⟨>⟩ 2,319

Write the numbers in order from least to greatest.

3. 598, 678, 590   4. 6,543, 7,585, 6,585
   590, 598, 678   6,543; 6,585; 7,585

Round each number to the given place.

5. 1,352 to the nearest ten   6. 567 to the nearest hundred
   1,350   600

7. $7.89 to the nearest dime   8. $6.29 to the nearest dollar
   $7.90 $6.00

Solve. Label your answer.

9. Jason collects toy dinosaurs. He has 485 toy
   dinosaurs in his collection. He plans to sell 243 toy
   dinosaurs. Round each number to the nearest ten to
   estimate how many he will have left.
   250 toy dinosaurs

UNIT 3   Test **175**

Student Activity Book page 175

Unit Test Name _____ Date _____

Use the bar graph to answer questions 10 and 11.

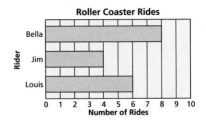

Roller Coaster Rides

10. How many more rides did Louis take than Jim? __2 rides__
11. How many rides did Bella and Louis take altogether? __14 rides__

This table shows the numbers of T-shirts of different
sizes a store had before a big sale, the number they
sold, and the number they had left.

T-shirt Sales

	Number Before Sale	Number Sold	Number Left After Sale
Small	645	587	58
Medium	435	390	45
Large	462	433	29

12. Fill in the blank cells.
13. How many more small T-shirts than large T-shirts did
    the store have before the sale?
    183 small T-shirts

176 UNIT 3   Test

Student Activity Book page 176

---

 45 MINUTES (more if schedule permits)

Goal: Assess student progress on unit objectives.

Materials: Student Activity Book pages 175–178; Assessment
Guide (optional)

▶ Review and Assessment

If your students are ready for assessment on the unit
objectives, use either the test on the Student Activity
Book pages or one of the forms of the Unit 3 Test in
the Assessment Guide to assess student progress. To
assign a numerical score for all of these test forms, use
5 points for each question.

The chart to the right lists the test items, the unit
objectives they cover, and the lesson activities in which
the objective is covered in this unit.

Unit Test Items	Unit Objectives Tested	Activities to Use for Reteaching
1–6, 9	**3.1** Compare, order, and round whole numbers and estimate sums and differences.	Lesson 1, Activities 1 and 2 Lesson 2, Activity 1 Lesson 3, Activity 1
7, 8, 17–20	**3.2** Find the value of and represent money amounts with coins and bills, count change, compare, round, and estimate with money.	Lesson 4, Activity 2 Lesson 5, Activity 1 Lesson 6, Activity 1 Lesson 7, Activities 1 and 2

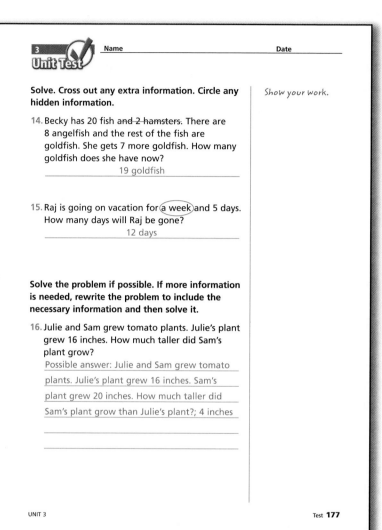

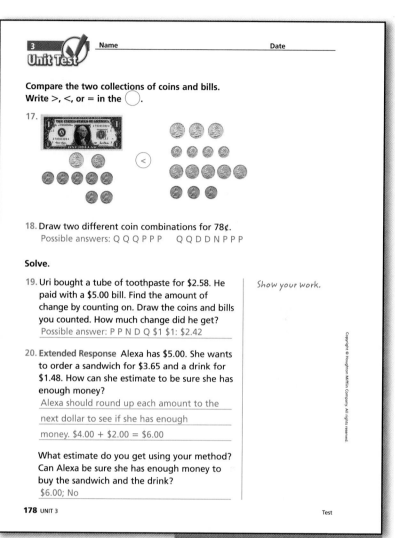

Unit Test Items	Unit Objectives Tested	Activities to Use for Reteaching
10–13	**3.3** Interpret data in a table or graph, make bar graphs, and complete tables.	Lesson 8, Activity 2 Lesson 9, Activity 2 Lesson 10, Activity 1 Lesson 16, Activity 2
14–16	**3.4** Solve word problems with two steps, multi-steps, extra or hidden information, and identify problems with not enough information.	Lesson 11, Activities 1 and 2 Lesson 12, Activity 1 Lesson 13, Activity 1 Lesson 14, Activity 1

► Assessment Resources

Form A, Free Response Test (Assessment Guide)

Form B, Multiple-Choice Test (Assessment Guide)

Performance Assessment (Assessment Guide)

► Portfolio Assessment

Teacher-selected Items for Student Portfolios:

- Homework, Lessons 2, 9, 14, and 16

- Class Activity work, Lessons 4, 7, and 12

Student-selected Items for Student Portfolios:

- Favorite Home or School Activity

- Best Writing Prompt

② Extending the Assessment

Unit Objective 3.1
Compare, order, and round whole numbers and estimate sums and differences.

Common Error: Rounds to an Incorrect Place

Students may transpose the place to be rounded with the place that is used to decide how to round the number.

Remediation Remind students to underline the place to which they are rounding and use Secret Code Cards and drawings to help them conclude that they need to look at the next smaller place to decide which way to round.

Common Error: Reverses Inequality Symbols

Students may have difficulty deciding whether the sign is pointing to the smaller or larger number.

Remediation Help students remember the difference between the symbols by pointing out that the symbols are like arrows and the small point of the arrow always points to the smaller number, or that the fish's mouth always faces the larger number.

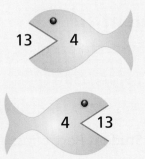

Unit Objective 3.2
Find the value of and represent money amounts with coins and bills, count change, compare, round and estimate with money.

Common Error: Counts Coins Incorrectly

Students must be proficient in skip counting by fives, tens, and twenty-fives to be successful with counting coins.

Remediation Have a group of students take turns saying the next number when counting by fives, tens, or twenty-fives. Then switch counting rules while students are counting. For example, when 4 students have counted by tens, say to the next student, "switch to fives."

Remind students always to count coins starting with the coins that have the greatest value.

Unit Objective 3.3
Interpret data in a table or graph, make bar graphs, and complete tables.

Common Error: Does Not Give Adequate Titles to Tables or Graphs

Students may not be able to use a table or bar graph to solve a problem because the information is not organized clearly.

Remediation Give students practice in saying titles and choosing the labels for the axes in bar graphs by giving various situations.

Unit Objective 3.4
Solve word problems with two steps, multi-steps, and extra or hidden information, and identify problems with not enough information.

Common Error: Has Difficulty with Multi-Step Problems

Students may have difficulty deciding when and how to break a problem into simpler parts.

Remediation Have students act out problems using lists, drawings, manipulatives, or money. This will allow them to see concretely which steps must be performed and how to order the steps.

Common Error: Unable to Identify the Relevant Information

Students may have difficulty identifying if there is too much or too little information in a problem.

Remediation Have students first identify what they need to find. Then have them go back to the beginning of the problem and circle the information they need, and cross out the information they do not need.

Patterns

UNIT C CONTINUES TO develop students' algebraic thinking through patterning. The activities in this unit give students the opportunity to identify, extend, and create repeating number patterns, repeating geometric patterns, growing and shrinking number patterns, and growing and shrinking geometric patterns. Students also explore transformations: flips, slides, and turns, and create motion geometry patterns with flips. Students apply their patterning skills to solve problems by using the strategy of solving a simpler related problem.

Planning Unit C

See pages xvii and xviii for a list of unit materials and manipulatives that are available in the *Math Expressions* Kit.

Lesson Title	Lesson Resources	Materials and Manipulatives	
		Math Expressions	**Other**
1 Motion Geometry Patterns	Family Letter Student Activity Book pages 179–184 Homework and Remembering pages 97–98	Centimeter Dot Paper (Copymaster M28) (optional), Pattern Blocks (Copymaster M27), Pattern Block Grid Paper (Copymaster M47)	Plastic mirror (optional), pattern blocks or Math Journals
2 Repeating Patterns	Student Activity Book pages 185–186 Homework and Remembering pages 99–100	Hundred Grid (Copymaster M48), Pattern Blocks (Copymaster M27)	Counters, pattern blocks, Math Journals, sheet protectors, dry-erase materials
3 Growing and Shrinking Patterns	Student Activity Book pages 187–190 Homework and Remembering pages 101–102	Skip Counting Circle (Copymaster M49)	Paper squares or square pattern blocks, Math Journals, *One Grain of Rice* by Demi (Scholastic Press, 1997)
✓ **Unit Review and Test**	Student Activity Book pages 191–192 Assessment Guide		

Unit C Assessment

✔ Unit Objectives Tested	Unit Test Items	Lessons
C.1 Recognize and describe slides, flips, and turns and recognize them in geometric patterns.	1, 2	1, 2
C.2 Identify the rule for number or geometric repeating patterns and continue the patterns.	3, 4, 5	2
C.3 Identify the rule for growing and shrinking number or geometric patterns and continue the patterns.	6, 7, 8, 9	3
C.4 Solve real-world problems with patterns.	10	3

Formal Assessment	Informal Assessment	Review Opportunities
Open or Free Response Tests • Unit Review and Test (Student Activity Book pages 191–192, Teacher's Guide pages 415–418) • Unit C Test Form A (Assessment Guide) • Unit C Open Response Test (Test Generator) • Test Bank Items for Unit C (Test Generator) **Multiple Choice Tests** • Unit C Test Form B (Assessment Guide) • Unit C Multiple Choice Test (Test Generator) • Test Bank Items for Unit C (Test Generator) **Performance Tasks** • Unit C Performance Assessment (Assessment Guide)	**Ongoing Assessment** • In every Teacher's Guide lesson **Performance Assessment** • Class discussions • Small-group work • Individual work on teacher-selected tasks **Portfolios** • See Unit C Review and Test for suggestions for selecting items for portfolios. • Some Homework pages are noted as suitable for portfolio inclusion.	**Homework and Remembering** • Homework pages provide review of recently taught topics. • Remembering pages provide spiral review. **Teacher's Guide** • Unit Review and Test (page 415) **Test Generator CD-ROM** • Test Bank Items can be used to create custom review sheets.

Unit C Teaching Resources

Differentiated Instruction

Reaching All Learners

English Learners
Lesson 2, page 403

Individualizing Instruction

Activities
- Intervention (in every lesson)
- On Level (in every lesson)
- Challenge (in every lesson)

Math Writing Prompts
- Intervention (in every lesson)
- On Level (in every lesson)
- Challenge (in every lesson)

Challenge Masters
- (for every lesson)

Cross-Curricular Links • Home or School Activities

 Language Arts Connection
Rhyming Patterns (Lesson 2, page 406)

 Literature Connection
One Grain of Rice by Demi (Scholastic Press, 1997) (Lesson 3, page 414)

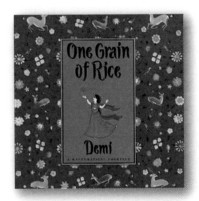

Teaching Unit C

Putting Research into Practice for Unit C

From Current Research: Transformations

Students in grades 3–5 should consider three important kinds of transformations: reflections, translations, and rotations (flips, slides, and turns). Younger students generally "prove" that two shapes are congruent by physically fitting one on top of the other, but students in grades 3–5 can develop greater precision as they describe the motions needed to show congruence ("turn it 90°" or "flip it vertically, then rotate it 180°"). They should also be able to visualize what will happen when a shape is rotated or reflected and predict the result.

National Council of Teachers of Mathematics. *Principles and Standards for School Mathematics.* Reston: NCTM, 2000. p. 167.

Patterns

Although *algebra* is a word that has not commonly been heard in grades 3–5 classrooms, the mathematical investigations and conversations of students in these grades frequently include elements of algebraic reasoning. These experiences and conversations provide rich contexts for advancing mathematical understanding and are also an important precursor to the more formalized study of algebra in the middle and secondary grades. In grades 3–5, algebraic ideas should emerge and be investigated as students—

- identify or build numerical and geometric patterns;
- describe patterns verbally and represent them with tables or symbols;
- look for and apply relationships between varying quantities to make predictions;
- make and explain generalizations that seem to always work in particular situations;
- use graphs to describe patterns and make predictions;
- explore number properties;
- use invented notation, standard symbols, and variables to express a pattern, generalization, or situation.

National Council of Teachers of Mathematics. *Principles and Standards for School Mathematics.* Reston: NCTM, 2000. p. 159.

Other Useful References: Patterns

Bay-Williams, Jennifer M. "What Is Algebra in Elementary School?" *Teaching Children Mathematics* 8.4 (Dec. 2001): p. 196.

Coburn, Terrence G., et al. *Patterns: Addenda Series, Grades K–6.* Reston: NCTM, 1993. p. 53.

Curcio, Frances R., et al. "Exploring Patterns in Nonroutine Problems." *Mathematics Teaching in the Middle School* 2.4 (Feb. 1997): p. 262.

Ferrini-Mundy, Joan, et al. "Experiences with Patterning." *Teaching Children Mathematics* 3.6 (Feb. 1997): p. 282.

National Council of Teachers of Mathematics. "Creating, Describing, and Analyzing Patterns to Recognize Relationships and Make Predictions: Making Patterns." *Principles and Standards for School Mathematics.* Reston: NCTM, 2000.

National Council of Teachers of Mathematics. *Teaching Children Mathematics* (Focus Issue: Algebraic Thinking) 3.6 (Feb. 1997).

Math Background

Transformations In the previous grade, students identified slides, flips, and turns, and created patterns using these transformations. In this unit, students draw flipped images of figures, describe slides, and describe and draw turned figures. When describing a turn, students use the vocabulary *quarter turn* and *half turn* and include an arrow showing the direction of the turn. The terms *clockwise* and *counterclockwise* are reserved for future work with transformations.

Repeating Patterns In the previous grade, students extended repeating number and shape patterns. They also had opportunities to create their own repeating patterns. In this unit, students extend repeating patterns, identify patterns on hundred grids, work with open-ended pattern problems, and write rules for patterns. The process of writing a pattern rule, telling how the pattern begins and how it continues, is an important stage in the development of algebraic thinking.

Growing and Shrinking Patterns In this unit, students' experiences with growing and shrinking patterns help them to continue making connections between physical representations and verbal descriptions. In the previous grade, students extended growing and shrinking patterns and created their own patterns but they were not required to describe the patterns. In this unit, students identify pattern rules as an integral part of the activities.

Problem Solving By developing proficiency in identifying and extending patterns, students acquire the skills and confidence to make sense of the regularities of their worlds. In the final lesson of this unit, students use simpler problems to help solve more complex problems, and solve real-world problems involving patterns. The goal at this grade is to have students recognize patterns, express the patterns they observe, and make predictions based on those patterns. In meeting those objectives, students think mathematically and begin to bridge the gap between arithmetic and algebra.

MINI UNIT C

LESSON

1

Motion Geometry Patterns

Lesson Objectives

- Recognize and describe slides, flips, and turns.
- Recognize slides, flips, and turns in geometric patterns and create patterns.

The Day at a Glance

Today's Goals	Materials	123 Math Talk
1 Teaching the Lesson **A1:** Recognize, describe, and draw flips of geometric figures. **A2:** Recognize, describe, and draw slides and turns of geometric figures. **2 Extending the Lesson** ▶ Differentiated Instruction **3 Homework and Spiral Review**	Rulers Plastic mirror (optional) Dot paper (optional) Pattern blocks or Pattern Blocks (Copymaster M27) Pattern Block Grid Paper (Copymaster M47) Student Activity Book pages 179–184 Homework and Remembering pages 97–98 Math Journals Family Letter	In today's activities, the students are involved in discussion as they ▶ describe and compare slides, flips, and turns ▶ talk about what happens when geometric figures slide, flip, or turn

Teaching the Lesson

Learn About Flips

 30 MINUTES

Goal: Recognize, describe, and draw flips of geometric figures.

Materials: Rulers (1 per student), Student Activity Book pages 179–180, plastic mirrors (optional), dot paper (optional)

✓ **NCTM Standards:**
Geometry
Representation

► **Describe Flips** WHOLE CLASS

Have students draw any figure on the bottom half of a sheet of paper. They should draw the figure using dark line segments so that they can see it through the paper to trace.

Ask students to fold the paper in half and trace the figure on the outside of the paper.

Then have them unfold the paper and redraw the tracing on the side of the paper facing them.

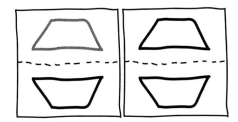

Explain that the new figure is called a flip of the original figure.

● Why do you think it's called a flip? The figure looks as if it has flipped over.

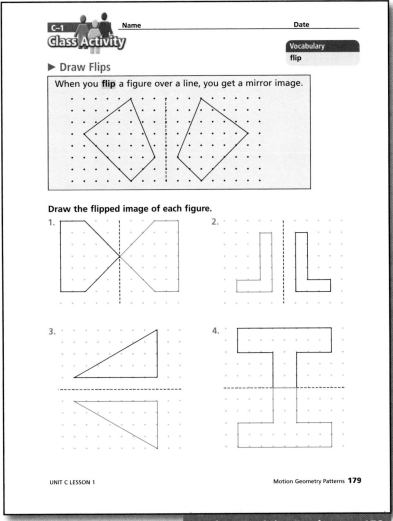

Student Activity Book page 179

● What happens to a figure when it is flipped? It gets reversed; it looks like a mirror image.

● What stays the same? size and shape

► **Draw Flips** WHOLE CLASS

Have students look at the flip of the figure on Student Activity Book page 179.

● What do you notice about matching corners of the figure and the flipped image? They are all the same distance from the dashed line.

● How will this help you to draw flips? I can measure the distance of each point from the dashed line.

Have the students complete exercises 1–4.

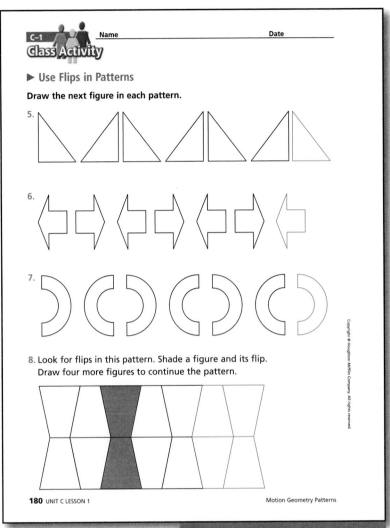

Student Activity Book page 180

▶ Use Flips in Patterns PAIRS

Have students look at the patterns in exercises 5–7 and discuss how the figures were moved to make the patterns. Ask students to draw the next figure in each pattern and then to complete exercise 8.

 Alternate Approach

Use a Plastic Mirror Have the students place the mirror on the dotted line on Student Activity Book page 179. When they look through the mirror, they will see that the image is exactly superimposed on the flipped figure.

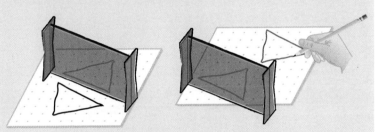

Students can draw a figure, choose a flip line, place the plastic mirror on the line, and trace the image they see when they look through the mirror. Using dot paper will help students to draw accurate images.

Activity 2

Explore Slides and Turns

 30 MINUTES

Goal: Recognize, describe, and draw slides and turns of geometric figures.

Materials: rulers (1 per student), Student Activity Book pages 181–182

✔ **NCTM Standards:**
Geometry
Representation

▶ Recognize Slides WHOLE CLASS

Draw a straight line on the board. Choose any flat object and slide it along the line without turning it.

● What changes when you slide along a straight line? The object moves to another place.

● What doesn't change? The object looks exactly the same after a slide. It's just in a different place.

● What words can you use to describe the new position of an object after a slide? left, right, up, down

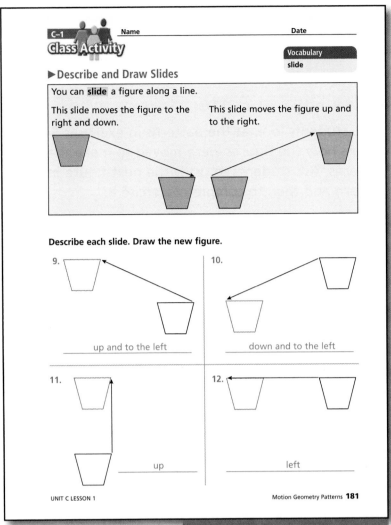

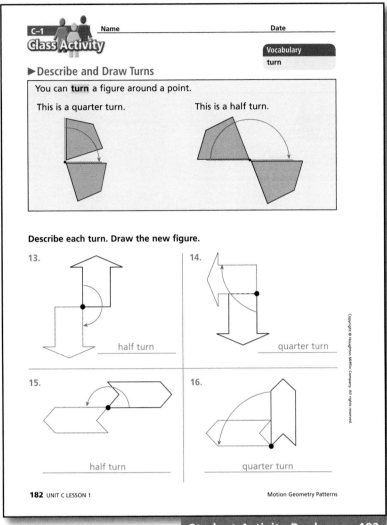

► Describe and Draw Slides [INDIVIDUALS]

Have the students complete exercises 9–12. Ask them to describe the new position of each figure.

Teaching Note

Language and Vocabulary The direction of a turn is described as clockwise or counterclockwise. Students need not use these terms, but they need to show the direction of a quarter turn they perform with an arrow.

✓ Ongoing Assessment

After students have completed Student Activity Book pages 180–182, ask them to write a large capital letter F.

► Show what the F would look like after a flip about a vertical line.

► Show what it would look like after a turn.

► Describe and Draw Turns [WHOLE CLASS]

Have students look at the figures at the top of Student Activity Book page 182.

● **Why is the first figure called a quarter turn?** It goes a quarter of the way around a circle.

● **What is a half turn?** a turn that goes halfway around a circle

● **Why is showing the direction of a quarter turn important?** The figure ends up in a different place if you turn it in the opposite direction.

● **Is this true for a half turn?** No, the figure ends up in the same place after a half turn in either direction.

Assign exercises 13–16, and have students describe each turn as a half or a quarter turn.

② Extending the Lesson

Differentiated Instruction | Activities for Individualizing

Intervention	**On Level**	**Challenge**
for students having difficulty	for students having success	for students seeking a challenge
PAIRS	PAIRS	INDIVIDUALS

Intervention
for students having difficulty

PAIRS

Model Transformations

Materials: pattern blocks or Pattern Blocks (Copymaster M27), Pattern Block Grid Paper (Copymaster M47)

Students use pattern blocks and Pattern Block Grid Paper to demonstrate slides, flips, and turns. They trace a pattern block on the grid and draw a line. They slide the pattern block along the line and trace it. Then they flip it over a line and trace it again. They turn it about one of its corners and trace it again.

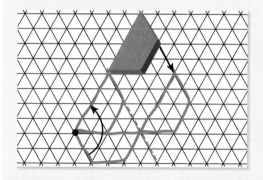

On Level
for students having success

PAIRS

Make a Pattern

Materials: pattern blocks or Pattern Blocks (Copymaster M27), Pattern Block Grid Paper (Copymaster M47)

Students use slides, flips, or turns to draw their own pattern on grid paper.

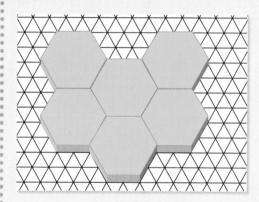

Challenge
for students seeking a challenge

INDIVIDUALS

Investigate Math

Materials: pattern blocks or Pattern Blocks (Copymaster M27)

Students trace white, blue, and orange pattern blocks and turn them around their centers until they fit on the tracings.

Ask them to describe the turns needed for the blocks to fit the tracings.

square: quarter turn
rhombus: half turn
parallelogram: half turn

Also Use
Challenge Master for C-1

 Math Writing Prompt

Intervention

Use Reasoning
Predict what you will see if you draw a flip about a vertical line of a capital Z. Will it still be a proper Z after this flip? Explain your thinking.

 Math Writing Prompt

On Level

Explain Your Thinking
How are turns and flips different? How are they the same? Use drawings to explain your thinking.

 Math Writing Prompt

Challenge

Investigate Math
Explain what happens when you turn a circle around its center.

③ Homework and Spiral Review

Homework **Goal:** Additional Practice

For homework, students practice with slides, flips, and turns.

Remembering **Goal:** Spiral Review

This Remembering page is appropriate anytime after today's lesson.

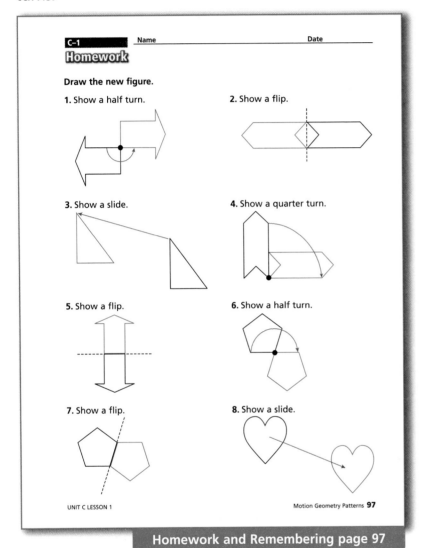

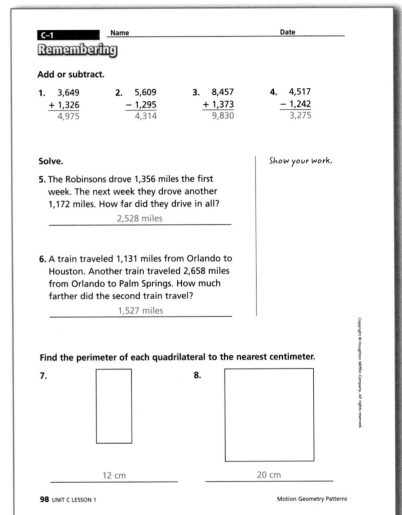

Home and School Connection

Family Letter Have students take home the Family Letter on Student Activity Book page 183. This letter explains how the concept of repeating, growing, and shrinking patterns is developed in *Math Expressions.* It gives parents and guardians a better understanding of the learning that goes on in math class and creates a bridge between school and home. A Spanish translation of this letter is on the following page in the Student Activity Book.

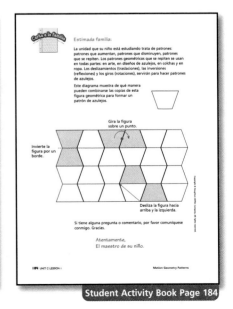

Student Activity Book Page 183

Student Activity Book Page 184

Repeating Patterns

Lesson Objectives

• Identify and continue a repeating number pattern.

• Identify and continue a repeating geometric pattern.

Vocabulary
repeating pattern

The Day at a Glance

Today's Goals	Materials	123 Math Talk
1 Teaching the Lesson **A1:** Recognize and describe a repeating number pattern. **A2:** Recognize and describe a repeating geometric pattern. **2 Extending the Lesson** ▶ Differentiated Instruction **3 Homework and Spiral Review**	Hundred Grid (Copymaster M48) Sheet protectors Dry-erase materials Counters Pattern blocks or Pattern Blocks (Copymaster M27) Student Activity Book pages 185–186 Homework and Remembering pages 99–100 Math Journals	In today's activities, the students are involved in discussion as they ▶ write rules for repeating number patterns ▶ explore patterns on a hundred chart ▶ describe repeating geometric patterns

Teaching the Lesson

Repeating Number Patterns

 30 MINUTES

Goal: Recognize and describe a repeating number pattern.

Materials: Student Activity Book page 185, Hundred Grid (Copymaster M48), sheet protectors, dry-erase materials, counters

✓ **NCTM Standards:**
Algebra
Reasoning and Proof

▶ Explore Repeating Number Patterns

WHOLE CLASS

Write a simple repeating pattern of numbers on the board.

2 4 4 2 4 4 2 4 4 2 4 4 2 4

● **Look at the list of numbers. What pattern do you notice?** Possible responses: It repeats the 3 numbers 2, 4, and 4 (or 2 and 44; or 24 and 4) or the number 244 repeats.

● **What is the next number in the pattern?** 4

● **Why isn't it 2?** because every 2 is followed by two 4s

Explain that you can write a rule to describe any pattern. The rule must say how the pattern starts and how it continues.

● **How does it start?** Possible responses: With the numbers 2, 4, and 4; with 244; with the numbers 2 and 44; with the numbers 24 and 4

● **How does it continue?** It repeats the starting numbers over and over.

Direct students' attention to Student Activity Book page 185 and have students complete exercises 1–4.

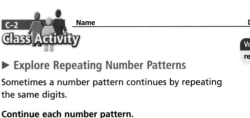

C–2
Class Activity

Name _____ Date _____

Vocabulary
repeating pattern

▶ **Explore Repeating Number Patterns**
Sometimes a number pattern continues by repeating the same digits.

Continue each number pattern.
1. 2 7 2 7 2 7   2 7 2 7 2 7 2 7 2 7 2 7 2 7 2
2. 1 2 2 1 2 2 1 2 2   1 2 2 1 2 2 1 2 2 1 2 2 1 2 2
3. 1 3 2 1 3 2 1 3 2   1 3 2 1 3 2 1 3 2 1 3 2 1 3 2
4. 1 0 0 1 1 0 0 1 1 0 0 1   1 0 0 1 1 0 0 1 1 0 0 1 1 0 0 1

▶ **Explore Repeating Patterns in Skip Counting**
Complete.
5. Skip count by 2s.
   2, 4, 6, 8, 10, _12_, _14_, _16_, _18_, _20_, _22_, _24_, _26_

6. Show the pattern in the ones digits when you skip count by 2s, starting at 2.
   _2_, _4_, _6_, _8_, _0_, _2_, _4_, _6_, _8_, _0_

7. Start at 1 and count by 2s.
   1, 3, 5, _7_, _9_, _11_, _13_, _15_, _17_, _19_

8. Show the pattern in the ones digits in exercise 7.
   _1_, _3_, _5_, _7_, _9_, _1_, _3_, _5_, _7_, _9_

9. Skip count by 5s.
   5, 10, 15, _20_, _25_, _30_, _35_, _40_, _45_, _50_, _55_, _60_

10. Show the pattern in the ones digits when you skip count by 5s, starting at 5.
    _5_, _0_, _5_, _0_, _5_, _0_, _5_, _0_

UNIT C LESSON 2   Repeating Patterns **185**

Student Activity Book page 185

▶ Explore Repeating Patterns in Skip Counting WHOLE CLASS

Distribute a Hundred Grid (Copymaster M48) and sheet protectors to students and have them explore patterns.

● **What pattern do you see in each column of the grid?** The tens digit repeats except for the last number in each column.

● **What pattern do you see in each row?** The ones digit repeats.

Ask the students to apply this pattern rule: "Start at 3 and count by 3s." Have them mark each number on the grid with an X.

● **Describe the pattern of the Xs in the grid.** The Xs go down one square and left one square and line up along diagonals.

Then have students erase their Xs and ask them to name other pattern rules and use the rules to mark the hundred grid.

● Choose a starting number from the first column of the grid, and then choose a number to skip count by. Mark the numbers on the chart.

● Describe the pattern your rule makes in the grid.

Explain that whenever you skip count by the same number, the ones digits will eventually make a repeating pattern. Have students complete exercises 5–10 on Student Activity Book page 185.

Alternate Approach

Counters If sheet protectors are unavailable, have students use counters to record the patterns on the Hundred Grid. This will allow students to reuse their grids.

Ongoing Assessment

Ask students to make a repeating number pattern. Have them choose a sequence of starting numbers that will repeat, and ask them to write the repeating pattern three times.

Differentiated Instruction

English Learners Explain to students that a *pattern rule* describes how to get the numbers or figures in a pattern. For example, "Start at 3 and count by three" or "triangle, flipped triangle, square, repeat." You can also describe the first pattern as "Each number increases by 3." All three activities on p. 405 are excellent for English Learners to practice describing patterns and reading decoded messages.

Activity 2

Repeating Geometric Patterns

🕐 **30 MINUTES**

Goal: Recognize and describe a repeating geometric pattern.

Materials: Student Activity Book page 186

✓ **NCTM Standard:**
Geometry

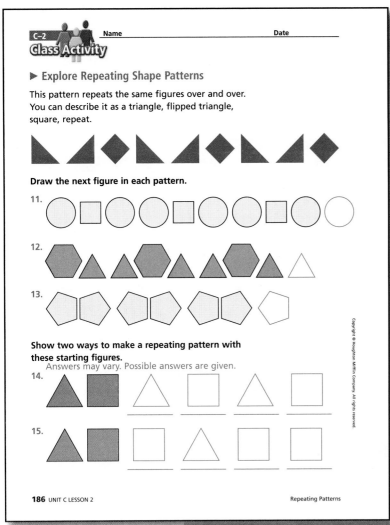

Student Activity Book page 186

▶ Explore Repeating Shape Patterns

INDIVIDUALS

Have students look at the pattern of figures at the top of Student Activity Book page 186.

● **Look at the figures. What pattern do you notice?** Groups of the same 3 figures repeat.

● **What is the next figure in the pattern?** a triangle that looks exactly like the first triangle

● **How are the first and second triangles related?** The second triangle is a flip of the first triangle.

● **What is the pattern rule?** a triangle, a flip of the triangle, and a square; **How does it start?** with a triangle

● **How does the pattern continue?** The first 3 figures repeat.

Assign exercises 11–13.

Open-ended Patterns Have students complete exercise 14 and discuss their patterns. Explain that without a given rule, there is no single correct pattern, especially when there are only a few starting numbers or figures. Any pattern that starts with a triangle and a square would be correct.

Teaching Note

Math Background Analyzing mathematical patterns is important to future success in algebra and geometry. A number pattern can usually be modeled as a simple algebraic function. When slides, flips, and turns are done on coordinate grids, the patterns in the coordinates can also be modeled using algebraic functions. Through patterns, these two branches of mathematics become interconnected.

② Extending the Lesson

Differentiated Instruction
Activities for Individualizing

Intervention
for students having difficulty

PAIRS

Describe a Pattern

Materials: pattern blocks or Pattern Blocks (Copymaster M27)

Students make repeating patterns with pattern blocks and ask their partners to write the rule. They can describe their patterns by shape, color, or transformations.

On Level
for students having success

PAIRS

Make Patterns

Students make a repeating pattern of 2-digit numbers where the pattern is different for each digit of the number. Give an example.

19, 38, 17, 39, 18, 37, …

Ask them to look at the first digit of each number and describe the pattern. Then ask about the second digit.

Pattern:

First digit: 1, 3, 1, 3, 1, 3,…

Second digit: 9, 8, 7, 9, 8, 7,…

Have students make their own patterns. Students challenge their partner to find the next number in a pattern. They can also try the activity using 3-digit numbers.

90, 81, 70, 91, 80, 71,…

Challenge
for students seeking a challenge

PAIRS

Make a Secret Code

Students use a repeating number pattern to make a coded message. For example:

> Number pattern: 1, 3, 1, 3, 1, 3, …
> Count on by each number to change each letter of your message.
> If the first letter is Y, Y+1 becomes Z.
> If the second letter is O, O+3 becomes R.
> If the third letter is U, U+1 becomes V,
> by going back to the beginning of the alphabet.
>
> Message:
>   YOU ARE MY BEST FRIEND
> Coded message:
>   ZRV DSH NB CHTW GUJHOG

Ask students to write a coded message to a partner, tell the partner the number pattern, and challenge the partner to decode the message.

Also Use
Challenge Master for C-2

 Math Writing Prompt

Intervention

Explain Your Thinking
What do you need to know to extend a pattern? Give an example.

 Math Writing Prompt

On Level

Use Reasoning
If you know the first three numbers in a number pattern, can you be sure what the next number will be? Give an example.

 Math Writing Prompt

Challenge

Investigate Math
Write a rule for a repeating number pattern and a rule for a repeating shape pattern. Use the rules to make the patterns.

③ Homework and Spiral Review

C-2
Homework **Goal:** Additional Practice

✓ Include students' work for page 99 as part of their portfolios.

C-2
Remembering **Goal:** Spiral Review

This Remembering page is appropriate anytime after today's lesson.

C-2   Name _____ Date _____
Homework

Write the next 3 numbers in the pattern.

1. 9 8 7 9 8 7 9 8 7 9 8 7 9 8   7   9   8

2. 1 0 1 1 0 1 1 0 1 1 0 1 1 0 1   1   0   1

3. 6 6 1 1 1 6 6 1 1 1 6 6 1 1   1   6   6

4. 1 2 3 4 3 2 1 2 3 4 3 2 1 2   3   4   3

Draw the next figure in the pattern.

5. ☐ ☐ ☐ ☐ ☐ ☐   ☐

6. △▽☐△▽☐△   ▽

7. ◁◇△◯◁◇△   ◁

How will you move the last figure to continue the pattern: slide, flip, or turn? Draw the next figure in the pattern.

8. F ꟻ F ꟻ F ꟻ F   flip

9. ⚡⚡⚡⚡⚡⚡⚡   slide

10. ☺ ☻ ☺ ☻ ☺ ☻   turn

UNIT C LESSON 2   Repeating Patterns **99**

Homework and Remembering page 99

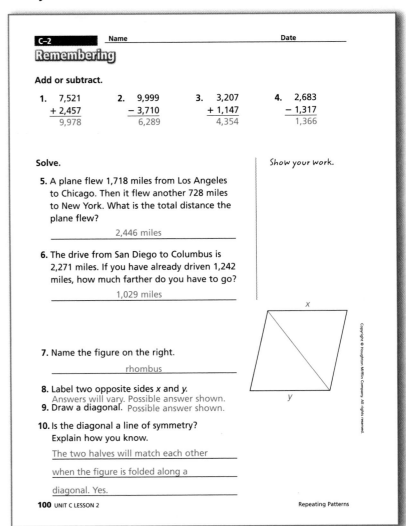

C-2   Name _____ Date _____
Remembering

Add or subtract.

1.   7,521
  + 2,457
  —————
  9,978

2.   9,999
  − 3,710
  —————
  6,289

3.   3,207
  + 1,147
  —————
  4,354

4.   2,683
  − 1,317
  —————
  1,366

Solve.   *Show your work.*

5. A plane flew 1,718 miles from Los Angeles to Chicago. Then it flew another 728 miles to New York. What is the total distance the plane flew?

   2,446 miles

6. The drive from San Diego to Columbus is 2,271 miles. If you have already driven 1,242 miles, how much farther do you have to go?

   1,029 miles

7. Name the figure on the right.

   rhombus

8. Label two opposite sides *x* and *y*.
   Answers will vary. Possible answer shown.
9. Draw a diagonal. Possible answer shown.

10. Is the diagonal a line of symmetry? Explain how you know.

   The two halves will match each other

   when the figure is folded along a

   diagonal. Yes.

100 UNIT C LESSON 2   Repeating Patterns

Homework and Remembering page 100

Home or School Activity

Language Arts Connection

Rhyming Patterns Find an example of a rhyming poem. Explain the rhyming pattern. For example, every other line rhymes (ABAB) or every pair of lines rhyme (AABB).

MY SHADOW

Robert Louis Stevenson

I have a little shadow that goes in and out with me, **A**

And what can be the use of him is more than I can see. **A**

He is very, very like me from the heels up to the head; **B**

And I see him jump before me, when I jump into my bed. **B**

Growing and Shrinking Patterns

Lesson Objectives

- **Identify and continue a number pattern that grows or shrinks.**
- **Identify and continue a geometric pattern that grows or shrinks.**

Vocabulary

growing pattern
shrinking pattern

The Day at a Glance

Today's Goals	Materials	123 Math Talk
1 Teaching the Lesson **A1:** Continue a number pattern that grows or shrinks. **A2:** Identify and use a table to analyze a growing pattern. **A3:** Solve a problem by solving a simpler problem using tables and patterns. **2 Extending the Lesson** ▶ Differentiated Instruction **3 Homework and Spiral Review**	Paper squares or square pattern blocks Skip Counting Circle (Copymaster M49) Student Activity Book pages 187–190 Homework and Remembering pages 101–102 Math Journals *One Grain of Rice* by Demi (Scholastic Press, 1997)	In today's activities, the students are involved in discussion as they ▶ describe, write rules for, and analyze repeating and growing patterns ▶ analyze growing and shrinking patterns ▶ solve problems that involve growing and shrinking patterns

1 Teaching the Lesson

Growing and Shrinking Number Patterns

 15 MINUTES

Goal: Continue a number pattern that grows or shrinks.

Materials: Student Activity Book page 187

✓ **NCTM Standards:**
Algebra
Reasoning and Proof

▶ **Continue a Growing or Shrinking Number Pattern** INDIVIDUALS

Remind students that they can write a rule to describe any pattern. The rule must say how the pattern starts and how it continues. Explain that some patterns grow by the same amount each time, while others grow by amounts that change.

Write this counting pattern on the board:

$$3, 6, 9, 12, 15, \ldots$$

● **What is the rule for this number pattern?** It starts at 3 and grows by 3 each time.

Write this counting pattern on the board:

$$1, 2, 4, 7, 11, 16, \ldots$$

● **What is the rule for this number pattern?** It starts at 1 and grows by 1, then by 2, then by 3, then by 4, and so on.

Have students look at Student Activity Book page 187. Explain that exercises 1 and 2 are about patterns that grow or shrink by the same amount, and exercises 3 and 4 are about patterns that grow or shrink by changing amounts. Emphasize that when the amount changes, students need to look for a pattern that tells how it changes. For example, in the pattern you discussed earlier (1, 2, 4, 7, 11, 16, …), the pattern changes by adding one more to the number added each time.

Have students complete exercises 5 and 6, and write the rule for each one. When they finish, invite volunteers to share their answers with the class.

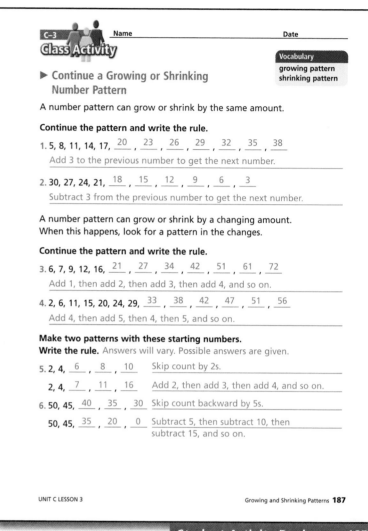

Student Activity Book page 187

 Ongoing Assessment

Observe the students as they analyze these number patterns and write the pattern rule. Do they try to continue a pattern before they determine the rule, or do they recognize that the rule can help them figure out what comes next? When they write a pattern rule, do they remember to tell how the pattern starts and how it continues? When a pattern grows or shrinks in a changing way, do they recognize that there is likely to be a pattern in the changes? (Students who recognize this will often jot small numbers above or below the pattern to show the changes.)

Growing and Shrinking Geometric Patterns

 15 MINUTES

Goal: Identify and use a table to analyze a growing pattern.

Materials: Student Activity Book page 188

 NCTM Standards:
Geometry
Algebra
Reasoning and Proof

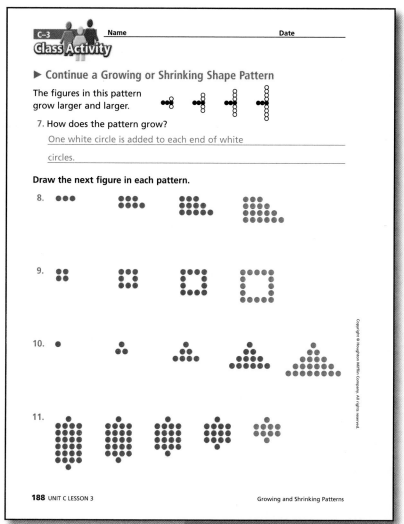

Student Activity Book page 188

► Continue a Growing or Shrinking Shape Pattern WHOLE CLASS

Discuss the pattern of figures at the top of Student Activity Book page 188.

● **How does the growing pattern start?** with a T-shape that has 3 black circles with 1 white circle on each side.

● **How does it continue?** The number of black circles is always the same, but the number of white circles increases by 2 each time.

Have students look at the pattern in exercise 8.

● **What is the rule for the pattern?** It starts with 1 row of 3 dots and adds a new row of dots each time. Each new row has 1 more dot than the row before it.

Ask students to draw the next figure. Ask a volunteer to draw the figure on the board. Then, give students time to complete the patterns in exercises 9 and 10. Ask volunteers to draw the figures on the board.

Next, direct students to the pattern in exercise 11.

● **How is this like the patterns in exercises 7–10?** It's a dot pattern.

● **How is it different?** The dot pictures get smaller instead of bigger.

● **What is the pattern?** Each time the pattern shrinks, 1 row of 4 dots is taken away.

Have students draw the next figure.

● **How many more times can this pattern repeat?** twice

● **What makes a shrinking pattern different from a growing pattern?** A growing pattern gets larger, but a shrinking pattern gets smaller. A growing pattern can continue forever, but a shrinking pattern ends.

If time allows, have students create a growing or shrinking dot pattern of their own and write the rule.

Activity 3

Patterns in the Real World

 30 MINUTES

Goal: Solve a problem by solving a simpler problem using tables and patterns.

Materials: Student Activity Book pages 189–190

 NCTM Standards:
Geometry
Algebra
Reasoning and Proof

▶ Solve a Simpler Problem [WHOLE CLASS]

Explain that sometimes we can solve a problem by looking for a pattern in a simpler problem. Then we can use the pattern to solve the original problem. You can often use a table like the one shown on Student Activity Book page 189 to help you see the pattern and extend it to solve the problem. Explain that you could draw the tenth triangle and count the small triangles, but it is easier and quicker to look for a pattern in a smaller number of triangles and extend the pattern.

Draw the table on chart paper or the board, and ask the students to help you complete it.

● **How does the table tell how the pattern starts?** The top row shows that the first figure has 1 triangle.

● **How does it show how the pattern continues?** The right column shows the number of small triangles in each figure: 1, 4, 9, 16.

● **What pattern do you see in the way the number of figures is growing?** Add 3, 5, 7, and so on.

Give students a few minutes to complete exercises 12–15. Then discuss the answers.

● **Write 1 for figure 1. How many triangles do you add to get figure 2?** 3

● **Write 1 + 3. How many triangles do you add to get figure 3?** 5

● **Write 1 + 3 + 5. How many triangles do you add to get figure 4?** 7

● **Write 1 + 3 + 5 + 7. How many triangles do you add to get figure 5?** 9

C–3

Class Activity

Name _____   Date _____

▶ **Solve a Simpler Problem**

How many small triangles will be in triangle number 10? One way to solve problems like this one is to solve a simpler problem and look for a pattern.

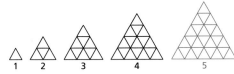

1   2   3   4   5

12. Complete the table to show how the number of small triangles grows.

13. Draw figure 5 in the pattern above. In the table, record the number of triangles it has.

14. Describe how the pattern grows.
The pattern grows by adding
3, 5, 7, 9, ... to the previous
number. Or, the triangle
number multiplied by itself.

Triangle Number	Number of Small Triangles
1	1
2	4
3	9
4	16
5	25

15. Use this pattern to find how many small triangles are in triangle number 10. _____100_____

Solve.

16. If 8 friends all shake hands with each other once, how many handshakes will take place?
_____28 handshakes_____

UNIT C LESSON 3   Growing and Shrinking Patterns **189**

Student Activity Book page 189

● **What do we call the numbers, 1, 3, 5, 7, and so on?** odd numbers

● **So figure 4 is the sum of the first 4 odd numbers. What will figure 5 be?** the sum of the first 5 odd numbers; 1 + 3 + 5 + 7 + 9

● **What will figure 10 be?** the sum of the first 10 odd numbers

Teaching Note

Math Background The number pattern in the table also represents square numbers. Square numbers will be studied in Unit 5.

- Now solve the problem. Tell students to look for numbers that make a ten to make adding easier.

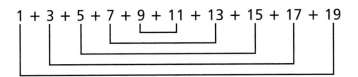

$$20 + 20 + 20 + 20 + 20 = 100$$

Ask these questions to help students solve problem 16. Encourage them to draw diagrams.

- How many handshakes would two friends have? 1

- three friends? 3

- four and five friends? 6; 10

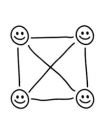 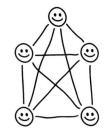

- The pattern is 1, 3, 6, 10, … What is the pattern rule? Add 2, then 3, then 4, and so on.

- Use the pattern rule to solve the problem.

	+2	+3	+4	+5	+6	+7
1	3	6	10	15	21	28

So with 8 friends, there would be 28 handshakes

▶ Make a Number-Chain Pattern

SMALL GROUPS

A "Number Chain" is a series of triangles with numbers inside them and at their corners. Draw this Number Chain on the board.

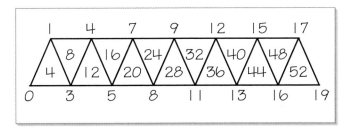

The sum of the numbers on the corners of each triangle is equal to the number inside.

- What pattern do you see inside the triangles? The numbers grow by adding 4 each time.

- What pattern do you see across the top? The numbers grow by adding 3, then 3, then 2, and repeating 3, 3, 2 each time.

- What pattern do you see across the bottom? The numbers grow by adding 3, then 2, then 3, and then repeating 3, 2, 3 each time.

- What zigzag pattern from bottom to top to bottom and so on do you see? The numbers grow by adding 1, then 2, then 1, and then repeating 1, 2, 1 each time.

- What will go inside the next triangle? 56

- What will be at the new corner of the next triangle? 20

Change the numbers in the chain, and ask students to describe the patterns and complete the missing triangles.

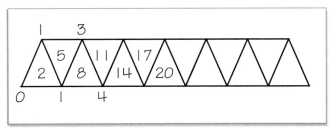

Challenge students to make up their own chains.

Activity continued ▶

Growing and Shrinking Patterns **411**

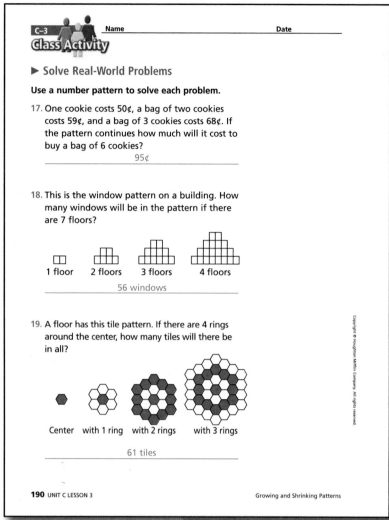

Student Activity Book page 190

▶ Solve Real-World Problems

INDIVIDUALS

Ask students to work independently on problems 17–19. Then discuss and summarize the results.

● What is the rule for the pattern in problem 17? Start at 50¢ and add 9¢ for each additional bag of cookies. A bag of 6 cookies would cost 95¢.

● What pattern do you see in the ones digits when you add 9¢ to each price? The ones digit decreases by 1.

● If I started with 63 and added 9, what would the ones digit be in the answer? 2 What is 63 + 9? 72

● What is the rule for the pattern in problem 18? Start at 2 and add 4, then 6, then 8, and so on.

To analyze this pattern, make a table like this:

Number of Floors	Number of Windows
1	2
2	2 + 4 = 6
3	2 + 4 + 6 = 12
4	2 + 4 + 6 + 8 = 20
5	2 + 4 + 6 + 8 + 10 = 30
6	2 + 4 + 6 + 8 + 10 + 12 = 42
7	2 + 4 + 6 + 8 + 10 + 12 + 14 = 56

Encourage students to discuss the patterns they see. A sample discussion follows.

 Math Talk in Action

What do you notice about the beginning of each addition sentence in column 2?

Melor: It has all the numbers from the row above it.

Samantha: And the last number in each sentence is double the number of the floor. For floor 6, the last number in the addition sentence is 12.

Great. How can you use that information to complete the chart without writing a long addition sentence?

Marshall: Double the number of the floor to get the number of windows to add, so for floor 8, it's 8 + 8, which is 16. Then add 16 to the number of windows that were on floor 7, which was 56. Then 56 + 16 = 72.

Then discuss problem 19.

● What is the rule for the pattern in problem 19? Start at 1 and add 6, then 12, then 18, and so on.

● What do you notice about all the numbers you're adding in this pattern? They're the "count-by-6" numbers.

● How did you find the number of tiles needed for four rings? 1 + 6 + 12 + 18 + 24 = 61

②Extending the Lesson

Intervention
for students having difficulty

PAIRS

Continue a Pattern

Materials: paper squares or square pattern blocks

Students use one square to represent their first figure. They then use three squares to make an L shape.

Students keep adding two squares at a time to make a larger L, and then write a number pattern to match the geometry pattern.

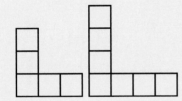

1, 3, 5, 7, 9, 11, …

On Level
for students having success

PAIRS

Make a Pattern

Materials: paper squares or square pattern blocks

Students use squares to make a geometric pattern of squares that grows, and then explain the rule for their pattern.

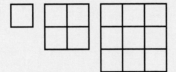

Start with 1. Add 3, add 5, add 7, and keep adding the next odd number. My pattern is 1, 4, 9, 16, . . .

Challenge
for students seeking a challenge

INDIVIDUALS

Make Patterns

Materials: Skip Counting Circle (Copymaster M49)

Students choose a skip-counting pattern that starts at 0. Beginning at 0 on the circle, they join the ones digits from their counting pattern with straight lines to change the number pattern into a geometric figure. Invite students to try some different counting patterns and write about what they discovered.

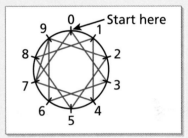

I skip counted by 3s. The figure traces over itself and makes the shape of a star.

Also Use
Challenge Master for C-3

 Math Writing Prompt

Intervention

Explain Your Thinking
How do you know if a pattern is growing or shrinking?

 Math Writing Prompt

On Level

Make a Pattern
Make a number pattern that grows or shrinks. Write your pattern rule.

 Math Writing Prompt

Challenge

Investigate Mathematics
Make a number pattern that grows by a different amount each time. What's your pattern rule?

③ Homework and Spiral Review

C–3

Homework **Goal:** Additional Practice

For homework, students continue practicing number patterns.

C–3

Remembering **Goal:** Spiral Review

This Remembering page is appropriate anytime after today's lesson.

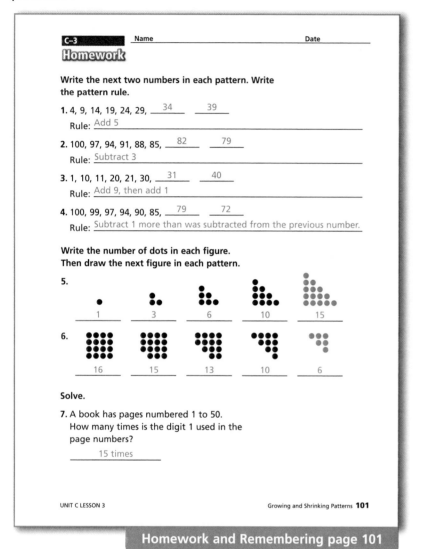

C–3 Name _____ Date _____
Homework

Write the next two numbers in each pattern. Write the pattern rule.

1. 4, 9, 14, 19, 24, 29, __34__ __39__
Rule: Add 5

2. 100, 97, 94, 91, 88, 85, __82__ __79__
Rule: Subtract 3

3. 1, 10, 11, 20, 21, 30, __31__ __40__
Rule: Add 9, then add 1

4. 100, 99, 97, 94, 90, 85, __79__ __72__
Rule: Subtract 1 more than was subtracted from the previous number.

Write the number of dots in each figure. Then draw the next figure in each pattern.

5. · / :· / :·: / ::·: / ::::·
1 3 6 10 15

6. 16 15 13 10 6

Solve.

7. A book has pages numbered 1 to 50. How many times is the digit 1 used in the page numbers?
15 times

UNIT C LESSON 3 — Growing and Shrinking Patterns **101**

Homework and Remembering page 101

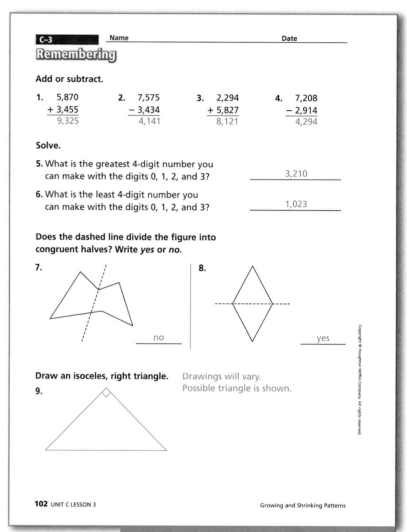

C–3 Name _____ Date _____
Remembering

Add or subtract.

1. 5,870 + 3,455 = 9,325   **2.** 7,575 − 3,434 = 4,141   **3.** 2,294 + 5,827 = 8,121   **4.** 7,208 − 2,914 = 4,294

Solve.

5. What is the greatest 4-digit number you can make with the digits 0, 1, 2, and 3? _____ 3,210

6. What is the least 4-digit number you can make with the digits 0, 1, 2, and 3? _____ 1,023

Does the dashed line divide the figure into congruent halves? Write *yes* or *no*.

7. _____ no   **8.** _____ yes

Draw an isoceles, right triangle.   Drawings will vary. Possible triangle is shown.
9.

102 UNIT C LESSON 3 — Growing and Shrinking Patterns

Homework and Remembering page 102

Home or School Activity

 Literature Connection

One Grain of Rice Have students read *One Grain of Rice,* by Demi (Scholastic Press, 1997). When you reach the part of the story where Rani asks for her reward, ask the students if they think her request (1 grain of rice the first day, 2 the second day, 4 the third day, and so on) is a wise one. Have them identify the pattern rule and continue the pattern for seven days to see how the amount of rice is growing. Then read the rest of the story.

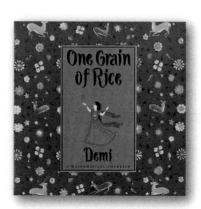

Unit Review and Test

Lesson Objective

● **Assess student progress on unit objectives.**

The Day at a Glance

Today's Goals	Materials
❶ Assessing the Unit ▶ Assess student progress on unit objectives. ▶ Use activities from unit lessons to reteach content. **❷ Extending the Assessment** ▶ Use remediation for common errors. There is no homework assignment on a test day.	Unit C Test, Student Activity Book pages 191–192 Unit C Test, Form A or B, Assessment Guide (optional) Unit C Performance Assessment, Assessment Guide (optional)

 Class Management

Review and Test Day You may want to choose a quiet game or other activity (reading a book or working on homework for another subject) for students who finish early.

Assessing the Unit

Assess Unit Objectives

🕐 **45 MINUTES** (more if schedule permits)

Goal: Assess student progress on unit objectives.

Materials: Student Activity Book pages 191–192; Assessment Guide (optional)

▶ Review and Assessment

If your students are ready for assessment on the unit objectives, you may use either the test on the Student Activity Book pages or one of the forms of the Unit C Test in the Assessment Guide to assess student progress.

If you feel that students need some review first, you may use the test on the Student Activity Book pages as a review of unit content, and then use one of the forms of the Unit C Test in the Assessment Guide to assess student progress.

To assign a numerical score for all of these test forms, use 10 points for each question.

You may also choose to use the Unit C Performance Assessment. Scoring for that assessment can be found in its rubric in the Assessment Guide.

▶ Reteaching Resources

The chart lists the test items, the unit objectives they cover, and the lesson activities in which the objective is covered in this unit. You may revisit these activities with students who do not show mastery of the objectives.

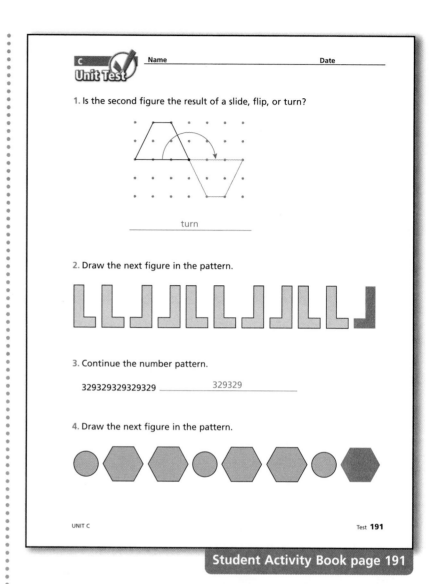

Student Activity Book page 191

Unit Test Items	Unit Objectives Tested	Activities to Use for Reteaching
1, 2	**C.1** Recognize and describe slides, flips, and turns and recognize them in geometric patterns.	Lesson 1, Activities 1 and 2 Lesson 2, Activity 2
3, 4, 5	**C.2** Identify the rule for number or geometric repeating patterns and continue the patterns.	Lesson 2, Activities 1 and 2

Student Activity Book page 192 content:

5. Write a rule for this pattern.

   □△△○□△△○

   square, triangle, triangle, circle, repeat _____

6. Continue this pattern.

   65, 62, 59, 56, 53, 50, 47, __44__, __41__, __38__, __35__, __32__

7. Continue this pattern.

   12, 16, 20, 24, 28, 32, 36, __40__, __44__, __48__, __52__, __56__

8. Continue this pattern.

   5, 6, 8, 11, 15, 20, 26, __33__, __41__, __50__, __60__, __71__

9. Write a rule for this pattern.

   69, 64, 59, 54, 49, 44, 39

   Start with 69. Then subtract 5. _____

10. **Extended Response** In September, Elisa walks dogs for $1.25 per walk. In October, she charges $1.50 per walk. In November, she charges $1.75 per walk. If the pattern continues, how much will she charge per walk in December and January? Describe the pattern rule you used to solve the problem.

    $2.00, $2.25; The pattern rule is that Elisa raises her price by $0.25 each month. December is the next month after November, so in December she will charge $1.75 + $0.25 = $2.00. January is the next month after December, so in January she will charge $2.00 + $0.25 = $2.25.

192 UNIT C   Test

Unit Test Items	Unit Objectives Tested	Activities to Use for Reteaching
6, 7, 8, 9	**C.3** Identify the rule for growing and shrinking number or geometric patterns and continue the patterns.	Lesson 3, Activities 1 and 2
10	**C.4** Solve real-world problems with patterns.	Lesson 3, Activity 3

▶ Assessment Resources

Free Response Tests
Unit C Test, Student Activity Book pages 191–192
Unit C Test, Form A, Assessment Guide

Extended Response Item
The last item in the Student Activity Book test and in the Form A test will require an extended response as an answer.

Multiple Choice Test
Unit C Test, Form B, Assessment Guide

Performance Assessment
Unit C Performance Assessment, Assessment Guide
Unit C Performance Assessment Rubric, Assessment Guide

▶ Portfolio Assessment
Teacher-selected Items for Student Portfolios:

- Homework, Lesson 2
- Class Activity work, Lessons 1, 3

Student-selected Items for Student Portfolios:

- Favorite Home or School Activity
- Best Writing Prompt

② Extending the Assessment

Unit Objective C.1
Recognize and describe slides, flips, and turns and recognize them in geometric patterns.

Common Error: Confuses Slides, Flips, and Turns

Some students may confuse slides, flips, and turns.

Remediation Have students make cutouts of the figures they are working with and mark a dot in one corner of each. Students can then note the position of the dot to help them determine if a transformation is a slide, flip, or turn.

Unit Objective C.2
Identify the rule for number or geometric repeating patterns and continue the patterns.

Common Error: Does Not Recognize a Visual Pattern

Sometimes students have difficulty identifying patterns that involve figures.

Remediation If students have difficulty recognizing visual patterns, encourage them to use words to describe the patterns. As they repeat the pattern aloud, they may begin to feel the rhythm of the words and more easily recognize the pattern.

For example: triangle, square, triangle, square, triangle, square, triangle, square . . .

• What comes next?

Unit Objective C.3
Identify the rule for growing and shrinking number or geometric patterns and continue the patterns.

Common Error: Does Not Correctly Identify a Pattern Rule for a Growing or Shrinking Pattern

Students may make errors in extending growing or shrinking patterns because they have not successfully found the pattern rule.

Remediation Encourage those students having difficulty finding pattern rules for growing or shrinking patterns to draw diagrams showing the change between consecutive numbers in the pattern.

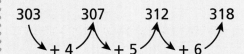

Common Error: Does Not Correctly Extend a Growing or Shrinking Pattern

Some students may correctly identify a growing or shrinking pattern rule but then make errors using the pattern rule to extend the pattern.

Remediation For students having difficulty extending number patterns using a pattern rule, suggest that they use an arrow with numbers to help them find the next number in the pattern

25   ─   ─   ─
    − 2   − 2   − 2

Unit Objective C.4
Solve real-world problems with patterns.

Common Error: Does Not Recognize the Information Given as a Pattern Rule

Some students may not recognize that a problem provides them with the information to extend a pattern.

Remediation Provide students with opportunities to practice identifying pattern rules in word problems. For example, consider the word problem in the Unit Test: In September, Elisa walks dogs for $1.25 per walk. In October, she charges $1.50 per walk. In November, she charges $1.75 per walk. If the pattern continues, how much does she charge per walk in December and January?

Ask students what the starting cost is per walk, and how much is added each time. Then ask them to determine how far they need to extend the pattern to solve the problem.

Common Error: Records Incorrect Information

Some students may incorrectly record information they are given so they are unable to identify patterns.

Remediation Remind students to check the numbers they write in their tables to be sure they are recording the correct information. Suggest that they have a partner check their data to be sure they entered the correct numbers in their tables before trying to find a pattern.

Student Glossary

Glossary

acute angle An angle whose measure is less than 90°.

acute triangle A triangle in which the measure of each angle is less than 90°.

addend A number to be added.

Example: $8 + 4 = 12$

    addend   addend

addition A mathematical operation that combines two or more numbers.

Example: $23 + 52 = 75$

  addend addend sum

adjacent (sides) Two sides that meet at a point.

Example: Sides *a* and *b* are adjacent.

A.M. The time period between midnight and noon.

angle A figure formed by two rays or two line segments that meet at an endpoint.

area The number of square units in a region.

The area of the rectangle is 6 square units.

array An arrangement of objects, pictures, or numbers in columns and rows.

Associative Property of Addition (Grouping Property of Addition) The property which states that changing the way in which addends are grouped does not change the sum.

Example: $(2 + 3) + 1 = 2 + (3 + 1)$

$5 + 1 = 2 + 4$

$6 = 6$

Associative Property of Multiplication (Grouping Property of Multiplication) The property which states that changing the way in which factors are grouped does not change the product.

Example: $(2 \times 3) \times 4 = 2 \times (3 \times 4)$

$6 \times 4 = 2 \times 12$

$24 = 24$

Glossary (Continued)

axis (plural: **axes**) A reference line for a graph. A bar graph has 2 axes; one is horizontal and the other is vertical.

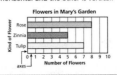

bar graph A graph that uses bars to show data. The bars may be horizontal or vertical.

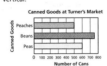

base (of a geometric figure) The bottom side of a 2-D figure or the bottom face of a 3-D figure.

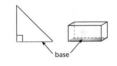

calculator A tool used to perform mathematical operations.

capacity The amount a container can hold.

cell A rectangle in a table where a column and row meet.

centimeter (cm) A metric unit used to measure length.

$100 \text{ cm} = 1 \text{ m}$

circle A plane figure that forms a closed path so that all points on the path are the same distance from a point called the center.

circle graph A graph that represents data as parts of a whole.

circumference The distance around a circle, about $3\frac{1}{7}$ times the diameter.

column A vertical group of cells in a table.

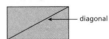

Commutative Property of Addition (Order Property of Addition) The property which states that changing the order of addends does not change the sum.

Example: $3 + 7 = 7 + 3$

$10 = 10$

Commutative Property of Multiplication (Order Property of Multiplication) The property which states that changing the order of factors does not change the product.

Example: $5 \times 4 = 4 \times 5$

$20 = 20$

comparison bars Bars that represent the larger amount, smaller amount, and difference in a comparison problem.

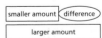

In Volume 2, we use comparison bars for multiplication.

cone A solid figure that has a circular base and comes to a point called the vertex.

congruent figures Figures that have the same size and shape.

Triangles A and B are congruent.

coordinates The numbers in an ordered pair that locate a point on a coordinate grid. The first number is the distance across and the second number is the distance up.

The coordinates 3 and 4 in the ordered pair (3, 4) locate Point A on the coordinate grid.

coordinate grid A grid formed by two perpendicular number lines in which every point is assigned an ordered pair of numbers.

cube A solid figure that has six square faces of equal size.

Glossary (Continued)

cup (c) A customary unit of measurement used to measure capacity.

2 cups = 1 pint
4 cups = 1 quart
16 cups = 1 gallon

cylinder A solid figure with two congruent circular or elliptical faces and one curved surface.

data Pieces of information.

decimal A number with one or more digits to the right of a decimal point.

Examples: 1.23 and 0.3

decimal point The dot that separates the whole number from the decimal part.

1.23

  decimal point

decimeter (dm) A metric unit used to measure length.

1 decimeter = 10 centimeters

degree (°) A unit for measuring angles or temperature.

degrees Celsius (°C) The metric unit for measuring temperature.

degrees Fahrenheit (°F) The customary unit of temperature.

denominator The bottom number in a fraction that shows the total number of equal parts in the whole.

Example: $\frac{1}{3}$ ⟵ denominator

diagonal A line segment that connects two corners of a figure and is not a side of the figure.

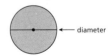

diameter A line segment that connects two point on a circle and also passes through the center of the circle. The term is also used to describe the length of such a line segment.

difference The result of subtraction or of comparing.

digit Any of the symbols 0, 1, 2, 3, 4, 5, 6, 7, 8, 9.

dividend The number that is divided in division.

Examples:

$12 \div 3 = 4$ $3\overline{)12}$

  dividend   dividend

division The mathematical operation that separates an amount into smaller equal groups to find the number of groups or the number in each group.

Example: $12 \div 3 = 4$ is a division number sentence.

divisor The number that you divide by in division.

Example: $12 \div 3 = 4$ $3\overline{)12}$

  divisor divisor

Student Glossary (Continued)

E

edge The line segment where two faces of a solid figure meet.

edge

elapsed time The time that passes between the beginning and the end of an activity.

endpoint The point at either end of a line segment or the beginning point of a ray.

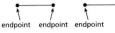
endpoint   endpoint   endpoint

equation A mathematical sentence with an equals sign.
Examples: 11 + 22 = 33
75 − 25 = 50

equilateral triangle A triangle whose sides are all the same length.

3 in.   3 in.
3 in.

equivalent Equal, or naming the same amount.

equivalent fractions Fractions that name the same amount.
Example: $\frac{1}{2}$ and $\frac{2}{4}$

equivalent fractions

estimate About how many or about how much.

even number A whole number that is a multiple of 2. The ones digit in an even number is 0, 2, 4, 6, or 8.

event In probability, a possible outcome.

expanded form A number written to show the value of each of its digits.
Examples:
347 = 300 + 40 + 7
347 = 3 hundreds + 4 tens + 7 ones

expression A combination of numbers, variables, and/or operation signs. An expression does not have an equals sign.
Examples: 4 + 7   a − 3

F

face A flat surface of a solid figure.

face

factors Numbers that are multiplied to give a product.
Example: 4 × 5 = 20

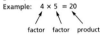
factor   factor   product

flip To reflect a figure over a line. The size and shape of the figure remain the same.

foot (ft) A customary unit used to measure length.
1 foot = 12 inches

Glossary **S5**

Glossary (Continued)

formula An equation with variables that describes a rule.
The formula for the area of a rectangle is:
$A = l \times w$
where A is the area, l is the length, and w is the width.

fraction A number that names part of a whole or part of a set.

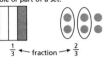
$\frac{1}{3}$ ← fraction → $\frac{2}{3}$

front-end estimation A method of estimating that keeps the largest place value in a number and drops the rest.
Example: 527 →   500
         + 673 → + 600
                   1,100
The 5 in 527 is the "front end" number
The 6 in 673 is the "front end" number

function table A table of ordered pairs that shows a function.

For every input number, there is only one possible output number.

Rule: add 2	
Input	Output
1	3
2	4
3	5
4	6

G

gallon (gal) A customary unit used to measure capacity.
1 gallon = 4 quarts = 8 pints = 16 cups

gram (g) A metric unit of mass, about 1 paper clip.
1,000 grams = 1 kilogram

greater than (>) A symbol used to compare two numbers.
Example: 6 > 5
6 is greater than 5.

group To combine numbers to form new tens, hundreds, thousands, and so on.

growing pattern A number or geometric pattern that increases.
Examples: 2, 4, 6, 8, l0…
1, 2, 5, 10, 17…

H

height A measurement of vertical length, or how tall something is.

horizontal Extending in two directions, left and right.

horizontal bar graph A bar graph with horizontal bars.

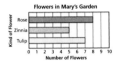
Flowers in Mary's Garden

hundredth One of the equal parts when a whole is divided into 100 equal parts.

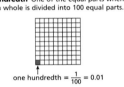
one hundredth = $\frac{1}{100}$ = 0.01

S6 Glossary

I

improper fraction A fraction in which the numerator is equal to or is greater than the denominator. Improper fractions are equal to or greater than 1.
$\frac{5}{5}$ and $\frac{8}{3}$ are improper fractions.

inch (in.) A customary unit used to measure length.
12 inches = 1 foot

isosceles triangle A triangle that has at least two sides of the same length.

K

key A part of a map, graph, or chart that explains what symbols mean.

kilogram (kg) A metric unit of mass.
1 kilogram = 1,000 grams

kilometer (km) A metric unit of length.
1 kilometer = 1,000 meters

L

less than (<) A symbol used to compare numbers.
Example: 5 < 6
5 is less than 6.

line A straight path that goes on forever in opposite directions.

line graph A graph that uses a straight line or a broken line to show changes in data.

Height of a Bean Plant

line of symmetry A line on which a figure can be folded so that the two halves match exactly.

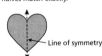
Line of symmetry

line plot A way to show data using a number line.

line segment A part of a line. A line segment has two endpoints.

liter (L) A metric unit used to measure capacity.
1 liter = 1,000 milliliters

Glossary **S7**

Glossary (Continued)

M

mass The amount of matter in an object.

mean (average) The sum of the values in a set of data divided by the number of pieces of data in the set.
Example: 3 + 5 + 4 + 8 = 20
20 ÷ 4 = 5   5 is the mean

mental math A way to solve problems without using pencil and paper, or a calculator.

meter (m) A metric unit used to measure length.
1 meter = 100 centimeters

method A procedure, or way, of doing something.

mile (mi) A customary unit of length.
1 mile = 5,280 feet

milliliter (mL) A metric unit used to measure capacity.
1,000 milliliters = 1 liter

mixed number A whole number and a fraction.
$1\frac{3}{4}$ is a mixed number.

mode The number that occurs most often in a set of data.
In this set of numbers {3, 4, 5, 5, 5, 7, 8}, 5 is the mode.

multiple A number that is the product of the given number and another number.

multiplication A mathematical operation that combines equal groups.
Example: 4 × 3 = 12

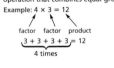
factor   factor   product
3 + 3 + 3 + 3 = 12
4 times

N

net A flat pattern that can be folded to make a solid figure.

This net can be folded into a rectangular prism.

number line A line on which numbers are assigned to lengths.

numerator The top number in a fraction that shows the number of equal parts counted.
Example: $\frac{1}{3}$ ← numerator

O

obtuse angle An angle that measures more than 90° but less than 180°.

obtuse triangle A triangle with one angle that measures more than 90°.

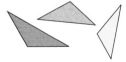

odd number A whole number that is not a multiple of 2. The ones digit in an odd number is 1, 3, 5, 7, or 9.

S8 Glossary

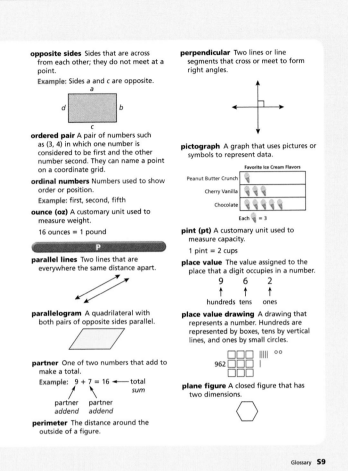

opposite sides Sides that are across from each other; they do not meet at a point.

Example: Sides a and c are opposite.

ordered pair A pair of numbers such as (3, 4) in which one number is considered to be first and the other number second. They can name a point on a coordinate grid.

ordinal numbers Numbers used to show order or position.

Example: first, second, fifth

ounce (oz) A customary unit used to measure weight.

16 ounces = 1 pound

P

parallel lines Two lines that are everywhere the same distance apart.

parallelogram A quadrilateral with both pairs of opposite sides parallel.

partner One of two numbers that add to make a total.

Example: 9 + 7 = 16 ← total
        sum
partner partner
addend   addend

perimeter The distance around the outside of a figure.

perpendicular Two lines or line segments that cross or meet to form right angles.

pictograph A graph that uses pictures or symbols to represent data.

Favorite Ice Cream Flavors

Peanut Butter Crunch
Cherry Vanilla
Chocolate

Each 🍦 = 3

pint (pt) A customary unit used to measure capacity.

1 pint = 2 cups

place value The value assigned to the place that a digit occupies in a number.

9   6   2
hundreds tens ones

place value drawing A drawing that represents a number. Hundreds are represented by boxes, tens by vertical lines, and ones by small circles.

962

plane figure A closed figure that has two dimensions.

Glossary (Continued)

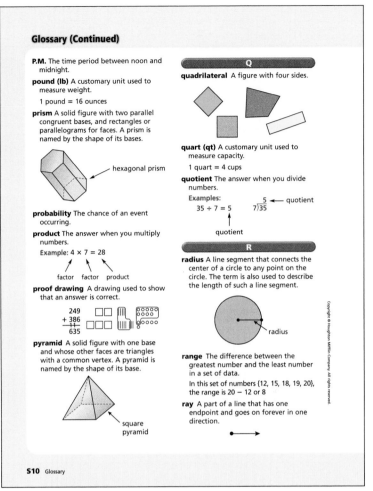

P.M. The time period between noon and midnight.

pound (lb) A customary unit used to measure weight.

1 pound = 16 ounces

prism A solid figure with two parallel congruent bases, and rectangles or parallelograms for faces. A prism is named by the shape of its bases.

→ hexagonal prism

probability The chance of an event occurring.

product The answer when you multiply numbers.

Example: 4 × 7 = 28

factor factor product

proof drawing A drawing used to show that an answer is correct.

249
+ 386
  11
 635

pyramid A solid figure with one base and whose other faces are triangles with a common vertex. A pyramid is named by the shape of its base.

square pyramid

Q

quadrilateral A figure with four sides.

quart (qt) A customary unit used to measure capacity.

1 quart = 4 cups

quotient The answer when you divide numbers.

Examples:
35 ÷ 7 = 5   5 ← quotient
            7)35
      quotient

R

radius A line segment that connects the center of a circle to any point on the circle. The term is also used to describe the length of such a line segment.

→ radius

range The difference between the greatest number and the least number in a set of data.

In this set of numbers {12, 15, 18, 19, 20}, the range is 20 − 12 or 8.

ray A part of a line that has one endpoint and goes on forever in one direction.

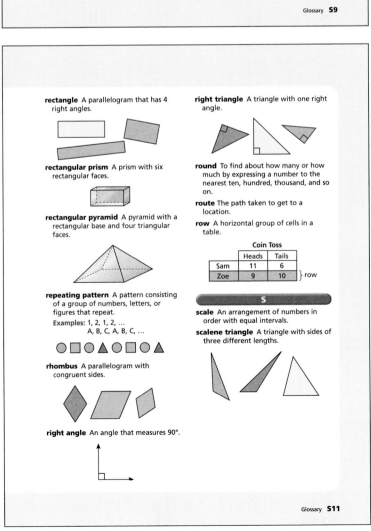

rectangle A parallelogram that has 4 right angles.

rectangular prism A prism with six rectangular faces.

rectangular pyramid A pyramid with a rectangular base and four triangular faces.

repeating pattern A pattern consisting of a group of numbers, letters, or figures that repeat.

Examples: 1, 2, 1, 2, …
          A, B, C, A, B, C, …

rhombus A parallelogram with congruent sides.

right angle An angle that measures 90°.

right triangle A triangle with one right angle.

round To find about how many or how much by expressing a number to the nearest ten, hundred, thousand, and so on.

route The path taken to get to a location.

row A horizontal group of cells in a table.

Coin Toss

	Heads	Tails
Sam	11	6
Zoe	9	10	} row

S

scale An arrangement of numbers in order with equal intervals.

scalene triangle A triangle with sides of three different lengths.

Glossary (Continued)

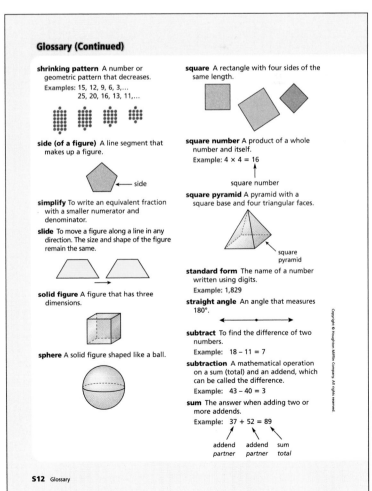

shrinking pattern A number or geometric pattern that decreases.

Examples: 15, 12, 9, 6, 3,…
          25, 20, 16, 13, 11,…

side (of a figure) A line segment that makes up a figure.

← side

simplify To write an equivalent fraction with a smaller numerator and denominator.

slide To move a figure along a line in any direction. The size and shape of the figure remain the same.

solid figure A figure that has three dimensions.

sphere A solid figure shaped like a ball.

square A rectangle with four sides of the same length.

square number A product of a whole number and itself.

Example: 4 × 4 = 16

square number

square pyramid A pyramid with a square base and four triangular faces.

→ square pyramid

standard form The name of a number written using digits.

Example: 1,829

straight angle An angle that measures 180°.

subtract To find the difference of two numbers.

Example: 18 − 11 = 7

subtraction A mathematical operation on a sum (total) and an addend, which can be called the difference.

Example: 43 − 40 = 3

sum The answer when adding two or more addends.

Example: 37 + 52 = 89

addend   addend   sum
partner   partner   total

Student Glossary (Continued)

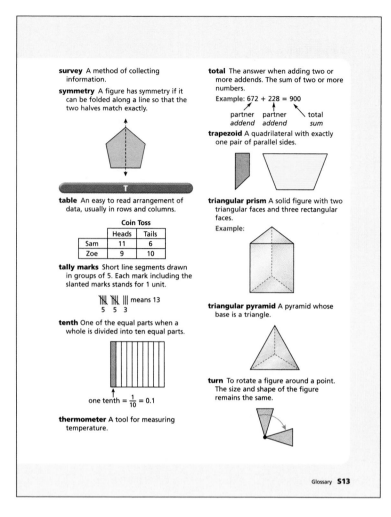

survey A method of collecting information.

symmetry A figure has symmetry if it can be folded along a line so that the two halves match exactly.

T

table An easy to read arrangement of data, usually in rows and columns.

Coin Toss

	Heads	Tails
Sam	11	6
Zoe	9	10

tally marks Short line segments drawn in groups of 5. Each mark including the slanted marks stands for 1 unit.

𝗧𝗛𝗟 𝗧𝗛𝗟 ||| means 13
  5   5   3

tenth One of the equal parts when a whole is divided into ten equal parts.

one tenth = $\frac{1}{10}$ = 0.1

thermometer A tool for measuring temperature.

total The answer when adding two or more addends. The sum of two or more numbers.

Example: 672 + 228 = 900

partner addend   partner addend   total sum

trapezoid A quadrilateral with exactly one pair of parallel sides.

triangular prism A solid figure with two triangular faces and three rectangular faces.

Example:

triangular pyramid A pyramid whose base is a triangle.

turn To rotate a figure around a point. The size and shape of the figure remains the same.

Glossary (Continued)

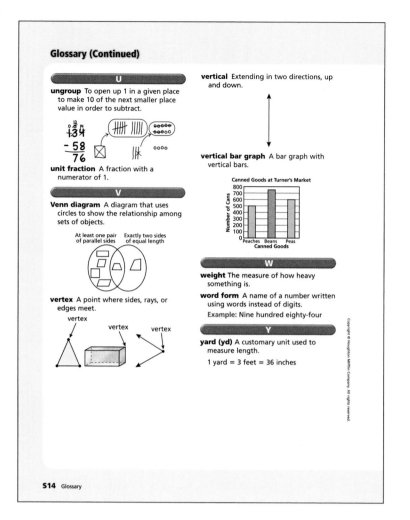

U

ungroup To open up 1 in a given place to make 10 of the next smaller place value in order to subtract.

unit fraction A fraction with a numerator of 1.

V

Venn diagram A diagram that uses circles to show the relationship among sets of objects.

At least one pair of parallel sides   Exactly two sides of equal length

vertex A point where sides, rays, or edges meet.

vertex   vertex   vertex

vertical Extending in two directions, up and down.

vertical bar graph A bar graph with vertical bars.

Canned Goods at Turner's Market

weight The measure of how heavy something is.

word form A name of a number written using words instead of digits.

Example: Nine hundred eighty-four

W

Y

yard (yd) A customary unit used to measure length.

1 yard = 3 feet = 36 inches

Teacher Glossary

5s shortcut A strategy for multiplying by numbers larger than 5. For example, to multiply 7 × 3, students think of the 5 count-by of 3, 15. They then think of the additional count-bys of 3, 18, 21. Therefore, 7 × 3 = 21.

7 times 3 equals 21

A

acute angle An angle whose measure is less than 90°.

acute triangle A triangle in which the measure of each angle is less than 90°.

addend A number to be added. In the equation 8 + 4 = 12, 8 and 4 are addends.

adjacent (sides) Two sides that meet at a point. In this example, sides *a* and *b* are adjacent.

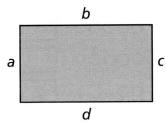

A.M. The abbreviation for *ante meridiem,* Latin for "before noon". Used to indicate a time between midnight and noon.

analog clock A clock with a face, a shorter hand, and a longer hand.

angle A figure formed by two rays or two line segments that meet at an endpoint.

area The number of square units in a region.

area model A model that uses square units to show a multiplication.

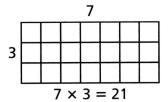

7 × 3 = 21

array An arrangement of objects, pictures, or numbers in columns and rows.

Associative Property of Addition Property which states that changing the grouping of addends does not change their sum. For all numbers *a*, *b*, and *c*, *a* + (*b* + *c*) = (*a* + *b*) + *c*.

Associative Property of Multiplication Property which states that changing the grouping of factors does not change their product. For all numbers *a*, *b* and *c*, *a* × (*b* × *c*) = (*a* × *b*) × *c*.

axis (plural: **axes**) A reference line for a graph. A bar graph has 2 axes; one is horizontal and the other is vertical.

B

bar graph A graph that uses bars to show data. The bars may be horizontal or vertical.

base (of a geometric figure) The bottom side of a 2-D figure or the bottom face of a 3-D figure.

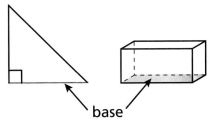

base

benchmark A reference whose size is familiar to students and approximately equal to a unit of measure. A benchmark helps students visualize the size of the unit. Comparing a known benchmark to an item of unknown size helps students to make a reasonable estimate.

Teacher Glossary (Continued)

C

capacity The amount a container can hold.

cell A rectangle in a table where a column and row meet.

centimeter (cm) A metric unit used to measure length. 100 cm = 1 m

change minus problem A problem that begins with a given quantity which is then modified by a change—something is subtracted—that results in a new quantity.

Sarah had 12 books. She loaned her friend 9 books. How many books does Sarah have now?

change plus problem A problem that begins with a given quantity which is then modified by a change—something is added—that results in a new quantity.
Alvin had 9 toy cars. He received 3 more for his birthday. How many toy cars does Alvin have now?

circle A plane figure that forms a closed path so that all points on the path are the same distance from a point called the center.

circle graph A graph that represents data as parts of a whole. (Also called a pie graph or pie chart.)

circumference The distance around a circle.

Class Multiplication Table A poster in table form that displays the multiplications for 1–9. Columns of the table are labeled 1–9 and rows are labeled 1–10. The product of the labels is found in the cells where the row and column meet.

clockwise A turn in the same direction as the hands of a clock move.

column A vertical group of cells in a table.

combinations Arrangements of elements

common denominator Any common multiple of the denominators of two or more fractions.

common multiplier The same number that multiplies the numerator and denominator of a fraction so that the resulting fraction is equivalent.

Commutative Property of Addition Property which states that the order in which numbers are added does not change the sum. For all numbers a and b, $a + b = b + a$.

Commutative Property of Multiplication Property which states that the order in which numbers are multiplied does not change the product. For all numbers a and b, $a \times b = b \times a$.

comparison bars Bars that represent the larger amount, smaller amount, and difference in a comparison problem.

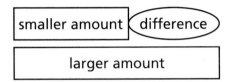

comparison language

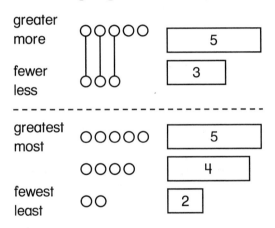

comparison situation A situation in which two amounts are compared by addition or by multiplication. An additive comparison situation compares by asking or telling how much more (how much less) one amount is than another. A multiplicative comparison situation compares by asking or telling how many times as many one amount is as another. The multiplicative comparison may also be made using fraction language. For example, you can say, "Sally has one fourth as much as Tom has," instead of saying "Tom has 4 times as much as Sally has."

compatible numbers Numbers that are close to the original numbers and are easy to compute with. The numbers 35 and 80 are compatible numbers for estimating 36 plus 82.

cone A solid figure that has a circular base and comes to a point called the vertex.

congruent figures Figures that have the same size and shape. In this example triangles A and B are congruent.

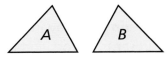

coordinate grid A grid formed by two perpendicular number lines in which every point is assigned an ordered pair of numbers.

coordinates The numbers in an ordered pair that locate a point on a coordinate grid. The first number is the distance across and the second number is the distance up. The coordinates 3 and 4 in the ordered pair (3, 4) locate Point A on the coordinate grid.

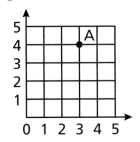

count-bys Products that are found by skip-counting a particular number; 5s count-bys would be 5, 10, 15, 20, 25, and so on; 3s count-bys would be 3, 6, 9, 12, and so on.

counter clockwise A turn in the opposite direction as the hands of a clock move.

count on An addition or subtraction strategy in which children begin with one partner and count on to the total. This strategy can be used to find an unknown partner or an unknown total.

$5 + 3 = \boxed{8}$

$5 + \boxed{3} = 8$

$8 - 5 = \boxed{3}$ Already **5**

cube A solid figure that has six square faces of equal size.

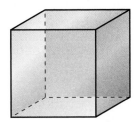

cubic unit A unit for measuring volume such as a cubic inch or cubic centimeter.

cup (c) A customary unit of measurement used to measure capacity. 2 cups = 1 pint
4 cups = 1 quart   16 cups = 1 gallon

cylinder A solid figure with two congruent circular faces and one curved surface.

D

data A set of information.

decimal A number with one or more digits to the right of a decimal point. 1.23 and 0.3

decimeter (dm) A metric unit used to measure length. 1 decimeter = 10 centimeters

degree (°) A unit for measuring angles or temperature.

degrees Celsius (°C) The metric unit of temperature.

degrees Fahrenheit (°F) The customary unit of temperature.

Demonstration Secret Code Cards A larger version of the Secret Code Cards for classroom use. (See **Secret Code Cards**.)

denominator The bottom number in a fraction that shows the total number of parts in a whole. In the fraction $\frac{1}{3}$, 3 is the denominator.

diagonal A line segment that connects two corners of a figure and is not a side of the figure.

Teacher Glossary (Continued)

diameter A line segment that connects two points on a circle and also passes through the center of the circle. The term is also used to describe the length of such a line segment.

difference The result of subtraction.

digit Any of the symbols 0, 1, 2, 3, 4, 5, 6, 7, 8, 9.

digital clock A clock that shows the hour and minutes with digits.

dimension A way to describe how a figure can be measured. A line segment has only length, so it has *one* dimension. A rectangle has length and width, so it has *two* dimensions. A cube has length, width, and height, so it has *three* dimensions.

dimensions The measurements of sides of geometric figures.

dimes place In dollar notation, the first place to the right of the decimal point. In the amount $3.47, 4 is in the dimes place.

Distributive Property of Multiplication The product of a factor and a sum (or difference) equals the sum (or difference) of the products. For all numbers *a*, *b* and *c*,
$a \times (b + c) = (a \times b) + (a \times c)$

dividend The number that is divided in division. In the equation $12 \div 3 = 4$, 12 is the dividend.

divisible A number is divisible by another number if the quotient is a whole number with no remainder. The number 6 is divisible by 3, but not 4.

divisor The number that you divide by in division. In the equation $12 \div 3 = 4$, 3 is the divisor.

dollars place In dollar notation, the first place to the left of the decimal point. In the amount $3.47, 3 is in the dollars place.

Dot Array An arrangement of dots in rows and columns.

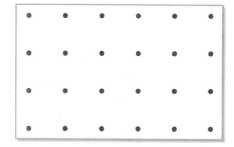

E

edge The line segment where two faces of a solid figure meet.

elapsed time The time that passes between the beginning and end of an event.

equal (=) Having the same value as that of another quantity or expression. $3 + 1 = 4$ is read as 3 plus 1 is equal to 4.

equal groups Concept used in multiplication and division situations. $5 \times 6 = 30$. There are 5 equal groups of 6 items.

Equal Shares drawing A drawing which children create that represents factors and products. It is a numerical form of a Repeated Groups drawing.

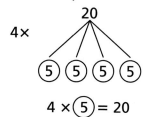

$4 \times \textcircled{5} = 20$

equally likely outcomes In probability, events that have the same chance of occurring.

equation A mathematical sentence with an equals sign. $11 + 22 = 33$ $75 - 25 = 50$

equilateral triangle A triangle whose sides are all the same length.

equivalence chain A series of equivalent fractions connected with equal signs.
$\frac{1}{2} = \frac{2}{4} = \frac{4}{8} = \frac{8}{16}$

equivalent fractions Fractions that name the same amount. $\frac{1}{2}$ and $\frac{2}{4}$ are equivalent fractions.

estimate A number close to an exact amount. About how many or about how much.

evaluate To find the value of a mathematical expression.

even number A whole number that is a multiple of 2. The ones digit in an even number is 0, 2, 4, 6, or 8.

event In probability, a possible outcome.

expanded form A number written to show the value of each of its digits.
Examples: 347 = 300 + 40 + 7
347 = 3 hundreds + 4 tens + 7 ones

expression A combination of numbers and operation signs. 4 + 7

F

face A flat surface of a solid figure.

face

factors Numbers that are multiplied to give a product. In the equation 4 × 5 = 20, 4 and 5 are factors.

Fast-Area drawing A representation of an area model that students can sketch quickly to label the units appropriately on a rectangle.

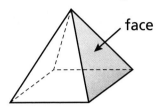

Fast-Array drawing A representation of an array that shows a missing factor or missing product.

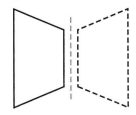

fewer Fewer is used to compare two quantities that can be counted. There are fewer red books than blue books. Less is used to compare two quantities that can be measured. There is less water than juice. *See comparison language.*

flip To reflect a figure over a line. The size and shape of the figure remain the same.

fluid ounce (fl oz) A customary unit of capacity equal to 2 tablespoons.

foot (ft) A customary unit used to measure length. 1 foot = 12 inches

formula An equation with variables that describes a rule. The formula for the area of a rectangle is: $A = l \times w$, where A is the area, l is the length, and w is the width.

fraction A number that names part of a whole or part of a set.

fraction bar A visual representation of a whole divided into equal parts. The fraction bar shown here represents one-third.

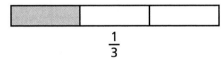
$\frac{1}{3}$

fraction strip Strips of paper divided into equal unit fractional parts that students can fold to explore equivalent fractions.

fracture To divide into smaller equal parts.

front-end estimation A method of estimating that uses the largest place value in a number. In the equation 527 + 673 = ☐, you would round 527 to 500 and 673 to 600 for a total of 1,100.

function A set of ordered pairs such that no two ordered pairs have the same first member.

function table A table of ordered pairs that shows a function.

Rule: add 2	
Input	Output
1	3
2	4
3	5
4	6

G

gallon (gal) A customary unit used to measure capacity. 1 gallon = 4 quarts = 16 cups

gram (g) A metric unit of mass.
1,000 grams = 1 kilogram

greater than (>) Having a value that is more than that of another quantity or expression. 6 > 5 is read as 6 is greater than 5.

group To combine numbers to form new tens, hundreds, thousands, and so on.

growing pattern A number or geometric pattern that increases.
Examples: 2, 4, 6, 8, 10 ...
1, 2, 5, 10, 17 ...

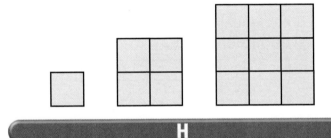

H

half turn A 180° rotation.

height In geometry, the length of a perpendicular line segment from a vertex to the opposite side of a plane figure.

hexagon A six-sided polygon.

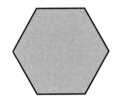

horizontal Extending in two directions, left and right parallel to the horizon.

hundred box In a place value drawing, a square box representing that 10 ten-sticks equal one hundred. A hundred box is a quick way of drawing 100.

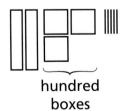

hundred
boxes

hundredth One of the equal parts when a whole is divided into 100 equal parts.

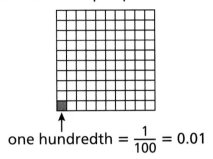

one hundredth = $\frac{1}{100}$ = 0.01

I

Identity Property of Multiplication The product of 1 and any number equals that number. 1 × 10 = 10

improper fraction A fraction in which the numerator is equal to or is greater than the denominator. Improper fractions are equal to or greater than 1. $\frac{8}{8}$ and $\frac{8}{3}$ are improper fractions.

inch (in.) A customary unit used to measure length. 12 inches = 1 foot

inequality A statement that two expressions are not equal.

input In a function or rule, the value that is entered into the function or rule to produce an output.

inverse operations Opposite or reverse operations that undo each other. Addition and subtraction are inverse operations. Multiplication and division are inverse operations.

isosceles triangle A triangle that has at least two sides of the same length.

K

key A part of a map, graph, or chart that explains what symbols mean.

kilogram (kg) A metric unit of mass.
1 kilogram = 1,000 grams

kilometer (km) A metric unit of length.
1 kilometer = 1,000 meters

L

less than (<) Having a value that is less than that of another quantity or expression. 5 < 6 is read as 5 is less than 6.

line A straight path that goes on forever in opposite directions.

line graph A graph that uses a straight line or a broken line to show changes in data.

line of reflection A line around or over which a figure is flipped to produce a mirror image of the figure. Each point of the original figure and flipped figure is the same distance from the line.

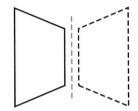

line of symmetry A line on which a figure can be folded so that the two halves match exactly.

line plot A way to show data using a number line.

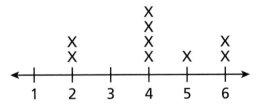

line segment A part of a line. A line segment has two endpoints.

line symmetry A figure has line symmetry if it can be folded along a line so the two halves match exactly.

liter (L) A metric unit used to measure capacity. 1 liter = 1,000 milliliters

M

Make a Hundred Strategy An addition or subtraction strategy in which the student finds the 100-partner of the larger addend and then breaks apart the other addend into that 100-partner and the rest to find the total.
To add 80 + 70 using the Make a Hundred strategy, the student finds the 100-partner for 80 which is 20, breaks apart 70, the other addend, into 20 + 50 and then adds the rest, 50, to 100. Thus, 100 + 50 = 150 so 80 + 70 = 150.

Make a Ten Strategy An addition strategy in which students find the 10-partner. To add 7 + 9, the student finds the 10-partner for 9 which is 1, breaks apart 7, the other addend, into 1 + 6 and then adds the rest, 6, to 10. Thus, 10 + 6 = 16, so 7 + 9 = 16.

Make a Thousand Strategy An addition strategy in which the student finds the 1,000-partner of the larger addend and then breaks apart the other addend into that 1,000-partner and the rest to find the total.
To add 800 + 700 using the Make a Thousand strategy, the student finds the 1,000-partner for 800 which is 200, breaks apart 700, the other addend, into 200 + 500 and then adds the rest, 500, to 1,000. Thus, 1,000 + 500 = 1,500 so 800 + 700 = 1500.

mass The amount of matter in an object. (Mass is constant; weight varies because weight is the effect of gravity on matter.)

Math Mountain A visual representation of the partners and totals of a number. The total (*sum*) appears at the top and the two partners (*addends*) that are added to produce the total are below to the left and right.

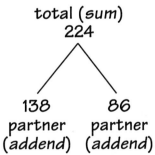

total (*sum*)
224

138   86
partner   partner
(*addend*) (*addend*)

mean (average) The number found by dividing the sum of a group of numbers by the number of addends. For the set of numbers 3, 5, 4, 8: 3 + 5 + 4 + 8 = 20, 20 ÷ 4 = 5, 5 is the mean.

median The middle number when a set of numbers is arranged in order from least to greatest. For an even number of numbers, the median is the average of the two middle numbers.

Teacher Glossary (Continued)

mental math A way to solve problems without using pencil and paper, or a calculator.

meter (m) A metric unit used to measure length. 1 meter = 100 centimeters

method A procedure, or way of doing something.

mile (mi) A customary unit of length. 1 mile = 5,280 feet

milliliter (mL) A metric unit used to measure capacity. 1,000 milliliters = 1 liter

mixed number A whole number and a fraction. $1\frac{3}{4}$ is a mixed number.

mode The number that occurs most often in a set of data. In this set of numbers {3, 4, 5, 5, 5, 7, 8}, 5 is the mode.

multiple A number that is the product of the given number and another number.

Multiplication Table An array of numbers with rows and columns labeled from 1 through 12. The product of the labels is found in the cell where the row and column intersect.

multiplier One of the factors in a multiplication equation. In the 9s count-bys or multiplications, each of the numbers that 9 is multiplied by, is the multiplier.

multiplier finger Used with the multiplication strategy Quick 9s strategy, the bent finger that indicates the number that 9 is being multiplied by.

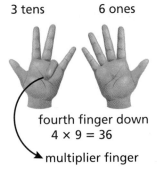

3 tens   6 ones

fourth finger down
4 × 9 = 36

multiplier finger

N

net A flat pattern that can be folded to make a solid figure. This net is for a rectangular prism.

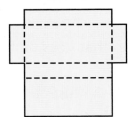

New Groups Above Method A strategy for multi-digit addition. The new groups are placed above the existing groups. This is the current, common method of addition.

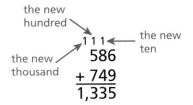

the new hundred
the new ten
the new thousand

111
586
+ 749
1,335

New Groups Below Method A strategy for multi-digit addition. The new groups are placed below the existing groups on the line waiting to be added.

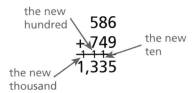

the new hundred
the new ten
the new thousand

586
+ 749
1 1 1
1,335

non-standard unit A unit of measure not commonly recognized, such as a paper clip. An inch and a centimeter are standard units of measure.

non-unit fraction A fraction that is built from unit fractions. $\frac{2}{3}$ is a non-unit fraction. It is built from the unit fractions $\frac{1}{3} + \frac{1}{3}$.

number sentence Numbers and expressions related to each other using one of these symbols: =, <, or >.

numerator The top number in a fraction that shows the number of equal parts counted. In the fraction $\frac{1}{3}$, 1 is the numerator.

O

obtuse angle An angle that measures more than 90° but less than 180°.

obtuse triangle A triangle with one angle that measures more than 90°.

octagon An eight-sided figure

odd number A whole number that is not a multiple of 2. The ones digit in an odd number is 1, 3, 5, 7, or 9.

operation A mathematical process. Addition, subtraction, multiplication, division, and raising a number to a power are operations.

opposite sides Sides that are across from each other; they do not meet at a point. In this example, sides *a* and *c* are opposite.

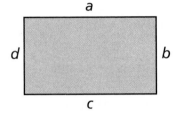

ordered pair A pair of numbers such as (3, 4) in which one number is considered to be first and the other number second. They can name a point on a coordinate grid.

Order of Operations A set of rules that state in which order operations should be performed.
- Compute inside parentheses first
- Multiply and divide in order from left to right
- Add and subtract in order from left to right

ordinal numbers Numbers used to show order or position. For example, first, second, fifth.

ounce (oz) A customary unit used to measure weight. 16 ounces = 1 pound

output In a function table, the value resulting from a specific input and rule.

parallel The same distance apart everywhere. This can describe lines, line segments, or faces of a solid figure.

parallelogram A quadrilateral with both pairs of opposite sides parallel.

partner One of two numbers that add to make a total. In the equation 9 + 7 = 16, 9 and 7 are the partners.

pennies place In dollar notation, the second place to the right of the decimal point. In the amount $3.47, the 7 is in the pennies place.

pentagon A five-sided figure.

perimeter The distance around the outside of a figure.

perpendicular Two lines, line segments, or rays that cross or meet to form right angles.

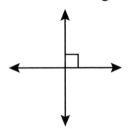

pictograph A graph that uses pictures or symbols to represent data.

pint (pt) A customary unit used to measure capacity. 1 pint = 2 cups

place value The value assigned to the place that a digit occupies in a number.

place value drawing A drawing that represents a number. Thousands are represented by a bar, hundreds are represented by boxes, tens by vertical lines, and ones by small circles.

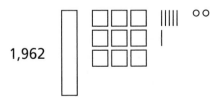

plane A flat surface that extends without end in all directions. It has no thickness.

plane figure A geometric figure that lies entirely in one plane.

P.M. The abbreviation for post meridiem, Latin for after noon. Used to indicate a time after noon.

polygon A closed plane figure make up of line segments.

pound (lb) A customary unit used to measure weight. 1 pound = 16 ounces

prism A solid figure with two parallel congruent bases, and rectangles or parallelograms for faces. A prism is named by the shape of its bases.

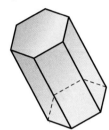

hexagonal prism

probability The chance of an event occurring.

product The answer when you multiply numbers. In the equation 4 × 7 = 28, 28 is the product.

proof drawing A drawing used to show that an answer is correct.

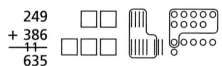

$$\begin{array}{r} 249 \\ + 386 \\ \underline{11} \\ 635 \end{array}$$

put together problem A problem that involves putting together (combining, joining) groups of things to form a total.

pyramid A solid figure with one base and whose other faces are triangles with a common vertex. A pyramid is named by the shape of its base.

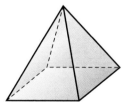

square pyramid

Q

quadrilateral A figure with four sides.

quart (qt) A customary unit used to measure capacity. 1 quart = 4 cups

quarter turn A 90° rotation.

Quick 9s A short-cut for multiplying by 9 in which students bend down one finger to represent the multiplier. The remaining fingers to the left of the bent finger represent the tens digit of the product and the fingers to the right of the bent finger represent the ones digit of the product.

3 tens   6 ones

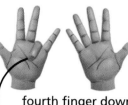

This method works because
3 × 9 = 3 × (10 − 1) = 30 − 3 = 27

fourth finger down
4 × 9 = 36

multiplier finger

quotient The answer when you divide numbers. In the equation 35 ÷ 7 = 5, 5 is the quotient.

R

radius A line segment that connects the center of a circle to any point on the circle. The term is also used to describe the length of such a line segment.

range The difference between the greatest number and the least number in a set of data. In this set of numbers {12, 15, 18, 19, 20}, the range is 20 − 12 or 8.

ray A part of a line that has one endpoint and goes on forever in one direction.

rectangle A parallelogram that has 4 right angles.

reflection (flip) A transformation that involves flipping a figure over a line. The size and shape of the figure remain the same.

reflectional symmetry See **line symmetry**.

remainder In division, the quantity that is left over which is not large enough to make another whole group. In the division example, 32 divided by 6, the quotient is 5 with a remainder of 2. There are 5 groups of 6 and one more group that has only 2 items (the remainder).

repeated addition An introduction to multiplication in which students add the same number (3) several times (4) to show that 3 + 3 + 3 + 3 produces the same result as 4 × 3.

Repeated Groups Drawing: A drawing which children create that represents factors and products.

4 × 5 = 20

repeated groups problem A type of multiplication word problem that involves multiple groups with the same number of items in each group.

repeating pattern A pattern consisting of a group of numbers, letters, or figures that repeat. Examples: 1, 2, 1, 2, ...
  A, B, C, A, B, C, ...

rhombus A parallelogram with congruent sides.

right angle An angle that measures 90°.

right triangle A triangle with one right angle.

rotation (turn) A transformation that involves a turn of a figure about a point. The size and shape of the figure remain the same.

round To find *about* how many or how much by expressing a number to the nearest ten, hundred, thousand, and so on.

route The path taken to get to a location.

row A horizontal group of cells in table.

rule In a pattern such as a function table or number sequence, what is done to the first number to get to the second number and so on. The rule *Add 3* is shown in the function table.

Add 3.	
0	3
1	4
2	5
3	6

The rule *n* + 7 is shown in the number sequence: 2, 9, 16, 23 . . . .

S

scale An arrangement of numbers in order with equal intervals.

scalene triangle A triangle with sides of three different lengths.

Secret Code Cards Cards printed with the digits 0 through 9, multiples of 10 from 10 through 90 and multiples of 100 from 100 through 1,000. The number is represented on the back of the card by dots, sticks, or boxes. The cards are used to teach place value.

Thousands Card   Hundreds Card   Tens Card   Ones Card

Assembled Cards

set A group of numbers or other things.

Show All Totals Method A method for finding a total of multi-digit numbers.

```
                    586
the new          + 749
thousand  →      1,200
the new
hundred    →       120
the new    →        15
ten
                  1,335
```

Teacher Glossary (Continued)

shrinking pattern A number or geometric pattern that decreases.

Example: 15, 12, 9, 6, 3,...
25, 20, 16, 13, 11,...

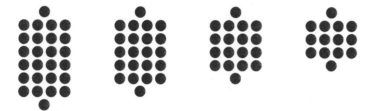

side (of a plane figure) A line segment that makes up a plane figure.

simplify To write an equivalent fraction with a smaller numerator and denominator.

situation equation An equation children write to represent a story problem. It represents a literal translation of the problem. It may or may not have the unknown isolated on one side of the equals sign.

slide To move a figure along a line. The size and shape of the figure remain the same.

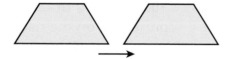

solid figure A figure that has three dimensions.

solution equation A situation equation that has been rewritten so that the unknown is on the right side of the equals sign. It is related to the operation needed to solve the problem rather than to a literal translation of the story problem.

sphere A solid figure shaped like a ball.

square A rectangle with four sides of the same length.

square number A product of a whole number and itself. $4 \times 4 = 16$, so 16 is a square number.

square unit Unit used to measure area that is 1 unit on each side. A square foot, for example, is a unit that is 1 foot on each side.

standard form The name of a number written using digits. For example, 1,829.

standard unit A recognized unit of measure, such as an inch or centimeter.

straight angle An angle that measures 180°.

strategy cards Cards that display a multiplication or division exercise on one side. The other side shows the answer to the exercise, the count-bys (up to the product) for both factors, and a Fast-Array drawing that shows the product and the two factors.

sum The answer when adding two or more addends. In the equation $37 + 52 = 89$, 89 is the sum.

survey A method of collecting information.

symmetry A figure has symmetry if it can be folded along a line so that the two halves match exactly.

T

table An easy to read arrangement of data, organized in rows and columns.

take apart problem A problem that involves separating a group of objects.

tally marks A group of lines drawn in order to count. Each mark stands for 1 unit.

 means 13
5   5   3

ten stick In a place value drawing a vertical line used to represent 10.

ten stick

tenth One of the equal parts when a whole is divided into ten equal parts.

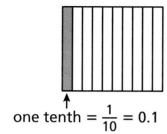

$$\text{one tenth} = \frac{1}{10} = 0.1$$

thousand bar In a place value drawing, a bar used to represent 1,000. A thousand bar is a quick way of drawing 1,000.

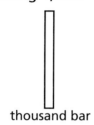

thousand bar

three-dimensional figure A figure with three dimensions.

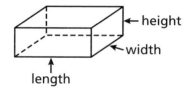

total The sum of two or more numbers. In the equation 672 + 228 = 900, 900 is the total.

transformation One of three basic motions: reflection (flip), rotation (turn), and translation (slide).

translation (slide) A transformation that involves sliding a figure along a line. The size and shape of the figure remain the same.

trapezoid A quadrilateral with exactly one pair of parallel sides.

turn To rotate a figure around a point. The size and shape of the figure remain the same.

two-dimensional figure A figure with two dimensions.

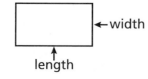

ungroup To break into a new group in order to be able to subtract.

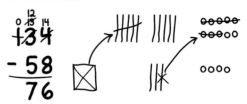

unit fraction A fraction with a numerator of 1.

Venn diagram A diagram that uses circles to show the relationship among sets of objects.

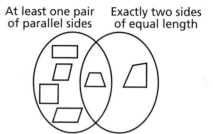

At least one pair of parallel sides Exactly two sides of equal length

vertex A point where sides, rays, or edges meet.

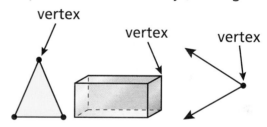

vertex   vertex   vertex

vertical Extending in two directions, up and down.

volume The measure of the amount of space occupied by an object.

weight The measure of how heavy something is. (Weight varies because weight is the effect of gravity on matter; mass is constant.)

word form A name of a number written using words instead of digits. For example, nine hundred eighty-four.

yard (yd) A customary unit used to measure length. 1 yard = 3 feet

Recommended Books

Unit A

Grandfather Tang's Story, by Ann Tompert, illustrated by Robert Andrew Parker (Bantam Doubleday Dell Books for Young Readers, 1997) (Lesson 3)

Unit 2

A Bundle of Beasts, by Mark Steele and Patricia Hooper, illustrated by Mark Steele (Houghton Mifflin, 1987) (Lesson 2)

Unit 3

The Greatest Gymnast of All, by Stuart J. Murphy (HarperTrophy, 1998) (Lesson 3)

Unit C

One Grain of Rice, by Demi (Scholastic Press, 1997) (Lesson 3)

Unit 4

Amanda Bean's Amazing Dream, by Cindy Neuschwander, illustrated by Liza Woodruff, Math Activities by Marilyn Burns (Scholastic Press, 1998) (Lesson 8)

Unit D

Spaghetti and Meatballs for All: A Mathematical Story, by Marilyn Burns, illustrated by Gordon Silveria (Scholastic Press, 1997) (Lesson 2)

Unit 5

Sea Squares, by Joy N. Hulme, illustrated by Carol Schwartz (Hyperion Books, 1993) (Lesson 8)

Unit E

Secret Treasures and Mathematical Measures: Adventures in Measuring: Time, Temperature, Length, Weight, Volume, Angles, Shapes, and Money, by Chris Kensler (Kaplan; Elementary edition, 2003) (Lesson 3)

Unit 6

The Big Orange Splot, by Daniel Manus Pinkwater (Rebound by Sagebrush, 1999) (Lesson 3)

Jump, Kangaroo, Jump, by Stuart J. Murphy, illustrated by Kevin O'Malley (HarperTrophy, 1999) (Lesson 5)

Mega-Fun Fractions, by Martin Lee and Marcia Miller (Teaching Resources, 2002) (Lesson 12)

The Fraction Family Heads West, by Marti Dryk, Ph.D., illustrated by Trevor Romain, D.M. (Bookaloppy Press, 1997) (Lesson 13)

Piece = Part = Portion: Fractions = Decimals = Percents, by Scott Gifford, photographs by Shmuel Thaler (Tricycle Press, 2003) (Lesson 16)

A Remainder of One: A Mathematical Folktale, by Elinor J. Pinczes, illustrated by Bonnie Mackain (Houghton Mifflin, 1995) (Lesson 18)

The Great Divide, by Dayle Ann Dodds, illustrated by Tracy Mitchell (Candlewick Press, 2005) (Lesson 20)

Unit 7

Room for Ripley, by Stuart J. Murphy, illustrated by Sylvie Wickstrom (HarperTrophy, 1999) (Lesson 5)

How Tall, How Short, How Faraway?, by David A. Adler, illustrated by Nancy Tobin (Holiday House, 2000) (Lesson 8)

Index

Index (Continued)

Index (Continued)

G

H

Index (Continued)

Index (Continued)

Index (Continued)